Patterns in Physics

Patterns in Physics

Second Edition

W. Bolton

McGRAW-HILL Book Company (UK) Limited

London · New York · St Louis · San Francisco · Auckland · Bogotá · Guatemala
Hamburg · Johannesburg · Lisbon · Madrid · Mexico · Montreal · New Delhi
Panama · Paris · San Juan · São Paulo · Singapore · Sydney · Tokyo · Toronto

Published by
McGRAW-HILL Book Company (UK) Limited
MAIDENHEAD · BERKSHIRE · ENGLAND

British Library Cataloguing in Publication Data

Bolton, W. (William), *1933–*
    Patterns in physics.—2nd ed.
    1. Physics
    I. Title
    530   QC21.2

    ISBN 0-07-084961-7

12345 RJA 89876

Phototypeset by Styleset Limited, Warminster, Wiltshire, and
printed and bound in Great Britain by R. J. Acford, Chichester, Sussex

Contents

CONTENTS

Preface to Second Edition

As with the First Edition, this book is addressed to all those who have an interest in learning about physics, something about a way of thinking. The level of the physics is intended to be that of pre-university courses in many countries, in particular the A-level courses in the United Kingdom.

Since the First Edition the concept of common cores between the various examining boards has emerged. The Second Edition covers in its entirety the common core syllabus. To make such identification clear the sequence of chapters adopted in this edition has been organized to conform with the common core sequence. The book does more than just cover the core—it covers in a comprehensive way all the physics both now covered by the Examining Boards and planned to be covered during the next few years. Some of the Boards are now complementing their extended core physics by topics, generally applied physics, from which a choice has to be made, e.g., the University of London School Examinations Board. A wide range of such material is covered within this Second Edition—all of those of the London Board being covered.

A considerable use has been made of questions drawn from the Examination Boards. To all the Boards I express my appreciation. Answers, and guides to answers, are given for all these questions. These are, however, my thoughts on the answers and not those of the Boards.

The Second Edition is not just the First with a few changes and bits of extra material. It is a major re-structuring of the physics and considerable changes have been made, the aim being to produce an edition which will stand for the next ten years, the First having just passed its tenth birthday.

The book owes much to the thoughts and writings of teachers in many countries. In particular my writing has been much influenced by the work of the Nuffield Foundation Advanced Physics project, of which I was one of the original team members. It has also benefited from my time overseas with Unesco and the Overseas Development Agency. My year with the Secondary Examinations Council and the GCSE Physics Grading Criteria Working Party provoked much thought about the nature of physics and I am grateful to the team members.

Finally, I must thank all those teachers and students who used the First Edition of *Patterns in Physics* over the last decade and hope they will enjoy this Second Edition.

Preface to Second Edition

Acknowledgements

The author and publishers have made every effort to trace the copyright holders of all material reproduced in this text. If any have been omitted they have our sincere apologies. We thank the following individuals and groups.

The Associated Examining Board
Joint Matriculation Board
Oxford and Cambridge Schools Examinations Board
Southern Universities' Joint Board
University of Oxford Delegacy of Local Examinations
University of Cambridge Local Examinations Syndicate
University of London Schools Examination Board

Oxford University Press: *The Second Law*.
Pergamon Press Ltd: 'A. Einstein (1905)' *Ann. Physik* **17**, 132. Translation in D. ter Haar (1967) *The Old Quantum Theory*.
Pilkington Brothers Limited: X-Ray diffraction pattern for glass; X-Ray diffraction pattern for distilled water.
Reyrolle Parsons Limited: Thorpe Marsh power station.
The Royal Society: *Bradley, Philosophical Transactions*.
The Science Museum: Photograph (Lent to the Science Museum by Professor E. O. Lawrence).
Professor Tabor: Radial Distribution For Liquid Argon, taken from *Gases, Liquids and Solids* (Cambridge University Press, 1985).
Dr Panchali Thakur: Photographs of X-ray diffraction arrangement; photograph of X-ray diffraction pattern with a single crystal of sodium chloride.
Sir George Thomson: Diffraction rings for gold; diffraction haloes for celluloid.
University of California Press: *Lectures on Gas Theory*.
The University of Chicago Press: Libby, Radiocarbon Dating.
University of Manchester: Photograph–the signal resulting from the bowl of the telescope sweeping across the plane of the milky way; photograph of Jodrell Bank Mk 1A radio telescope.
University of Washington: Photograph of Tacoma Narrows Bridge.
R. J. van de Graff: *Reports On Progress In Physics*.
Van Nostrand Reinhold (UK): R. H. Baker *Astronomy 8/e*.
Victor Gollancz Limited: *Darwin's Century*.
E. W. Wichman: *Quantum Physics*.
Wykeham Publications (London) Limited: *Gravity and the Earth*.
Addison-Wesley Publishers Co. Inc.: *Development of Concepts of Physics*—F. W. Sears and M. W. Zemansky; *The Feynman Lectures in Physics*, Vol. 1.

Australia House/Australian News and Information Bureau: Photograph of Gladesville Bridge, Sydney.
Lord Blackett: Photographs, scattering in hydrogen; scattering in helium; scattering in nitrogen.
J. Allan Cash: Photographs of Roman bridge at Rimini; the iron bridge over the Severn at Ironbridge; The Severn Bridge.
Century Hutchinson Limited: Marconi—*Master of Space*.
Collins Sons and Co. Ltd: *The ABC Murders*.
D. Dieckmann: *Ergonomics*, Vol. 1.
Doubleday and Co.: *Darwin's Century*.
Educational Development Center Inc: Strobe photograph of a simple pendulum; Berkeley Physics Course electron diffraction patterns.
K. W. Ford: *The World of Elementary Particles*.
Hale Observatories: Photographs of reflecting telescope and Palomar reflecting telescope.
Harvard Apparatus Ltd: Diffraction pattern from random array; diffraction pattern from regular array. *Note: Diffraction plates no longer available.*
PSSC Physics 2/e, 1965; D. C. Heath & Co. with Education Development Center, Inc., Newton, MA.
Kelvin Hughes, a division of Smith Industries Limited: Echo sounder chart.
Professor arch Italo Insolera: Photograph of the viaduct at Brusseau sur Creuse.
The Institute of Physics: L. de Broglie (1971) *Physics Bulletin*.
R. S. Longhurst: Photographs, diffraction at slits.
Macmillan, London and Basingstoke; Viking Penguin Inc: *A Star Called The Sun*.
Meitner and Frisch: *Nature*.
F. J. Morin and J. P. Naita, *Phys. Rev:* 'Intrinsic carrier concentration for silicon'.
Nuffield Foundation (1972) *Advanced Physics, Change and Chance;* Nuffield Foundation (1971) *Advanced Physics, Waves, Particles and Atoms*.

The cover photograph is reproduced by courtesy of the Meteorological Office, Bracknell and P.P.H. Versclure.

We should like to point out that all illustrations in the text that have been taken from *PSSC Physics* 2/e, 1965, and attributed to D. C. Heath & Co should also be attributed to the Education Center, Inc., Newton, MA. The latter holds the copyright to these illustrations.

Part 1
Mechanics

0 Patterns and language of physics

A note   Why is this called chapter zero?

' "Rule Forty-two. All persons more than a mile high to leave the court."

Everybody looked at Alice.

"I'm not a mile high," said Alice.

"You are," said the King.

"Nearly two miles high," added the Queen.

"Well, I shan't go, at any rate," said Alice: "besides, that's not a regular rule: you invented it just now."

"It's the oldest rule in the book," said the King.

"Then it ought to be Number One," said Alice.'

L. Carroll (1865)
Alice's Adventures in Wonderland.

This is not a 'regular' chapter but it is the 'oldest' chapter in physics.

Intuition

Many scientific discoveries can be called accidents; for example Jansky's discovery of radio waves originating from outside the earth. Jansky was investigating radio interference at the time and not looking for extra-terrestrial radio waves. Other discoveries have arisen from scientists feeling that something is not quite right, an experimental fact does not quite fit a theory or a theory seems to have some strange predictions—Leverrier and Adams predicted the existence of a new planet, Neptune, on the basis of slight irregularities of the orbit of the planet Uranus, irregularities which did not fit with the theoretical prediction based on Newton's theory of gravitation (see Chapter 12). Scientific intuition might be the right phrase to describe many discoveries.

' "My friend Hastings will tell you that from the moment I received the first letter I was upset and disturbed. It seemed to me at once that there was something very wrong about the letter."

"You were quite right" said Franklin Clarke dryly.

"Yes. But there, at the very start, I made a grave error. I permitted my feeling—my very strong feeling about the letter to remain a mere impression. I treated it as though it had been an intuition. In a well-balanced, reasoning mind there is no such thing as an intuition—an inspired guess! You can guess, of course—and a guess is either right or wrong. If it is right you call it an intuition. If it is wrong you usually do not speak of it again. But what is often called an intuition is really an impression based on logical deduction or experience. When an expert feels that there is something wrong about a picture or a piece of furniture or the signature on a cheque he is really basing that feeling on a host of small signs and details. He has no need to go into them minutely—his

3

experience obviates that—the net result is the definite impression that something is wrong. But it is not a guess, it is an impression based on experience." '

Agatha Christie (1936) *The ABC Murders,* Collins/Dodd, Mead and Co. Inc.

To be a scientist you have to be a detective, a Hercule Poirot (the detective in the above extract) or Sherlock Holmes. Detective stories seem to follow a general sequence:

1. A fact requiring explanation; perhaps a murder.
2. Investigations to yield data; gathering clues.
3. Forming a hypothesis, a pattern; putting the clues together to give a pattern and so a suspect for the crime.
4. Looking for evidence to confirm the hypothesis, seeking the vital evidence to give a cast-iron case.
5. The successful theory and the arrest of the murderer. There will almost inevitably be false data and false hypotheses which lead in the wrong direction, if only to make certain that the reader does not 'guess' the identity of the murderer too soon.

The above steps describe not only detective stories but also much of the way in which science progresses. The following is a physics sequence described in more detail in chapter 18.

1. A fact; the spectrum lines of an element are characteristic of that element—they serve as a fingerprint.
2. Determination of the wavelengths of all the lines in the hydrogen spectrum.
3. Balmer derives an empirical relationship between the wavelengths—a pattern has emerged.
4. Bohr produces a theory of the atom out of which Balmer's relationship emerges.
5. Bohr's theory of the atom proves unsatisfactory.
6. A wave theory replaces Bohr's theory, Balmer's relationship still comes out of this theory.
7. The wave theory enables other predictions

to be made—these check with experiments (e.g., the emission of alpha particles from nuclei).
8. We have, for the present, a successful theory.

In one sense physics is a search for patterns among data. The data may have been in existence many years but no pattern seen, or regrouping of existing patterns of data may lead to a bigger simpler pattern.

Kepler used Tycho Brahé's data on planets to give a simple pattern for planetary behaviour. Newton combined the patterns of Kepler for the movements of the planets with the pattern of Galileo for the behaviour of objects falling to the surface of the earth to give a general simple pattern of universal gravitation.

In one sense physics is the search for patterns with which to describe the physical events of the world, and universe, around us. The patterns enable us to give order to events and make predictions. We expect that the sun will rise every morning in the east and set every evening in the west. We feel we can predict this because in our experience it always has done—what we mean is that we have made a large number of observations of the sun rising and setting and established a pattern and feel confident enough to make predictions based on this pattern. The immediate purpose of physics, indeed science, is to make predictions of events in nature. It is through this ability of man to make predictions that he has survived—he could not outrun or outfight other animals but he could outwit them.

The rest of this chapter is a consideration of the language of physics and some of the common patterns.

Terms used in physics

The following are some terms used in physics.

1. A *fact* results from experimental observation and can be reproduced if the experiment is repeated. Thus, for example, a fact might be that the length of a piece of copper wire is 1.0 m. You perhaps obtained this from a measurement and if you, and other, people repeat the measurement the same value is obtained.

2. A *hypothesis* is a tentative idea put forward to explain phenomena and which has not been fully tested by experiment. You might perhaps carry out the experiment of measuring the thickness of a thin film of oil on water and then put forward the hypothesis, based on just this result, that the size of the oil molecule is about 10^{-10} m.

3. A *law* is a statement that summarizes a range of observations and presents a general idea of importance. Thus, for example, Ohm's law describes a simple mathematical relationship between the two measured quantities of current and potential difference.

4. A *model* is an imaginative picture used to aid discussion of some phenomena. It generally gives a highly simplified view of the phenomena. Thus the magnetic field surrounding a permanent magnet may be pictured in terms of lines radiating out from one end of the magnet and converging on the other end.

5. A *theory* is an imaginative picture used to describe the process which gives rise to observed behaviour. Kinetic theory is an example involving the imaginative picture of a gas in terms of a very large number of small, randomly moving particles colliding with each other and the walls of a container. This is then used to explain the relationships observed between pressure, volume and temperature, i.e., the gas laws.

Physical quantities

Before a measurement can be made and any statement made about a physical quantity, such as perhaps a length, units have to be defined. Measurements can then be made in terms of that unit and the physical quantity then expressed as a value with a unit, e.g., 20 mm for the length. Without a unit the value for a physical quantity has no significance.

The international scientific community has adopted a system of units, with symbols for them, which is known as the SI system. The system is based on seven basic units with other units being obtained from these by multiplication and division. The basic units are for seven basic physical quantities which by definition are considered to be independent of each other. The following table shows these quantities and units.

Physical quantity	Name of SI unit	Symbol of unit
Mass	kilogram	kg
Length	metre	m
Time	second	s
Electric current	ampere	A
Temperature	kelvin	K
Luminous intensity	candela	cd
Amount of substance	mole	mol

The units of any other physical quantity can be derived from those of the basic quantities by the equation used to define that quantity. Thus, for example, velocity is rate of change of displacement, the defining equation thus being (see Chapter 2)

$$v = \frac{ds}{dt}$$

Hence the unit of velocity is given by

$$\text{unit of velocity} = \frac{\text{unit of displacement}}{\text{unit of time}}$$

The unit of displacement is that of length, i.e., metre, and the unit of time is the second. Hence

$$\text{unit of velocity} = \frac{\text{metre}}{\text{second}}$$

This can be expressed as metres per second, or m/s, or m s^{-1}.

Acceleration a is rate of change of velocity with time (see Chapter 2), i.e.

$$a = \frac{dv}{dt}$$

Hence the unit of acceleration is given by

$$\text{unit of acceleration} = \frac{\text{unit of velocity}}{\text{unit of time}}$$
$$= \frac{(\text{metre/second})}{\text{second}}$$
$$= \frac{\text{metre}}{\text{second} \times \text{second}}$$

This can be expressed as m/s^2 or $m\,s^{-2}$.

Force F is defined as the product of mass m and acceleration a (see Chapter 3). Hence

$$F \doteq ma$$

Unit of force = (unit of mass) × (unit of acceleration)

$$= kg \times m\,s^{-2}$$

$$= kg\,m\,s^{-2}$$

This unit is given a special name, the newton (symbol N).

The following table gives some more common derived units and their defining equations.

Quantity	Defining equation	SI unit
Area	$A = L^2$	m^2
Volume	$V = L^3$	m^3
Momentum	momentum $= m\,v$	$kg\,m\,s^{-1}$
Density	$\rho = m/V$	$kg\,m^{-3}$
Pressure	$p = F/A$	$kg\,m^{-1}\,s^{-2} = N\,m^{-2}$ $= Pa$ (pascal)
Stress	stress $= F/A$	$kg\,m^{-1}\,s^{-2} = N\,m^{-2}$ $= Pa$ (pascal)
Energy, work	work $= F\,s$	$kg\,m^2\,s^{-2} = N\,m$ $= J$ (joule)

In addition to the basic and derived units there are some units referred to as 'supplementary units'. These could have been derived but would have ended up with no unit. Thus the quantity plane angle θ is defined by arc length s divided by radius r, i.e.

$$\theta = \frac{s}{r}$$

hence

$$\text{unit of plane angle} = \frac{\text{unit of length}}{\text{unit of length}}$$

$$= \text{a ratio and so no unit}$$

The two supplementary units are

Physical quantity	Name of SI unit	Symbol
Plane angle	radian	rad
Solid angle	steradian	sr

Definitions of SI basic units

(1) Mass

The kilogram is the mass of the international prototype kilogram preserved at the International Bureau of Weights and Measures in France. This is in the form of a solid cylinder of platinum–iridium alloy.

(2) Length

The metre is the length equal to 1 650 763.73 wavelengths in a vacuum of a specified radiation from an atom of krypton-86.

(3) Time

The second is the duration of 9 192 631 770 periods of a specified radiation from an atom of caesium-133.

(4) Electric current

The ampere is that constant current which, if maintained in two straight parallel conductors of infinite length, of negligible circular cross-section, and placed 1 m apart in a vacuum, causes each to exert a force of 2×10^{-7} N on 1 metre length of the other.

(5) Temperature

The kelvin is the fraction 1/273.16 of the thermodynamic temperature of the triple point of water.

(6) Luminous intensity

The candela is the fraction 1/60 of the luminous intensity per square centimetre of a specified radiator.

(7) Amount of substance

The mole is the amount of substance of a system which contains as many elementary units as there are carbon atoms in 0.012 kg (i.e., 12 g) of carbon-12.

Unit prefixes

The size of units is sometimes not convenient for a quantity being measured. Thus, for example, a small object may have a mass of 0.000 52 kg. While the measurement can be written in that form, an alternative way of writing it is in what is called 'standard form'. This means writing the number in terms of a whole number not less than 1 but less than 10 multiplied by an appropriate power of 10. Thus the small object has a mass of 5.2×10^{-4} kg. A large object might have a mass of 230 000 kg. In standard form this is 2.3×10^5 kg.

Another way of writing such measurements is to use prefixes to the units. The prefix indicates the standard form number by which the unit has been multiplied. The following table gives the prefixes.

Multiple	Prefix to unit	Symbol
10^{-18}	atto	a
10^{-15}	femto	f
10^{-12}	pico	p
10^{-9}	nano	n
10^{-6}	micro	μ
10^{-3}	milli	m
10^{3}	kilo	k
10^{6}	mega	M
10^{9}	giga	G
10^{12}	tera	T
10^{15}	peta	P
10^{18}	exa	E

The above are the preferred prefixes, involving indices of ± 3, ± 6, ± 9, etc. Other prefixes are, however, used on occasions.

Multiple	Prefix to unit	Symbol
10^{-2}	centi	c
10^{-1}	deci	d
10^{1}	deca	da
10^{2}	hecto	h

An electric current of 0.000 002 3 A can be written as 2.3×10^{-6} A or 2.3 μA. A pressure of 1200 Pa can be written as 1.2×10^3 Pa or 1.2 kPa.

Physical equations

In a correct physical equation not only must the numbers on both sides of the equation balance but so also must the units. Thus if we take the equation

$$\text{kinetic energy} = \tfrac{1}{2}mv^2$$

and consider a mass of 10 g with a velocity of 20 m s^{-1}, then we might obtain the kinetic energy by

$$\text{kinetic energy} = \tfrac{1}{2} \times 10 \times 20^2$$

This has the value of 2000. The units must be

$$\text{unit of kinetic energy} = \text{unit of mass} \times (\text{unit of velocity})^2$$

$$= g \times (m\ s^{-1})^2$$
$$= g\ m^2\ s^{-2}$$

While kinetic energy can be expressed in such a unit it is not the conventional unit of the joule, i.e., kg m^2 s^{-2}. Thus, if we had written

$$\text{kinetic energy} = 2000\ J = \tfrac{1}{2} \times 10 \times 20^2\ g\ m^2\ s^{-2}$$

then we would have the numbers balancing on either side of the equation but the units would not. That would be wrong.

To obtain a correct equation we need the same units on each side. Hence if we write the mass in kilograms we can have a balanced equation.

$$\text{kinetic energy} = \tfrac{1}{2} \times 10 \times 10^{-3} \times 20^2$$

$$\text{unit of kinetic energy} = kg \times (m\ s^{-1})^2$$

Hence the answer is 2.0 kg m^2 s^{-2}, or 2.0 J.

Dimensions

The dimension of any physical quantity can be expressed in terms of the dimensions of the basic measures, such as mass, length, time, etc., from which it is derived. The dimension of a physical quantity is established by the way it is defined; this is not, however, the same as the unit of a physical quantity since that depends on particular values of quantities. Thus, for example, the dimension of length is length but the unit of

MECHANICS

length could be anything—metre, inch, etc. Volume is defined by the cubing of length and so has the dimension of length cubed. This is often written as

$$[\text{volume}] = [L^3]$$

The 'square' brackets indicate that we are only considering the dimensions. Capital letters are always used for a basic dimension.

Velocity is the rate of change of displacement with time and so has the dimension

$$[\text{velocity}] = \frac{[\text{displacement}]}{[\text{time}]}$$

$$= [LT^{-1}]$$

Acceleration is the rate of change of velocity with time and so has the dimension

$$[\text{acceleration}] = \frac{[\text{velocity}]}{[\text{time}]}$$

$$= \frac{[LT^{-1}]}{[T]}$$

$$= [LT^{-2}]$$

Since force = mass × acceleration, the dimension of force is

$$[\text{force}] = [\text{mass}] \times [\text{acceleration}]$$

$$= [M] \times [LT^{-2}]$$

$$= [MLT^{-2}]$$

In any valid physical equation, every term must have the same dimensions. Such an equation is said to be 'dimensionally homogeneous'. Consider the equation for straight line motion (see Chapter 2)

$$v = v_0 + at$$

If we write the dimensions for each term:

$$[LT^{-1}] = [LT^{-1}] \text{ and } [LT^{-2} \times T]$$

$$[LT^{-1}] = [LT^{-1}] \text{ and } [LT^{-1}]$$

the equation is dimensionally homogeneous.

Consider another example, the equation for the periodic time of a sample pendulum (see Chapter 6):

$$T = 2\pi \sqrt{\frac{L}{g}}$$

If we write the dimensions for each term:

$$[T] = \left[\frac{L}{LT^{-2}}\right]^{\frac{1}{2}}$$

The 2π has no dimensions. Hence

$$[T] = [L^{\frac{1}{2}}L^{-\frac{1}{2}}T] = [T]$$

The equation is dimensionally homogeneous.

This 'method of dimensions' for checking equations can also be used to predict the form of an equation. The following example illustrates this method.

An object accelerating from rest with a uniform acceleration a will reach a velocity v after some time t which could be supposed to be a function of both a and t. What type of relationship could be feasible? We can write for the equation

$$v = ka^x t^y$$

where k is a dimensionless constant, and x and y are some powers to which a and t are raised. If we now write the dimensions for each term:

$$[\text{velocity}] = [\text{acceleration}]^x \times [\text{time}]^y$$

$$[LT^{-1}] = [LT^{-2}]^x \times [T]^y$$

Equating the indices of L gives

$$1 = x$$

Equating the indices of T gives

$$-1 = -2x + y$$

Hence $x = 1$ and $y = 1$, and the equation has the form

$$v = kat$$

Vectors

Quantities for which we need to know the direction as well as the magnitude in order to determine their effect on some object are called *vectors*.

Those quantities for which a specification of the magnitude alone suffices to specify the effect are called *scalar quantities*.

Displacements, velocities, and accelerations are examples of vectors; mass, volume, and temperature are examples of scalar quantities.

A convenient representation of a vector quantity is an arrow-headed line segment, the length of which is representative of the magnitude of the vector quantity and the direction of which specifies the direction of the vector quantity (Fig. 0.1(a)).

All vector quantities are found to combine in the same way—by what is called the parallelogram law. The vectors to be combined are represented by the arrow-headed line segments placed tail-to-tail. For a pair of vectors the resultant effect is equivalent to a vector represented by the line segment completing the diagonal of the parallelogram (Fig. 0.1(b)) resulting from using the two line segments as two adjacent sides in a parallelogram.

An alternative way of specifying the combination rule is to place the vector line segments head-to-tail and the resultant is the line segment completing the triangle (Fig. 0.1(b)).

As an example, what is the resultant of a displacement of an object from its rest position of 3 km to the north followed by 4 km to the east? The parallelogram or triangle construction (Fig. 0.2) gives a resultant of 5 km displacement in a direction making an angle θ north of east, where θ is given by

$$\tan \theta = \tfrac{3}{4}$$

The total journey is, however, 7 km; journeys are not vector quantities.

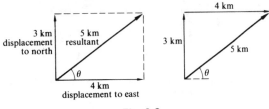

Fig. 0.2

Velocities are vector quantities. Suppose you were to swim across a river, always keeping your body at right angles to the river bank (Fig. 0.3), at a velocity of 3 km h^{-1}. There is a current, parallel to the bank, of 4 km h^{-1}. What is your effective velocity? 5 km h^{-1} at an angle θ to the bank, where

$$\tan \theta = \tfrac{3}{4}$$

A single vector can be resolved into two other vectors by doing the above procedure in reverse (Fig. 0.1(c)). Thus a velocity v can be resolved into two velocities $v \cos \theta$ and $v \sin \theta$ at right angles to each other. We can obtain the same effect as the velocity v by considering the effects of the two independent velocities $v \cos \theta$ and $v \sin \theta$.

If we have more than two vectors to be combined we can use the parallelogram for combining pairs of vectors and continue combining

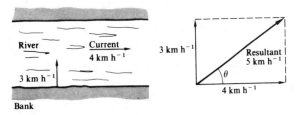

Fig. 0.3

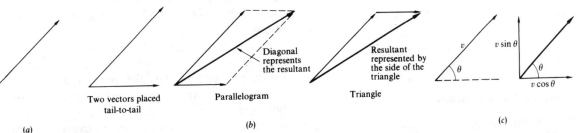

Fig 0.1   (a) Arrow representing a vector. (b) Finding the resultant of two vectors. (c) Resolving a vector into two other vectors

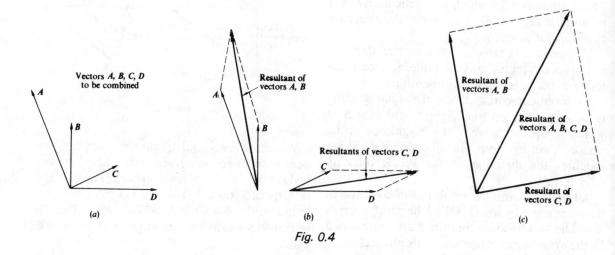

Fig. 0.4

pairs until we are left with just one resultant (Fig. 0.4 shows an example of this). A probably simpler way of combining the vectors is to use the 'triangle' construction but putting all the vectors tail-to-head and taking the resultant as the vector needed to join the last head to the first tail (Fig. 0.5). This is equivalent to combining A and B, then combining the resultant with C, then this resultant with D.

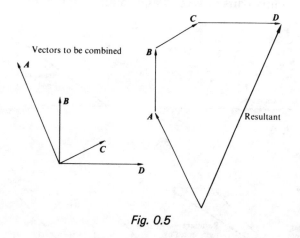

Fig. 0.5

Errors in measurements

When a physical quantity is measured, the result will be a value and a unit. But there will also be a possible error associated with that value. The error in a measurement is defined as the algebraic difference between the measured value and the true value.

Errors which might occur can be systematic or random. Systematic errors are those which occur because of some fault in the instrument used or the technique of measurement. Thus, for example, a meter might have a zero error and all readings with that instrument are high by the same amount. Another cause of systematic errors is an incorrectly calibrated instrument. Another possibility is that the observer making a measurement is persistently misreading an instrument, perhaps reading the wrong scale on a multi-scale meter, or using the wrong measurement technique. Repeating the measurement will not eliminate or reveal a systematic error. Such an error can only be revealed by varying the instrument or technique of measurement. Thus if a meter is incorrectly calibrated or has a zero error, repeating the measurement with another meter can show up the error since a different reading will be obtained.

A systematic error might be always positive, i.e., the measured value is always higher than the true value, or negative, i.e., the measured value is always lower than the true value. A random error, however, has an equal chance of being positive or negative. Random errors can be caused by the very fact that human beings are making the measurement—thus, for example, if ten students measure the length of an object with a rule then some variation in the results is very likely. Other random errors can be caused by fluctuations in the environment. Random errors can be revealed and eliminated by making repeated measurements. Thus in, for example, a measurement of the time taken for 10 oscillations of a simple pendulum, repeating the measurement for, say, 5 times and then taking the average value is likely to eliminate much of the random error.

Unless it is unavoidable or you are fairly certain that subsequent measurements will give the same result, more than one measurement should be made. With a single measurement, assuming systematic errors are insignificant, the possible error can be taken to be that given by the limited sensitivity of the instrument concerned. This is one scale division for the instrument. Thus for an ammeter with scale divisions of 0.2 A, a reading taken as 6.4 A would be indicated as having a possible error of ± 0.2 A, i.e., 6.4 ± 0.2 A. Where a measurement involves determination of some position, perhaps the distance of an image from a lens, then the possible error may well be greater than the sensitivity indicated by the rule used because of a difficulty in determining the precise position. The image might seem to be in focus over the range of distance 30–36 cm and so the measurement can be quoted as 33 ± 3 cm.

With a measurement where several readings are taken, statistical techniques can be used to indicate the probable error. A simple way is to calculate the average of the readings and then the mean of all the deviations of each reading from the average value. This mean deviation can then

Length measurement /cm	Deviation /cm
20.2	0.0
20.4	0.2
20.0	0.2
20.3	0.1
20.1	0.1
20.2	0.0
Sum 121.2	0.6
mean 20.2	0.1

be taken as the probable error. Thus, for example, where a length is measured six times and in the table readings obtained, the average is 20.2 cm and the mean of the deviations, ignoring the sign of the deviations, is 0.1 cm. Hence the result can be quoted as 20.2 ± 0.1 cm.

The final result of an experiment might involve combining a number of measurements, each with a possible error. The maximum possible error in compound quantities can be determined as follows:

1. When adding or subtracting measurements, add the numerical errors. For example, where a distance is to be determined by subtracting two position measurements of 10.1 ± 0.1 cm and 25.3 ± 0.1 cm, then the distance is 15.2 ± 0.2 cm.

2. When multiplying or dividing measurements, add the percentage errors. The percentage error is

$$\frac{\text{error}}{\text{value}} \times 100$$

Thus, for example, the error in a resistance value obtained from measurements of potential difference and current by the use of $R = V/I$ is derived as follows:

$$V = 6.4 \pm 0.2 \text{ V}$$

$$I = 0.55 \pm 0.05 \text{ A}$$

The percentage error for V is $(0.2/6.4) \times 100$ or about 3 per cent. The percentage error in I is $(0.05/0.55) \times 100$ or about 9 per cent. Hence the error in R obtained when V is divided by I is 12 per cent. The resistance is thus quoted as $11.6 \, \Omega$ with a percentage error of 12 per cent, i.e., $11.6 \pm 1.4 \, \Omega$.

3. When a measurement is raised to a power, multiply the percentage error by that power. Thus, if we have the fourth power of a radius then the percentage error of the radius is multiplied by four. If we have the square root of a length then the percentage error of that length is multiplied by a half.

The above rules can be deduced in the following way. Consider the error in the compound quantity $x + y$ if the errors in the quantities are Δx and Δy. The possible sum is then $x \pm \Delta x + y \pm \Delta y$. The worst possible error is when we have $x + \Delta x + y + \Delta y$ or $x - \Delta x + y - \Delta y$. Hence the compound quantity can be expressed as $x + y \pm (\Delta x + \Delta y)$, i.e., the errors are added. The same type of argument applies if we have the compound quantity $x - y$.

Consider the error in the compound quantity xy if the errors in the quantities are Δx and Δy. The compound quantity could be as large as $(x + \Delta x)(y + \Delta y)$ or as small as $(x - \Delta x)(y - \Delta y)$. The spread of the product is thus between about $xy + x\Delta y + y\Delta x + \Delta x\Delta y$ and $xy - x\Delta y - y\Delta x + \Delta x\Delta y$. If we neglect $\Delta x\Delta y$ as being small, then the error is between $x\Delta y + y\Delta x$ and $-(x\Delta y + y\Delta x)$, i.e., $\pm(x\Delta y + y\Delta x)$. The possible fractional error is thus

$$\text{fractional error} = \pm \frac{(x\Delta y + y\Delta x)}{xy}$$

$$= \pm \left(\frac{\Delta y}{y} + \frac{\Delta x}{x} \right)$$

This is the sum of the possible fractional errors. Hence the possible percentage error is the sum of the percentage errors.

Relationships

The equation $y = mx$, where y and x are variables and m a constant, describes the relationship between y and x and tells us that x is proportional to y. Thus, if y is doubled then x is doubled, if y is trebled then x is trebled. A physics relationship of this form is $V = RI$, where R is the constant and V and I are variables. If the potential difference V across a resistor is doubled then the current I through it must also be doubled.

The equation $y = mx^2$ describes a relationship where y is proportional to x^2. If x is doubled then y increases by a factor of 4. A physics relationship of this form is Power $= RI^2$. If the current I through a resistor is doubled then the power is increased by a factor of 4.

Graphs can be used to pictorially depict how a pair of variables are related. They can also be used, if we know how the two quantities are related, to determine the constants in the equation describing the relationship.

The equation $y = mx$ describes a straight line graph that passes through the origin, i.e., when $x = 0$ then $y = 0$, with m being the gradient of the line. The equation $y = mx + c$, with both m and c being constants, is also the equation of a straight line. The line, however, does not pass through the origin unless $c = 0$. When $x = 0$ then $y = c$ and thus the line intercepts the y-axis of the graph at $y = c$ (Fig. 0.6). When $y = 0$ then $x = -c/m$. When c is not zero then x is not proportional to y, i.e., doubling y does not double x.

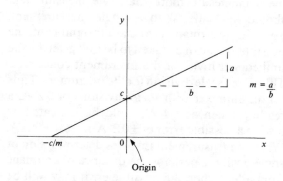

Fig. 0.6 The straight line graph y = mx + c

To illustrate the above, consider a heat flow per second Q into an object of mass m, specific heat capacity c, which results in a temperature rise of $\Delta\theta$ per second. The heat losses per second are h. Thus

$$Q = mc\,\Delta\theta + h$$

A graph of Q against $\Delta\theta$ will give a straight line graph with a gradient of mc and an intercept on the Q-axis of h.

For many physical situations there is not a linear relationship between the two variables and so a graph plotted between them would not give a straight line. Thus if we consider the equation for the periodic time T of a simple pendulum

$$T = 2\pi \sqrt{\frac{L}{g}}$$

where L is the length of the pendulum and g the acceleration due to gravity, a graph of T against L

does not give a straight line graph. However, there is a linear relationship between T and $\sqrt{L}$

$$T = \left(\frac{2\pi}{\sqrt{g}} \right) (\sqrt{L})$$

The gradient of such a graph is $(2\pi/\sqrt{g})$ and it passes through the origin.

Suppose we had a relationship of the form $y = Ax^n$ where A and n are constants. If y is plotted against x, a straight line does not result. We can have a straight line graph if y is plotted against x^n. However, we may be trying to determine A and n, and so such a graph would not be feasible. An alternative is to consider a log graph. For that relationship we have

$$\lg y = \lg(x^n) + \lg A$$
$$= n \lg x + \lg A$$

A graph of $\lg y$ against $\lg x$ will give a straight line with a gradient of n and an intercept of $\lg A$.

Differential equations

If we say that the velocity of an object is constant then we can write this as an equation of the form

$$v = C$$

where C represents the constant. But velocity is the rate of change of position with time. If the object covers a distance Δx in time Δt then the velocity is given by

$$v = \frac{\Delta x}{\Delta t}$$

This v is the average velocity over a distance Δx and time Δt. We can make this approximate to the instantaneous velocity by making Δt small. If we make Δt vanishingly small (dt) we have what we can call the 'velocity at an instant'.

Instantaneous velocity $v = dx/dt$.

For the case under consideration the velocity is a constant, thus

$$\frac{dx}{dt} = C$$

This is known as a differential equation and describes the motion of the object. Differential equations can be used to describe the rate of change of many quantities. We can describe the rate at which a radioactive isotope decays by the differential equation

$$\frac{dN}{dt} = -\lambda N$$

where N is the number of atoms at some instant and λ a constant. We can describe the rate at which the electric potential V varies with distance r from a charge by the differential equation

$$\frac{dV}{dr} = -\frac{q}{4\pi\varepsilon_0 r^2}$$

where q is the charge and ε_0 a constant.

Let us look at another example connected with motion. A freely falling object has a uniform acceleration.

$$\text{Acceleration} = \text{a constant } C$$

But acceleration is the rate of change of velocity with time.

$$\text{Acceleration} = \frac{dv}{dt}$$

The same arguments about instantaneous acceleration apply as occurred for velocity. Velocity is the rate of change of position with time, thus

$$\text{Acceleration} = \frac{d(dx/dt)}{dt}$$

We can rewrite this as

$$\text{Acceleration} = \frac{d^2x}{dt^2}$$

Thus the differential equation describing the constant acceleration of a freely falling object can be written as

$$\frac{d^2x}{dt^2} = C$$

This is known as a second-order differential equation, the ones previously considered being first-order equations.

If we take a graph of distance x against time t, what can we identify as both the first-order and second-order differential equations? The first-order equation involves dx/dt, the velocity. dx/dt is the rate at which x changes with time and thus is represented by the slope of the graph. The first-order equation thus tells us how the slope of the distance–time graph is varying with time. The second-order equation tells us how the velocity varies with time and thus how the rate of change of the slope with time depends on the time.

Another way of looking at this is to consider finite differences in x and t instead of the infinitesimally small. A $\Delta x/\Delta t$ equation tells us how much we should change x for each small incremental change in t of Δt. Thus if the differential equation states that dx/dt is a constant C, then in each interval of time Δt the value of x increases by Δx, where

$$\frac{\Delta x}{\Delta t} = C$$

or change in $x = \Delta x = C \, \Delta t$.

Thus if we had a constant velocity of 20 m s^{-1} and took time intervals of 0.1 s, then the change in x in the first time interval would be

$$\Delta x = C \, \Delta t = 20 \times 0.1 = 2 \text{ m}$$

If at time $t = 0$ the x value is 0, then we can use the change in x value to arrive at the position after 0.1 s (Fig. 0.7). Because C is a constant, the change in x in the next 0.1 s time interval will be 2 m, and

2 m in the next 0.1 s interval, and so on. The graph gives the solution of the differential equation.

In this case we could have arrived at the solution by using a standard integration form

$$\frac{dx}{dt} = C = 20$$

$$\int_0^x dx = \int_0^t 20 \, dt$$

$$x = 20t$$

This is the equation of the graph in Fig. 0.7. Standard integral forms are not always possible; the previous method, known as numerical integration, can be used in quite complicated cases.

An important use of numerical integration is the solution of second-order differential equations. For an object freely falling from rest we can, under laboratory conditions, assume a constant value for the acceleration due to gravity, say 10 m s^{-2}.

$$\text{Acceleration} = \frac{d^2x}{dt^2} = C = 10$$

We can rewrite this as

$$\frac{d}{dt}\left(\frac{dx}{dt}\right) = 10$$

dx/dt is the slope of the x against t graph

$$\frac{d}{dt}(\text{slope}) = 10$$

The rate of change of the slope is 10. The slope is the velocity.

For finite small changes we can write

$$\frac{\Delta}{\Delta t}(\text{slope}) = 10$$

or the change in slope is

$$\Delta(\text{slope}) = 10 \, \Delta t$$

Figure 0.8 shows a graph produced by taking Δt intervals of 0.1 s. In each successive time interval the slope changes by $10 \times 0.1 = 1$ m s^{-1}.

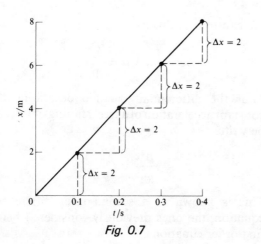

Fig. 0.7

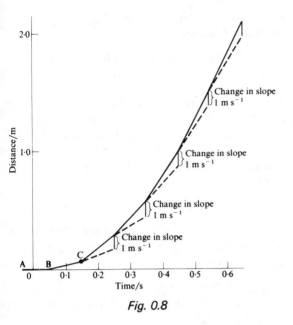

Fig. 0.8

The exponential

Figure 0.9 shows how the world population has been changing with time. At present the growth rate is about 2.55 per cent per year. We can write this as the following equation

(Change in population per year)

$$= \frac{2.55}{100} \times \text{population}$$

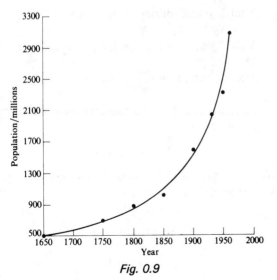

Fig. 0.9

or in symbols

$$\frac{\Delta N}{\Delta t} = kN$$

where ΔN is the change in population, initially N, occurring in a time interval Δt, and k is the constant. This equation is in fact telling us how the slope of the population–time graph changes with time (the slope is kN). The slope is directly proportional to N and thus, as t increases and more and more ΔN increments are added to N, the slope becomes steeper as time progresses. The equation describes how the number N changes with time, considered in intervals of Δt, when the change (ΔN) in any interval of time is some fixed fraction (or percentage) k of the number present at that time. Let us consider another example, the way in which a sum of money earning interest changes with time. Suppose we have £100 in an account which gives 10 per cent interest per year.

Initially £100.
After 1 year the interest paid will be $\frac{1}{10}$ of £100 per year or

$$\frac{\Delta N}{1} = \frac{1}{10} 1 \times 100$$

$$\Delta N = £10$$

After 1 year the money will have grown to £110.
After 2 years the interest paid will be

$$\frac{\Delta N}{1} = \frac{1}{10} \times 110$$

$$\Delta N = £11$$

After 2 years the money will have grown to £121.
After 3 years the interest paid will be

$$\frac{\Delta N}{1} = \frac{1}{10} \times 121$$

$$\Delta N = £12.1$$

After 3 years the money will have grown to £133.1.

And so the money will keep on growing. The change in money, i.e., the interest paid, will

15

increase each year because the total money is increasing each year. We can plot a graph showing how N, the total money, varies with time (Fig. 0.10). Rather than just plot the points given by the above calculations we will build up the graph step by step. The reason for doing this is that the technique gives a greater insight into the significance of the operation specified by the growth equation.

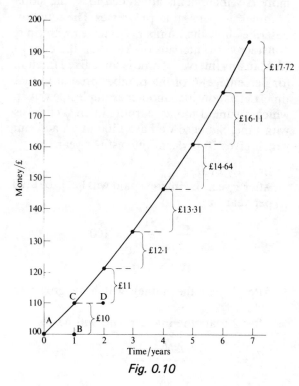

Money/£

Time/years

Fig. 0.10

At time $t = 0$ the total money is £100. If there was no growth, i.e., no interest, then after 1 year there would still be £100. The rate of growth at 1 year would be zero. This would mean no change in money from the value at time $t = 0$. The value at time $t = 0$ is zero and represented on the graph by the point A. The unchanged value at $t = 1$ year is given by continuing the line to B. But interest is earned and the slope of the graph becomes

$$\text{Slope} = kN = £10 \text{ per year}$$

If we just consider 1 year then the change in the amount of money is

$$\text{Change in money} = \Delta N = kN\,\Delta t$$
$$= £10$$

This change is represented on the graph by the line going from A to C instead of A to B. If no further interest was earned in the next year the graph would progress to point D. But because interest is earned we must add to point D an amount ΔN given by

$$\text{Change in money} = kN\Delta t = £11$$

In the next interval of time we must add £12.1. In this way we can build up the graph, the procedure being:

> read off from the graph the last value of N
> calculate the change in N during the next time interval
> use this value to plot the new value of N.

Our growth equation tells us, at each value of N, the change in N that will occur in the next interval of time.

What is the equation relating money (N) and time (t)? This would be the equation represented by the graph, Fig. 0.10.

After 0 years, money $= N_0$
After 1 year, money $= N_0 + kN_0 = N_0(1 + k) = N_1$
After 2 years, money $= N_1 + kN_1 = N_1(1 + k) = N_0(1 + k)^2 = N_2$
After 3 years, money $= N_2 + kN_2 = N_0(1 + k)^3$
After t years, money $= N_0(1 + k)^t$

Thus we can describe the graphical curve by the equation

$$N = N_0(1 + k)^t$$

After 10 years our £100 would, at 10 per cent per year interest, have grown to

$$N = 100\left(1 + \frac{1}{10}\right)^{10}$$
$$= £259.4$$

16

An alternative way of writing the equation is

$$N = N_0 a^t$$

where a is a constant.

$$a = 1 + k$$

Thus in the case of the £100 at 10 per cent interest the equation can be written as

$$N = 100(1.1)^t$$

If the interest rate had been 20 per cent then the equation would be

$$N = 100(1.2)^t$$

There is another way of writing this equation where the interest rate is in the power term.

$$N = N_0 e^{kt}$$

k is the interest rate and 'e' a number. For this equation to be identical with our previous equation we must have

$$e^{kt} = a^t = (1 + k)^t$$

For the 10 per cent interest rate this means that

$$e^{0.1} = 1.1$$

For the 20 per cent interest rate

$$e^{0.2} = 1.2$$

Are these two values of 'e' identical? With the 10 per cent interest 'e' has the value 2.59, with 20 per cent the value is 2.49. The following table shows the values of 'e' for different interest rates.

Interest rate /per cent	e
100	2
20	2.49
10	2.59
1	2.70
0.1	2.717
0.01	2.718

As the interest rate becomes low so the value of 'e' seems to be tending to a value of 2.718. What is the significance of this?

The value of 'e' becomes constant when we have small interest rates. This is when we have a smooth graph relating money and time. We could have achieved a smooth curve by taking smaller intervals of time, e.g., calculating the interest every month or every day. Our equation

$$N = N_0 e^{kt}$$

where 'e' is a constant having the value 2.718, is thus for the case where our N or t intervals between plotted points are very small, i.e., in the limiting case when $\Delta t \to 0$.

This equation can also be used to describe the way in which the population increases with time, if there is a constant growth rate.

As $\Delta N / \Delta t = kN$ we must be able to write, for our limiting case when $\Delta t \to 0$

$$\frac{dN}{dt} = kN_0 e^{kt}$$

The rate at which N varies with time t is also proportional to e^{kt} and thus a graph of dN/dt against t should be a similar shape to the graph of N against t. The graph is of the same form, that given by e^{kt}, but multiplied by a different constant, kN_0 instead of just N_0.

Whenever some quantity (N) changes by an amount (ΔN) that is directly proportional to how much of that quantity was already present, then the growth is called *exponential*. An exponential growth can be described by the equations

$$\frac{dN}{dt} = kN$$

$$N = N e^{kt}$$

A graph of the logarithm of the quantity N against time t is a straight line.

Another way of considering an exponential is as a constant ratio graph. In successive intervals of time the value of N changes from N to $N + \Delta N$ (Fig. 0.11).

$$\frac{N + \Delta N}{N} = \frac{N + kN\Delta t}{N} = 1 + k\Delta t$$

17

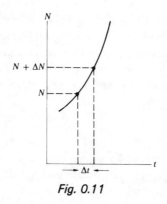

Fig. 0.11

Thus the ratio of values of N at times separated by an interval of Δt is a constant.

At time t_1 value of N is N_1.
At time t_2 value of N is N_2.

$$t_2 - t_1 = \Delta t$$

$$\frac{N_2}{N_1} = 1 + k \; \Delta t = \text{a constant}$$

At time t_3 value of N is N_3.

$$t_3 - t_2 = \Delta t$$

$$\frac{N_3}{N_2} = 1 + k \; \Delta t = \text{the same constant}$$

Similarly for values of N spaced at successive intervals of Δt

$$\frac{N_2}{N_1} = \frac{N_3}{N_2} = \frac{N_4}{N_3} = \frac{N_5}{N_4} = \text{a constant}$$

The curve grows by constant ratios in successive equal intervals of time.

The equations and examples so far considered have all involved growth. We can, however, describe a decay by means of the exponential equation. The equations then become

$$\frac{dN}{dt} = -kN$$

$$N = N_0 e^{-kt}$$

The minus sign tells us that when a change takes place that we subtract rather then add the change.

Consider an example—radioactive decay and the equation in the form

$$\frac{\Delta N}{\Delta t} = -kN$$

where ΔN is the change in the number of atoms in a time interval Δt, N is the number of atoms present and k the disintegration rate. The minus sign is because in each succeeding time interval the number N is getting less. The value of ΔN we calculate will be negative, indicating that it has to be subtracted from the preceding value of N.

Suppose we have 1000 radioactive atoms with a decay constant of 0.1 per minute (i.e., a 10 per cent decrease per minute).

At $t = 0$ number of atoms = 1000.
At $t = 1$ minute

Change in number of atoms $\Delta N = -\dfrac{1000}{10}$

and thus the number of atoms will be 1000 − 100 = 900.
At $t = 2$ minutes

Change in number of atoms $\Delta N = -\dfrac{900}{10}$

and thus the number of atoms will be 900 − 90 = 810.
At $t = 3$ minutes

Change in number of atoms $\Delta N = -\dfrac{810}{10}$

and thus the number of atoms will be 810 − 81 = 729.
At $t = 4$ minutes

Change in number of atoms $\Delta N = -\dfrac{729}{10}$

and thus the number of atoms will be 729 − 73 = 656.

Problems

1. What pattern can you discern in the following data:

	Melting point, /K	Molar latent heat of fusion/kJ mol^{-1}
Lead	600	4.77
Copper	1360	13.05
Nickel	1730	17.61
Platinum	2040	19.66
Iridium	2730	26.36
Tungsten	3650	35.23

What molar latent heats would you forecast for the following:

Magnesium, melting point 923 K
Vanadium, melting point 2190 K?

2. There is an error in the following data. Which is the incorrect boiling point? The information given in question **1** may help. Use your intuition to guess which point is in error and then try to analyse why you consider that point to be in error.

Boiling point, /K	
Lead	2824
Copper	2855
Nickel	3100
Platinum	4100
Iridium	4400
Tungsten	5880

3. This question is about describing different kinds of scientific statements. Here are some possible descriptions of such statements:

"states an experimental fact"
"makes a hypothesis"
"quotes a scientific law"
"is a rough estimate"
"is a deduction from earlier statements".

You are asked to give a brief description of each of the numbered statements in the passage below. Your descriptions should use phrases like those given above; you may use, combine or adapt the phrases above or invent others of your own.

1. If we assume that in a gas the atoms have a radius of about 10^{-10} m and a mean separation of about ten atomic diameters . . .
2. . . . it is clear that an alpha particle in traversing several centimetres of the gas must encounter some thousands of atoms of gas.
3. Only a minute fraction of such encounters however produce any appreciable deflection of the alpha particle.
4. It is difficult to avoid the conclusion that the greater part of the atomic volume is effectively empty.

(Oxford and Cambridge Schools Examination Board, Nuffield, Short answer paper, 1970)

4. Suppose the basic physical quantities chosen had been length, force and time with units of metre, newton and second. What would have been the units of (a) mass, (b) density, (c) momentum?

5. What are the dimensions of the following quantities: (a) density, (b) momentum, (c) energy?

6. A body moving through air at high speed v experiences a retarding force F given by

$$F = kA\rho v^x$$

where A is the surface area of the body, ρ is the density of the air and k is a numerical constant. Deduce the value of x.

A sphere of radius 50 mm and mass 1.0 kg falling vertically through air of density 1.2 kg m^{-3} attains a steady velocity of 11.0 m s^{-1}. If the above equation then applies to its fall, what is the value of k in this instance?

(University of London, Q5, Paper 2, June 1980)

7. Which of the following equations represents a valid relationship between the velocity v of an object after moving a distance s with a constant acceleration a? k is a numerical constant.

$$v = kas; \quad v = kas^2; \quad v = ksa^2; \quad v^2 = kas$$

8. Under certain conditions the distance s covered by a falling object is found to be proportional to the time t from the start of the fall. Write an equation relating s and t and give the dimensions of the proportionality constant.

9. When a sphere of radius a and density d falls through oil contained in a tank, it descends with uniform velocity v. The relation between v, a and d is

$$v/a^2 = Ad - B$$

where A and B are constants.

Figure 0.12 shows the results of some experiments. Determine from the graph the numerical values of A and B. What is the radius of a steel sphere of density 7.5 g cm^{-3} which falls through the oil with velocity 3.9 cm s^{-1}?

(Southern Universities, Q3, Paper 1, June 1980)

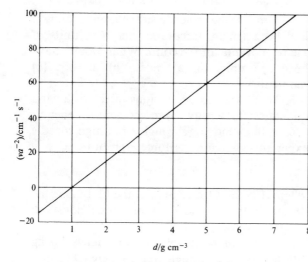

Fig. 0.12

10. For the following relationships, what should be plotted along the axes if a straight line graph is to be produced? For each graph state the gradient of the line and its intercept with the y-axis.

(a) $p = p_0 + \rho gh$, where p and h are the variables.

(b) $v = \sqrt{(2GM/R)}$, where v and R are the variables.

(c) $F = q_1q/4\pi\varepsilon_0 r^2$, where F and r are the variables.

(d) $v_0^2 = v^2 + 2as$, where v and s are the variables.

11. (a) Explain what is meant by:

(i) a random error

(ii) a systematic error.

For each type of error, describe one example of the experimental procedure used to reduce its effect.

(b) An experimenter wishing to determine the volume of glass in a length of glass tubing obtains the following readings:

Length, l	40 ± 1 mm
External diameter, D	12.0 ± 0.2 mm
Internal diameter, d	10.0 ± 0.2 mm

The volume V of the glass is calculated using the formula

$$V = \tfrac{1}{4}\pi l(D^2 - d^2)$$

(i) What is the greatest possible percentage error in each reading?

(ii) Calculate the volume V of the glass.

(iii) Estimate the greatest possible percentage error in the value of V calculated from these readings.

(iv) Suggest a different experimental method (other than the use of a more precise measuring instrument) which would give a more accurate value for the volume of the glass, and estimate the accuracy of the method.

(Oxford Local Examinations, Q2, Paper 1, June 1981)

12. The periodic time T of a simple pendulum of length L is given by

$$T = 2\pi \sqrt{\frac{L}{g}}$$

where g is the acceleration due to gravity. An experimenter obtains the following results for a simple pendulum

Time for 10 oscillations 20 ± 1 s

Length L $\qquad$ 0.995 ± 0.005 m

What is the value of g and its possible error?

13. Read the following account of an experimental investigation and then answer the questions at the end.

In one method for the determination of the surface tension, γ, of a liquid, a glass sphere of radius R is suspended from an arm of a balance and weighed. A trough containing the liquid is then raised until the liquid surface just touches the bottom of the sphere; the mass of the sphere appears to increase by m where

$$m = 4\pi\rho a^2\left(R - \frac{\sqrt{(aR)}}{3} - \frac{a}{3}\right) \quad (1)$$

In this formula, $a = (\gamma/\rho g)^{1/2}$, where ρ is the density of the liquid and g is the acceleration of free fall (9.80 m s^{-2}). Unfortunately, equation (1) cannot be solved to give an expression for a from which γ could be calculated. However, an approximate value of a may be obtained by using the expression

$$m = 4\pi\rho a^2 R \quad (2)$$

and a more accurate value then be obtained by a graphical method.

The following data were obtained during measurements on benzene.

Apparent increase in mass of sphere in contact with benzene 1.461 g

Radius of sphere 43.8 mm

Density of benzene 878 kg m^{-3}

Questions

(a) Show using equation (2), that the approximate value of a for benzene is 1.74 mm.

(b) Choose four convenient values of a within the range 1.74×10^{-3} m ± 10% and draw up a table to include values of a, $4\pi\rho a^2$, $\frac{1}{3}\sqrt{(aR)}$, $\frac{1}{3}a$, and z, where

$$z = 4\pi\rho a^2\left(R - \frac{\sqrt{(aR)}}{3} - \frac{a}{3}\right)$$

Plot a graph of z against a. Read off the value of a for which $z = m$, that is, the value satisfying equation (1).

Hence calculate the surface tension (γ) of benzene.

(c) Using the above method the following values of a were obtained for various water-alcohol mixtures.

% Water	% Alcohol	Density /kg m^{-3}	a/m
100.0	0.0	1000	2.71×10^{-3}
81.0	19.0	970	2.09×10^{-3}
60.0	40.0	947	1.81×10^{-3}
42.8	57.2	914	1.73×10^{-3}
0.0	100.0	792	1.71×10^{-3}

Plot a graph of surface tension against percentage of alcohol, and hence determine the surface tension of a mixture containing 30.0% alcohol.

Estimate the rate of change of surface tension with percentage of alcohol for mixtures containing 30% alcohol.

(University of London, Q8, 9, 10, Paper 3, June 1981)

14. Read the following account of an experimental investigation and then answer the questions at the end.

Corresponding measured values of potential difference, V, and current, I, for a semiconductor diode are given in Table 1.

Potential difference, V/V	Current, I/μA
0.255	0.40
0.315	1.60
0.345	3.6
0.385	8.9
0.410	18.2
0.455	52.2
0.475	90.3
0.495	140
0.505	182
0.515	223
0.530	310

Table 1

Questions

(a) Using the values in Table 1, plot a graph with I as ordinate against V as abscissa.

Determine, for the point on the graph corresponding to $V = 0.500$ V

(i) the rate of change of I with V, and hence
(ii) the percentage change in I corresponding to a 1% change in V.

(b) The following theoretical equation (the 'rectifier equation') applies for certain types of semiconductor diode:

$$I = I_0(e^{\alpha V} - 1) \qquad (1)$$

where I and α are constants.

If V is sufficiently large, $I \approx I_0 e^{\alpha V} \qquad (2)$

so that

$$\ln I \approx \ln I_0 + \alpha V \qquad (3)$$

or

$$\log_{10} I \approx \log_{10} I_0 + 0.434\alpha V \qquad (4)$$

From an appropriate table of values plot either a graph of $\ln(I/\mu A)$ as ordinate against V as abscissa, or a graph of $\log_{10}(I/\mu A)$ as ordinate against V as abscissa. From your graph derive values for I_0 and α.

(c) Explain for which value of potential difference in Table 1 the approximation made in equation (2) will be most serious. Using the values of I_0 and α derived in question (b), calculate the current at this p.d. using the exact equation (1) ($e = 2.72$). Plot the corresponding point on your second graph.

State, giving your reasons, whether you consider that use of the approximate equation (4) was justified in analysing the results in Table 1.

(University of London, Q6, 7, 8, Paper 3, June 1980)

15. Which of the graphs in Fig. 0.13 are of exponential changes?

16. How would you describe what an exponential variation with time is, to say an arts student who has never met the term or studied physics?

17. What two quantities would you plot to obtain straight line graphs for

(a) $y = e^{-cx}$?
(b) $y = e^{-c/x}$?

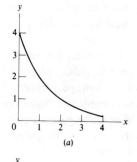
(a)

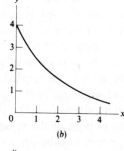
(b)

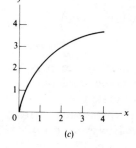
(c)

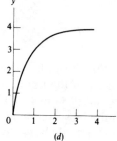
(d)

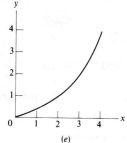
(e)

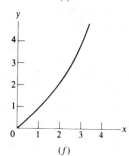
(f)

Fig. 0.13

18. A particle is projected at 100 m s^{-1} up a sloping plane, as shown in the diagram [Fig. 0.14], so that it is moving along a line inclined at 30° to the horizontal. By considering the velocity changes that happen during successive short time intervals begin to construct a distance–time graph for

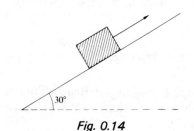
Fig. 0.14

the particle. Your construction need not be accurate, but you should give enough notes to explain how an accurate plot would be made. Ignore friction forces between the plane and the particle, and assume that gravity exerts a force of 9.8 N kg^{-1} which does not vary with height.

(Oxford and Cambridge Board, Nuffield, Special paper, 1971)

19. The damping of an object oscillating with simple harmonic motion decreases according to the equation

$$\frac{\Delta A}{\Delta t} = -CA$$

where A is the amplitude and C a constant.

(a) Describe how the amplitudes of successive oscillations change with time.

(b) If the value of C was doubled how would the oscillation change?

(c) Sketch a graph relating A and t.

1 Static forces

Equilibrium

Civil engineers are very much concerned with what can be called static equilibrium, i.e., they have to design objects such as bridges and buildings so that though acted on by forces they remain at rest (when seen by an observer on earth). They have to analyse situations, identifying all the external forces that act or may act on the structure, and establish that it will remain at rest and so tolerate the forces concerned.

In any discussion of equilibrium we need to distinguish between translational and rotational equilibrium. *Translational equilibrium* is when an object has zero translational acceleration and zero translational velocity, so that it remains at rest relative to the observer. The term 'translational' means in just one direction, without rotation. *Rotational equilibrium* is when an object has zero rotational acceleration and zero rotational velocity, so that it is not rotating relative to the observer.

Translational equilibrium

If we take a small object to which are attached a number of spring balances, as in Fig. 1.1, and consider their readings when the object is at rest then the result is always that there is no resultant forces, all the applied forces cancelling each other out. Forces are vector quantities and so the condition for translational equilibrium can be given as

> The vector sum of all the external forces acting on the body is zero when it is in translational equilibrium

The 'vector sum' means that when the forces are added their directions have to be taken into account. Thus for the forces shown in Fig. 1.1, one way of taking directions into account is to resolve the forces into two convenient directions and consider the sums of the forces in those directions. Thus if we take the Y and X directions, then for the Y direction we have

$$F_1 \cos \theta_1 - F_3 \cos \theta_3$$

If there is static equilibrium then the sum must be zero, hence

$$F_1 \cos \theta_1 - F_3 \cos \theta_3 = 0$$

For the X direction we have

$$F_1 \sin \theta_1 - F_2 + F_3 \sin \theta_3 = 0$$

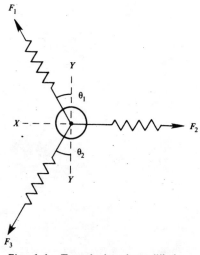

Fig. 1.1 *Translational equilibrium*

Other methods of summing forces and establishing their vector sum is zero are the triangle of forces, the parallelogram of forces and the polygon of forces. Chapter 0 includes an introduction to these methods. They all rely on a force being represented by an arrow-headed line whose length and direction represents the magnitude and direction of the force. If there are three forces acting on a body, it will be in static translational equilibrium if these arrow-headed lines when drawn head-to-tail form a closed triangle. If they are not in equilibrium the triangle will not close. If more than three forces are involved the same technique will result in a closed polygon for equilibrium. Figure 1.2 illustrates both these methods.

The parallelogram method involves, for three forces, determining the sum of two of the forces, i.e., the resultant, and showing that it is opposite and equal to the third force. Figure 1.3 illustrates this method. The parallelogram law can be stated as

Two vector quantities V_1 and V_2 can be replaced by an equivalent vector which is the diagonal of the parallelogram formed by V_1 and V_2 as its two sides

Rotational equilibrium

In discussing rotational equilibrium we need to talk of moment or torque of a force. The moment or torque of a force T about an axis is the product of the force and the perpendicular distance r of the line of action of that force from the axis (Fig. 1.4).

$$T = Fr$$

Torque, or moment, has the units of N m, when the force is in newtons (N) and the distance in metres (m).

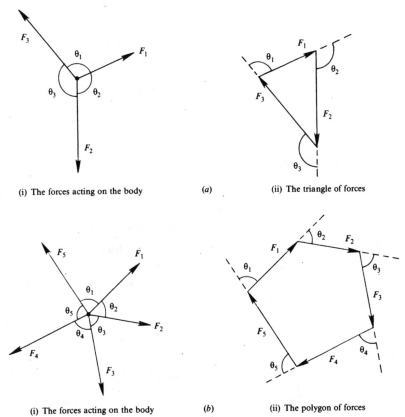

(i) The forces acting on the body   (a)   (ii) The triangle of forces

(i) The forces acting on the body   (b)   (ii) The polygon of forces

Fig. 1.2 (a) Three forces in translational equilibrium. (b) Five forces in translational equilibrium

25

MECHANICS

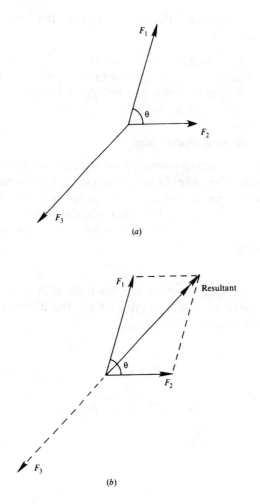

(a)

(b)

Fig. 1.3 (a) The forces acting on the body. (b) The parallelogram

The condition for rotational static equilibrium that there be no rotational acceleration means that there must be no resultant external rotational torque or moment of force acting on the body. Hence, since we need to take the direction of rotation into account for a torque, or moment of force:

The vector sum of all the external torques acting on the body must be zero when it is in rotational equilibrium

Another way of putting this, often referred to as the principle of moments, is

The algebraic sums of the moments of the forces acting on a body about all axes is zero when it is in rotational equilibrium, i.e., clockwise moments of forces about any axis equals anticlockwise moments of forces about the same axis

Consider the simple example of a light beam balanced across a pivot with a force of 100 N applied downwards at one end, 200 mm from the pivot, and a force of 120 N to be applied somewhere along the beam so that it balances and is horizontal (Fig. 1.5). The clockwise moment about the pivot is 100×200 N mm and the anticlockwise moment is $120 L$. For rotational equilibrium

$$120L = 100 \times 200$$

$$L = 167 \text{ mm}$$

The normal force

When an object rests on a table there are just two forces acting on it, a gravitational force due to the mass of the object and a force resulting from the

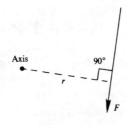

Fig. 1.4 Definition of movement of a force

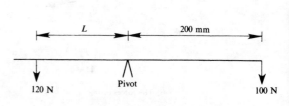

Fig. 1.5

26

deformation of the table due to the object resting on it. This deformation force is upwards, the gravitational force being downwards. Since the object is at rest, then the upward force due to the deformation must just balance the downward force due to gravity. This upward force is called the normal force since it is perpendicular to the surface of the table. The term 'reaction force' is sometimes used, but this can lead to confusion with the term 'reaction' which is used sometimes with Newton's third law of motion. The normal force acts on the same object that is responsible for it coming into effect, the reaction force in Newton's third law of motion acts on another body.

Conditions for equilibrium

For an object in static equilibrium, when all the forces are coplanar, i.e., in the same plane, we must have:

1. The sums of the resolved components of the forces in any two convenient directions are zero.
2. The algebraic sums of the moments of the forces acting on the body about all axes are zero.

A consequence of the above two conditions when there are only three forces acting on a body is that, if the body is in equilibrium the lines of action of the forces must be concurrent, i.e., all pass through a single point.

It is possible to apply the above conditions to all the component parts of a body, as well as the body as a whole, since all parts are also in equilibrium.

The following examples illustrate the ways some equilibrium problems can be tackled.

(a) A rigid beam of negligible mass is hinged to a wall and held horizontally by a wire attached to one end, as shown in Fig. 1.6. If a weight of 50 N is hung from the free end of the beam, what is (i) the tension in the wire, (ii) the compression in the beam?

Since the free end of the beam is in static equilibrium we can solve this problem by considering the vertical and horizontal components

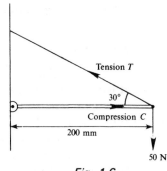

Fig. 1.6

of the forces acting on this end of the beam. Thus

$$T \sin 30° = 50$$

Hence

$$T = 100 \text{ N}$$

$$C = T \cos 30°$$

Hence

$$C = 87 \text{ N}$$

An alternative method for solving the problem would have been to draw the triangle of forces for the three forces at the end of the beam.

(b) Figure 1.7 shows one end of a bridge. What must be the relationships between the forces F_1 and F_2 acting along the parts of the bridge and the normal force N acting on the end of the bridge?

Since the end of the bridge is in static equilibrium then the vertical and horizontal components of the forces must be zero. Thus

$$N = F_1 \sin 60°$$

$$F_2 = F_1 \cos 60°$$

If we needed N in terms of F_2 we can obtain the

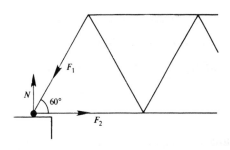

Fig. 1.7

27

relationship by dividing the equations and so obtaining

$$N = F_2 \tan 60°$$

(c) Figure 1.8 shows an object being held at rest in a person's hand with the forearm horizontal. Superimposed on the figure are the forces acting at the different distances. F_1 is the force exerted by the muscle, F_2 the force exerted at the elbow joint and the gravitational force due to the mass of the forearm is 20 N. What are F_1 and F_2?

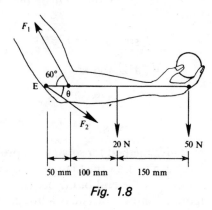

Fig. 1.8

Taking moments about the axis through the elbow joint E, then

$$F_1 \times 50 \sin 60° = 20 \times 150 + 50 \times 300$$

Hence $F_1 = 416$ N

For static equilibrium there must be no net horizontal force acting on the arm, hence considering the horizontal components we have

$$F_1 \cos 60° = F_2 \cos \theta$$

Similarly for the vertical components

$$F_1 \sin 60° = F_2 \sin \theta + 20 + 50$$

Hence we have, for the two equations

$$F_2 \sin \theta = 290$$

$$F_2 \cos \theta = 208$$

Dividing these equations gives $\tan \theta = 1.39$ and so $\theta = 54.4°$. Thus $F_2 = 357$ N at this angle.

(d) A ladder of length 4.0 m and having a weight of 250 N rests with its upper end 3.5 m up a smooth vertical wall and its lower end on rough horizontal ground. If the weight of the ladder can be considered to act through its mid point and the force exerted by the wall is at right angles to the wall, what is the force exerted on the ladder by the ground?

Figure 1.9 shows the situation. Since there are just three coplanar forces acting on the ladder, their lines of action must meet at a single point. Hence the angle θ must be given by

$$\tan \theta = \frac{3.5}{\frac{1}{2}L}$$

Since $L^2 = 4.0^2 - 3.5^2$ (Pythagoras theorem), then $L = 1.9$ m. Hence $\theta = 75°$.

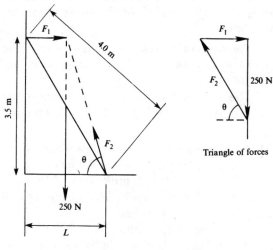

Fig. 1.9

If we consider the triangle of forces, then we must have

$$F_2 \sin \theta = 250$$

and so $F_2 = 259$ N.

Note, the reason for the force acting on the ladder at the ground not being at right angles to the ground is that, because the ground is rough, there are two forces acting at that point—the normal force and a frictional force along the ground. It is the resultant of these two forces which is F_2.

The problem could also have been solved by taking moments about the point of contact of the ladder with the ground, summing the vertical forces and summing the horizontal forces.

(e) The brake pedal of a car is as shown in Fig. 1.10. If a foot applies a force of 800 N to the pedal, what will be the tension T in the brake cable?

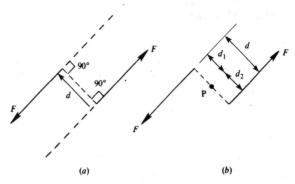

(a)   (b)

Fig. 1.11   A couple acting on a lamina

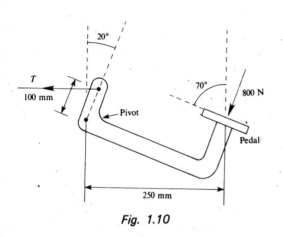

Fig. 1.10

If we take moments about an axis through the pivot, then

$$T \times 100 \cos 20° = 800 \times 250 \sin 70°$$

$$T = 2000 \text{ N}$$

The important point in this problem is to realise that what is required is the perpendicular distance from the line of action of the force to the axis about which the moment is taken.

Couples

The term *couple* is used to describe a pair of forces which produce only a turning effect, no translational effects. Such forces are equal in magnitude but opposite in direction and do not pass through a point, being parallel as shown in Fig. 1.11. An example of a couple are the forces applied to the steering wheel of a car to rotate it.

The torque or moment of a couple about, say, an axis mid way between the forces (Fig. 1.11a) is $F \times \frac{1}{2}d + F \times \frac{1}{2}d = Fd$. About any other axis the

moment of the couple is the same

$$\text{Moment of a couple} = Fd$$

For example, about P (Fig. 1.11b)

$$\text{Moment} = Fd_1 + Fd_2 = F(d_1 + d_2) = Fd$$

To illustrate the calculation of the moment of a couple, consider the chair castor illustrated in Fig. 1.12. The chair has four such castors and when a person is sitting in the chair the force applied through the chair leg to each castor is 2000 N. What is the moment of the couple acting on the castor?

The normal force at the point of contact between the ground and the wheel of the castor must be 2000 N upwards. Hence there is a couple and the moment of the couple is $2000 \times 40 \times 10^{-3}$ = 800 N m.

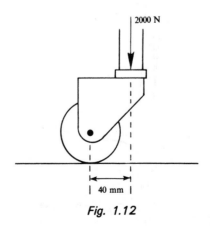

Fig. 1.12

Centre of gravity

If you take an object and suspend it then, after some initial movement, it settles down to a rest position. This means that in that position, since we have static equilibrium, the clockwise moments of all the particles in the object to the right of the pivot line must be balanced by the anticlockwise moments of all the particles in the object to the left of the pivot line (Fig. 1.13). It is as though the entire weight of the object is situated somewhere along this pivot line. If the object is suspended from different points, further pivot lines can be found and they all meet in just one single point. At this point we can consider the line of action of the weight of the object to always act, however the object is orientated. This point is called the *centre of gravity* of the object.

The centre of gravity of an object is the single point through which the line of action of the weight passes, however the object is orientated.

Suspending an object from different points and finding the pivot lines is an experimental way of determining the position of the centre of gravity of an object. The position can, however, be calculated using the principle of moments.

The object is considered to be made up of a number of segments each having mass and so weight, each at different distances from an axis about which we can take moments. The total

moment of all these segments is thus

$$w_1x_1 + w_2x_2 + x_3x_3 + \text{etc.}$$

where w_1 is the weight of particle 1 and x_1 its distance from the axis, w_2 and x_2 the corresponding weight and distance for particle 2, etc. The total moment can thus be represented by

$$\text{total moment} = \Sigma(wx)$$

The Σ sign is used to mean 'sum' of. If we replaced the entire object by a weight acting at a single point such that it gave the same moment then, if W is this weight and $\bar{x}$ its distance from the axis, we must have

$$W\bar{x} = \Sigma(wx)$$

and so

$$\bar{x} = \frac{\Sigma(wx)}{W}$$

By carrying out such summations the position of the centre of gravity can be determined.

For symmetrical homogeneous objects the centre of gravity is the geometrical centre. Thus for a sphere, the centre of gravity is at the centre. For a uniform rod of length L, the centre of gravity is a distance of ½L from each end. For a uniform rectangular laminar, the centre of gravity is at the intersection of the diagonals.

For composite objects, the centre of gravity can be determined by considering the object to be made up of a number of homogeneous objects, each with its weight concentrated at its geometric centre. Thus for the object shown in Fig. 1.14, a homogeneous sphere at the end of a homogenous rod, we can consider the centre of gravity of the sphere to be at its centre, A, and the centre of

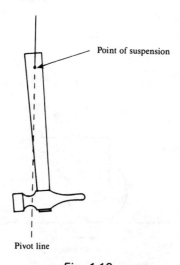

Point of suspension

Pivot line

Fig. 1.13

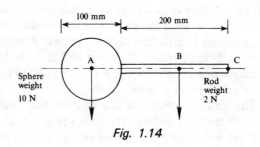

Fig. 1.14

gravity of the rod at its centre, B. Hence if we take moments about some axis, say C, then

$$\text{total moment} = 10 \times 250 + 2 \times 100$$

$$= 2700 \text{ N mm}$$

If the centre of gravity is x from C then, since the total weight is 12 N

$$12x = 2700$$

$$x = 225 \text{ mm}$$

Stability of equilibrium

A cone resting base down on a horizontal surface is stable in that it does not topple over but remains at rest. However, a cone stood point down on a horizontal surface is not stable but topples over with the greatest of ease. What determines whether an object is stable?

If a block of wood is placed on an incline and the angle of the incline slowly increased (see Fig. 1.15), the block will be found to be stable and not topple over until the centre of gravity of the block fails to lie above the base area of the block. Then it topples.

An object is in stable equilibrium when its centre of gravity lies above the base area defined by its supports or edges.

Problems

1. A street lamp of mass 5.0 kg is held suspended over the road by two wires of negligible mass, as shown in Fig. 1.16. What is the tension in each wire? ($g = 9.8$ m s^{-2})

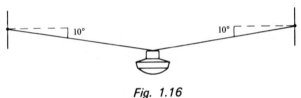

10°   10°

Fig. 1.16

2. A pub sign of mass 10.0 kg is suspended above the pub door by the arrangement shown in Fig. 1.17. What is the force exerted by the wall on the tie rod? ($g = 9.8$ m s^{-2})

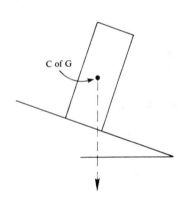

C of G

(a) Does not topple

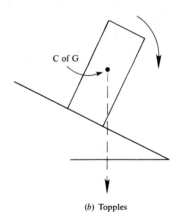

C of G

(b) Topples

Fig. 1.15

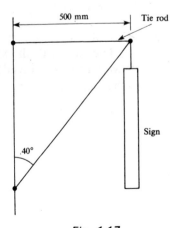

500 mm   Tie rod

40°

Sign

Fig. 1.17

3. Determine the tension in the supporting cable and the force on the pin at A for the jib crane shown in Fig. 1.18. ($g = 9.8$ m s^{-2})

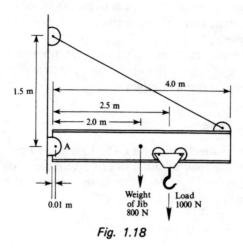

Fig. 1.18

4. What is the maximum load the tow truck shown in Fig. 1.19 can lift vertically without the front wheels coming off the ground?

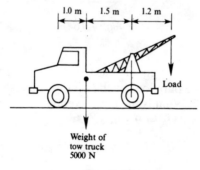

Fig. 1.19

5. The two sides of a step ladder have equal lengths of 2.0 m. The side with the steps has a weight of 160 N which can be considered to act 1.1 m up from the base. The other side has a weight of 50 N which acts mid way along its length. What are the normal forces exerted on the ground by each side when the feet are 0.60 m apart?

6. A chain of mass 4.0 kg has its ends fixed at the same height to two parallel vertical walls and hangs loosely between them. If the angle to the horizontal made by the end links at each end is 30°, what is the tension in the chain? ($g = 9.8$ m s^{-2})

7. A hiker has a mass of 70 kg and carries a rucksack of mass 15 kg. The centre of gravity of the hiker, without the pack, is 1.1 m above the ground. The centre of gravity of the rucksack is 0.2 m above its base, and when carried the base is 1.2 m above the ground. At what height above the ground is the centre of gravity of the hiker plus rucksack?

8. A four-legged table has a square top of mass 15 kg and side 1.0 m. The uniform legs each have a mass of 1.5 kg and length 0.7 m and are positioned at each corner of the top. Where is the centre of gravity of the table? At what angle to the horizontal can the table be tipped on two legs before it will topple over?

9. For the vase shown in Fig. 1.20, how far can the top of the vase be pushed from the vertical before it topples over?

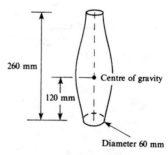

Fig. 1.20

2 Motion

Describing motion

What is meant by motion? Anybody answering this question would probably talk of position changing with time. But if we look at how the position of objects or parts of objects change with time it seems very complex. Look at the position–time traces for the planet Mars (Fig. 2.1a), for a point on the rim of a car wheel as the car moves steadily along a road (Fig. 2.1b), and for a tennis ball during a game of tennis (Fig. 2.1c). To find laws governing motion and its causes we need ways of describing motion and of simplifying it,

so that relationships can be readily established. Having arrived at relationships for a simplified case we can then try to apply them to complex motions.

For our simplified case we take the motion of a point in a straight line. We chose a point because we do not have to bother with the structure of the object and possible rotation. We chose a straight line because it seems to be the simplest. How can we describe the motion of a point? One way is to determine the position of the point at various instants of time and use the position–time data to specify the motion.

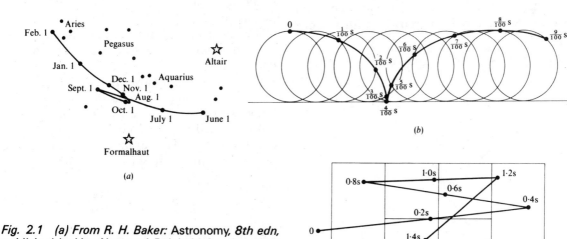

Fig. 2.1 (a) From R. H. Baker: Astronomy, 8th edn, published by Van Nostrand Reinhold Co., Copyright 1964 by Litton Educational Publishing. The position–time trace for the planet Mars with respect to the fixed stars. (b) The position–time trace for a point on the rim of a wheel. (c) The position–time trace for a tennis ball

Let us take an example:

Position of point/m	0	0	2	4	6	10	15
Time/s		0	1	2	3	4	5	6

Position of point/m	18	20	22	23	23	23
Time/s	7	8	9	10	11	12

The table could be presented diagrammatically as a graph, Fig. 2.2. What is happening to the point? When we start our timing the point is at the zero on our distance scale. After 1 s the point is still at the zero position. During the next second the point moves a distance of 2 m. We can describe this motion by saying that the point has an average speed of 2 m s^{-1} during the time interval 1 to 2 s.

Average speed =

$$\frac{\text{distance covered in a time interval}}{\text{time interval}}$$

The word average is necessary because the point could have higher, and lower, speeds during the time interval. If our time interval had been from zero to 2 s then the average speed would have been 1 m s^{-1}: for part of this interval the speed was zero, for part 2 m s^{-1}.

Over the time intervals 2–3 s and 3–4 s the distance covered in a second remains constant. We say that the point is moving with uniform

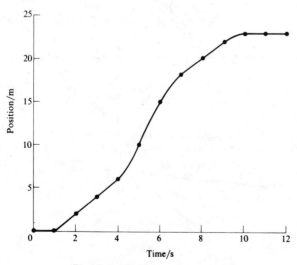

25

20

Position/m

15

10

5

0   2   4   6   8   10   12
Time/s

Fig. 2.2 Position–time graph

speed. The average speed is uniform when equal distances are covered in equal intervals of time. The speed is uniform if equal distances are covered in equal time intervals, however short the time intervals are.

We supposed our point to be moving in a straight line; would our definition of speed and that of uniform speed be changed if the point moved in any other path? Can we use the terms for, say, an object moving in a circular path? The term speed is used regardless of any change of direction of an object. We can have an object moving with constant speed round a circular path. A car could go round a race track with a constant speed of 100 km h^{-1} (at least theoretically, if not in practice). Uniform speed can describe the motion of an object moving in a circular path—all that is required is that the object changes its position by equal distances in equal intervals of time, however short the time intervals.

The term velocity is used, instead of speed, to describe motion when we are concerned with the position of an object after some time. Instead of being concerned with distance we are concerned with displacement, i.e., for a particular time interval the straight line distance between the start and finish points regardless of the path the object actually followed during that time. Thus, the average velocity is the displacement in a time interval divided by the time interval.

The velocity is uniform if equal displacements occur in equal time intervals, however short the time intervals are. An object can only have a constant velocity if it moves in a straight line and covers equal distances along that line in equal intervals of time. Thus an object may have a uniform speed but need not necessarily have a uniform velocity. The car moving round the race track with uniform speed is not moving with a uniform velocity.

When the velocity of an object changes we say it has accelerated.

Average acceleration =

$$\frac{\text{change of velocity in a time interval}}{\text{time interval}}$$

If the velocity was 2 m s^{-1} at the beginning of a one-second time interval and 4 m s^{-1} at the end, then the average acceleration was $+2$ m s^{-2}. The acceleration is positive because the velocity is increasing in the time interval. A negative acceleration would mean a decreasing velocity—the object was slowing down.

The acceleration is uniform when equal changes in velocity occur in equal intervals of time, however small the time intervals.

Distance–time relationships

This section is only concerned with motion in a straight line.

Suppose we determine experimentally the positions of an object at different instants of time. The data can be used to plot a graph of distance, from some starting point, against time. What is the significance of the slope of such a graph?

Over a straight line portion of the graph, Fig. 2.3, the slope is

$$\frac{s_2 - s_1}{t_2 - t_1}$$

where s_1 is the distance at time t_1, and s_2 the distance at time t_2. The slope is the change in s divided by the change in t. This can be written as

$$\frac{\Delta s}{\Delta t}$$

The Δ (delta) sign is used to denote a finite bit of some quantity.

The slope tells us the distance covered in the time taken. This quantity is known as velocity.

$$\text{Velocity} = \frac{\Delta s}{\Delta t}$$

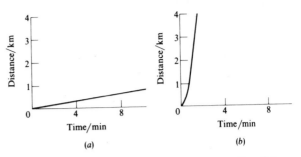

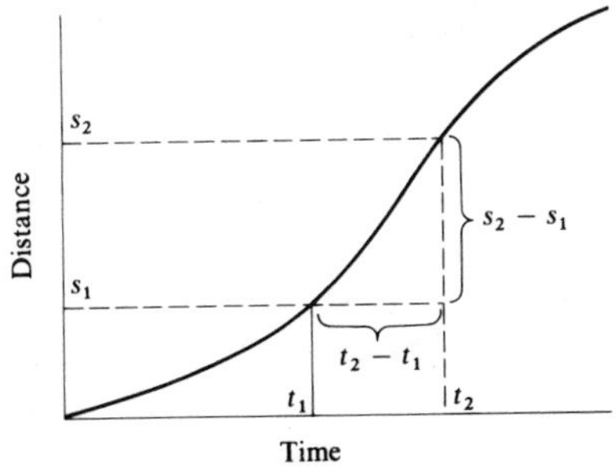

Fig. 2.4   Distance-time graphs: (a) a cyclist, (b) a car

The greater the velocity the greater the slope of the distance–time graph (Fig. 2.4).

If the velocity is not constant the graph will not be a straight line, i.e., the slope will not be constant. What about our velocity definition now? If we take large values of Δt in order to compute the slope then we are averaging out the velocity over the time interval Δt. The smaller the value of Δt the more accurate will be our value of the velocity for an instant of time. The velocity at some instant of time is the value of $\Delta s/\Delta t$ when Δt is very small, i.e., when Δt is nearly zero.

$$\text{Velocity} = \lim_{\Delta t \to 0} \frac{\Delta s}{\Delta t}$$

The above is the mathematical way of writing this, 'limit as Δt approaches zero' of $\Delta s/\Delta t$. A shorter way of writing this is ds/dt.

$$\text{Velocity} = \frac{ds}{dt}$$

The Δ's and the d's are part of the notation, like sine or cosine, and are not arithmetical symbols which can be cancelled. ds/dt is called the derivative of s with respect to t.

Suppose we have a distance–time graph which can be represented by the equation (Fig. 2.5)

$$s = Kt^2$$

where K is some constant. How can we calculate the velocity at some instant of time? The velocity is the slope of the graph at the instant concerned. How then can we calculate the slope?

Fig. 2.3

35

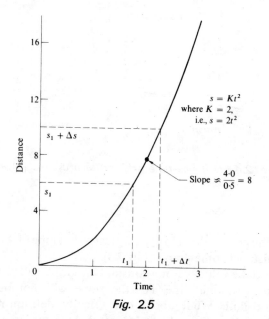

Fig. 2.5

Let s_1 be the distance at time t_1.

$$s_1 = Kt^2_1 \qquad (1)$$

If we increase the time to $t_1 + \Delta t$, then the distance must also increase to, say, $s_1 + \Delta s$. If both these values lie on the graph then

$$s_1 + \Delta s = K(t_1 + \Delta t)^2$$

Expanding the term in the brackets

$$s_1 + \Delta s = Kt^2_1 + 2Kt_1\Delta t + K(\Delta t)^2$$

If Eq. (1) is subtracted from this

$$\Delta s = 2Kt_1\,\Delta t + K(\Delta t)^2$$

$$\frac{\Delta s}{\Delta t} = 2Kt_1 + K\,\Delta t$$

As Δt tends to zero so this value of $\Delta s/\Delta t$ will come nearer to being the value of the velocity at the time t_1. But the smaller we make Δt the smaller will the $K\,\Delta t$ term become. Hence in the limit when Δt is near to zero the velocity will be given by

$$\text{Velocity (at } t_1) = \frac{ds}{dt} = 2Kt_1$$

This process is known as differentiation.

With $K = 2$ this gives at $t_1 = 2$ a velocity or slope

of distance–time graph of 8; this checks with a measurement of the graphical slope at $t = 2$.

The equation shows that the velocity depends on the time elapsed. The object whose motion is described by this equation must therefore be accelerating—a velocity depending on the time is not constant.

Velocity is the rate at which distance along a straight line is covered, with respect to time, and is the slope at any instant of the distance–time graph. If there is uniform velocity then equal distances along a straight line are covered in equal intervals of time, however short, and the slope of the graph is the same at all instants, during the constant velocity. When the velocity is not constant then the slope of the distance–time graph is not constant. Figure 2.6 shows several

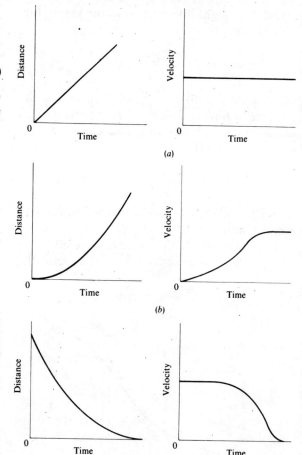

Fig. 2.6

distance-time graphs and their corresponding velocity-time graphs. The velocity has been obtained from measurements of the slopes at various times of the distance-time graphs.

When the slope of the velocity-time graph is zero then the velocity is constant, there is no acceleration. If the slope of the velocity-time graph is positive, i.e., the velocity is increasing as the time increases, then there is a positive acceleration. If the slope is negative, i.e., the speed is decreasing as the time increases, then there is a negative acceleration. Acceleration is defined as

Acceleration =

$$\frac{\text{change in velocity in a time interval}}{\text{time interval}}$$

$$= \frac{\Delta v}{\Delta t}$$

Acceleration is the slope of a velocity-time graph. In Fig. 2.6a the slope of the velocity-time graph is zero and thus there is no acceleration. In Fig. 2.6b the slope increases initially and then decreases to zero; the initial acceleration thus decreases to zero. In Fig. 2.6c the slope decreases to zero. The slope is negative and thus there is a negative acceleration.

Uniformly accelerated motion

The slope at any instant of the velocity-time graph gives the acceleration at that instant. For a uniform or constant acceleration we have a constant slope (Fig. 2.7).

Suppose we have a velocity of v_0 at time $t = 0$ and v at time t. Then

$$\text{Slope} = \frac{v - v_0}{t}$$

and thus acceleration, a, is given by

$$a = \frac{v - v_0}{t}$$

or

$$v = v_0 + at$$

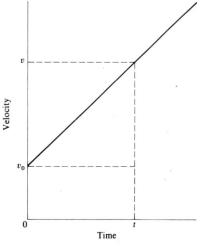

Fig. 2.7

The velocity is increasing uniformly with time, hence the average velocity $\bar{v}$ is given by

$$\bar{v} = \frac{v + v_0}{2}$$

But during time t the object moves a distance s. Hence

$$\bar{v} = \frac{s}{t}$$

Eliminating $\bar{v}$ from these two equations gives

$$\frac{s}{t} = \frac{v + v_0}{2}$$

$$s = \frac{v_0 t}{2} + \frac{vt}{2}$$

Eliminating v by use of the equation $v = v_0 + at$ gives

$$s = v_0 t + \tfrac{1}{2}at^2$$

If instead of eliminating v we had eliminated t the result would be

$$v^2 = v_0^2 + 2as$$

The three equations

$$v = v_0 + at$$

$$s = v_0 t + \tfrac{1}{2}at^2$$

$$v^2 = v_0^2 + 2as$$

37

for straight line, uniformly accelerated motion are used in many problems. The following illustrates such use.

(a) A car· is accelerated at 2.0 m^{-2} from a velocity of 8.0 m s^{-1}. Calculate (i) the time required to attain a velocity of 20 m s^{-1}, (ii) the distance travelled in this time?
(i) Using $v = v_0 + at$, with $v = 20$ m s^{-1}, $v_0 = 8.0$ m s^{-1} and $a = 2.0$ m s^{-2}, then $t = 6.0$ s.
(ii) Using $v^2 = v^2_0 + 2as$, with $v = 20$ m s^{-1}, $v_0 = 8.0$ m s^{-1} and $a = 2.0$ m s^{-2}, then $s = 84$ m.
(b) A car starts from rest and accelerates uniformly at 2.0 m s^{-2} in first gear until it attains a velocity of 10 m s^{-1}. The motorist then changes to second gear and accelerates uniformly at 4.0 m s^{-2} until a velocity of 30 m s^{-1} is attained. Calculate (i) the time for which the car is in first gear, (ii) the time for which it is in second gear and (iii) the total distance travelled by the car.
(i) Using $v = v_0 + at$, with $v = 10$ m s^{-1}, $v_0 = 0$, $a = 2.0$ m s^{-2}, then the time t in first gear is 5.0 s.
(ii) Using $v = v_0 + at$, with $v = 30$ m s^{-1}, $v_0 = 10$ m s^{-1}, $a = 4.0$ m s^{-2}, then the time t in second gear is 5.0 s.
(iii) During the time in first gear, $v = 10$ m s^{-1}, $v_0 = 0$, $a = 2.0$ m s^{-2}, and so using $v^2 = v^2_0 + 2as$ we have $s = 25$ m.
During the time in second gear, $v = 30$ m s^{-1}, $v_0 = 10$ m s^{-1}, $a = 4.0$ m s^{-2}, and so using $v^2 = v^2_0 + 2as$ we have $s = 100$ m. Hence the total distance travelled is $25 + 100 = 125$ m.

Area under velocity–time graph

Consider an object moving with uniform velocity. Figure 2.8a shows the velocity–time graph for the motion. The distance travelled, s, during a time, t, is given by

$$s = vt$$

if $s = 0$ at time $t = 0$. But vt is the area under the graph between the times $t = 0$ and t. Is this a general rule—is the area under the velocity–time graph the distance travelled?
What about a uniformly accelerated object? Figure 2.8b shows the velocity–time graph. The area under the graph between $t = 0$ and t is $\frac{1}{2}vt$.

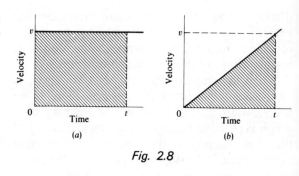

Fig. 2.8

How does this compare with the calculated distance?

$$s = \frac{1}{2}at^2, \qquad v = at$$

If we eliminate a from the two equations we have

$$s = \frac{1}{2}vt$$

The area is equal to the distance covered.
Suppose we have a non-uniformly accelerated motion. Figure 2.9 shows a typical velocity–time graph for the first stage of a rocket. Can we determine the distance–time graph? We can find the distance covered in the first 10 s by estimating the area under the graph between time zero and time 10 s, in this case approximately 125 m. The distance covered in the first 20 s is the area between the time zero and time 20 s lines, 1000 m.

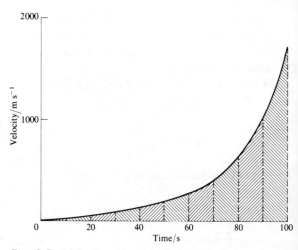

Fig. 2.9 Velocity–time graph for the first stage of a rocket

In a similar manner we find the distance covered at various times and so plot the distance-time graph. Figure 2.10 shows the result. After 100 s the rocket has covered a distance of about 38 km. The first stage of the rocket, Saturn, which put the first men on the moon burns for 159 s and gives the rocket a speed of about 140 000 m s⁻¹. At the end of the time the rocket has covered a distance of about 61 km.

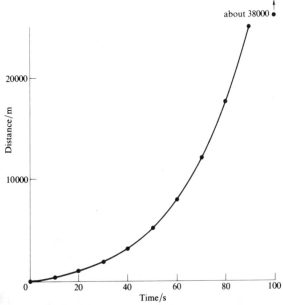

Fig. 2.10   Distance-time graph for the first stage of a rocket

Fig. 2.11   Photograph from PSSC Physics, 2nd edn, D. C. Heath and Co. Strobe photograph of a falling billiard ball. The position scale is in centimetres, and the time interval between the successive positions of the ball is 1/30 s

The acceleration due to gravity

Figure 2.11 shows a strobe photograph of a freely falling object. The photograph shows the positions occupied by the object at equally spaced successive time intervals. Figure 2.12 shows the distance-time graph for the motion. As can be seen, the object certainly does not cover equal distances in equal time intervals and so does not have a constant velocity.

We can read off from the graph the distances covered in short time intervals and so obtain values of the average velocity at different times during the fall. The velocities are in fact the slopes of the graph at the time instants concerned.

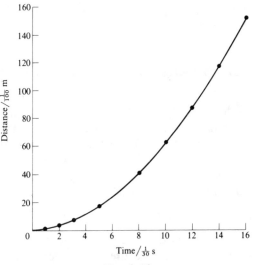

Fig. 2.12

Measure for yourself. The velocity is directly proportional to the time. Equal increases of velocity occur in equal intervals of time—there is constant acceleration. The velocity changes by about 10 m s^{-1} for each second change—the acceleration is about 10 m s^{-2}.

Not only is the acceleration constant for a freely falling object but all freely falling objects, *in vacuo*, have the same acceleration (symbol g). We need to specify a vacuum because an object falling in a medium has its motion affected by the medium. For dense objects falling in air over relatively short distances the effect of the medium is generally not noticeable. Galileo comments on a test of this acceleration being the same for all objects.

> 'But I, . . . , who have made the test can assure you that a cannon ball weighing one or two hundred pounds, or even more, will not reach the ground by as much as a span ahead of a musket ball weighing only half a pound, provided both are dropped from a height of 200 cubits.'

G. Galileo (1638)
Dialogues concerning two new sciences.
If two objects take the same time to accelerate over the same distance then they must have the same acceleration. Galileo is reputed to have dropped objects from the Leaning Tower of Pisa in test of this constant acceleration idea. This, however, is considered by many to be a legend.

The accurate measurement of the acceleration due to gravity

Why do we bother about an accurate value for the acceleration due to gravity? The acceleration can be measured in terms of standard lengths and times and if the acceleration is accurately known it is possible, with a known standard mass, to specify a force standard.

$$\text{Force} = \text{weight} = mg$$

Such a standard is required in calibrating machines used to measure forces such as those occurring when rocket motors are fired. The current balance used to specify the ampere requires an accurate value of g in that the force between two current-carrying conductors is measured in terms of weights put in a balance pan.

Recent measurements of g have involved direct measurements on a falling body, whereas earlier measurements had been concerned with measurements on a pendulum. The time taken for a pendulum to complete one oscillation is related to the acceleration due to gravity. The measurements on a falling body were of the time taken for a freely falling body to cover a measured distance. A graduated scale has been used as the falling object and a photograph taken using a very sharp pulse of light occurring at known time intervals. Such free fall methods have given g results with uncertainties of about 1 or 2 parts in a million. Thulin at the International Bureau of Weights and Measures (1961) and Faller at the Palmer Laboratory, Princeton (1963) have used this method. Another method which has been used, by Cook at the National Physical Laboratory (1967), involves throwing an object upwards and measuring the time intervals at two points between the object passing them on the way up and on the way down. The uncertainty in this method for the g value is about a few parts in ten million.

Figure 2.13 illustrates the principle of this last method. T_A is the time interval between the object passing A on its way up and on its way down. $T_A/2$ is thus the time taken for the object to go from A to the top of its path. It is also the time taken for the object to freely fall from the top of its path to A. The velocity at A, in either the upwards or the

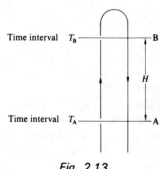

Fig. 2.13

downwards direction, is thus (using $v = v_0 + at$ with $v_0 = 0$)

$$v_A = g \frac{T_A}{2}$$

Similarly from point B

$$v_B = g \frac{T_B}{2}$$

But

$$v^2_B = v^2_A - 2gH$$

hence

$$g = \frac{8H}{T^2_A - T^2_B}$$

The height H is sufficiently small for the variations with height of g to be insignificant.

Projectiles

The photograph, Fig. 2,14, shows an object falling freely from rest and another object which although freely falling has also received an initial horizontal motion. An interesting point emerges from an examination of the stroboscopic photograph—the two objects are at the same horizontal level at the same time. They are both falling with the same acceleration, the accleration due to gravity. The conclusion from this is that motions at right angles to each other are independent. The motion in one direction does not influence the motion in a direction at right angles to it.

The motion of a projectile is considerably simplified by considering it as due to two motions at right angles to each other.

Let us consider a specific example of a projectile—an object projected horizontally with a velocity of 15 m s^{-1}. We can determine the position of the object at any instant of time by working out how far in the horizontal direction it moves in the time and also how far in the vertical direction it has fallen due to gravity.

In the first second the object falls through a distance of $\frac{1}{2} \times 9.8 \times 1^2$

$$s = \tfrac{1}{2}at^2$$

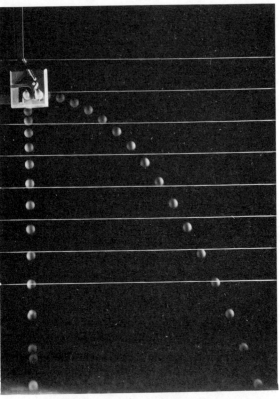

Fig. 2.14 PSSC Physics, *2nd edn, D. C. Heath and Co. A flash photograph of two golf balls, one projected horizontally at the same time that the other was dropped. The strings are 15 cm apart and the interval between flashes was 1/30 s*

Thus the vertical distance moved in one second is 4.9 m downwards. The horizontal distance moved is 15 × 1 m.

$$s = ut$$

Thus we can plot on a graph the position of the object after one second (Fig. 2.15).

After two seconds the object has fallen through a distance of $\frac{1}{2} \times 9.8 \times 2^2$ or 19.6 m. The horizontal distance moved is 15 × 2 or 30 m.

After three seconds the object has fallen through a distance of $\frac{1}{2} \times 9.8 \times 3^2$ or 44.1 m. The horizontal distance moved is 15 × 3 or 45 m. In this way we can construct a picture resembling the stroboscopic photograph.

The stroboscopic photograph gives a graph of vertical distance against horizontal distance—what is the equation of the line joining the images?

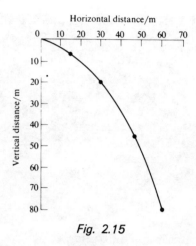

Fig. 2.15

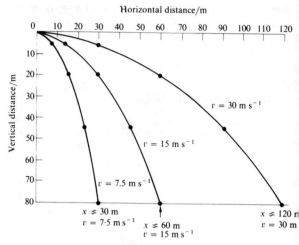

Fig. 2.16

For the vertical motion $s = \frac{1}{2}gt^2$. Let us put this in the form where vertical distances are represented by y. Then

$$y = \frac{1}{2}gt^2$$

This equation gives the y ordinates of the object, considered as a point, at different times.

For the horizontal motion $s = vt$, where v is the horizontal velocity. If we use x to represent distances in the horizontal direction, then

$$x = vt$$

Eliminating t between two equations gives

$$y = \frac{1}{2}g\left(\frac{x}{v}\right)^2$$

$$y = \frac{g}{2v^2}x^2$$

This is the equation of the graph. It is in fact the equation of a parabola.

Satellites

The distance travelled along a horizontal plane by a projectile, given an initial horizontal velocity of v, is vt. The value of the time t is determined by the height from which the object falls. If we keep the height constant how does the distance depend on the horizontal velocity?

$$\text{Distance} \propto v \qquad \text{(Fig. 2.16)}$$

Now consider a projectile being given a horizontal velocity from the top of a high mountain on the earth. If the earth is flat then the distance from the mountain at which the projectile will hit the earth is directly proportional to the velocity. But the earth is not flat—what effect does this have? The projectile will move further along the surface of the earth than would occur with a flat earth. If the velocity is high enough it will not come down to earth—it will go into orbit (Fig. 2.17). During the entire motion of the projectile, it is falling with the acceleration due to gravity.

How long would it take for the projectile to orbit the earth? We will assume that the satellite is

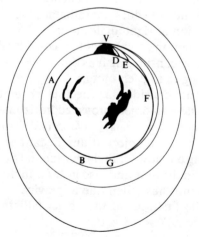

Fig. 2.17 *I. Newton (1686).* Principia, *Vol. 2*

close to the surface of the earth and that the acceleration due to gravity is therefore the same for the satellite as at the earth's surface. Consider a satellite 160 km above the earth's surface. The radius of the earth is approximately 6400 km. If the satellite remains the same distance from the earth, i.e., a circular orbit, then we know the path of our projectile. Figure 2.18 shows a scale diagram. But we can calculate how far the projectile should fall in, say, 200 s.

$$
\begin{aligned}
s &= \tfrac{1}{2}at^2 \\
&= \tfrac{1}{2} \times 9.8 \times 200 \times 200 \\
&= 1.96 \times 10^5 \text{ m} \\
&= 196 \text{ km}
\end{aligned}
$$

This is the 'fall distance' at right angles to the path of the satellite. The force of gravity is always at right angles to the circular path; on our diagram this can only be the case when the satellite has reached the position P. During this time the satellite must have travelled a distance of about 1600 km. This distance was measured from the diagram. This means that the speed of the satellite must be

$$
\text{speed} = \frac{1600}{200} = 8 \text{ km s}^{-1}
$$

How long will it take to go round the earth? The orbit has a radius of 6400 + 160 and hence the total distance covered in one orbit is $2\pi \times 6560$ or 41 200 km. At 8 km s^{-1} the time taken to cover this

distance is therefore

$$
\frac{41\,200}{8} = 5150 \text{ s}
$$

This is about 86 minutes. This is a rough estimate because of the limited accuracy with which the diagram was drawn.

The first artificial satellite was launched on 4 October 1957 by the USSR. The time to cover one orbit was 96.2 minutes; the orbit was, however, not circular but an ellipse. The height above the earth's surface varied from 215 to 939 km. The first manned space flight, by Yuri Gagarin in 1961, was in an orbit whose height varied between 169 and 315 km above the earth's surface and had an orbital time of 89.3 minutes.

Further reading

G. Gamow (1962) *Gravity*, Heinemann, Science Study Series No. 17.

Supplementary material

The motion of the planets

The sun rises in the morning in the east and in the evening sets in the west. It seems the most natural thing to consider the earth stationary and the sun orbiting the earth. After all if the earth was moving surely we would somehow feel the motion. These views held the scene until the seventeenth century. Though superficially they seem to be the simplest answer they did introduce many complications. A simpler answer turned out to be that the earth is moving round the sun. In the following we briefly examine the arguments advanced both for and against the idea of the moving earth.

Ptolemy, AD 85–165, considered the earth to be the central item in the universe and all the other planets and the sun to revolve round the earth. The motion of the planets could not, however, be as simple as a circle because this conflicted with observations (see Fig. 2.1a). The planets had to move in epicycles round the earth. A simple epicycle is traced out by a point on the rim of a wheel which is rolling round the circumference of a circle. To describe the entire solar system

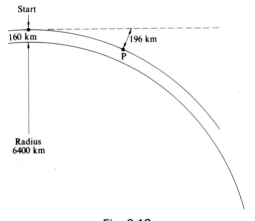

Fig. 2.18

necessitated many epicycles. The model was, however, adequate for the precision of the data then known. With its aid tables were constructed giving the positions of the planets in the sky—a vital navigational aid.

Copernicus, 1473–1543, proposed a new model for the universe—the planets, including the earth, orbiting the sun. Figure 2.18 shows how this model gives an explanation for the motion of Mars described in Fig. 2.1a. His model turned out to be a stimulus to science and the start of new advances in astronomy, even if as a model it proved no better than that of Ptolemy in forecasting planetary positions. In concept it was simpler than Ptolemy's model.

An argument against the Copernican view that the earth rotated round the sun was that freely falling objects would always fall to the west of the vertical. An object dropped from the mast of a moving ship should fall not at the base of the mast but behind the mast as during the time it was falling the ship would have moved. In 1640 Gassendi tried the experiment with a stone being dropped from the mast of a ship—the result was that the stone always hit the deck of the ship at the same position, regardless of whether the ship was moving or not. The explanation was that the stone before being released has the same horizontal velocity as the ship. When it falls it has a vertical acceleration, that due to gravity, and the horizontal velocity. In the horizontal direction it thus keeps pace with the ship. The path of the stone from the point of view of an observer not moving with the ship is that of a projectile, i.e., a parabolic path. From the point of view of a man on the ship who has the same horizontal velocity as the stone, the stone appears to be falling vertically. We on earth see falling objects in the same way that the man on the ship sees the stone falling from the top of the mast.

In 1609 Johann Kepler published the first two of what are known as Kepler's three planetary laws. The third law appeared in 1619. These laws can be written as:

1. All planets follow elliptical orbits with the sun located at one of the foci.
2. An imaginary line connecting the sun and a planet sweeps over equal areas of the planetary orbit in equal intervals of time.

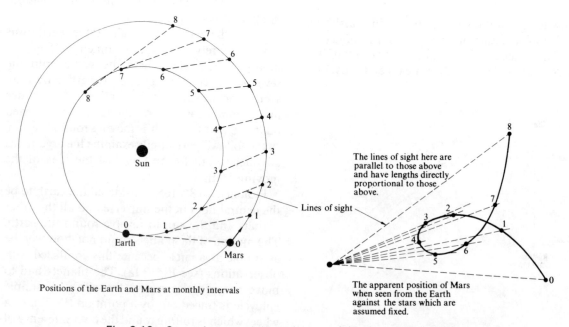

Positions of the Earth and Mars at monthly intervals

The apparent position of Mars when seen from the Earth against the stars which are assumed fixed.

Fig. 2.19 Copernicus model used to explain the motion of Mars

3. The square of the periods of revolution of any two planets are as the cubes of their mean distances from the sun.

$$\frac{T_1^2}{R_1^3} = \frac{T_2^2}{R_2^3}$$

where T_1 is the period of revolution for planet 1, T_2 is the period for planet 2, R_1 is the mean distance from the sun of planet 1, and R_2 is the mean distance from the sun of planet 2. An alternative way of expressing it is:

(planetary year)$^2 \propto$ (mean distance from sun)^3

These were laws arrived at from an examination of experimental data—a search for simple models to fit the data. They were not arrived at as a result of some grand theoretical line of argument.

Kepler had an advantage over earlier astronomers: he had much better data on planetary positions. This was the result of work by Tycho Brahe (1546–1601).

Further reading

A. Koestler (1964) *The Sleepwalkers*, Penguin.
Nuffield O-level physics background book. *Astronomy*, Penguin.
S. Toulmin and J. Goodfield (1961) *The Fabric of the Heavens*, Penguin.

Problems

1. Figure 2.20 shows the distance–time graph for a car with automatic transmission accelerating from rest.

(a) Sketch the velocity–time graph.
(b) Sketch the acceleration–time graph.
(c) How does the acceleration depend on the velocity of the car? This is a vital factor in deciding how good a car would be at overtaking other cars.

2. A car starts from rest and is accelerated at a constant 1.5 m s^{-2} for 6.0 s. What distance will the car have covered in that time and what will be its velocity at the end of the time?

3. A car moving with a velocity of 12 m s^{-1} accelerates uniformly at 1.2 m s^{-2} until it attains a

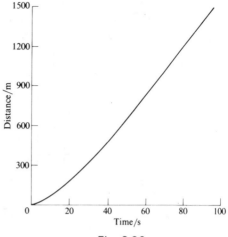

Fig. 2.20

velocity of 16 m s^{-1}. What is (a) the time taken to reach this velocity, (b) the distance travelled?

4. A train travelling at 35 m s^{-1} slows down with a uniform retardation until, after a distance of 500 m, it has reached a velocity of 20 m s^{-1}. What time does it take to reach this velocity and, if it continued with the same retardation, what further time would be needed before the train comes to rest?

5. In the absence of air resistance, how long will it take an object to fall from rest through a distance of 2.0 m? ($g = 9.8$ m s^{-2})

6. A ball is thrown vertically upwards with a velocity of 12 m s^{-1}. If air resistance is ignored, what will be (a) the maximum height attained, (b) the time taken before the ball returns to the thrower? ($g = 9.8$ m s^{-2})

7. A stone is thrown from the edge of a cliff with a horizontal velocity of 2.0 m s^{-1}. How long will it take to reach the sea 50 m below and at what horizontal distance from the thrower? ($g = 9.8$ m s^{-2})

8. Show that the displacement x at time t of a particle moving with uniform acceleration a is given by the equation $x = ut + \frac{1}{2}at^2$, where $x = 0$ and $dx/dt = u$ when $t = 0$.

A light rubber ball of mass 0.08 kg is thrown vertically upward at 14 m s^{-1} and Fig. 2.21 represents the velocity–time graph for part of the ensuing motion.

(a) Describe this motion briefly.

45

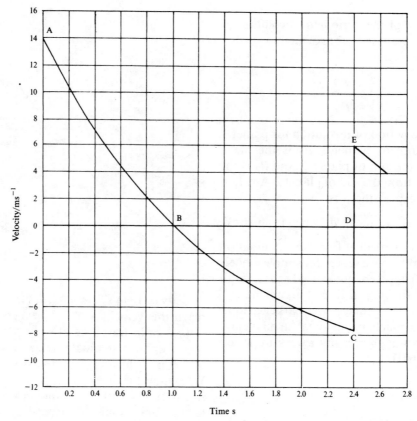

Fig. 2.21

(b) Estimate the initial acceleration at A, and the accelerations at B and at C. How do you account for the differences between them?

(c) Estimate the height to which the ball rises above the point of projection. (g = 9.8 m s^{-2})
(Oxford Local Examinations, Part Q1, Paper II, Summer 1977)

9. A ball dropped from a height of 2.0 m to the ground rebounds to a height of 1.6 m. What is (a) the velocity with which the ball hits the ground, (b) the velocity with which it rebounds, (c) the time taken from release of the ball to it reaching the height of 1.6 m after rebounding? (g = 9.8 m s^{-2})

10. A ball set rolling on a horizontal table falls off and hits the ground 15 cm out from the table edge. If the table top is 70 cm high, with what velocity did the ball roll off the table edge((g = 9.8 m s^{-2})

11. A rifle is firing bullets at a target 100 m away. How high above the target bull do you think the rifle should be aimed to allow for the fall of the bullet under the action of gravity? Try guessing the data you need. You might argue that the effect of the air through which the bullet was travelling would be insignificant over a distance of 100 m.

12. Data on the orbits of the planets.

Planet	Mean orbital radius/ AU	Time for an orbit/ year
Mercury	0.387	0.241
Venus	0.723	0.615
Earth	1.000	1.000
Mars	1.524	1.881
Jupiter	5.203	11.862
Saturn	9.539	29.46
Uranus	19.182	84.01
Neptune	30.058	164.79
Pluto	39.439	248.43

1 AU = 149.6 × 10^9 m

(a) Do the above data confirm Kepler's third law?

(b) There is a law called the Bode law, or sometimes the Titius–Bode law, which states that

$$r_n = 0.4 + 0.3 \, (2)^{n-1}$$

where r_n is the radius of the orbit of the nth planet, the planets being numbered in sequence from the earth as one outwards. How well is this law obeyed? A group of asteroids occurs between the orbit of Mars and Jupiter.

(c) The asteroid belt extends from about an orbital radius of 2.5 to 3.0 AU. Calculate the range of times taken for the asteroids to orbit the sun.

13. A query is posed in R. B. Feynman, R. P. Leighton and M. Sands (1963) *The Feynman Lectures on Physics, Vol. 1,* Addison-Wesley, Reading, Mass., page 8–3:

'A lady in a car was stopped by a cop. The cop goes up to her and says, "Lady, you were going 60 miles an hour!" She says, "That's impossible, sir, I was travelling for only seven minutes. It is ridiculous—how can I go 60 miles an hour when I wasn't going an hour?" How would you answer her if you were the cop?'

(For an answer look at the Feynman reference.)

The above question is really asking you to say what you understand by the term speed.

3 Forces and motion

The cause of motion

What causes motion? What stops motion? Is any cause necessary for things to move? Why when you push an object along the bench does it soon stop moving? Why do the planets keep moving round the sun?

'A moving body comes to a standstill when the force which pushes it along can no longer so act as to push it.' This was the view of Aristotle. This seems to be reasonable—when you cease to push an object along a bench it comes to rest soon after you cease pushing. A force seems to be necessary to keep an object in motion. However, let us look at the situation more critically. We will start with the object, say a block of wood, at rest on the bench (Fig. 3.1). We apply a small force to the block—nothing happens. We increase the force and then at some particular value the block moves. If we increase the force, by pushing or pulling more, the object moves faster. When we stop pushing the block rapidly comes to rest. The result is, however, different if we put wheels on the block of wood: a very small force causes the block to move. Why the difference? Wheels—but why? Friction? Perhaps friction complicates the results and we have some force other than our push acting on the block.

It is possible to achieve nearly friction-free conditions by floating the block on a cushion of gas (like the hovercraft), Fig. 3.2. One way of doing this is by blowing air upwards through holes in the base on which the object floats. In an air table a flat base containing the holes is used. An alternative is for the object to blow gas downwards onto the base. An upturned tin lid containing solid carbon dioxide is one form. The carbon dioxide is very cold and on warming up vaporizes, the tin lid shape forcing the escaping gas downwards. What happens when we push an object in the absence of friction? It keeps on moving with a uniform velocity, when no resultant force is acting on it. (We are only concerned with forces and motion in the horizontal plane—gravity still acts on the object but no motion in the vertical plane is possible.) In the absence of a resultant force an object keeps moving with a uniform velocity or it remains at rest. This is known as *Newton's first law of motion*.

Consider a ball rolling down a curved piece of track. When the rail is in the form of a U the ball rolls down one side of the U and up the other side to almost the same height. This occurs regardless of the shape of the U and regardless of whether the slopes of each arm of the U are the same. If it

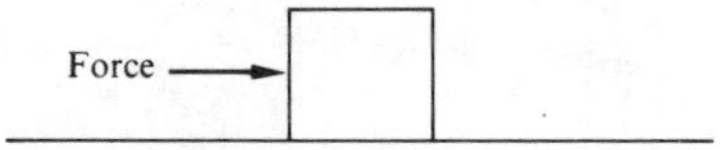

Force →

Fig. 3.1

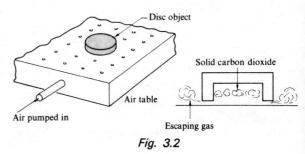

Fig. 3.2

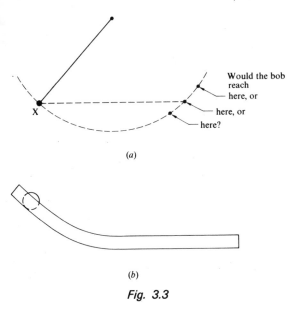

Would the bob reach
here, or
here, or
here?

X

(a)

(b)

Fig. 3.3

rolls down one side and the other side of the U is horizontal then the ball should keep rolling until it reaches the same height again—in fact in the absence of friction, never. It continues in motion with a uniform velocity.

What does a force do? It causes a change in velocity. So for no resultant force we have rest or uniform velocity, and when a force is applied the velocity is changed. What now do we think about the situation where an object was pushed along the bench. When the force was small no motion occurred. But a force should cause motion—the conclusion we are forced to is that there must be another force acting on the object which just cancels out the effect of the force we have applied (forces are vector quantities). As we increase our force so this opposing force increases, until at some particular value the opposing force ceases to increase and motion occurs because there is a resultant force acting on the object. This opposing force is known as the *force of friction*.

Change of velocity

Is there any simple relationship between force and the change in motion produced by the force? Let us simplify the matter—what happens when a constant force acts on an object? The first problem is how to produce a constant force. If we

pull a piece of rubber between our hands and keep it stretched by the same amount—is the stretching force constant? A constant extension of a piece of rubber would seem to be a convenient way of defining a constant force. Now let us apply our constant force to an object and study its motion. A trolley is a convenient object and its motion can be studied if ticker tape is attached to it (Fig. 3.4) and passed through a vibrator which produces marks on the tape at regular time intervals. Figure 3.5 shows the ticker tape trace produced for a constant force. When this is plotted as a distance-time graph, a curve is found. A velocity-time graph of the motion, however, is a straight line. The motion is one of constant acceleration. A constant force produces a constant acceleration. Try this analysis with Fig. 3.6.

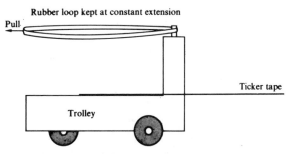

Rubber loop kept at constant extension

Pull

Ticker tape

Trolley

Fig. 3.4   Trolley being pulled with a constant force

We have met constant acceleration before—a freely falling object. The conclusion would seem to be that a constant force is acting on the object during free fall.

What happens if, for the same object, we double the force? Double the force can be produced by using two identical lengths of rubber (Fig. 3.7) and giving both the same extension. Double the force gives double the acceleration. If we use three times the force we get three times the acceleration. The acceleration, a, is directly proportional to the force F

$$a \propto F$$

We can write this as

$$F = ma$$

where m is the constant of proportionality. We

49

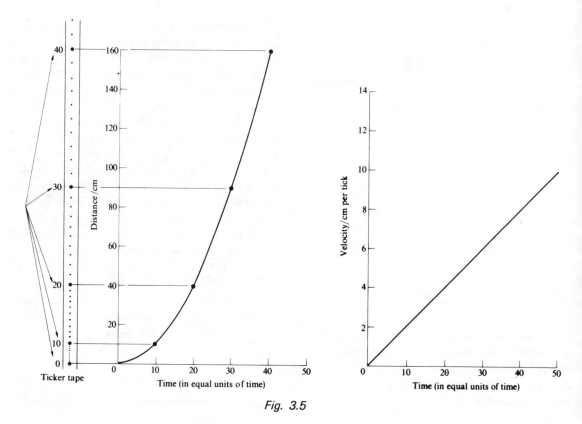

Fig. 3.5

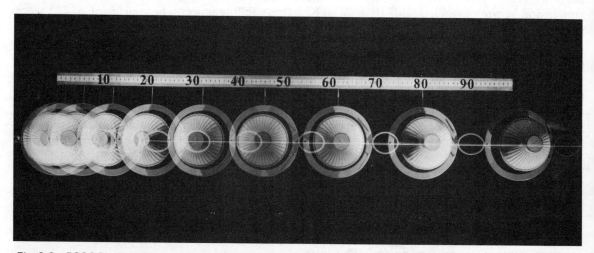

Fig. 3.6 PSSC Physics, *2nd edn, D. C. Heath and Co. The flash photographs show the puck being pulled to the right using a rubber ring which shows a constant deformation*

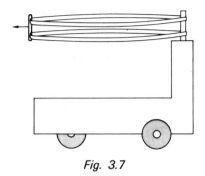

Fig. 3.7

call the constant *m* mass. The bigger this constant for a given force the smaller the acceleration. The greater the constant the more difficult it is to accelerate an object. What factors change this constant?

Suppose instead of using one trolley being pulled by the piece of rubber we use two trolleys stacked together, one on top of the other. The acceleration with the two trolleys is half that with the single trolley. With three trolleys the acceleration is one-third of that with the single trolley. *F* is kept constant.

Number of trolleys	Acceleration	Value of m
1	a	m
2	$a/2$	$2m$
3	$a/3$	$3m$

The product of a number representing the number of trolleys and the acceleration is a constant with a constant force. The value of *m*, the constant of proportionality in $F = ma$, is determined by the number of trolleys. Doubling the number of trolleys doubles the value of *m*.

What do we mean by saying that force is a vector quantity? If we apply two lengths of rubber to our trolley the resulting acceleration will depend on the directions in which the rubber strips pull on the trolley (Fig. 3.8). Our equation is concerned with the resultant force. The equation is one form of what is known as *Newton's second law of motion*.

The units of acceleration are $m\ s^{-2}$; what are the units of mass and force? As the two quantities are related by the equation we need only specify a standard for one; the other can be defined in terms of it. In fact we adopt a piece of material as a standard mass, called 1 kg. The unit of force, called the newton (N), is then defined as that force which produces an acceleration of $1\ m\ s^{-2}$ for a mass of 1 kg.

The international standard of mass, the kilogramme, is kept in Paris. Many countries keep copies of this standard and compare their copies with the standard in Paris.

Action and reaction

Let us take a closer look at the forces acting when we pulled the trolley with a length of rubber. The rubber pulled the trolley—after all the trolley did

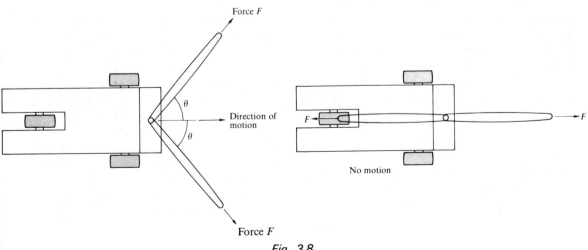

Fig. 3.8

accelerate. Are there any other forces? If we pull on one end of a length of rubber—does it extend? Forces in opposite directions are needed at each end of the piece of rubber. When we pull the trolley a force is applied to the trolley and a force in the opposite direction is applied to our hand. What are the relative magnitudes of the two forces?

Newton dealt with this in what he called the *third law of motion*.

If one body exerts a force on a second, the second exerts an equal and opposite force on the first.

The force exerted by the first body on the second is known as the action, the opposite and equal force acting on the first object is known as the reaction. Briefly the law can be described as— action and reaction are always equal.

Let us take a closer look at a horse drawing a stone tied by a rope, an example used by Newton (Fig. 3.9). There is a force acting on the rope at the horse's end. Because the rope resists being extended, there will be an oppositely directed force at the stone's end of the rope. If the rope is of insignificant mass, by comparison with the stone and the horse, then the forces at each end of the rope are opposite and equal. What would happen if they were not? There would be a resultant force acting on the rope. A force acting on something of insignificant mass would mean an infinite acceleration ($F = ma$), certainly a much greater acceleration than the stone. If the rope is not of insignificant mass then there will be a resultant force acting on the rope. This does not mean that the third law of motion is incorrect—it specified two bodies and here we are considering three. If we look at the forces in pairs then the law is correct. The force on the horse is equal to the force on the rope at the horse's end. The force on the rope at the stone's end is equal to the force on the stone. A simpler example is a case where there is no rope—one magnet attracting another magnet. The force on one magnet is equal to the force on the other. If you doubt the existence of these forces hold one magnet near another—there is a force acting on both magnets: you can feel it and see the resulting accelerations when the magnets are released.

Mass and weight

We have defined mass in terms of a standard piece of matter and called this standard 1 kg. A 1 N resultant force acting on this mass gives it an acceleration of $1\ \mathrm{m\ s^{-2}}$. If we have a 2 kg mass then the 1 N force only produces an acceleration of 0.5 $\mathrm{m\ s^{-2}}$. Our scale of mass is determined by the acceleration produced by a force. Mass is the property of a body which represents its inertia. Our definition of mass has been defined independently of its situation: on the moon or on the earth the same force is needed to accelerate a 1 kg mass at $1\ \mathrm{m\ s^{-2}}$.

If we allow a mass to fall freely it will accelerate with the acceleration due to gravity, about 9.8 $\mathrm{m\ s^{-2}}$ near the surface of the earth. An accelerating mass means a force—the force of gravity.

$$\text{Gravitational force} = mg$$

Because the acceleration due to gravity is the same for all masses, then the gravitational force is directly proportional to the mass.

What is weight? If we put a mass on the pan of a spring balance, the spring becomes extended and the amount of the extension can be used to tell us the force necessary to keep the mass at rest relative to the earth's surface. This force is called the weight of the object. An object has weight when we prevent it freely accelerating under the action of the gravitational force. The object is weightless when it is freely falling. Astronauts when they are weightless are freely falling under the action of the local gravitational force.

If we prevent an object accelerating we must apply a force equal to the gravitational force. Thus

$$\text{weight} = \text{gravitational force} = mg$$

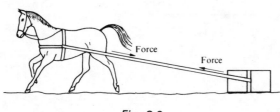

Force

Force

Fig. 3.9

The weight of an object is thus proportional to the mass of the object. The weight, however, depends on the value of the acceleration due to gravity. A 1 kg mass on earth has a weight of about 9.8 N, on the moon its weight is only 1.6 N because the acceleration due to gravity is only 1.6 m s^{-2} on the surface of the moon.

Momentum

An alternative way of looking at the experiments, on page 49, with the trolleys is to consider the changes in velocity produced by forces and not the acceleration. The experiments thus become as follows. With one length of rubber stretched to a constant extension, we pull the trolley for a specified interval of time and measure its change in velocity. This can be done with the aid of the ticker tape. Then with double the force, two identical lengths of rubber both stretched the same amount as before, we measure the change in velocity produced in the same time interval as before. Then with three times the force, four times, etc.

Force	Change in velocity in time t
F	v
2F	2v
3F	3v
4F	4v

The change in velocity is proportional to the force acting on the trolley.

What happens if we keep the force constant and for a particular trolley increase the time over which we determine the change in velocity?

Time	Change in velocity
t	v
2t	2v
3t	3v
4t	4v

The change in velocity is directly proportional to the time.

Suppose we now keep the force and time constant and use first one trolley, then two trolleys stacked together, then three, etc.

Number of trolleys	Change in velocity
1	v
2	v/2
3	v/3

The change in velocity is inversely proportional to the number of trolleys used. Let us say that this factor associated with number of trolleys is mass. The bigger the mass the less the change in velocity in a given time.

These various relationships can be summarized as

Change in velocity $\Delta v \propto F$

with mass m, time interval Δt, constant.

Change in velocity $\Delta v \propto \Delta t$

with mass m, force F, constant.

Change in velocity $\Delta v \propto \dfrac{1}{m}$

with force F, time interval Δt, constant.

These three relationships can be brought together in one equation

$$\Delta v \propto \frac{F(\Delta t)}{m}$$

or

$$F \propto \frac{m(\Delta v)}{\Delta t}$$

The proportionality sign can be replaced by an equality sign by introducing a constant of proportionality. However, we can choose to make this constant of proportionality one. Thus

$$F = \frac{m(\Delta v)}{\Delta t}$$

We can thus define a force unit, the newton, as that resultant force which acting on a standard mass, called 1 kg, causes it to change its velocity by 1 m s^{-1} in a time interval of 1 s. This is the same definition of force as we obtained using the equation $F = ma$. Either can be used as a basis for the definition.

The product of mass and velocity, mv, is given a name—momentum. $m(\Delta v)$ is the change in momentum produced by the force in time Δt, assuming m to remain constant.

$$F = \text{rate of change of momentum}$$

Thus momentum, like velocity and force, is a vector quantity.

Newton's second law of motion can therefore appear in the form—the rate of change of momentum of a body is proportional to the force acting on it, and occurs in the direction in which that force is acting. This is essentially the form in which Newton first wrote the law.

We can have conditions where both velocity and mass are changing or even just the mass changing by mass being ejected from a system (see the section in this chapter on rocket propulsion). Our force equation works in all these cases if we take the change in momentum as the change in the product m.

$$\text{Force} = \frac{\Delta(mv)}{\Delta t}$$

The momentum changes in a time Δt, the time over which the force is considered to act. The product $F \Delta t$ is known as the impulse

$$\text{Impulse} = F \Delta t = \Delta(mv)$$

A big impulse means a big change in momentum.

If you jump off a wall and land on the ground 'stiffly' you may break a bone or in some way suffer damage. If, however, you land with your knees flexing as you hit the ground there is less chance of damage. In both cases there was the same change in momentum and so the same impulse. In the 'stiff' interaction between you and the earth Δt was smaller than when you flexed your knees. Thus the force acting on you was greater in the 'stiff' landing.

Newton's laws

Newton's laws of motion can be written as:

First Law

In the absence of a resultant force an object keeps moving with a uniform velocity or it remains at rest.

Second Law

The rate of change of momentum of a body is proportional to the resultant force acting on it, and occurs in the direction in which the force is acting.

This can be worded in a different manner as

the product of the mass and acceleration of a body is proportional to the force acting on it, the acceleration occurring in the direction in which the force is acting.

Third Law

If one body exerts a force on a second, the second exerts an equal and opposite force on the first.

This is often worded as

to every action there is an opposite and equal reaction.

These laws were of considerable importance in the development of physics.

The following illustrates some of the types of problems that might be encountered involving the application of Newton's laws.

(a) A force of 500 N has to be applied to push a box of mass 100 kg along a horizontal floor. If there is a constant frictional force of 450 N, what is the acceleration of the box?

The resultant force acting on the box is (500 − 450) = 50 N. It is this resultant force which results in an acceleration. Hence acceleration $a = F/m = 50/100 = 0.50 \text{ m s}^{-2}$.

(b) An object of mass 4.0 kg is suspended from a spring balance which is attached to the ceiling of a lift. If the spring balance is calibrated in newtons, what will be the readings on that balance when (a) the lift is stationary, (b) the lift is moving with a constant velocity of 0.20 m s^{-1}, (c) accelerating upwards with an acceleration of 0.15 m s^{-2}, (d) accelerating downwards with an acceleration of 0.15 m s^{-2}? ($g = 9.8 \text{ m s}^{-2}$).

The forces acting on the object are the tension in the spring and the gravitational force due to its weight, i.e., mg. When the lift is stationary the mass has no acceleration and thus there must be no resultant force acting on it. Hence the tension in the spring must equal mg, i.e., $4.0 \times 9.8 = 39.2$ N, and this is the balance reading.

When the lift is moving with constant velocity there must also be no resultant force acting on it (Newton's first law). Hence the spring balance must read 39.2 N.

When the lift is accelerating there must be a resultant force acting on the object since it also is accelerating. When it is accelerating upwards the resultant force is $(T - mg)$, where T is the tension in the spring. This force causes the object to accelerate and so $(T - mg) = ma$, where a is the acceleration. Thus $T = ma + mg = 39.8$ N.

When the lift is accelerating downwards the resultant force acting on the object is $(mg - T)$. Hence $(mg - T) = ma$ and so $T = mg - ma = 38.6$ N.

Incidently, if the lift cable were to break and the lift fell freely with the acceleration due to gravity, we would have $(mg - T) = mg$ and so $T = 0$. The spring balance would give a zero force reading. This is the weightless condition, that of free fall.

(c) Sand falls vertically at 0.15 kg s^{-1} onto a horizontal conveyor belt which is moving at a constant velocity of 0.040 m s^{-1}. What is the horizontal force acting on the belt due to the sand?

In 1 s sand of mass 0.15 kg falls onto the belt. Before reaching the belt the sand has a horizontal velocity of zero, when on the belt 0.040 m s^{-1}. Hence the change in horizontal momentum of the sand in 1 s is $mv = 0.15 \times 0.040$ kg m s^{-1}. The force needed to cause this momentum change every second is, according to Newton's second law, the rate of change of momentum, i.e., 0.15×0.040 N. But this must also be the force exerted on the belt due to the sand (Newton's third law). Hence the answer is 6.0×10^{-3} N.

(d) Water is ejected from a hose pipe nozzle, at the rate of 1.2 kg s^{-1}, with a velocity of 20 m s^{-1}. What is the resulting force on the nozzle?

In 1 s, water of mass 1.2 kg leaves the nozzle. Hence the momentum change of the water per second is 1.2×20 kg m s^{-1}. Thus, using Newton's second law, the force acting on the water is 1.2×20 N. Hence, using Newton's law, the force on the jet is 24 N.

Conservation of momentum

What happens when two bodies collide—what can we say about the forces? According to Newton's third law the force exerted by the first body on the second body must at any instant of time be equal and opposite to the force exerted by the second body on the first body. This must apply however the force varies during the approach and collision of the two bodies. Thus at every instant the rate of change of momentum of the first body must be opposite and equal to that of the second body.

$$F_1 = -F_2$$
$$\frac{\Delta(mv)_1}{\Delta t} = -\frac{\Delta(mv)_2}{\Delta t}$$

If we take the same time interval, then the change of momentum of the first body must be opposite and equal to the change in momentum of the second body. If the velocity of the first body before any interaction between the two bodies was v_1 and after the collision the velocity is v'_1 when the two bodies no longer interact, similarly v_2 before the collision and v'_2 after the collision for the second body, then

$$m_1(v'_1 - v_1) = -m_2(v'_2 - v_2)$$
$$m_1v_1 + m_2v_2 = m_1v'_1 + m_2v'_2$$

The vector sum of the momentum before a collision is equal to the sum after the collision. This is known as the *conservation of momentum*.

Measurements of momentum before and after collisions all show that momentum is conserved. Newton's third law has led to the conservation of momentum law. We could have started with the experimental results showing the conservation of momentum and deduced Newton's third law. It is the experimental fact that momentum is conserved that establishes the third law.

Conservation of momentum seems to be applicable to all linear events. Collisions between billiard balls or between balloons or electrons or atoms, these all obey the conservation of momentum law. Anywhere a change in momentum occurs for one object there must be a corresponding change in momentum for another body. You drop a book—the book accelerates and so its momentum is increasing. The book accelerates because of the gravitational attraction of the earth. The earth, however, is also attracted by the book, the forces are opposite and equal, and thus the earth accelerates towards the book and gains momentum at the same rate as the book; momentum is conserved. A speeding car brakes and comes to a halt—its momentum decreases and becomes zero (relative to the earth). The loss in momentum of the car is exactly balanced by the change in momentum of the earth. One way of visualizing the fact that there must be an interaction between the car and the earth for the car to stop is to consider the car to be speeding along on a sheet of ice—an almost no-interaction situation.

Collisions

We have argued that in any collision momentum is conserved. We can therefore write down a relationship involving the velocities of the colliding bodies both before and after the collision. These are the velocities before the bodies collide, or interact, and after. What happens during the collision time? During the collision time, object 1 experiences a force because of the proximity of object 2, and vice versa. Because they both experience forces they will accelerate. This acceleration will continue until the separation of the two objects is such that the forces become insignificant. Let us look at a specific case—two trolleys held together with a spring in compression between them (Fig. 3.10). When the trolleys are released they spring apart. They accelerate under the action of the force they impart to each other.

$$F_1 = m_1 a_1 \text{ and } F_2 = m_2 a_2$$

But at any instant these forces must be opposite and equal

$$F_1 = -F_2$$
$$m_1 a_1 = -m_2 a_2$$

The forces decrease as the trolleys fly apart; after some particular separation the forces will be zero when the trolleys are no longer coupled by the spring. Because of this the accelerations of the two trolleys will change with time. When the trolleys are no longer coupled by the spring the forces will be zero and thus the accelerations will be zero. The above equation thus indicates the relationship between the accelerations at any instant of time.

Figure 3.11a shows a typical distance–time graph for two such trolleys. When 'contact' ceases the distance–time graph shows a constant velocity for each trolley. Figure 3.11b shows the corresponding velocity–time graph and Fig. 3.11c the acceleration–time graph.

What would happen if we changed the spring between the trolleys and so changed the 'contact' time? If the 'contact' time is shortened the trolleys reach their constant velocities more quickly (Fig. 3.12). The values of the velocities depend only on the masses of the trolleys and not on the 'contact' time.

Does the conservation of momentum apply at any instant during the collision time? The momentum before the collision, in this case, is zero. Therefore if momentum is conserved at any instant we must have

$$m_1 v_1 = m_2 v_2$$

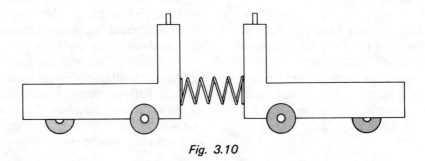

Fig. 3.10

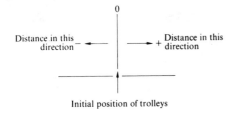

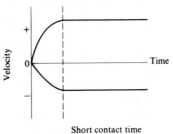

Short contact time

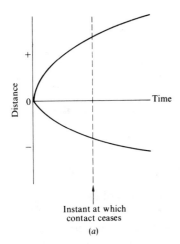

Instant at which
contact ceases

(a)

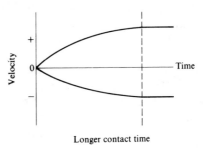

Longer contact time

Fig. 3.12

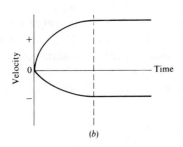

(b)

where v_1 and v_2 are the velocities at some particular instant of time. Rearranging the equation gives

$$\frac{v_1}{v_2} = \frac{m_2}{m_1}$$

The ratio of the velocities at any instant is the inverse ratio of the masses. This we can check on the velocity–time graph. At any instant the ratio of the velocities is a constant (Fig. 3.13)—we can apply the conservation of momentum to any instant in a collision.

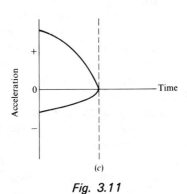

(c)

Fig. 3.11

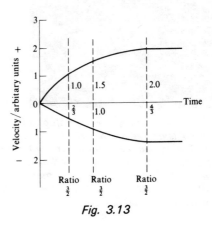

Fig. 3.13

Here in fact is a method of comparing masses which does not rely on a measurement of force.

So far only collisions involving motions along a single straight line have been considered. What happens if the collisions are not restricted to a single line but can involve any directions in a plane, i.e., in two dimensions? Figure 3.14 shows the results of a collision between two balls, the dotted ball entering the picture at the bottom and striking the initially stationary striped ball. The momentum of the striped ball after the collision was 0.481 kg m s^{-1}, the dotted ball had a momentum of 0.559 kg m s^{-1} before the collision and 0.247 kg m s^{-1} afterwards. If we sum the momenta before the collision, 0.559 kg m s^{-1}, and those afterwards, 0.728 kg m s^{-1}, without regard to direction they are not equal. Taking directions into account, i.e., treating momentum as a vector quantity, does show (Fig. 3.15) that momentum is conserved.

An alternative to the drawing of the vector diagram (see Chapter 0) is to resolve the momenta into two perpendicular directions. Momentum

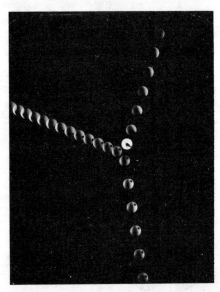

Fig. 3.14 *A multiple flash photograph of an off-centre collision between two balls, each of mass 173 g. The dotted ball entered at the bottom of the picture and struck the striped ball at rest. The flash rate was 30 per second and the camera was pointed straight down, the balls moving horizontally* (PSSC Physics, *2nd edn, D. C. Heath and Co.)*

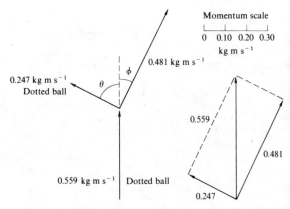

Fig. 3.15 *Adapted from* PSSC Physics, *2nd edn, D. C. Heath and Co.*

must be conserved for the components in both the directions.

$$0.247 \sin \theta = 0.481 \sin \phi$$

$$0.559 = 0.247 \cos \theta + 0.481 \cos \phi$$

The conservation of momentum law or principle is considered to be valid in all circumstances. If the results of an experiment appear to conflict with the conservation of momentum law then we suspect the results, not the law. The emission of beta particles from radioactive substances appeared at one time not to follow the conservation laws (energy as well as momentum). A particle was invented to account for the 'missing' momentum—the neutrino. It was quite some time later before the neutrino was found.

Rocket propulsion

A balloon blown up and then released so that the air can escape moves around a room quite rapidly. Why does it move? When the balloon is blown up we increase the air pressure in the balloon to above the atmospheric pressure. When the balloon is released the difference in air pressure causes air to leave the balloon. It is this air leaving the balloon which causes the balloon to move—in the opposite direction to which the air leaves the balloon. Air moving away from the balloon means mass moving away with a velocity, i.e., momentum in a direction away from the balloon. Conservation of momentum indicates that we must have an opposite and equal momentum for the balloon; the initial momentum was zero.

If we assumed that all the air left the balloon with a constant velocity v (a big assumption)

$$mv = -MV$$

where m is the total mass of the air leaving the balloon, M the mass of the balloon and V its velocity when all the air has left. This has made a simplifying assumption that all the air leaves the balloon with the same velocity; the velocity will in fact decrease as the air leaves the balloon and the pressure in the balloon comes nearer to the atmospheric pressure. In addition, we assumed that the mass of the balloon remained constant—the initial mass will be $M + m$ and this will decrease to M.

The balloon has behaved like a rocket. A rocket moves because fuel is burnt inside the rocket and the products of combustion emerge from the rear of the rocket with a high velocity. The term thrust is used for the rate of change of momentum.

Consider a small interval of time Δt during which mass Δm of fuel is ejected from a rocket. Let m be the mass of the rocket plus fuel during this instant. Δm is considered to be so small that the mass of rocket plus fuel can be considered constant during this small time interval. The ejection of this fuel causes an increase in the velocity of the rocket of ΔV. The velocity of the ejected fuel is taken as being at constant velocity v.

By the conservation of momentum law

$$m \, \Delta V = -(\Delta m)v$$

The change in momentum of the rocket is equal and opposite to the momentum change produced by the movement of the fuel. In many rocket motors v is a constant, during the time the fuel is being consumed.

Rearranging the equation gives

$$\frac{\Delta m}{m} = -\frac{\Delta V}{v}$$

As m decreases, owing to the fuel being used, the change in velocity of the rocket will increase.

How does the velocity of the rocket vary with time? In each successive interval of time Δt, a mass Δm is ejected and the rocket's mass decreases by Δm. Let us work out a rough solution for this change in mass to be $\Delta m = M/10$. This assumes that the rate at which the rocket uses fuel is constant, i.e., Δm is the same for each interval of time. This is generally the case. Also we will take a particular value for v of 1.5×10^3 m s^{-1}.

Starting from rest, the mass of rocket plus fuel is M. Hence the change in velocity of the rocket is given by

$$\frac{M}{10} \cdot \frac{1}{M} = \frac{-\Delta V}{1.5 \times 10^3}$$

$$\Delta V = -150 \text{ m s}^{-1}$$

The velocity of the rocket after a time Δt is therefore 150 m s^{-1}. The minus sign is because the rocket's velocity is in the opposite direction to that of the fuel.

In the next interval of time the mass of the rocket plus fuel is

$$M - \frac{M}{10} = \frac{9M}{10}$$

Hence the change in velocity of the rocket is given by

$$\frac{M}{10} \cdot \frac{10}{9M} = \frac{-\Delta V}{1.5 \times 10^3}$$

$$\Delta V = -167 \text{ m s}^{-1}$$

The velocity of the rocket after a time $2 \, \Delta t$ is therefore 317 m s^{-1}.

In the next interval of time the mass of the rocket plus fuel is

$$\frac{9M}{10} - \frac{M}{10} = \frac{8M}{10}$$

Hence the change in velocity of the rocket is given by

$$\frac{M}{10} \cdot \frac{10}{8M} = \frac{-\Delta V}{1.5 \times 10^3}$$

$$\Delta V = -188 \text{ m s}^{-1}$$

The velocity of the rocket after a time $3 \, \Delta t$ is therefore 505 m s^{-1}.

In a similar manner we find that:

After 4 Δt, $\Delta V = -214$ m s^{-1} and the rocket velocity is 719 m s^{-1};

after 5 Δt, $\Delta V = -250$ m s^{-1} and the rocket velocity is 969 m s^{-1};

after 6 Δt, $\Delta V = -300$ m s^{-1} and the rocket velocity is 1269 m s^{-1};

after 7 Δt, $\Delta V = -375$ m s^{-1} and the rocket velocity is 1644 m s^{-1}.

This would be the final velocity of the rocket if the fuel initially constituted 70 per cent of the total mass of the rocket plus fuel. The graph (Fig. 3.16)

of velocity against time would be much smoother if smaller time intervals, and hence smaller values of Δm, had been considered.

All rockets, whether they be fireworks or those used to put men on the moon, work on the same principle: the expulsion of mass at a high velocity from the rear of the rocket. In chemical propellant rockets, the fuel and the oxidant when mixed together at the right temperature react and the resulting product emerges from the rocket exhaust with a high velocity. A typical fuel would be a hydrocarbon, such as kerosene, and as oxidant liquid oxygen (LOX). Liquid oxygen boils at 89 K, i.e., −184°C, and it is this which is responsible for the ice which forms, and the clouds of white condensed water vapour, before launch. The fuel oxidant are stored in separate tanks within the rocket and only mix during firing, when they are forced into the combustion chamber by either gas stored under high pressure or by pumps driven by a turbine (Fig. 3.17). Such an arrangement would constitute a rocket engine. A large rocket would have more than one such engine.

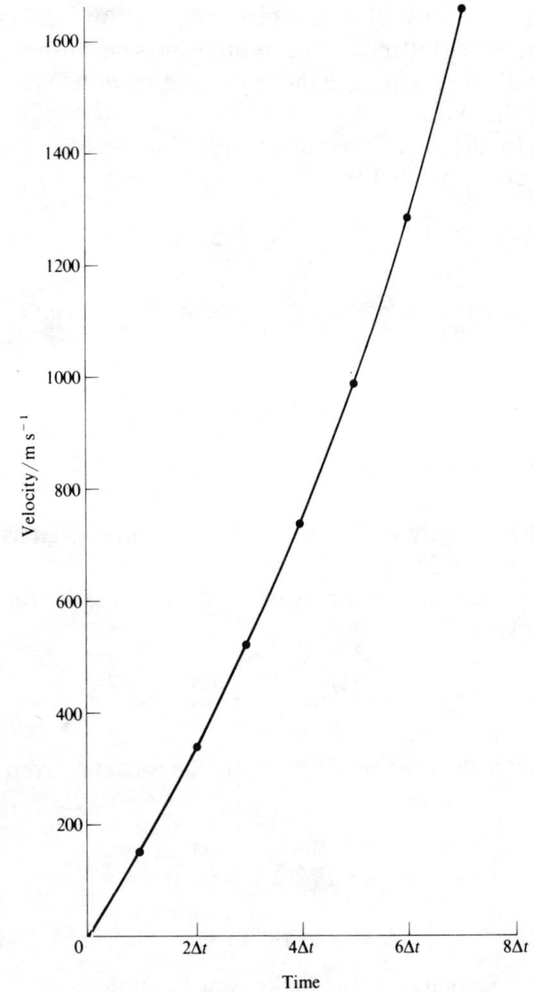

Fig. 3.16

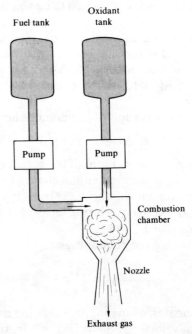

Fig. 3.17 Simplified sketch of a rocket engine

The recoil of rifles

When a rifle is fired the butt jerks back against the shoulder. This recoil is a consequence of the bullet being fired; momentum must be conserved. Two factors contribute to the recoil—the momentum given to the bullet and the momentum given to the gases produced by the explosion. This last item can amount to some 40 per cent of the total forward momentum.

If the momentum of the bullet, after being fired, is mv, and the momentum of the gases leaving the barrel after the explosion $m'v'$, then the momentum of the gun is given by

$$MV = mv + m'v'$$

For a typical rifle, $M = 3.6$ kg, $V = 3.8$ m s^{-1}, $m = 10$ g, $v = 900$ m s^{-1}. This gives as the momentum due to the gases leaving the barrel

$$m'v' = 3.6 \times 3.8 - 0.01 \times 900$$

$$= 4.7 \text{ kg m s}^{-1}$$

This is about 34 per cent of the total momentum given to bullet and gas.

If the momentum of the gas can be reduced, then the recoil momentum will be reduced. The momentum of the gas is due to the rapid build-up of gas pressure behind the bullet while it is in the barrel. The gas is produced by the explosion and the high temperature produced contributes to the pressure build-up. Pressures above atmospheric pressure of the order of 10^5 N m^{-2} are produced. The pressure is needed to get the bullet going, but need not give all its momentum to the recoil if it does not all stream from the end of the barrel after the bullet has left. In recoil control devices the gas is diverted out of vents to the side or upwards instead of straight forward.

Frictional forces

When a block of wood on a bench is given a push it may well not move—our push has to be big enough to overcome the frictional force. Frictional forces always oppose relative motion between two surfaces.

Suppose we pull the block with a spring balance, so that we know the force being applied to the block. At, perhaps, 1.0 N there is no movement. There must therefore be no resultant force acting on the block, otherwise it would accelerate. Therefore we conclude that the frictional force has a value of 1.0 N, in the opposite direction to the applied force. At, perhaps, 2.0 N there is still no movement. The frictional force must then be 2.0 N in the opposite direction to the applied force. At, perhaps, 6.0 N the block begins to move and at higher values it accelerates. The frictional force when the block just begins to move is called the limiting frictional force since it is the maximum value of that force. If we apply a force of, say 8.0 N when the limiting frictional force is 6.0 N, then there is a resultant force of 2.0 N to accelerate the block and we can calculate the acceleration using this value and $F = ma$.

The value of the limiting frictional force depends on the normal force. This is the reaction force, i.e., the force of the surface on the block, and is opposite and equal to the force of the block at right angles to the surface, i.e., the force holding the block on the surface. Figure 3.18 shows a block on a sloping surface, the normal force N in this case being opposite to, and having the value of, $mg \cos \theta$ which is the component of the block weight at right angles to the surface. For a horizontal surface, N would have the value mg.

The limiting frictional force F is proportional to the normal force N, i.e., $F = \mu N$, where μ is called the static coefficient of friction.

If we take a particular block and measure the limiting frictional forces when its various surfaces, with different areas, are in contact with the surface over which sliding is to occur, then we find that the limiting frictional force is independent of surface area.

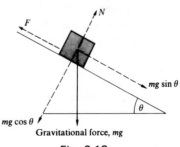

Fig. 3.18

The laws of friction between solids are thus:

1. The frictional force between two surfaces always opposes relative motion.
2. The frictional force is independent of the area of contact between the two surfaces.
3. The limiting frictional force is proportional to the normal force and depends on the two surfaces concerned.

So far we have only considered the forces necessary to start motion. When an object is moving, a force is necessary to maintain a constant velocity. For a constant velocity there must be no resultant force (Newton's first law). Thus the frictional force must be opposite and equal to the applied force. The same laws of friction apply as for the static situation, with the limiting frictional force in this situation being the frictional force when there is a constant velocity. The coefficient of friction in such a case is called the dynamic coefficient and generally has a value lower than the static coefficient.

Typical values of these coefficients are given below.

	Static coefficient	Dynamic coefficient
Steel sliding on steel	0.74	0.57
Glass sliding on glass	0.94	0.40
Oak on oak (parallel to grain)	0.62	0.48

One way of measuring the static coefficient is to place a block of the material on the surface concerned and tilt the surface until the block just begins to slide, then the angle of the surface to the horizontal is measured. For such a case, see Fig. 3.18; the frictional force must be opposite and equal to the component of the block weight down the slope, i.e., $F = mg \sin \theta$. The normal force N must be opposite and equal to the component of the block weight at right angles to the slope, i.e., $N = mg \cos \theta$. Thus

$$\frac{F}{N} = \frac{mg \sin \theta}{mg \cos \theta}$$

and so

$$\mu = \tan \theta$$

Problems

1. A crate having a mass of 40 kg is lifted by means of a rope of negligible mass. What is the tension in the rope when the crate is lifted with (a) constant velocity, (b) an upward acceleration of 0.8 m s^{-2}, and (c) held suspended in mid-air? ($g = 9.8$ m s^{-2})

2. A person, of mass 50 kg, is standing in a lift which accelerates upwards at 0.40 m s^{-2}. What is the force exerted on the lift floor by the person? ($g = 9.8$ m s^{-2})

3. A block of mass 2.0 kg rests on a frictionless horizontal table and is attached to a string which passes horizontally along the table and over a frictionless, massless, pulley at the edge of the table to hang vertically. If an object of mass 3.0 kg is attached to the free end of this string, what is the acceleration of the 2.0 kg block? ($g = 9.8$ m s^{-2})

4. Mass, length and time are base quantities, whereas momentum, acceleration and force are derived ones. Define each of these derived quantities and express each of them in terms of the base ones.

In a collision, linear momentum is conserved. Outline an experiment to illustrate this conservation law. Give two further examples of conservation laws.

By considering a collision as one body exerting a constant force F on another for a time t, show that the conservation of linear momentum is a direct result of Newton's laws of motion.

A rocket with its motors burning is moving in space in a straight line with constant acceleration. Sketch graphs to show how (a) acceleration, (b) velocity, (c) momentum, and (d) distance moved change with time.

(University of London, Q12, Paper 2, June 1978)

5. A ball of mass 50 g moving with a velocity of 4.0 m s^{-1} collides head on with another ball of mass 200 g which is at rest. What is their common velocity after the collision if both balls move off together?

6. A car of mass 1400 kg moving with a velocity of 60 km h^{-1} collides head on with a truck of mass 4200 kg coming in the other direction with a velocity of 40 km h^{-1}. What is their common

velocity after the collision if they become locked together?

7. A bullet of mass 10 g is fired horizontally with a velocity of 300 m s^{-1} into a suspended stationary wooden block of mass 500 g. If the bullet becomes embedded in the block, what is the common velocity of bullet and block immediately after the collision?

8. A rocket out in space and moving with a velocity of 1000 m s^{-1} explodes and breaks into two pieces, one of mass 12 kg and the other 6 kg. If the 12 kg piece moves off in the same direction as that of the rocket with a velocity of 1600 m s^{-1}, what must be the velocity of the other piece?

9. What is the force acting on a firework rocket due to it discharging gases at the rate of 4.0 g s^{-1} with a velocity of 400 m s^{-1}?

10. What must be the mass of gas ejected per second from a rocket if it is to be launched vertically from the earth with an initial acceleration of 18 m s^{-2}. The rocket plus fuel has a mass of 7000 kg and the exhaust gases have a velocity of 2000 m s^{-1}. (g = 9.8 m s^{-2})

11. (a) A person standing at one end of a rowing boat, floating at rest on a lake, walks to the other end of the boat. Explain what happens to the boat.
(b) A person jumps from a rowing boat onto the bank of a river, explain what happens to the boat.

12. A block of mass 30 kg rests on a horizontal surface, the coefficient of friction between the block and the surface being 0.50. What happens when the block is given a horizontal push of (a) 100 N, (b) 150 N, (c) 200 N? (g = 9.8 m s^{-2})

13. A block of wood of mass 50 g rests on a wooden plank which is slowly tilted. When the plank reaches an angle of 30° to the horizontal, the block begins to slide down the plank. What is the static coefficient of friction between the two surfaces? (g = 9.8 m s^{-2})

14. A wooden block of mass 1.6 kg is at rest on a wooden plane inclined at 30° to the horizontal.
(i) Write down the component of its weight acting parallel to the plane, the component of its weight acting at right angles to the plane, and the frictional force between the block and the plane.
(ii) When the block is given a sharp tap directed down the plane, it begins to move with speed 0.3 m s^{-1} and thereafter slides down the plane with uniform acceleration 0.2 m s^{-2}. Calculate the impulse applied to the block and the frictional resistance to the ensuing motion. (g = 9.8 m s^{-2})

(Oxford Local Examinations, Part Q1, Paper I, Summer 1979)

15. A cliff railway is designed as a double track, giving a rise of 120 m in a track length 240 m. The two cars, which make the ascent and descent simultaneously, are linked by a stout, endless, wire cable which passes round pulleys at each end of the track.

Beneath the cabin of each car is installed a tank, of triangular cross-section, which can hold 4 m^3 of water, as shown in the outline diagram of Fig. 3.19. To set the cars in motion, the tank in the upper car is filled with water from a river while the tank in the lower car is emptied. The cars are held stationary by brakes until this process is completed. The brakes are then released by the drivers who ride on each car. The cars uniformly accelerate to 5 m s^{-1}, then maintain a constant speed and are finally brought to rest with a uniform deceleration of 0.5 m s^{-2}. Each car weighs 2 × 10^4 N and has a maximum passenger load of 1.5 × 10^4 N.

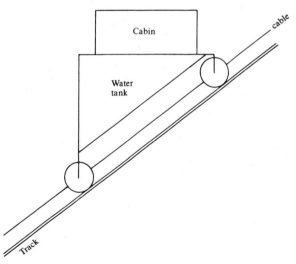

Fig. 3.19

Neglecting frictional resistance, determine the journey times of the rail cars when carrying the greatest number of downward passengers per hour.

Hence determine the maximum number of passengers per hour that can be carried down the railway.

You may assume a 'turn round' time of two minutes after each journey, and that the average passenger weights 750 N.

State, giving a reason, whether more, less or the same number of passengers per hour can be carried up the railway. What safety precautions do you think are necessary in the operation of this system? (g = 10 N kg^{-1}, density of water = 10^3 kg m^{-3})

(JMB, Engineering Science, Q11, Paper III, June 1978)

4 Energy

What is energy?

It is hard to give a general definition of energy. The following quotations are the ways a number of authors have defined energy.

'We shall now start with a very earthy, and rather vague, description of energy as something we pay for, the product of fuel.'

E. M. Rogers (1960)
Physics for the Inquiring Mind, OUP.

'For the moment we shall say that energy is the essential thing involved in jobs—not the creation of energy but its transfer from one form to another.'

PSSC Physics, Heath.

' "Energy" is not a substance, fluid, paint, or fuel which is smeared on bodies and rubbed off from one to another. We use this term to denote a construct—numbers, calculated in a certain prescribed way, that are found by theory and experiment to preserve a remarkably simple relationship in very diverse physical phenomena.'

A. B. Arons (1965) *Development of Concepts of Physics*, Addison-Wesley, Reading, Mass.

'It is important to realize that in physics today, we have no knowledge of what energy is. We do not have a picture that energy comes in little blobs of a definite amount. It is not that way. However, there are formulas for calculating some numerical quantity, and when we add it all together it gives "28"—always the same number. It is an abstract thing in that it does not tell us the mechanism or the reasons for the various formulas.'

R. B. Feynman, R. P. Leighton and M. Sands (1963)
The Feynman Lectures in Physics, Vol. 1, Addison-Wesley, Reading, Mass.

Energy—the product of fuels, the essential 'thing' involved in jobs, a number calculated in a certain prescribed way. This chapter is concerned with the search for these numbers and the ways of calculating them. They will all describe the result of a fuel being expended. In addition they will always add up to the same number.

Transferring energy

If fuel is burnt, i.e., used up, cars can be made to move, aeroplanes fly, machines 'run' and do jobs. Fuel enables jobs to be done. The fuel provides something we call energy.

When a fuel provides energy—what are the results? If the fuel is the petrol in a car the result is motion. The petrol could be supplied to a motor operating a hoist which lifts bricks up the side of a building under construction. Here the fuel results in a gain in height for bricks. The fuel could be used in a furnace to provide a change in temperature. A change in velocity, a change in height, and a change in temperature are three possible outcomes of energy being released by a fuel. The cornflakes you ate for breakfast are a fuel supplying energy to enable you to run, to climb steps, to keep warm, and just to exist.

The motor could be used to lift bricks up to the top of a building, a gain in height, and then the bricks could fall down to the ground again, a gain in velocity. It appears as if the fuel supplies energy which results in a height change, and that the bricks somehow at the new height have energy which can be released and result in a change in velocity. There is energy associated with height of an object. This is called *potential energy*. There is energy associated with velocity of an object, called *kinetic energy*. The process of transferring energy from a fuel to an object and producing a change in potential or kinetic energy is known as *work*.

Work

We say we are working, in the physical sense, when we move objects against the force of gravity (lifting objects) or friction (pushing objects) or against some force. To do work we require energy. This we obtain by eating, food is the fuel which enables us to work. When we work we are transferring the 'food energy' from us to some object—we lose energy and the object gains energy. A heavy manual worker needs more food fuel than an office worker.

In physics the term work is used to denote the energy transferred either to or from an object. After the movement both the objects involved are in some way in a different state—a different level above the ground, a different velocity etc. Work measures the energy transferred from object X to object Y which results in a force moving an object through some distance.

Work is defined as the product of the force and the distance moved, along the line of action of the force. Thus if a weight of 5 N is lifted vertically through 10 m the energy transferred to the object by work is $5 \times 10 = 50$ N m. A newton metre (N m) is known as a joule (J). If we pull a trolley with a constant horizontal force of 5 N along a norizontal table a distance of 10 m then the work done is 50 J.

Why is work defined in this way? If we did experiments with a motor doing work, perhaps lifting objects, we would find that, approximately, for the same quantity of fuel used the same value of force–distance product was obtained. Thus, for the same fuel quantity, doubling the force

halves the distance through which it moves the object.

Why do we have the term work in physics? Why do we want to calculate it? If we know the work done then we know the amount of energy being transferred to or from some object. This does not tell us what the result will be, i.e., whether the object will move faster or gain height or both, but it does tell us the total energy being transferred by mechanical means. As will be seen in the sections in this chapter on potential energy and kinetic energy, the work definition enables us to calculate what the changes in velocity and height can be if we know which one, or how both, are changing.

The definition of work as the force–distance product gives us a quantity that is found by theory and experiment to preserve a remarkably simple relationship in very diverse phenomena: a relationship called the *conservation of energy*.

Getting tired

If we lift a weight, a force is being moved through a distance and energy is needed to do the work. This energy is supplied by the food fuel we 'burn' inside us. This seems an obvious case of fuel energy being used and a reason for eating. But what about the situation when we do no work but still get tired? Getting tired would seem to be a reasonable indication that we are using energy. If we hold a weight and do not move it then no force is moved through a distance and thus no work done—however, we still get tired. If the weight were on a table, still at rest, no work is done—why should there be any difference between the table supporting the weight and us supporting the weight? The answer is that 'physiological' work is done for us to support a weight. The muscles in our arms need to be continuously supplied with nerve impulses for a muscle to remain in the 'tense' position for supporting weights. The muscle is not able to remain in the 'tense' position without nerve impulses; when they cease the muscle relaxes. Some animals have muscles which will remain in the 'tense' or 'set' position without being fed with nerve impulses. The muscles in the clam are of this type, the shell can be kept open at any position without energy being expended to keep it at that position.

Power

Power is the rate at which energy is transferred from one object to another. The unit of power is the watt and is 1 J s^{-1}. A typical car engine has a possible power of about 75 kW whereas a man only averages out at about 25 W. The first stage of the Saturn rocket used to put the first men on the moon had a power of 1.2×10^{11} W at lift-off.

Potential energy

If we push a mass against a spring and compress the spring we need to expend energy. If we release the spring and mass, the spring pushes the mass through some distance. In compressing the spring we transferred energy to the spring from us; when the spring is released it transfers energy to the mass and causes it to move. We can talk about the compressed spring having a store of energy, elastic energy, or strain energy. A general term used to describe the energy which a body possesses by virtue of being in some particular position is called potential energy.

For masses near the earth's surface there is a force due to the earth's gravitational pull on the mass. As this force is product of the mass and acceleration due to gravity or gravitational field strength, mg, lifting a weight through a vertical height h means an energy transfer to the mass of mgh. The energy transferred is known as gravitational potential energy.

$$\text{Potential energy} = mgh$$

This assumes that the force remains constant over the distance h. If this is not the case the total potential energy in moving through h can be obtained by considering the mass to be moved through a number of small steps in h and summing the result of all the steps.

Potential energy $= F_1 \Delta h_1 + F_2 \Delta h_2 + F_3 \Delta h_3 +$ ... where F_1 is the force acting over the small distance Δh_1, F_2 the force over distance Δh_2, etc. In calculus notation

$$\text{Potential energy} = \int_0^h F \, \mathrm{d}h$$

If we squash a piece of rubber, energy is needed and the squashed rubber has potential energy. The rubber is just like the spring. If we squash a gas we can consider the squashed gas to have potential energy—energy is used to squash the gas. Suppose we think of the gas enclosed by a piston in a cylinder. When we push the piston in by an amount Δh we need to supply an energy of $F \Delta h$, where F is the force opposing the movement of the piston. The force is provided by the gas pressure P.

$$P = \frac{F}{A}$$

where A is the surface area of the piston. Hence the energy supplied is $PA \Delta h$. But $A \Delta h$ is the change in volume of the gas, ΔV, thus we can write

$$\text{Energy needed} = P \Delta V$$

If there is no temperature rise of the gas, this will be the potential energy stored in the gas due to the movement of the piston.

Force–distance graphs

...ɔject acted on by a constant force moves through a distance then the energy transfer, the work, is the product of the force and the distance

$$\text{Energy transfer} = Fs$$

On a graph of the force against distance (Fig. 4.1a) Fs is the area under the line between the distance equal to zero and equal to s lines. The area gives the energy transferred.

If the force is not constant over the distance, the energy transfer can be obtained from the area

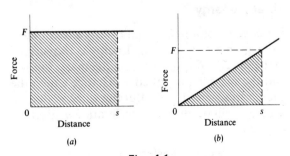

Fig. 4.1

under the graph. For example, when a spring is extended the force is proportional to the extension. Figure 4.1b shows the force–distance graph. The energy transferred when the extension is changed from zero to s is therefore in this case $\frac{1}{2}Fs$, where F is the force at extension s.

We can write a general equation for the area under a force–distance graph:

$$\text{Energy transfer} = \int_{s_1}^{s_2} F \, ds$$

or in words, the energy transferred in moving from distances s_1 to s_2 is the area under the graph of force against distance between the distance equal to s_2 and the distance equal to s_1 lines. The energy transferred can be obtained from determining the area under the graph or, in the case where the equation relating F and s is known, by integration.

As an example we will look at the energy transfer for a spring being extended. If the spring obeys the relationship $F = ks$, i.e., the extension is proportional to the force, then the energy transfer in extending it from $s = 0$ to s is

$$\text{Energy transfer} = \int_0^s F \, ds = \int_0^s ks \, ds$$

$$= \frac{ks^2}{2}$$

This can be written as $\frac{1}{2}Fs$, when the equation $F = ks$ is used to eliminate the k. This is the same result as we obtained from looking at the area under the graph.

Kinetic energy

Suppose a motor pulls a mass along a frictionless table, perhaps an air table. Energy is transferred to the mass. If F is the force on the mass, Fig. 4.2, and the mass, m, is pulled a distance s then the energy transferred is Fs. But the force acting on the mass will produce an acceleration a, given by $F = ma$.

$$\text{Energy transfer} = Fs = mas$$

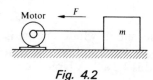

Fig. 4.2

The mass accelerates over a distance s, hence the velocity v at the end of that distance will be given by

$$v^2 = v_0^2 + 2as$$

where v_0 is the initial velocity. Hence the energy transfer can be written as

$$\text{Energy transfer} = mas = \frac{1}{2}m^2 - \frac{1}{2}mv_0^2$$

$$= (\text{value of } \tfrac{1}{2}mv^2 \text{ after energy transfer})$$

$$- (\text{value before the transfer})$$

$$= \Delta(\tfrac{1}{2}mv^2)$$

$\Delta(\frac{1}{2}mv^2)$ is the gain in energy of the mass as a result of the energy transferred to it from the motor. This is the energy used to change the state of motion of the mass. It is called kinetic energy.

The above argument still applies when the mass is not moving along a frictionless table.

Conservation of mechanical energy

What happens when an object slows down? The object must lose kinetic energy—where does it go? Let us take a simple case—a ball being thrown vertically upwards. As the ball moves upwards it slows down, its kinetic energy decreases. It is, however, gaining height against the force of gravity and thus gaining potential energy. Is the gain in potential energy related to the loss in kinetic energy? If the initial velocity was v_0 and the velocity at a vertical distance h above the point of release v, then

$$\text{Change in kinetic energy} = \tfrac{1}{2}mv^2 - \tfrac{1}{2}mv_0^2$$
$$= \tfrac{1}{2}m(v^2 - v_0^2)$$

Using the equation $v^2 = v_0^2 + 2as$, we can write

$$v^2 = v_0^2 - 2gh$$

Hence the change in kinetic energy = $\frac{1}{2}m(2gh)$ = mgh. The change in kinetic energy is equal to the gain in potential energy.

In the absence of forces other than gravitational forces, i.e., there are, for example, no frictional forces, the sum of the kinetic energies and potential energies in an isolated system remains constant. This is called the *law of conservation of mechanical energy.*

But often there are forces other than gravitational forces, e.g., friction. Then mechanical energy is not conserved. It becomes diminished as energy is transferred to random molecular potential and kinetic energy and becomes dissipated. Such energy is called internal energy, being internal to some substance.

What happens when a ball drops? There is a gain in kinetic energy at the expense of the potential energy. What happens when the ball hits the ground and stops? The potential energy has been changed into kinetic energy, but what happens to this kinetic energy when the ball is stopped by the ground? If you hit an object with a hammer both the object and the hammer become warm. The same thing occurs when the ball hits the ground— there is a rise in temperature. The kinetic energy has been transferred to increased internal energy in the ball and the ground.

Forms of energy and conservation

Petrol in a car engine enables the car to gain kinetic and perhaps potential energy. The energy in the fuel is transformed into mechanical energy. A fuel could, however, have been used just to provide a temperature change, e.g., coal on a fire. In that case the energy is transferred by means of heat to give a temperature change. The heating or the movement of the car could have been produced by using electricity. Electricity is another way by which energy can be transferred. Nuclear reactors can be used to provide energy—thus we have another form of energy.

Energy can exist in many forms and can be changed from one form to another. There is a firm belief that whatever the form and whatever the changes we make, energy is always conserved. That is, if we add up all the energy in some system before an event and then add up all the bits after the event we will have the same amount of energy. This is known as the *law of conservation of energy.* The belief in this law is so strong that physicists will believe something to be wrong with their experiments or that they have missed something if calculations in an experiment seem to show that energy is not conserved.

Energy as an additive property

A very important property of energy is that it is additive. If we take 5 ml of water and add a further 3 ml then the result is 8 ml—volume is an additive property. Mass is another additive property. Temperature is, however, not an additive property— the temperature of an object is not equal to the sum of the temperatures of the constituent parts. If we take two beakers of water, each at a temperature of 20°C, and pour them into just one of the beakers the result is still a temperature of 20°C— not 40°C. If a certain mass of fuel will release 50 J of energy and another mass 30 J, then putting the two masses together will give 80 J of energy— energies are additive.

The following are examples of some problems involving energy considerations.

(a) A goods train, total mass 100 000 kg, is accelerated from rest to a speed of 15 m s^{-1} in a distance of 1000 m. What is the gain in kinetic energy? What constant force must be supplied over the 1000 m by the engine?

Kinetic energy = $\frac{1}{2}mv^2$ = $\frac{1}{2} \times 100\,000 \times 15^2$
$$= 1.1 \times 10^7 \text{ J}$$

This energy is gained as a result of work being done by the engine. Hence 1.1×10^7 = force $\times$ distance, and so the force is $1.1 \times 10^7/1000 = 1.1 \times 10^4$ N.

(b) Figure 4.3 shows the side view of a roller coaster track. The roller coaster car, together with the passenger, has a mass of 300 kg and starts with zero velocity at A and moves solely over the run under the action of gravity. (g = 9.8 m s^{-2})

(i) What will be the speed of the car at B and C?

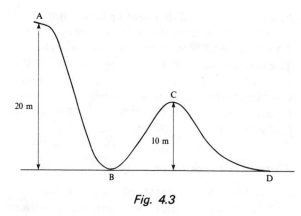

Fig. 4.3

(ii) At the end of the run the car runs against brakes at D. What energy will have to be lost by the car for it to come to a stop at D?

(iii) In the above questions it has been assumed that no energy is dissipated in overcoming friction. How would the answer be changed if friction was taken into account?

(i) At B the loss of potential energy = mgh, where h is 20 m. This results in a gain in kinetic energy of $\frac{1}{2}mv^2$. Hence $\frac{1}{2}mv^2 = mgh$ and so $v^2 = 2gh$ and $v = 20$ m s^{-1}.

At C the loss in potential energy in going from A to C is mgh, where h is $(20 - 10) = 10$ m. Hence the resulting gain in kinetic energy means that $v^2 = 2gh$ and $v = 14$ m s^{-1}.

(ii) Energy lost in going from A to D = mgh, where $h = 20$ m. Hence energy = $300 \times 9.8 \times 20 = 5.9 \times 10^4$ J.

(iii) The effect of friction is to include another term in each of the above calculations. Thus, at B we have $mgh = \frac{1}{2}mv^2 + E$, where E is the energy dissipated as a result of friction. This has the effect of giving a lower value for the velocity at B. Similarly the velocity at C will be reduced. The energy of the car at D will also be less.

(c) Sand falls at a uniform rate of 12 kg s^{-1}, and with negligible kinetic energy, onto a conveyor belt moving horizontally at a constant speed of 4.0 m s^{-1}. What is the power required to maintain this constant speed?

The sand initially has no horizontal velocity and gains one of 4.0 m s^{-1} when it falls onto the belt. Hence the gain in momentum of the sand per second is $mv = 12 \times 4.0 = 48$ kg m s^{-1}. The force acting on the sand to give this change is equal to the rate of change of momentum of the sand, i.e., 48 N. According to Newton's third law the force acting on the belt must also be 48 N.

In one second, sand is moved a distance of 4.0 m. Thus the work done per second is $48 \times 4 = 192$ J. Power is the rate of doing work and so is 192 W.

(d) A train of mass 1.8×10^5 moves with a constant velocity of 20 m s^{-1} up an incline of 1 in 100. If the train develops a power of 600 kW for this climb, how big is the frictional force which the engine is having to overcome? ($g = 9.8$ m s^{-2})

An incline of 1 in 100 means that for every 100 metres up the slope there is an increase in vertical height of 1 metre. The gravitational force component parallel to the slope is $mg \sin \theta = 1.8 \times 10^5 \times 9.8 \times (1/100) = 1.8 \times 10^4$ N. The resultant force down the slope is thus $(1.8 \times 10^4 + F)$, where F is the frictional force.

In 1 s the train covers a distance of 20 m and so the work done per second is $(1.8 \times 10^4 + F) \times 20$. Power is the rate of doing work and therefore $600 \times 10^3 = (1.8 \times 10^4 + F) \times 20$ and hence $F = 1.2 \times 10^4$ N.

Collisions

Collisions between two objects in which the sum of the kinetic energies of the objects before the collision is equal to the sum after are said to be elastic collisions. Collisions where kinetic energy is 'lost' are said to be inelastic. In both types of collisions momentum is still conserved.

Thus if two billiard balls of equal mass collide head on and the collision is elastic, then if they have initial velocities of 0.40 m s^{-1} and 1.00 m s^{-1} we can calculate the velocities of each after the collision by first applying the conservation of momentum which gives

$$0.40m - 1.00m = mv_1 + mv_2$$

The minus sign for the momentum of one ball before the collision is because the collision is head on and so they must be coming from opposite directions. v_1 and v_2 are the velocities after the collision.

Conservation of kinetic energy then gives

$$\tfrac{1}{2}m(0.40)^2 + \tfrac{1}{2}m(1.0)^2 = \tfrac{1}{2}mv_1^2 + \tfrac{1}{2}mv_2^2$$

The kinetic energies before the collision are both positive since energy is a scalar quantity, unlike momentum which is a vector. Hence we have the two equations, following some simplification, of

$$v_1 + v_2 = 0.60 \tag{1}$$

$$v_1^2 + v_2^2 = 1.16$$

$$(v_1 + v_2)(v_1 - v_2) = 1.16$$

$$v_1 - v_2 = \frac{1.16}{0.60} \tag{2}$$

Hence adding Eqs (1) and (2) gives $v_1 = 1.27$ m s^{-1} and so $v_2 = -0.67$ m s^{-1}.

Atomic particle collisions

Cloud chambers enable us to see the paths followed by atomic particles. The particles leave tracks in the vapour used in the chamber, like the vapour trails left by aircraft in the sky. Figure 4.4 shows photographs taken for alpha particles in different gases. The photographs show, in addition to the normal alpha tracks, collisions between alpha particles and gas atoms. Figure 4.4a shows an alpha particle colliding with a hydrogen atom. The short dense track after the collision is the alpha particle and the long thin track is that due to the hydrogen atom. Figure 4.4b shows an alpha particle colliding with a helium atom. The angle between the tracks after the collision, in hydrogen was significantly less than 90°. The third photograph, Fig. 4.4c shows an alpha particle colliding with a nitrogen atom; the tracks after the collision are now more than 90° apart. Can we explain these results?

Let us assume that we can apply the conservation of momentum and the conservation of kinetic energy to such collisions.

Taking the momentum components in the incident direction (Fig. 4.5), we have

$$mv_1 = mv_2\cos\phi + MV\cos\theta$$

and for momentum components in the direction at right angles to the incident direction

$$0 = mv_2\sin\phi - MV\sin\theta$$

Conservation of kinetic energy gives

$$\tfrac{1}{2}mv_1^2 = \tfrac{1}{2}mv_2^2 + \tfrac{1}{2}MV^2$$

The three velocity terms v_1, v_2, and V can be eliminated to give

$$\frac{m}{M} = \frac{\sin(2\theta + \phi)}{\sin\phi}$$

When $m = M$ the equation simplifies to $\phi + \theta = 90°$. The alpha particle collision in helium gave 90° between the tracks—evidence that alpha particles are in fact helium nuclei. In hydrogen we can measure the angles and we get the result that the alpha particle mass is 3.96 times that of a hydrogen atom. In nitrogen the angles give us that the alpha particle mass is about 4/14 that of a nitrogen atom.

In the case of the collision between an alpha particle and a helium atom, when the masses of the particles are all the same we can use the triangle or parallelogram of vectors to show that the angle between the tracks must be 90° after the collision. With equal masses the conservation of kinetic energy equation becomes

$$v_1^2 = v_2^2 + V^2$$

The only way we can draw the vector diagram for v_1, v_2, and V so that this equation applies, is for v_1 to be the hypotenuse of a right-angled triangle (Fig. 4.6).

Supplementary material

Machines and engines

When you lift some object you are using a machine, the muscle–bone machine of your arm. When you row a boat using oars you are using a machine, the pivoted oars. Pulleys, screws, water wheels, gears, are all examples of machines—machines that have been in use for many centuries. A machine can be defined as a 'contrivance for redirecting effort to better advantage' (A. R. Ubbelohde *Man and energy*, Hutchinson (1954)). Thus a large force applied over a short distance

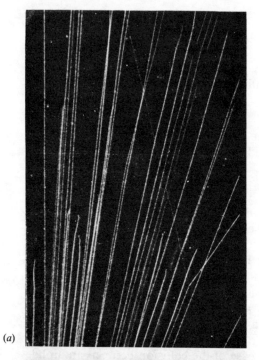

(a)

(c)

Fig. 4.4 (a) Scattering in hydrogen. (b) Scattering in helium. (c) Scattering in nitrogen. (Photographs Science Museum, London, reproduced by permission of Lord Blackett)

(b)

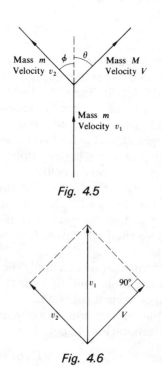

Fig. 4.5

Fig. 4.6

may be redirected to give a small force applied over a long distance, and a small force over a long distance may be redirected to give a large force over a short distance. The contrivance for making such changes is called a machine.

One of the simplest machines is the lever. Figure 4.7 shows some forms of lever. In all the examples we have the product of the force applied and the distance of the point of application to the pivot equal to the product of the load force and its point of application distance from the pivot. The product of a force and the distance, along the line of action of the force, through which its point of application moves is called work and is a measure of the energy transferred. The energy taken from the 'source', e.g., the man in (a) and (b), is transferred to the load and as energy is conserved, then that energy transferred at one end of the system is equal to that transferred at the other end, hence the identity of the force–distance product. The lever is a means of transferring energy.

In Fig. 4.7a the force applied by the man is less than that applied to the stone, the distance of the point of application of the man's force from the pivot being greater than that from the point of application of the force to the stone from the pivot. In Fig. 4.7b the force applied by the man is greater than that applied to the water by the oar, the distance of the point of application of the man's force from the pivot being less than that from the point of application of the force to the water from the pivot. In Fig. 4.7c the force applied by the muscle is greater than that applied to the load. Figures 4.7c and b are examples of what might be called 'distance magnifier' machines, Fig. 4.7a being an example of a 'force magnifier' machine.

A pulley wheel acts like a lever where the distances from the force applied by the man and that applied to the object to the pivot are equal, the pulley merely giving a change in direction of the force (Fig. 4.8). The distance through which the force applied by the man moves must be equal to the distance moved by the load; they are at the

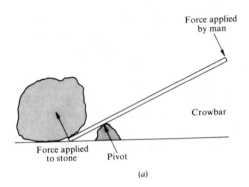

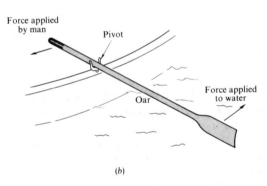

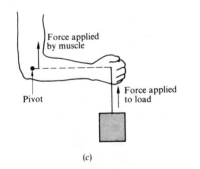

Fig. 4.7 (a) Using a crowbar to move a large stone. (b) Using an oar to propel through water. (c) Lifting a load

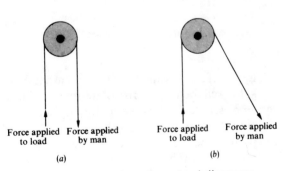

Fig. 4.8 Single pulley wheel diagrams

opposite ends of the same rope. If we take energy to be conserved then this means that the forces must be equal. This applies regardless of whether we have the situation represented by Fig. 4.8a or b.

Figure 4.9 shows two more complex pulley systems. For the system represented by (a) the distance through which the man's force moves is twice that which the load moves through. The force applied to the load is thus twice that exerted by the man. In (b) the distance through which the man's force moves is four times that which the load moves through, hence the force applied to the load is four times that applied by the man. One way of working out these distances is to consider how each of the ropes must be shortened if the load is to be lifted through, say, 1 m. The total amount of shortening must be equal to the distance over which the man must exert his pull if the rope remains taut.

and a half million stones, the mass of each being about 2½ tonnes (1 tonne is 1000 kg). A force of 2.5 × 10⁶) N has thus to be applied to lift one of these stones vertically. To push it along an inclined plane the force needed is that to overcome the component of the gravitational attraction down the plane, $mg \sin \theta$ for a plane making an angle θ with the horizontal, and the frictional force, $\mu mg \cos \theta$, where μ is the coefficient of friction. The frictional term can be made quite low by using lubricants; the Egyptians poured water under the runners on which they slid the stone blocks. With a plane inclined at 10° and taking μ as 0.1 the force needed to slide a 2½ tonne block is about 0.75 × 10⁶ N, about one-third of that needed for direct lifting.

A screw can be considered as an inclined plane wrapped round a cylinder (Fig. 4.10). With a helical thread of constant pitch, one revolution of the screw changes the height of the screw by the pitch. The angle of this inclined plane is thus

$$\tan \theta = \frac{p}{2\pi r}$$

where r is the mean radius of the screw and p the pitch. Archimedes invented a screw pump for lifting water (Fig. 4.11); such pumps are still used in some countries.

Many Greek and Roman inventions were concerned with the raising of water. During the first century BC water wheels for this purpose were in use in many parts of the Roman Empire (Fig. 4.12). The rotating wheel, rotated by hand or horse, trapped water in its buckets and carried it up out of the river before spilling it into a channel at the top of the wheel. Such wheels, generally

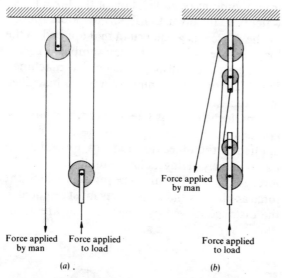

Force applied by man   Force applied to load

Force applied by man

Force applied to load

(a)   (b)

Fig. 4.9   Multiple pulley wheel diagrams

The use of pulleys and levers as machines dates back to well before Christ. Archimedes (third century BC) devised some pulley systems. In erecting the pyramids (3000–200 BC) the Ancient Egyptians used a very simple machine, the inclined plane. The Great Pyramid at Giza is about 160 m high and is constructed of some two

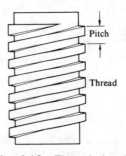

Pitch

Thread

Fig. 4.10   Threaded rod

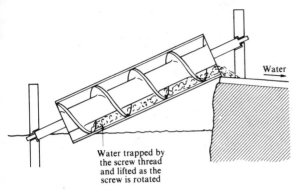

Fig. 4.11 *Screw thread lifting water*

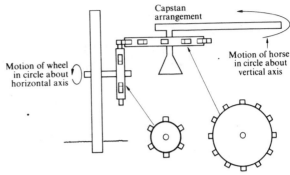

Fig. 4.13 *Water wheel with a capstan*

driven by oxen or donkeys, are still in use in many countries. The animals walk in a horizontal circular path and turn a capstan. This converts the rotation about a vertical axis into a rotation about a horizontal axis (Fig. 4.13).

The Romans were responsible for the spread of water mills throughout their empire—these utilized water power to produce rotation of a wheel. In one form the rotation was produced by blades on the wheel dipping into a flowing river, in another form where there was a drop in the water level the water from the upper level was passed along a chute to the top of the wheel and caused the rotation by falling onto the blades (Fig. 4.14).

An essential feature of water mills was the use of gearing. By this means the water wheel was able to rotate at a different speed to that of the working wheel, perhaps for grinding corn. When two different diameter wheels, in contact at a point of their circumferences, rotate without

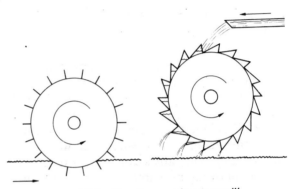

Fig. 4.14 *Two forms of water mill*

slipping then the ratio of their angular speeds is in the inverse ratio of their diameters. Contact without slipping, or very little, is achieved by putting teeth on the wheels (Fig. 4.15).

Water mills probably originated in the first century BC. They and the later windmill, probably

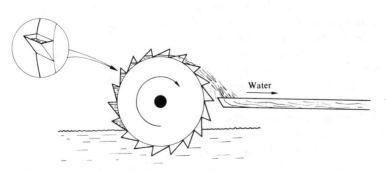

Fig. 4.12 *Water-raising wheel*

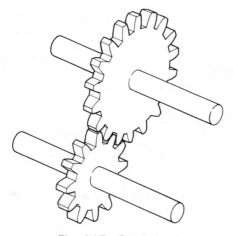

Fig. 4.15   Gear wheels

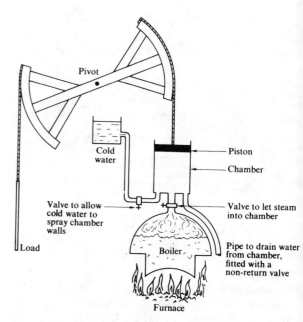

Fig. 4.16   Simplified diagram of a Newcomen engine

developed about the seventh century AD, allowed men to harness energy sources other than those of their fellow humans or beasts. These early mills were only capable of producing power of some 500 W. The eighteenth century saw the emergence of another energy source which man was able to utilize, steam. The early steam engines functioned on the following principle: when steam is used to expel a piston from a chamber, the steam condenses and so produces a partial vacuum; this drop in pressure to below atmospheric pressure on one side of the piston causes it to be pulled into the chamber, the steam is then admitted to the chamber and expels the piston, and so the cycle repeats itself. Figure 4.16 shows the engine invented by T. Newcomen which worked on this principle. The steam was made to condense by water being injected into the chamber.

With the Newcomen engine the steam pressure remains reasonably constant as the piston is pushed outwards; the steam from the boiler is flowing into the chamber during the entire operation. When the steam is condensed there is an abrupt drop in pressure followed by the piston moving back into the chamber. The pressure-volume changes can be roughly represented by Fig. 4.17. The work done at each stroke is the area under the graph (see earlier in this chapter). In this case this will be the product of the steam pressure and the chamber volume. The Newcomen engine of 1712 had a piston 0.54 m in diameter

and a chamber 2.4 m long, hence the chamber volume was about 0.55 m^3. The steam was at atmospheric pressure, 10^5 N m^{-2}, and thus the theoretical energy per stroke was 0.55×10^5 J. The engine made a stroke every 5 seconds so the power would be 0.11×10^5 W or 11 kW. The engine in fact was able to lift 46 kg of water through 46 m on each stroke; this means about 0.21×10^5 J at each stroke, a power of about 4.2 kW. Newcomen was able to increase the power of his engines by increasing the volume of the chamber—this

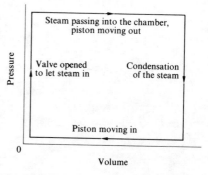

Fig. 4.17   Pressure-volume   relationship   for   a Newcomen engine

meant a much larger boiler to produce the steam. Later workers made significant power improvements by increasing the steam pressure.

The higher pressure is produced by higher boiler temperatures. Steam at one atmosphere pressure means the water boiling at 100°C, twice the atmospheric pressure means a temperature of about 121°C, six atmospheres means 159°C (see Chapter 16 and the section in which vapour pressure is discussed). J. Watt made a significant improvement when he made the engine double acting—the steam was applied first to one side and then to the other of the piston. The early engines, even with these improvements, still had very low efficiencies—less than 5 per cent. Efficiency is the percentage of the energy input which is available at the output, i.e., as mechanical energy. Much of the energy liberated by the fuel in the boiler was used in increasing the temperature of the surroundings or when the steam was produced not all the steam was used to produce the expansion. Only about 12 per cent of the steam in the Newcomen engine was available for the expansion, the rest condensed on the colder walls of the chamber.

The efficiencies of steam engines show a significant increase over the years, as the following table shows.

Year	Efficiency (approx.) /per cent
Newcomen	1712	2
Watt	1770	3
Watt	1796	4
Cornish engines	1830	10
Cornish engines	1846	14
Triple expansion	1890	18
Parsons' turbine	1910	20
Steam turbine	1950	30
Steam turbine	1955	38

A steam turbine is essentially the windmill with steam as the moving fluid which produces the rotation (Fig. 4.18). For steam with a mass per second m impinging on a blade, we can write for the change in momentum of the blade per second.

$$mv_1 \cos \theta$$

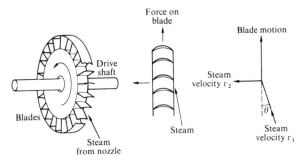

Fig. 4.18 Impulse turbine

where θ is the angle the incident steam makes with the blade. This assumes that the emerging steam is at right angles to the blade. We must also have

$$mv_1 \sin \theta = mv_2$$

The force acting on the blade is thus $mv_1 \cos \theta$. If the nozzle through which the steam emerges to hit the blade has an area A and the steam has a density ρ then

$$m = Av_1\rho$$

Hence

$$\text{force} = Av_1^2\rho \cos \theta$$

Typical figures for these quantities might be $\theta = 20°$, $A = 5 \times 10^{-4}$ m^2, $v_1 = 500$ m s^{-1}, $\rho = 4$ kg m^{-3}. The steam would be emerging from the nozzle with a pressure of about 8 atmospheres for these conditions to occur. This results in a force of about 500 N on a single blade.

The above form of turbine is known as an impulse turbine in that the steam strikes the blades and gives them an impulse. Another form of turbine is the reaction turbine (Fig. 4.19). In the impulse turbine the steam must have a high velocity when it impinges on the blades; in the reaction turbine the steam supply has to be at high pressure (this does not involve steam molecules having a high velocity in some particular direction). The steam can escape from the high to a low pressure region by passing through the blades of the turbine. The steam emerges at high velocity. The situation is comparable to a garden hosepipe or sprinkler, the water at high pressure passes through the nozzle to emerge as

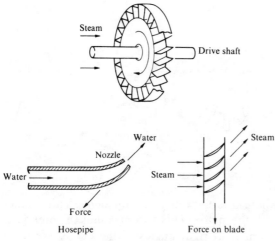

Fig. 4.19 Reaction turbine

high speed water. As is certainly evident with the water sprinklers which revolve, the nozzle experiences a force. This is the so-called reaction force that is experienced by the blades of the turbine. The force causing rotation will be equal to the rate of change of momentum of the steam in a direction at right angles to the drive shaft.

Many of the large turbines use both the impulse and the reaction methods of operation, having a number of stages each with a number of turbine rotors with blades. Turbines are used with steam or water or hot gases. In the gas turbine hot gas at high pressure is generated by internal combustion and then passed to the turbine section. Turbines with powers of the order of many thousands of kilowatts are now quite common (Fig. 4.20).

One engine that must not be omitted in this brief survey is the internal combustion engine. Figure 4.21 shows the basic sequence of operations in a four-stroke engine. The sequence is briefly— intake of a mixture of air and vaporized petrol; compression of this mixture, raising the temperature of the mixture; ignition by a spark, the mixture burns and the hot gases push the piston down; the gases remaining in the chamber are ejected. Figure 4.22 shows the pressure–volume graph for the gases in the cylinder. Compression gives an increase in pressure, a decrease in volume, and an increase in temperature. At

Fig. 4.20 Thorpe Marsh Power Station (Central Electricity Generating Board). View of the turbines with the upper covers removed to show the blades. (Reyrolle Parsons)

ignition there is a sudden increase in pressure and then the pressure drops as the piston moves down. The area enclosed by the graph is a measure of the energy made available. This can be made larger by increasing the compression ratio, i.e., reducing the volume by a greater fraction during the compression part of the sequence. A limit on this ratio is set by the fact that the temperature rise resulting from the compression must not become so high that the gas ignites.

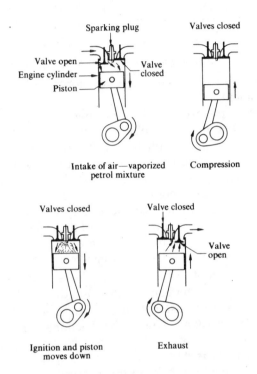

Fig. 4.21

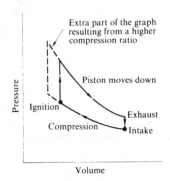

Fig. 4.22

Further reading

H. Hodges (1970) *Technology in the Ancient World*, Penguin. This is useful for details of ancient machines.

J. F. Sandfort (1964) *Heat Engines*, Science Study Series, No. 22, Heinemann.

Problems

1. A stone is projected vertically upwards and eventually returns to the point of projection. Ignoring any effects due to air resistance, draw sketch graphs to show the variation with time of the following properties of the stone: (i) velocity, (ii) kinetic energy, (iii) potential energy, (iv) momentum, (v) distance from point of projection, (vi) speed.

(AEB, QA2, Paper 3, June 1982)

2. A stone of mass 80 g is released at the top of a vertical cliff. After falling for 3 s it reaches the foot of the cliff, and penetrates 9 cm into the ground. What is (a) the height of the cliff, (b) the average force resisting penetration of the ground by the stone? ($g = 9.8$ m s^{-2})

(Southern Universities, Q2, Paper 1, June 1980)

3. A bullet of mass 10 g is fired horizontally with a velocity of 200 m s^{-1} into a block of wood of mass 4.0 kg at rest on a horizontal surface. If the coefficient of friction between the block and the surface can be taken as 0.30, how far will the block be moved by the impact if the bullet comes to rest in the block?

4. A truck of mass 1500 kg travelling at 20 m s^{-1} on a horizontal surface is brought to rest in a distance of 14 m when the brakes are applied. Calculate the average retarding force exerted by the brakes.

5. A pendulum bob has a mass of 0.50 kg and when hit by a bullet of mass 5.0 g swings through an arc which results in the bob rising through a vertical height of 15 cm. If the bullet remains embedded in the bob, what was its original speed? ($g = 9.8$ m s^{-2})

6. A car can develop a power of 200 kW. If the car has a mass of 1000 kg how fast can it climb a 30° incline with a coefficient of friction 0.2? ($g = 9.8$ m s^{-2})

79

7. A cyclist, of mass 60 kg, pedals a bike, of mass 15 kg, up an incline of 5 in 100 at a constant velocity of 2.6 m s^{-1}. What power is the cyclist expending if frictional forces can be ignored? ($g = 9.8$ m s^{-2})

8. Coal drops vertically onto a horizontal conveyor belt moving at a constant velocity of 2.0 m s^{-1} at the rate of 120 kg s^{-1}. What power has to be expended to keep the belt moving at this velocity?

9. (a) Outline an experiment to show that linear momentum is conserved in collisions.

(b) In each of the following processes are both momentum and kinetic energy conserved during the impacts?

(i) A collision between two gas molecules.
(ii) A steel ball dropped onto a stone floor and rebounding to about three-quarters of its original height.
(iii) A lump of Plasticene being dropped onto a stone floor and not rebounding at all.

For case (ii) discuss the momentum and energy transfers which occur throughout the process.

Sketch two graphs showing how the momentum and kinetic energy of the ball vary with time from initial release.

(University of London, Q11, Paper 2, January 1979)

10. (a) Define linear momentum and state the principle of conservation of linear momentum.

(b) Discuss the application of the principle to the following cases:

(i) A dart is thrown at a board and remains stuck in the board.
(ii) A billiard ball makes a perfectly elastic collision, striking the cushion of a billiard table at right angles.
(iii) A tennis ball strikes the ground at an angle and rebounds to a smaller height than that from which it was released.

(c) Distinguish between elastic and inelastic collisions and give an example of each type. Two similar billiard balls are in contact and at rest on a billiard table. A third similar ball is travelling with a velocity v along the line joining the centres of the stationary balls. Assuming an elastic colli-

sion to take place, explain why it is not possible for the moving ball to stop and the two stationary balls to move off each with a velocity of $v/2$.

(d) In an experiment to measure its speed a bullet is fired horizontally at a block of wood suspended from a vertical string. On striking the block, the bullet is embedded and the block rises to a vertical height of 6.00 cm above its rest position. The mass of the bullet is 10.0 g and that of the block 390.0 g. Calculate the speed of the bullet. ($g = 9.8$ m s^{-2})

(AEB, QB11, Paper 3, November 1982)

11. State the principle of conservation of momentum.

A particle of mass m moving with speed v makes a head-on collision with an identical particle which is initially at rest. How would you tell from the subsequent motion of the particles whether they had made (a) an elastic, (b) a completely inelastic, collision? In each case, work out how (if at all) the kinetic energy of the first particle, and the kinetic energy of the system as a whole, is affected by the collision.

The neutrons in a beam from a reactor have an average energy of 6.0×10^{-13} J. This is reduced to 6.0×10^{-21} J by causing the neutrons to make a series of collisions with carbon nuclei in a moderator. On average, the fractional loss of kinetic energy of a neutron at each collision in the moderator is 0.14. About how many collisions must a neutron make in this process?

(University of Cambridge, Q13, Paper 1, June 1980)

12. State Newton's laws of motion, and show how the principle of conservation of linear momentum may be derived from them.

A particle P of mass 3 kg and a particle Q of mass 1 kg are connected by a light elastic string and initially held at rest on a smooth horizontal table with the string in tension. They are then simultaneously released. The string gives up 24 J of energy as it contracts to its natural length. Calculate the velocity acquired by each of the particles, assuming no energy is lost.

A helicopter of mass 810 kg supports itself in a stationary position by imparting a downward velocity v to all the air in a circle of area 30 m^2. Given that the density of air is 1.20 kg m^{-3}, calculate the value of v. What is the power needed to support the helicopter in this way, assuming no energy is lost?

(Southern Universities, Q1, Paper 2, June 1980)

13. (a) A steady stream of balls each of mass 0.2 kg hits a vertical wall at right angles. If the speed of the balls is 15 m s^{-1} and 600 hit the wall in 12 s and rebound at the same speed, what is the average force acting on the wall? Sketch a graph to show how the actual force on the wall varies with time over a period of 0.10 s. Explain how the average force on the wall could be obtained from this graph.

Explain briefly how the above problem can lead to an understanding of how a gas exerts a pressure on the walls of its container.

(b) A car travelling along a level road at a speed of 10 m s^{-1} crashes head on into a wall. If the mass of the car is 1000 kg, calculate the kinetic energy and momentum of the car just before the collision.

Describe as carefully as you can the energy changes that occur in this collision.

If the impact time (the time taken for the car to come to rest) is 0.2 s, calculate the average force acting on the wall and explain why it is an average.

Why is it advantageous for a passenger if the impact time is increased? Make a calculation to support your point. How in practice could car design be improved to achieve an increase in impact time?

(University of London, Q12, Paper 2, June 1980)

14. 'A conservation law is a statement of constancy in nature. . . .

. . . The strong hint emerging from recent studies of elementary particles is that only inhibition imposed upon the chaotic flux of events in the world of the very small is that imposed by the conservation laws. Everything that can happen without violating a conservation law does happen.

This review of democracy in nature—freedom under law—represents a revolutionary change in man's view of natural law. The older view of a fundamental law of nature was that it must be a law of permission. It defined what can (and must) happen in natural phenomena. According to the new view, the more fundamental law is a law of prohibition. It defines which cannot happen. A conservation law is, in effect, a law of prohibition. It prohibits any phenomenon that would change the conserved quantity. . . .'

K. W. Ford (1963) *The World of Elementary Particles*, Blaisdell, page 81.

(a) How would you define a conservation law, without using the word 'conserved'?

(b) Give examples of laws of permission and of prohibition that occur in everyday life.

(c) Are Newton's laws of motion laws of permission or prohibition?

5 Angular motion

Describing angular motion

A particle moving in a circular path or a point on a spinning rigid body can have its motion described in terms of the angle swept out in unit time. We defined (Chapter 2) linear velocity as the distance covered, in a straight line, in unit time—in a similar manner we can define angular velocity as the angle of rotation in unit time.

$$\text{Linear velocity} = \frac{\text{distance change}}{\text{time taken}}, \quad v = \frac{\Delta s}{\Delta t}$$

$$\text{Angular velocity} = \frac{\text{angle rotated}}{\text{time taken}}, \quad \omega = \frac{\Delta \theta}{\Delta t}$$

The angular velocity tells us how far a point has gone round a circle in unit time. The angle is usually measured in radians and thus the angular velocity could have units of radians per second.

If a point moves along the arc of a circle, Fig. 5.1, then the angle of rotation, in radians, is equal to the distance moved along the arc divided by the radius.

$$\theta = \frac{\text{distance moved along arc}}{\text{radius}}$$

Thus for one complete rotation the distance covered is the circumference, $2\pi r$, and thus

$$\theta = \frac{2\pi r}{r} = 2\pi$$

One complete rotation is a movement through $360°$ and thus 2π radians are equal to $360°$.

Hence

$$1 \text{ radian} = \frac{360°}{2\pi} = 57.3°$$

If a shaft completes three revolutions in 4 s then the angle through which the shaft has rotated is $3 \times 2\pi$ radians and so the average angular velocity over that time is $3 \times 2\pi/4 = 4.7$ rad s^{-1}.

If there are f revolutions per second then the angle covered in one second is $2\pi f$ and so the angular velocity ω is

$$\omega = 2\pi f$$

It is quite common to refer to angular velocity as being so many revolutions per second rather than multiply the number of revolutions per second by 2π to give the angular velocity in its correct units of radians per second.

If T is the time taken for one complete revolution, the number of revolutions per second f is $1/T$.

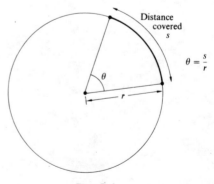

Fig. 5.1

Hence

$$f = 1/T$$

and so

$$\omega = \frac{2\pi}{T}$$

Thus if a shaft takes 0.2 s to complete one revolution then the average angular velocity over that time is $2\pi/0.2 = 31$ rad s^{-1}.

Angular acceleration is defined as the rate of change of angular velocity with time.

Angular acceleration $\alpha = $

$$\frac{\text{change in angular velocity}}{\text{time taken}}$$

$$\alpha = \frac{d\omega}{dt}$$

The unit of angular acceleration is rad s^{-2}. Angular acceleration has a positive value if the change in angular acceleration is such that the angular velocity is increasing, negative if it is decreasing.

Thus if a shaft has an angular acceleration of 2 rad s^{-2}, it is changing angular velocity at such a rate that if it continued at that rate for a second the angular velocity would have changed by 2 rad s^{-1}.

A car wheel increases its speed from 2 revolutions per second to 20 revolutions per second in a time of 40 s, what is the average angular acceleration over that time? For such a problem we need to convert frequency of rotation to angular velocity. Thus

Initially $\quad \omega_1 = 2\pi f_1 = 2\pi \times 2$ rad s^{-1}

After 40 s $\quad \omega_2 = 2\pi f_2 = 2\pi \times 20$ rad s^{-1}

Hence average angular acceleration

$$\alpha = \frac{\omega_2 - \omega_1}{t}$$

$$\alpha = \frac{(2\pi \times 20) - (2\pi \times 2)}{40}$$

$$= 2.8 \text{ rad s}^{-2}$$

Relationship between linear and angular motion

If a wheel rotates with a constant angular velocity ω, then in time t a point on the rim of the wheel will sweep out an angle θ, where

$$\omega = \frac{\theta}{t}$$

The point on the rim will have moved a distance s round the arc in that time (Fig. 5.1). But the speed v of the point, referred to as the *linear speed* to distinguish it from angular speed, is the distance covered divided by the time taken.

$$v = \frac{s}{t}$$

The arc length is related to the angle θ by the relationship

$$s = r\theta$$

where r is the radius of the wheel. Thus

$$v = \frac{r\theta}{t}$$

$$v = r\omega$$

Thus for a car wheel rotating with an angular velocity of 15 rad s^{-1}, and having a radius of 0.35 m, a point on the rim of the wheel will have a linear speed of $v = 0.35 \times 15 = 5.25$ m s^{-1}.

If the point on the rim of the wheel had an initial speed v_0 and an initial angular velocity ω_0, then

$$v_0 = r\omega_0$$

If after some time interval t the same point had a speed v_1 and an angular velocity ω_1, then

$$v_1 = r\omega_1$$

The average *linear acceleration* a during this time is

$$a = \frac{v_1 - v_0}{t}$$

$$= \frac{r\omega_1 - r\omega_0}{t}$$

But the angular acceleration α is given by

$$\alpha = \frac{\omega_1 - \omega_0}{t}$$

Hence
$$a = r\alpha$$

If the angular acceleration of a car wheel is 2 rad s^{-2} and the wheel has a radius of 350 mm (i.e., 0.35 m), then the linear acceleration of a point on the tyre tread is $0.35 \times 2 = 0.70$ m s^{-2}.

The following examples illustrate the types of problems in which the above equations might be required.

(a) A flywheel rotates at 15 revolutions per second. If the flywheel has a radius of 150 mm, what is the linear speed of a point on the rim of the wheel?

$$\omega = 2\pi f$$
$$= 2\pi \times 15$$
$$= 30\pi \text{ rad s}^{-1}$$
$$v = r\omega$$
$$= 0.15 \times 30\pi$$
$$= 14.1 \text{ m s}^{-1}$$

(b) The wheels of a car increase their angular speed from 40 rev min^{-1} to 500 rev min^{-1} in 20 s. Calculate the average angular acceleration of the wheels and, if the wheels have a radius of 350 mm, the linear acceleration of a point on the tyre tread.

$$\omega = 2\pi f$$

Thus initial angular velocity $\omega_0 = 2\pi \times (40/60)$ rad s^{-1}

Final angular velocity $\omega_1 = 2\pi \times (500/60)$ rad s^{-1}

Average angular acceleration $= \dfrac{\omega_1 - \omega_0}{t}$

$$= \frac{2\pi \times (500/60) - 2\pi \times (40/60)}{20}$$
$$= 2.41 \text{ rad s}^{-2}$$

Linear acceleration $a = r\alpha$
$$= 0.35 \times 2.41$$
$$= 0.84 \text{ m s}^{-2}$$

(c) A driver brakes and brings his car, which was moving at 60 km h^{-1} to rest in a distance of 80 m. The car has tyres of radius 350 mm. Calculate
(i) the average retardation,
(ii) the initial angular velocity of a wheel,
(iii) the average angular retardation of a wheel.

·(i) Initial velocity $= 60$ km h^{-1}
$$= \frac{60 \times 10^3}{60 \times 60} \text{ m s}^{-1}$$
$$= 16.7 \text{ m s}^{-1}$$
$$v^2 = v_0^2 + 2as$$

Hence

$$0 = 16.7^2 + 2 \times a \times 80$$
$$160a = -16.7^2$$
$$a = -\frac{16.7^2}{160}$$
$$a = -1.74 \text{ m s}^{-2}$$

(ii) Initially the circumference of the tyre has a linear velocity of 16.7 m s^{-1}. Thus initially

$$v = r\omega$$
$$16.7 = 0.35\omega$$
$$\omega = \frac{16.7}{0.35}$$
$$\omega = 47.7 \text{ rad s}^{-1}$$

(iii) The linear retardation of the circumference of the tyre is 1.74 m s^{-2}.

$$a = r\alpha$$
$$1.74 = 0.35\alpha$$
$$\alpha = \frac{1.74}{0.35}$$
$$= 4.97 \text{ rad s}^{-2}$$

Equations for uniformly accelerated motion

If there is uniformly accelerated motion then, from the definition of angular acceleration, when the angular velocity changes from ω_0 to ω_1 in a time t

$$\alpha = \frac{\omega_1 - \omega_0}{t}$$

$$\omega_1 = \omega_0 + \alpha t$$

Compare this with the equation for linear motion (Chapter 2) of

$$v = v_0 + at$$

The angle covered when the angular velocity changes from ω_0 to ω_1 in time t is

$$\theta = (\text{average angular velocity}) \times (\text{time})$$

$$= \tfrac{1}{2}(\omega_1 + \omega_0)t$$

But $\omega_1 = \omega_0 + \alpha t$, and so

$$\theta = \tfrac{1}{2}(\omega_0 + \alpha t + \omega_0)t$$

$$\theta = \omega_0 t + \tfrac{1}{2}\alpha t^2$$

Compare this with the equation for linear motion (Chapter 2) of

$$s = v_0 t + \tfrac{1}{2}at^2$$

We can obtain a third equation for this motion by squaring the equation $\omega_1 = \omega_0 + \alpha t$, i.e.

$$\omega_1^2 = \omega_0^2 + 2\omega_0 \alpha t + \alpha^2 t^2$$

$$= \omega_0^2 + 2\alpha(\omega_0 t + \tfrac{1}{2}\alpha t^2)$$

Hence

$$\omega_1^2 = \omega_0^2 + 2\alpha\theta$$

Compare this with the equation for linear motion (Chapter 2) of

$$v^2 = v_0^2 + 2as$$

The following example illustrates the use of these equations. A car wheel has an initial angular velocity of 50 rad s^{-1} and when the brakes are applied it comes to rest in 15 s. If the angular acceleration can be assumed to be uniform, what is its value and the number of revolutions the wheel makes in coming to rest?

Since $\qquad \omega_1 = \omega_0 + \alpha t$

$$0 = 50 + 15\alpha$$

$$\alpha = -3.3 \text{ rad s}^{-2}$$

The minus sign indicates that the wheel is slowing down.

Since $\quad \theta = \omega_0 t + \tfrac{1}{2}\alpha t^2$

$$\theta = 50 \times 15 + \tfrac{1}{2} \times (-3.3) \times 15^2$$

$$\theta = 379 \text{ rad}$$

Since one revolution is 2π rad, the number of revolutions per second f is

$$f = \frac{379}{2\pi} = 60.3$$

Torque and angular motion

In Chapter 1, torque or moment of a force about an axis, T, is defined as the product of the force and the perpendicular distance of that force from the axis. If you want to push open a door, i.e., cause rotation of the door about the hinges axis, it is easiest if the push is applied as far from the hinges as possible. Door handles are usually situated as far from the hinges as possible because least effort is then needed. (Try opening a door by pushing near the hinges.) Applying a force at the largest distance from the axis of rotation means a bigger torque than if the distance is made small for the same size force. Thus the angular acceleration of the opening door depends on the applied torque.

We could do experiments with a door, or better still a turntable, by applying forces at different distances from the axis and determining the change in angular velocity produced, i.e., establishing the relationship between torque and angular acceleration. Experimentally the outcome is

$$\text{angular acceleration} \propto \text{torque}$$

The constant of proportionality, i.e., the amount of angular acceleration produced by a given torque, depends on the mass of the object being accelerated and the way the mass is distributed.

We can deduce the above relationship if we consider a rigid body which is rotating about some axis, see Fig. 5.2. A particle of mass m of that body, at A, rotates through a circular arc of radius r. If F is the tangential force acting on this particle

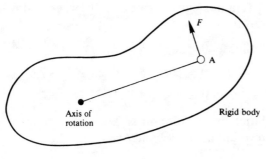

Fig. 5.2

at A, then using Newton's second law of motion, the acceleration a is given by $F = ma$ and since $a = r\alpha$, where α is the angular acceleration, we have

$$F = mr\alpha$$

Hence the torque T acting on the particle is

$$T = Fr = mr^2\alpha$$

The rigid body is made up of a large number of small particles, each being at different distances from the axis. The total torque acting on the body is the sum of the torques acting on all these small particles, Thus

Total torque T = sum of all $(mr^2\alpha)$ terms

Since α is the same for all the particles in a rigid body

$$T = (\text{sum of } mr^2 \text{ terms}) \times \alpha$$

The sum of all the mr^2 terms is called the *moment of inertia*, symbol I, of the body. Hence

$$T = I\alpha$$

This equation for angular motion can be compared with $F = ma$ for linear motion. Torque is the angular equivalent of force for linear motion, angular acceleration the equivalent of linear acceleration, and moment of inertia the equivalent of mass. Mass tells us how easy it is to accelerate (linearly) an object. The moment of inertia tells us how easy it is to rotationally accelerate an object.

Moments of inertia

The moment of inertia of a body about a particular axis is defined by

$$I = \Sigma mr^2$$

where r is the distance of each particle of mass m in the body from the axis of rotation considered. For a uniform sphere rotating about a diameter the moment of inertia is $\frac{2}{5} Mr^2$, where M is the total mass of the sphere and r its radius. For a uniform disc, mass M and radius r, about an axis perpendicular to its plane and through its centre, the moment of inertia is $\frac{1}{2}Mr^2$. For a ring of mass M and radius r, the moment of inertia about a central axis perpendicular to its plane is Mr^2.

The moment of inertia of any body depends on the position of the axis about which the moment is considered. If the moment of inertia I_0 about some particular axis is known, then the moment of inertia I about some parallel axis a distance d away is given by

$$I = I_0 + Md^2$$

where M is the total mass of the body. This relationship is known as the theorem of parallel axes. Thus for a sphere of radius r and mass M, the moment of inertia about an axis perpendicular to its plane, and through its centre is $\frac{2}{5} Mr^2$. Hence the moment of inertia of the same sphere about an axis tangential to its circumference is $\frac{2}{5} Mr^2 + Mr^2 = \frac{7}{5} Mr^2$ (Fig. 5.3).

Some objects can be considered to be made up of a number of simple objects. Thus a dumbbell, for instance, consists of two spheres mounted at the ends of a slender rod (Fig. 5.4). The moment of

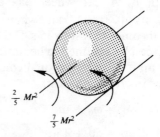

Fig. 5.3 *Moments of inertia of a sphere about different axes*

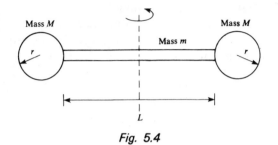

Mass M

Mass m

Mass M

r

r

L

Fig. 5.4

inertia of such an object about an axis through the centre of the rod is the sum of the moments of inertia of the component parts about the same axis. The moment of inertia of the rod is $\frac{1}{12}mL^2$ about the specified axis. The moment of inertia of a sphere is $\frac{2}{5}Mr^2 + M(\frac{1}{2}L + r)^2$. As there are two spheres, the total moment of inertia is thus

$$\frac{1}{12}mL^2 + 2\left[\frac{2}{5}Mr^2 + M\left(\frac{1}{2}L + r\right)^2\right]$$

Radius of gyration

Whatever the form of an object it is always possible to represent its moment of inertia in the form $I = Mk^2$, where M is its mass and k a distance from the axis concerned which is called the *radius of gyration*. The significance of this radius is that we can consider, for rotational purposes, the body effectively to have all its mass concentrated at a point a distance k from the axis of rotation.

Thus if a flywheel has a mass of 400 kg and a radius of gyration of 1.2 m about some axis, then the moment of inertia of the flywheel about that axis is $\frac{1}{2}Mk^2 = \frac{1}{2} \times 400 \times 1.2^2 = 288$ kg m^2. Given the radius of gyration we do not need any information about how the mass of the flywheel is distributed in order to obtain the moment of inertia.

The following examples illustrate some of the types of problems that can be encountered.

(a) The rotor of an electric motor has a moment of inertia of 6.2 kg m^2, what torque is

needed to give the rotor an angular acceleration of 0.20 rad s^{-2}?

$$\text{Torque} = I\alpha = 6.2 \times 0.20 = 1.4 \text{ N m}$$

(b) A flywheel has a mass of 280 kg and a radius of gyration of 0.50 m. What is the uniform torque needed to bring such a wheel to rest in 25 s when it is rotating at 5.0 rev s^{-1}?

$$I = Mk^2 = 280 \times 0.50^2 \text{ kg m}^2$$

$$\omega_1 = \omega_0 + \alpha t$$

Hence

$$0 = (2\pi \times 5.0) + 25\alpha$$

$$\alpha = -10\pi/25 \text{ rad s}^{-2}$$

Thus torque $T = I\alpha = 280 \times 0.50^2 \times (10\pi/25)$

$$= 88 \text{ N m}$$

Energy and rotation

Consider an object being rotated by tangentially applied forces, as in Fig. 5.5. When the force at point A causes it to move through an arc of angle θ then the work involved is

$$\text{work} = F \times \text{distance round the arc } (AB)$$

But this distance round the arc is $r\theta$. Hence

$$\text{work} = Fr\theta$$

But the torque $T = Fr$, hence

$$\text{work} = T\theta$$

This is in fact the work done by a couple, there being oppositely directed but equal size forces at the ends of the diameter.

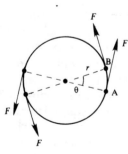

F

F

B

r

θ

A

F

F

Fig. 5.5

If this work results in a constant angular velocity ω, then in 1 s the angle covered in ω. Thus the work done per second is $T\omega$. But power is work done per second. Hence

$$\text{power} = T\omega$$

As an example of the use of this equation, consider the power needed to keep a wheel rotating at 10 rad s^{-1} when acted on by a constant torque of 30 N m.

$$\text{Power} = 30 \times 10 = 300 \text{ W}$$

Each particle of a rotating rigid body will have kinetic energy of $\frac{1}{2}mv^2$, where m is the mass of the particle and v its velocity. If such a particle is a distance r from the axis of rotation then, since $v = r\omega$ we can write

$$\text{kinetic energy} = \frac{1}{2}m(r\omega)^2$$

The total kinetic energy of the rotating body will be the sum of the kinetic energies of all its constituent particles. Thus

$$\text{total kinetic energy} = \Sigma\frac{1}{2}m(r\omega)^2$$

All the particles will have the same angular velocity, thus

$$\text{total kinetic energy} = \frac{1}{2}\omega^2(\Sigma mr^2)$$

But $\Sigma mr^2 = I$, the moment of inertia about the axis concerned. Hence the kinetic energy of the rotating body is

$$\text{kinetic energy} = \frac{1}{2}I\omega^2$$

Thus if a flywheel is rotating at 2.0 revolutions per second and the moment of inertia about the axis of rotation is 60 kg m^2, then the flywheel has rotational kinetic energy of $\frac{1}{2} \times 60 \times (2\pi \times 2.0)^2$ = 4.7 kW

Many machines use rotating flywheels as a means of storing energy. Such 'stores' can be used to 'iron out' input energy fluctuations to the machine. Thus, for example, if the energy input to a machine with a flywheel rises, the drive shaft will start to increase in angular velocity. But a large energy input is required to cause a change in the angular velocity of the flywheel and so the energy input causes less change in angular velocity than otherwise would have been the case.

Similarly, if the energy input to the machine decreases, energy is taken from the flywheel with little change in its angular velocity. The significant factor in this use of a flywheel is that the kinetic energy of the flywheel is proportional to the square of the angular velocity and large changes in kinetic energy are needed to cause significant changes in angular velocity.

Kinetic energy of a rolling object

When an object rolls along a plane it has both translational kinetic energy and rotational kinetic energy. Consider the problem of a uniform cylinder rolling down an incline (Fig. 5.6). It is assumed that the cylinder does not slip but purely rolls. The total kinetic energy of the cylinder at some instant is

$$\text{total kinetic energy} = \frac{1}{2}mv^2 + \frac{1}{2}I\omega^2$$

where I is the moment of inertia about the central axis of the cylinder. Since $v = r\omega$

$$\text{total kinetic energy} = \frac{1}{2}mv^2 + \frac{1}{2}I(v/r)^2$$

$$= \frac{1}{2}v^2\left(m + \frac{I}{r^2}\right)$$

This kinetic energy is gained as a result of a loss of potential energy. If the cylinder starts from rest and has rolled a distance s along the plane, then the vertical height through which it has fallen is $s \sin\theta$ and so the loss in potential energy is $mgs \sin\theta$. Hence, since this must equal the gain in kinetic energy

$$\frac{1}{2}v^2\left(m + \frac{I}{r^2}\right) = mgs \sin\theta$$

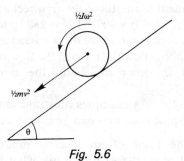

Fig. 5.6

If a is the linear acceleration down the plane, then $v^2 = 2as$ and so

$$a = \frac{mg \sin \theta}{\left(m + \dfrac{I}{r^2}\right)}$$

If there had been no rolling, only sliding down the plane, then there would have been no rotational energy term and we would have had

$$a = g \sin \theta$$

A common problem is to consider a solid cylinder and a hollow cylinder rolling down a plane, and consider which would reach the bottom the first. A uniform solid cylinder has a moment of inertia of $\frac{1}{2}mr^2$ about its central axis, m being its mass and r the radius. A uniform hollow cylinder open at both ends has a moment of inertia about its central axis of mr^2, where m is its mass and r its radius. If both cylinders have the same mass, then for the solid one $I/r^2 = \frac{1}{2}m$ and for the hollow one $I/r^2 = m$. Thus for the solid cylinder $a = \frac{2}{3}g \sin \theta$ and for the hollow one $a = \frac{1}{2}g \sin \theta$. Thus the solid cylinder has the greater acceleration and so will reach the bottom of the incline the faster.

Angular momentum

If you sit in one of those swivelling typist's chairs with your arms outstretched and large masses in your hands, whirl round and then pull your hands, and the masses, close in to your body a remarkable thing happens—your angular velocity increases (you go round faster). A skater slowly spinning with arms outstretched spins much faster when he pulls his arms in. In both these cases the moment of inertia has been changed by the movement of the arms. This is one of the important differences between mass and moment of inertia—the mass of a body cannot be changed, the moment of inertia can be. Why does changing the moment of inertia change the speed of spinning? For this we will introduce a term called *angular momentum*.

Consider a rotating rigid body and some particle of it a distance r from the axis of rotation

(Fig. 5.7). If this particle has a mass m and at some instant a tangential velocity v, then the linear momentum of the particle is mv. But $v = r\omega$, where ω is the angular velocity. Therefore linear momentum $= mr\omega$. If there is a change in linear momentum then there must be a force acting, force being equal to rate of change of momentum (see Chapter 3). Thus

Force F = rate of change of $(mr\omega)$

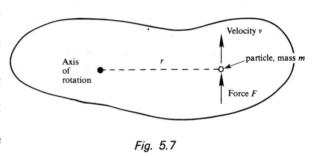

Fig. 5.7

Since the torque $T = Fr$

$$T = r \times \text{rate of change of } (mr\omega)$$

$$= \text{rate of change of } (mr^2\omega)$$

This is for just one particle in the rotating body. For all the particles the torque will be the sum of the rates of change of all the $(mr^2\omega)$ terms.

$$T = \text{rate of change of } (\Sigma mr^2\omega)$$

But ω will be the same for all particles in the rotating body and Σmr^2 is the moment of inertia I. Hence

$$T = \text{rate of change of } (I\omega)$$

We define angular momentum to be

$$\text{angular momentum } L = I\omega$$

with units of $\text{kg m}^2 \text{ s}^{-1}$. Then we have an equation similar to that for force, when it is defined as rate of change of linear momentum, of

$$T = \text{rate of change of angular momentum}$$

Thus in the case of somebody sitting in a typist's chair with outstretched hands holding masses and slowly rotating, the angular momentum will be $I\omega$. However, if the hands are pulled in, so bringing the masses closer to the axis of rotation, then the moment of inertia is decreased. The angular velocity increases. This is because in the absence of any external torque acting, the rate of change of angular momentum must be zero. Hence if I is decreased then ω must be increased, so that the angular momentum remains unchanged. Angular momentum is conserved.

Consider a horizontal disc of moment of inertia 2.0×10^{-4} kg m^2 which is rotating at 33 revolutions per minute about a central vertical axis (perhaps it is a record player turntable). What will be the new number of revolutions per minute if a small piece of material, mass 0.030 kg, drops onto the disc at a distance of 0.15 m from its axis?

$$\text{Initial angular velocity} = 2\pi f$$
$$= 2\pi \times 33/60 \text{ rad s}^{-1}$$

$$\text{Initial angular momentum} = I\omega = 2.0 \times 10^{-4} \times$$
$$(2\pi \times 33/60)^2 \text{ kg m}^2 \text{ s}^{-1}$$

When the material drops onto the disc the moment of inertia is increased.

$$\text{New moment of inertia} = 2.0 \times 10^{-4} + 0.030 \times 0.15^2$$

$$\text{Hence new angular momentum} = (2.0 \times 10^{-4} + 0.030 \times 0.15^2)\omega$$

where ω is the new angular velocity. Since angular momentum is conserved, the new angular momentum must equal the initial angular momentum. Hence ω is 2.73 rad s^{-1}. This means a frequency of rotation of $f = \omega/2\pi = 0.434$ s^{-1} or 26.1 revolutions per minute.

Motion in a circle

An object continues in uniform motion in a straight line, i.e., constant velocity, or remains at rest if no force is acting on it. Thus when an object moves in a circular path there must be a force acting on it, moving it from the straight line path. This force can be provided by the tension in a string, for an object being whirled round in a horizontal circle on the end of a string, or gravity

for the earth orbiting the sun. The force, whatever its origin, is known as a *centripetal force*. Objects moving in circular paths are not in equilibrium, there must be a resultant force otherwise there would be only straight line motion.

Consider an object of mass m, moving in a horizontal circular path of radius R with a speed v (Fig. 5.8). At some instant it is at point P, with a velocity v in the direction shown by the arrow. Some time t later the object is at Q with a velocity in the direction shown by the arrow at Q. The direction has changed. To get this new velocity at Q we must have added another velocity to the one at P. We can find what must be added to the velocity at P to give a resultant velocity of that at Q by using the parallelogram of vectors (see Chapter 0). Figure 5.8 shows the parallelogram and this added velocity of Δv. This is the velocity that has to be added in the time taken to cover the angle θ. The direction of this addition is towards the centre of the circle.

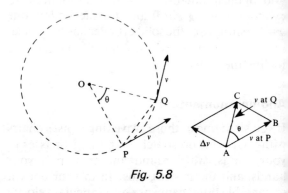

Fig. 5.8

The triangles OPQ and ABC are similar triangles and thus

$$\frac{\Delta v}{\text{PQ}} = \frac{v}{R}$$

The arc distance PQ is the distance covered by the object in time t and hence $v = $ arc PQ$/t$. If we consider only small time intervals, then the distance PQ approximates to the arc PQ and so

$$\frac{\Delta v}{vt} = \frac{v}{R}$$

There is a change in velocity of Δv in time t and so the average acceleration over that time is $\Delta v/t$. Since we are considering very small intervals of time, this can then be considered to be the instantaneous acceleration. Hence the object accelerates with an acceleration given by

$$a = \frac{v^2}{R}$$

The direction of the acceleration is towards the centre of the circle.

The centripetal force produces this acceleration and hence this force is

$$F = \frac{mv^2}{R}$$

If the centripetal force is made zero the object will fly off along a tangent to the circle.

The term centrifugal force is often used incorrectly, to denote a force acting outwards, along a radius, to balance the centripetal force. The forces on a rotating object are not balanced—if there was a centrifugal force, acting on the object, opposite and equal to the centripetal force, then the object would not move in a circular path. An unbalanced force is necessary for motion in a circle. But it can be argued that because to every action there is an opposite and equal reaction there must be another force somewhere. The action and reaction do not act on the same body. The reaction force acts on the object supplying the centripetal force. In the case of the earth orbiting the sun, the centripetal force acts on the earth and the reaction force acts on the sun. For an object being whirled round in a horizontal circle on the end of a string, the centripetal force acts on the object and the reaction force on the string and so on the hand of the person holding the string (Fig. 5.9).

For a stationary observer an object moves in a circular path because it is acted on by a centripetal force: there is no centrifugal force. If, however, the observer rotates at the same angular speed as the moving object then the object will appear to be stationary. The rotating observer can then argue that there is no resultant force acting on the rotating object and thus the centripetal force must

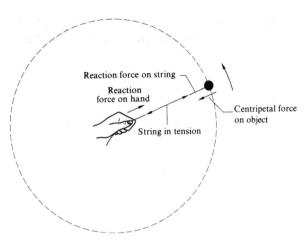

Fig. 5.9 Rotating object viewed by a stationary observer

be balanced by an opposite and equal force, the centrifugal force. This centrifugal force only occurs because we chose to view the moving object from a rotating frame of reference instead of a stationary frame of reference.

Motion round corners

Consider a car turning round a horizontal corner of radius r at a speed v, as in Fig. 5.10. The forces acting on the car are its weight mg, the normal force N and a frictional force F (neglecting any consideration of forces due to air resistance). The frictional force F is the force which supplies the centripetal acceleration; without friction the

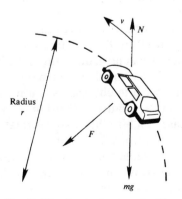

Fig. 5.10 Cornering on the flat

cornering could not take place. Since $F = \mu N$ and $N = mg$, then the maximum frictional force is μmg and so

maximum centripetal force = μmg

This must be equal to mv^2/r and so the maximum velocity with which the corner can be traversed without sliding is

$$\frac{mv^2}{r} = \mu mg$$

$$v = \sqrt{(\mu gr)}$$

Turning a horizontal corner thus relies on friction. However, if the corner is banked it is possible to turn the corner without relying in any way on friction. Figure 5.11 shows a car turning a banked corner and the forces acting. If the frictional forces F_1 and F_2 are to be zero, then there must be no side-slip of the wheels. Hence the force responsible for the centripetal acceleration is the resolved horizontal component of the normal forces at the wheels, N_1 and N_2. Hence

$$(N_1 + N_2) \sin \theta = \frac{mv^2}{r}$$

But $\qquad (N_1 + N_2) \cos \theta = mg$

Hence, by dividing the two equations, we have

$$\tan \theta = \frac{v^2}{rg}$$

This is the angle of banking required for no side-slip when the speed is v for the corner of radius r.

Planes and birds are held aloft by lift forces resulting from the flow of air over their bodies. When they are in horizontal flight the lift force is vertical and so equal to the weight. However, when they wish to change direction, actions are instituted which cause the bird or plane to bank. In the case of a bird this involves rotating a wing or the tip of a wing, for a plane the movement of ailerons (movable surfaces on the trailing edges of the wings). When banked, the lift force is no longer vertical and there is a horizontal component (see Fig. 5.12).

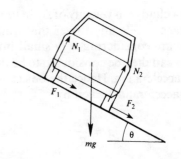

Fig. 5.11 Turning a banked corner

Horizontal lift force component = $L \sin \theta$

This component provides the centripetal acceleration. Hence

$$L \sin \theta = \frac{mv^2}{r}$$

But, for the vertical component of the lift force we must have

$$L \cos \theta = mg$$

Hence, dividing these equations gives

$$\tan \theta = \frac{v^2}{rg}$$

θ is the angle at which the wings have to be banked in order for the bird or plane to execute the turn.

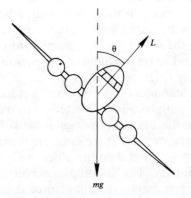

Fig. 5.12 A banked plane executing a turn

Motion in a vertical circle

Consider an object, mass m, on the end of a string and being whirled round in a vertical circle of radius r (Fig. 5.13). At the top of its path A, the force causing the centripetal acceleration is the sum of the tension in the string T_1 and the weight mg. Hence

$$T_1 + mg = \frac{mv^2}{r}$$

$$T_1 = \frac{mv^2}{r} - mg$$

At the bottom of the path B the tension and weight are in opposite directions. Hence

$$T_2 - mg = \frac{mv^2}{r}$$

$$T_2 = \frac{mv^2}{r} + mg$$

The tension at the bottom of the path is thus greater than that at the top of the path, by an amount $2mg$.

At the point C the centripetal acceleration is provided entirely by the tension T_3. Hence

$$T_3 = \frac{mv^2}{r}$$

Thus to keep an object moving in a vertical circular path with a constant speed the tension in the string must be varied, being greatest at the top of the path and least at the bottom.

The object being rotated in this vertical circle might be a bucket containing water. If the speed of rotation is high enough the water remains in the bucket and does not fall out, even when the bucket is at the top of its path and so upside down. This is because the weight of the water, Mg, is less than the centripetal force of Mv^2/r, the total force acting on the water being the sum of Mg and the reaction force of the base of the bucket on the water and this must equal Mv^2/r. If, however, Mg is greater than Mv^2/r, the excess of force above the Mv^2/r value gives the water an acceleration out of the bucket.

The conical pendulum

Consider an object of mass m on the end of a string and being whirled round in a horizontal circle with a constant speed v but with the string not horizontal but making some angle θ to the vertical (Fig. 5.14). Such an arrangement is known as a *conical pendulum*. The horizontal component of the tension T in the string provides the centripetal acceleration. Hence

$$T \sin \theta = \frac{mv^2}{r}$$

But for the vertical components we must have

$$T \cos \theta = mg$$

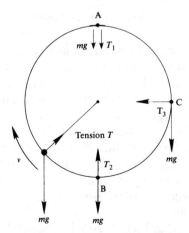

Fig. 5.13 Motion in a vertical circle

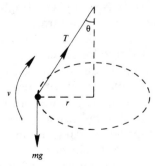

Fig. 5.14 The conical pendulum

Hence dividing these equations gives

$$\tan \theta = \frac{v^2}{rg}$$

Thus if such an object is whirled round in a circle with a constant speed v, it will ride up into a circle to give some angle θ such that the above equation is satisfied.

Problems

1. What torque has to be applied to a flywheel having a moment of inertia of 20 kg m^2 about some axis in order to give it an angular acceleration of 0.4 rad s^{-2} about that axis?

2. For a disc of radius r the moment of inertia about an axis through the centre of the disc and normal to its plane is given by $I = \frac{1}{2}Mr^2$, where M is the disc mass. Calculate the moment of inertia of the disc about its central axis if it has a radius of 100 mm, a thickness of 10 mm and is made of material having a density of 8400 kg m^3.

3. A flywheel has a mass of 50 kg and a radius of gyration of 200 mm, what is its moment of inertia?

4. A flywheel has a mass of 300 kg and a radius of gyration of 0.50 m. What is the constant torque needed to bring such a wheel to rest in 50 s when it is rotating at 3.0 revolutions per second?

5. Two spheres of the same radius and the same mass are rotated about a diameter; one of them is, however, solid and the other hollow. Which one will have the greater moment of inertia?

6. A force of 50 N is applied at right angles to the arm of a car jack at a turning radius of 300 mm. What is the work done if 20 revolutions of the arm are needed to raise the car?

7. What is the torque developed by a motor with its shaft rotating at 100 revolutions per second and developing a power of 2.0 kW?

8. A drive shaft supplies a torque of 200 kN m to a ship's propeller at 6.0 revolutions per second. What is the power developed?

9. A flywheel with a moment of inertia of 0.20 kg m^2 is kept rotating at a constant angular velocity of 100 rad s^{-1} by an electric motor of power 50 W. What is (a) the rotational kinetic energy of the flywheel and (b) the frictional couple opposing the rotation?

10. An ice skater spins about a vertical axis at 2 revolutions per second with arms outstretched. When the arms are folded the rate of spinning increases to 6 revolutions per second. By what factor did the skater change his moment of inertia?

11. A gramophone record rotates about a vertical axis at 33 revolutions per second. A small piece of putty of mass 20 g falls vertically onto the record at a distance of 150 mm from the axis. This has the result of decreasing the rate at which the record revolves to 30 revolutions per second. What is the moment of inertia of the record?

12. A horizontal turntable in a children's playground has a moment of inertia of 180 kg m^2. If it is initially at rest when three children, total mass 60 kg, climb on to it, what will be the angular velocity attained by the turntable when the children start to run round it at a speed of 2.5 m s^{-1} when 1.6 m from the axis?

13. The moment of inertia of the earth about its axis of rotation is 8.0×10^{37} kg m^2. Estimate (a) the earth's angular momentum and (b) the earth's angular kinetic energy.

Due to the frictional effects of tides on the ocean bed, the length of the earth's day is very slowly increasing. What effect does this have on the kinetic energy and the angular momentum of the earth?

(University of London, Q4, Paper 2, January 1982)

14. A flywheel rotates about a horizontal axis fitted into friction-free bearings. A light string, one end of which is looped over a pin on the axle, is wrapped ten times round the axle and has a mass of 1.5 kg attached to its free end. Discuss the energy changes as the mass falls. If the moment of inertia of the wheel and axle is 0.10 kg m^{-2} and the diameter of the axle 5.0 cm, calculate the angular velocity of the flywheel at the instant when the string detaches itself from the axle after ten revolutions.

(AEB, QA1, Paper 3, November 1982)

15. (a) For a rigid body rotating about a fixed

axis, explain with the aid of a suitable diagram what is meant by angular velocity, kinetic energy and moment of inertia.

(b) In the design of a passenger bus, it is proposed to derive the motive power from the energy stored in a flywheel. The flywheel, which has a moment of inertia of 4.0×10^2 kg m^2, is accelerated to its maximum rate of rotation of 3.0×10^3 revolutions per minute by electric motors at stations along the bus route.

(i) Calculate the maximum kinetic energy which can be stored in the flywheel.
(ii) If, at an average speed of 36 kilometres per hour, the power required by the bus is 20 kW, what will be the maximum possible distance between stations on the level?

(JMB, Q1, Paper I Section (2), June 1979)

16. (a) Explain why a particle moving with constant speed along a circular path has a radial acceleration.

The value of such an acceleration is given by v^2/r, where v is the speed and r is the radius of the path. Show that this expression is dimensionally correct.

(b) Explain, with the aid of clear diagrams, the following.

(i) A mass attached to a string rotating at a constant speed in a horizontal circle will fly off at a tangent if the string breaks.
(ii) A cosmonaut in a satellite which is in a free circular orbit around the earth experiences the sensation of weightlessness even though he is influenced by the gravitational field of the earth.

(c) A pilot 'banks' the wings of his aircraft so as to travel at a speed of 360 km h^{-1} in a horizontal circular path of radius 5.0 km. At what angle should he bank his aircraft in order to do this?

(University of London, Q12, Paper 2, June 1982)

Part 2

Oscillations and waves

6 Oscillations

What are oscillations?

What is an oscillation? Something that goes wig-wag! Can we produce a scientist's description? If we study the motion of a number of objects we can perhaps answer the question. If a mass is suspended from a spring, pulled down and then released, oscillations occur (Fig. 6.1). If a marble is rolling in a curved track, the marble oscillates backwards and forwards about its rest position. For a mass suspended from the end of a piece of string (a simple pendulum), when the mass is displaced from its rest position and released oscillations occur. A trolley tethered between two supports on a horizontal bench by springs will oscillate when the trolley is displaced from its rest position and then released. A ruler clamped at one end to a bench oscillates when the free end is depressed and then released. What do we do, for these and other examples, to get oscillations? The masses are pulled away from their rest position and then released. A restoring force then pulls them back and they seem to overshoot the rest position. This restoring force must exist otherwise they would not move when released. Because there is a force then we must have an acceleration. The restoring force is always directed towards the central rest position—thus the acceleration is always directed towards the central rest position.

We can determine the distance–time graph for an oscillating object by taking a strobe photograph—Fig. 6.2 shows one for a pendulum—or using ticker tape and a vibrator. A vibrating metal strip puts marks on a strip of paper at regular intervals and if the tape is attached at one end to, say, the trolley, a trace similar to Fig. 6.3 is obtained as the trolley moves from its maximum displacement on one side of the rest position to its maximum displacement on the other.

Isochronous oscillations

Some oscillations seem to have the property that the same time is taken for each complete oscillation. Such oscillators are known as isochronous,

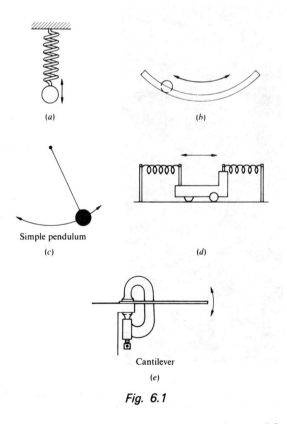

Simple pendulum
(c)

Cantilever
(e)

Fig. 6.1

Fig. 6.3   Ticker tape trace

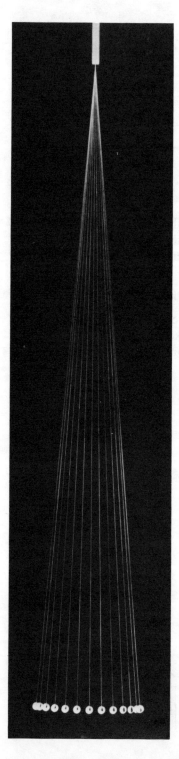

Fig. 6.2   Strobe photograph of a simple pendulum. (Educational Development Center Inc.)

and they maintain this constant time property regardless of amplitude changes due to damping.

How do we know that these masses take the same time for each oscillation? Because we measured it with a clock. But what is a clock? Something that keeps regular time owing to the regular oscillation of some device such as a spring or a pendulum. Are our oscillations constant time oscillations because we use this property to measure time and in fact have a closed circle argument? What was used to measure time before people knew of isochronous oscillators? The movement of the sun across the sky and the passage of day and night—we could define a unit of time as the time occurring between two successive appearances of the sun at maximum elevation (a day). We could define our time unit in terms of our heart or pulse beat. Both these definitions give reasonable agreement regarding the regularity of time, the day is a constant number of heart beats. We thus have natural time units which we can use to determine whether an oscillation is isochronous.

Galileo is reputed to have watched a swinging lamp during a service in the Cathedral of Pisa in 1538 and timed the oscillations by the use of his pulse. The period of time taken for one complete oscillation was found constant regardless of the amplitude (not, however, the very large amplitude).

Consider an isochronous oscillation. The time taken to complete an oscillation, i.e., the time to move from an extreme displacement to the rest position, is a constant regardless of the amplitude of the oscillation. Thus in Fig. 6.4 the same time is taken for the mass to move from A to P as from B to P or C to P. In this argument let us take BP = 2 AP (the amplitude is doubled) and CP = 3 AP (the amplitude is trebled). Doubling the amplitude makes no difference to the time taken to cover the distance, hence the average speed over the distance BP must be double that over the distance

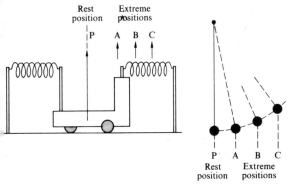

Fig. 6.4

must be proportional to the displacement, from the rest position.

This can readily be checked from the ticker tape or stroboscopic results obtained with isochronous oscillations. These are distance-time records. As velocity is the rate of variation of distance with time, the slope of the graph of distance against time, then a velocity–time graph can be produced. Acceleration is the rate of change of velocity with time, the slope of the graph of velocity with time. Hence we can obtain the accelerations at different displacements (Fig. 6.6). The acceleration really is proportional to the displacement from the rest position.

$$\text{Acceleration} \propto -\text{displacement}$$

The minus sign is because the acceleration is always opposing an increase in displacement.

Solving the acceleration equation

An object oscillating freely with a motion described by the following relation is said to be describing simple harmonic motion.

$$\text{Acceleration } a \propto -\text{displacement } x$$

$$(\text{or} \quad \text{Restoring force} \propto -\text{displacement } x)$$

or using the constants of proportionality ω^2, see later for an explanation,

$$a = -\omega^2 x$$

(or $F = ma = -kx$, thus $a = -kx/m$ and $\omega^2 = k/m$) But acceleration is the change of velocity with time

$$a = \frac{\Delta v}{\Delta t}$$

where Δv is the velocity change occurring in time Δt. Velocity is the rate at which distance is covered with time

$$v = \frac{\Delta x}{\Delta t}$$

where Δx is the distance covered in time Δt. Thus we can write for acceleration

$$a = \frac{\Delta(\Delta x/\Delta t)}{\Delta t}$$

AP. This double average speed has to be acquired in the same time as the single amplitude motion, so doubling the amplitude means doubling the average acceleration. The speed and acceleration will not be constant during the motion. If we have double the average acceleration then we must have doubled the average force. This can be produced by the force being proportional to the displacement so that the force acting on the mass at the extreme end of the double amplitude motion is twice that at the end of the single amplitude motion (Fig. 6.5). If we consider the treble amplitude motion then the force at the end of its motion is three times that at the end of the single amplitude motion.

If the trolley starts at a displacement C then we can say that there is a force of $3F$ acting on it. As it passes through point B the force has dropped to $2F$ and when it reaches A the force is only F. As the acceleration at any instant is proportional to the force acting on the mass then the acceleration

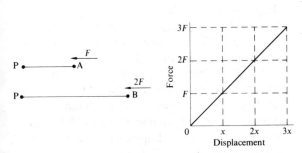

Fig. 6.5

101

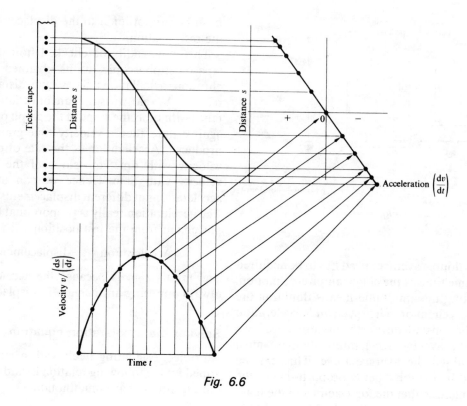

Fig. 6.6

i.e., acceleration is the rate of change with time of $(\Delta x/\Delta t)$. Thus for our simple harmonic motion equation we can write

$$\frac{\Delta(\Delta x/\Delta t)}{\Delta t} = -\omega^2 x$$

On a graph of displacement x against time t, $(\Delta x/\Delta t)$ is the average slope over an interval of time Δt.

(For this solution it is convenient to use finite intervals, hence the Δ sign, instead of infinitesimally small intervals. Hence all the velocities and accelerations are average values over some finite time interval.)

Thus our equation can be written

$$\frac{\Delta(\text{slope})}{\Delta t} = -\omega^2 x$$

or

$$\text{Change in slope} = -\omega^2 x \ \Delta t$$

To plot a graph of x against t we start at some arbitrary value of the slope, calculate the change in slope during the next time interval, plot the new x position given by this new slope, use the new x value to find the change in slope that will occur in the next time interval, and so on. Let us take a specific case; at time $t = 0$ the displacement to be a maximum of 10 cm, thus velocity (initial slope) to be zero, and $\omega^2 = 20$ s^{-2}. We will take time intervals of 0.1 s. (See Fig 6.7 for the step by step plotting.)

Time 0.0 s, slope 0.

Time 0.1 s, slope change $= -20 \times 10 \times 0.1 = -20$ cm s^{-1}. Over a time interval of 0.1 s this change in slope means a drop of 2 cm.

Time 0.2 s, slope change $= -20 \times 8 \times 0.1 = -16$ cm s^{-1}. Over a time interval of 0.1 s this is a drop from the previous slope of 1.6 cm.

Time 0.3 s, slope change $= -20 \times 4.4 \times 0.1 = -8.8$ cm s^{-1}. This is a drop of 0.88 cm, in the next 0.1 s, from the previous slope.

Time 0.4 s, slope change $= -20 \times (-0.08) \times 0.1$

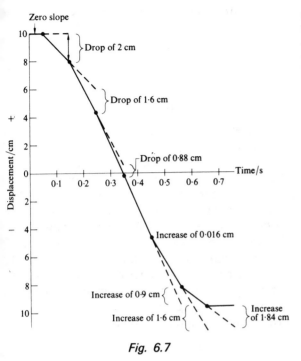

Fig. 6.7

acceleration varies with distance by differentiation. The variation of distance with time is certainly not a straight line relationship. What is it? Because I know the answer I am going to suggest that we try the following method to arrive at the equation. We take the ticker tape trace and draw a semicircle equal to the amplitude of the oscillation (Fig. 6.8). The tape is then placed along the diameter, with the end marks on the circle, and perpendiculars drawn from the marks on the tape to cut the circle, at points A, B, C, etc. Now these points are each joined by a line to the centre of the circle O. The distance of any one mark from the rest position is therefore the projection of a point on the circle onto the diameter. The marks on the tape were made at equal time intervals, the angles through which the points on the circle have moved are equal ($\theta_1 = \theta_2 = \theta_3 =$ etc.). So the displacements of the oscillator are the projections onto a diameter of a point which moves round a circle, radius equal to the amplitude, with a constant angular velocity (Fig. 6.9).

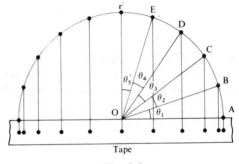

Fig. 6.8

= $+0.16$ cm s^{-1}. This is an increase in slope and hence, in the next 0.1 s, an increase of 0.016 cm from the previous slope.

Time 0.5 s, slope change = $-20 \times (-4.5) \times 0.1 =$ $+9$ cm s^{-1}. This is an increase of 0.09 cm, in the next 0.1 s, from the previous slope.

Time 0.6 s, slope change = $-20 \times (-8) \times 0.1 =$ $+16$ cm s^{-1}. An increase of 1.6 cm, in the next 0.1 s, from the previous slope.

Time 0.7 s, slope change = $-20 \times (-9.2) \times 0.1 =$ $+18.4$ cm s^{-1}. An increase of 1.84 cm, in the next 0.1 s, from the previous slope.

This last result starts the graph moving back towards the axis again. The result of our graph plotting is the displacement–time graph. Our oscillating object takes about 2×0.7 s to complete one oscillation.

Mapping the motion onto a circle

If we know the equation relating the displacement with time we can arrive at the way the

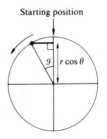

Fig. 6.9

This gives the displacement x, from the rest position, as $r \cos \theta$, where θ is the angle through which the point on the circle has moved in time t. At time $t = 0$ the oscillator is at an extreme position. But the radius is equal to the amplitude of the motion, A. Hence

$$x = A \cos \theta$$

For one complete oscillation the point moves completely round the circle. If T is the time for one complete oscillation (known as the *periodic time*) then the angle covered in this time is 2π radians (2π radians equal $360°$). In time t the point has moved through angle θ. If ω is the angular velocity then

$$\omega = \frac{2\pi}{T} = \frac{\theta}{t}$$

Hence we can write θ as

$$\theta = \omega t = \frac{2\pi}{T}$$

and the displacement as

$$x = A \cos \omega t = A \cos \frac{2\pi t}{T}$$

Figure 6.10 shows the graph of this equation.

Differentiation can be used to obtain the velocity and acceleration variations with time. The velocity is the slope at an instant of the distance–time graph, i.e., dx/dt. Hence

$$v = \frac{dx}{dt} = -A\omega \sin \omega t$$

This agrees with the graph obtained in Fig. 6.6. Acceleration is the slope at any instant of the velocity–time graph, i.e., dv/dt. Hence

$$a = \frac{dv}{dt} = -A\omega^2 \cos \omega t$$

But $x = A \cos \omega t$, hence

$$a = -\omega^2 x$$

The acceleration is directly proportional to the displacement.

What is the significance of the minus sign in the velocity and acceleration equations? As the displacement from the rest position increases the velocity decreases. As the displacement increases so the acceleration becomes more negative, i.e., the retardation increases. As the displacement becomes smaller, the mass is approaching the rest position, the acceleration becomes smaller and at the rest position is zero (look again at Fig. 6.6).

The force trying to restore the mass to its original rest position will therefore be

$$F = ma = -m\omega^2 x$$

The restoring force is proportional to the displacement from the rest position and always directed towards that position (the mass always accelerates towards the rest position).

Object suspended from a spring

Consider a mass on the end of a spring, as in Fig. 6.1a, then provided the spring is only extended or compressed within the elastic region

$$F \propto x$$

The force is proportional to the extension,

or $$F = -kx$$

where k is the force constant. Hence

$$k = m\omega^2$$

But

$$\omega = \frac{2\pi}{T}$$

Therefore

$$T = 2\pi \sqrt{\frac{m}{k}}$$

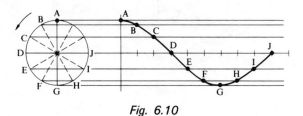

Fig. 6.10

This is the periodic time of the oscillator. This equation tells us how the time taken to complete one oscillation depends on the mass and force constant of the spring. Often the term frequency is used instead of periodic time. Frequency, f, is the number of oscillations per second and hence

$$f = \frac{1}{T}$$

as T is the time for one oscillation. The frequency unit is the hertz (Hz). One oscillation or cycle per second is one hertz.

$$f = \frac{1}{2\pi}\sqrt{\frac{k}{m}}$$

If we do an experiment with a mass on the end of a vertically suspended spring then doubling the mass on the spring increases the time for one oscillation by a factor of $\sqrt{2}$ and decreases the frequency by $1/\sqrt{2}$. If the mass is quadrupled then the frequency is halved. Suppose we double the force constant of the spring (sometimes loosely referred to as the stiffness of the spring) by using two identical springs, side by side, to support the mass, then the frequency increases by a factor of $\sqrt{2}$.

The simple pendulum

With the simple pendulum the force trying to restore the bob (the mass at the end of the thread) to its rest position when it is pulled to one side is gravity (Fig. 6.11a). The weight of the bob can be broken down into two components, one along the thread keeping it taut and the other perpendicular to the thread moving it towards the rest position, i.e., the restoring force. From the similar triangles in Fig. 6.11b

$$\frac{F_r}{mg} = \frac{d}{L}$$

Therefore

$$F_r = \frac{mg}{L}d$$

As long as the arc through which the pendulum swings is small, the displacement along the arc x

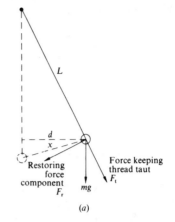

(a)

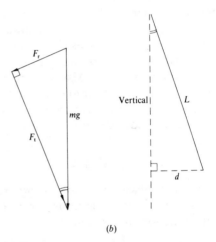

(b)

Fig. 6.11

is a reasonable approximation to d. Hence we can write

$$F_r = \frac{mg}{L}x$$

The restoring force is proportional to the displacement and thus the motion is isochronous.

By comparison with our equation for the restoring force for the spring, i.e., $F = kx$, our force constant with a simple pendulum is $k = mg/L$. Hence the frequency of oscillation is given by

$$f = \frac{1}{2\pi}\sqrt{\frac{g}{L}}$$

or periodic time T by

$$T = 2\pi \sqrt{\frac{L}{g}}$$

Simple harmonic motion

The isochronous motion of the spring-supported mass, the tethered trolley, the pendulum, and many others, all have a displacement–time graph in the form of a cosine (or sine) curve if damping is insignificant. Because of this they all have an acceleration proportional to the displacement from the rest position and directed towards it. This type of motion is known as simple harmonic motion. It is important because it is a very common form of motion. Also any repetitive motion can be broken down into simple harmonic components (this is known as Fourier's theorem).

The equations used to describe simple harmonic motion are

$$\text{acceleration } a = -\omega^2 x$$

where x is the displacement and $\omega = 2\pi f$ or $2\pi/T$. f being the number of oscillations per unit time and T the time for one oscillation.

$$\text{Restoring force} = -m\omega^2 x$$

where m is the mass of the displaced object.

$$\text{Displacement } x = A \cos \omega t$$

where A is the amplitude. This assumes a maximum displacement at $t = 0$. If the displacement at $t = 0$ is zero then

$$x = A \sin \omega t$$

For this displacement equation the velocity v is given by

$$v = \omega A \cos \omega t$$

Hence, since $\sin \omega t = x/A$ and $\cos \omega t = v/\omega A$, and using $\sin^2 \omega t + \cos^2 \omega t = 1$, we can derive the relationship

$$v = \pm\omega\sqrt{(A^2 - x^2)}$$

For the displacement equation $x = A \cos \omega t$, we

have the velocity equation

$$v = -A\omega \sin \omega t$$

and the same relationship between v, A and x.

A general way of writing the displacement equation is

$$x = A \sin(\omega t + \phi)$$

where ϕ is some angle (Fig. 6.12), generally referred to as the phase angle. The inclusion of ϕ tells us how the starting displacement of a particular oscillation relates to one given by $x = A \sin \omega t$. Thus, for example, one with ϕ having the value of 90° or, in radian terms ½π, would have a displacement variation with time given by (Fig. 6.12b)

$$x = A \sin(\omega t + 90°)$$

But this means that the displacement graph starts off with a maximum value, sin $(\omega t + 90°)$ being the But this means that the displacement graph starts off with a maximum value, sin $(\omega t + 90°)$ being the same as cos ωt. Figure 6.12c shows how the

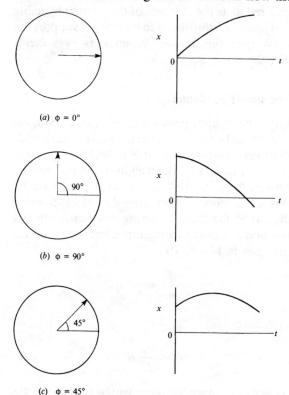

(a) $\phi = 0°$

(b) $\phi = 90°$

(c) $\phi = 45°$

Fig. 6.12 Oscillations with different phase angles

displacement would vary with time for $\phi = 45°$.

The following examples illustrate some of the types of problem in simple harmonic motion that might be encountered.

(a) If the displacement x of an object oscillating with simple harmonic motion is given by $x = 12 \cos 5\pi t$, where x is in millimetres and t in seconds, what is (i) the amplitude, (ii) the periodic time and (iii) the maximum value of the velocity.

(i) the equation can be compared with $x = A \cos \omega t$ and so the amplitude is 12 mm.
(ii) Similarly, since $\omega = 2\pi/T$ then $x = A \cos 2\pi t/T$ and so $T = 1/5$ s.
(iii) $v = \pm\omega\sqrt{(A^2 - x^2)}$ and so the maximum value of v occurs when $x = 0$. The maximum value is thus $v = \pm\omega\sqrt{(A^2)}$ and so ±377 mm s^{-1}.

(b) A small, light coin rests on a horizontal platform which is vibrating with simple harmonic motion with a periodic time of 0.40 s. What is the maximum amplitude of this motion which will allow the coin to remain in contact with the platform at all times? ($g = 9.8$ m s^{-2})

In the absence of the platform the coin would fall freely with the acceleration due to gravity. Thus the coin will lose contact with the platform when the acceleration downwards of the platforms exceeds the acceleration due to gravity. The maximum value of the platform acceleration occurs when its displacement is a maximum, i.e., when $a = -\omega^2 x$ with $x = A$ the amplitude. Hence the maximum amplitude occurs when $a = -g$ and so

$$\omega^2 A = 9.8$$

$$(2\pi/T)^2 A = 9.8$$

$$A = 0.040 \text{ m}$$

(c) A simple pendulum oscillates with simple harmonic motion of amplitude 40 mm and a periodic time 1.5 s. What is the velocity of the pendulum bob when the displacement is (a) a maximum, (b) zero, (c) 20 mm? ($g = 9.8$ m s^{-2})

The velocity is given by the equation

$$v = \pm\omega\sqrt{(A^2 - x^2)}$$

(i) When $x = A$ then $v = 0$.

(ii) When $x = 0$ then $v = \pm\omega\sqrt{(A^2)} = \pm(2\pi/T)A = 168$ mm s^{-1}.
(iii) $v = \pm(2\pi/1.5)\sqrt{(40^2 - 20^2)} = 145$ mm s^{-1}.

(d) When an object of mass 0.50 kg is hung from the lower end of a vertical spring, an extension of 10.0 cm is produced. When the object is pulled down a further amount and released, it executes simple harmonic motion. What is the frequency of the oscillation? ($g = 9.8$ m s^{-2})

$$f = \frac{1}{2\pi}\sqrt{\frac{k}{m}}$$

where k is given by $F = kx$. Hence $k = mg/x = 0.50 \times 9.8/(10.0 \times 10^{-2}) = 49$ N m^{-1}. Hence

$$F = \frac{1}{2\pi}\sqrt{\frac{49}{0.5}}$$

$$= 1.6 \text{ Hz}$$

(e) A solid cylinder with a cross-sectional area A and height L floats upright in a liquid with a height H immersed in the liquid. If the solid has a density ρ and the liquid a density σ show that, in the absence of frictional effects, the cylinder will execute simple harmonic motion when pushed slightly into the liquid and released. What is the periodic time of the motion?

The basic procedure that can be adopted for such problems is to find the restoring force, and hence the acceleration of the object and its relationship to displacement.

When the cylinder is at rest, the weight mg must be balanced by the upthrust of $HA\sigma g$ (Archimedes' principle—the upthrust equals the weight of fluid displaced). Hence

$$LA\rho g = HA\sigma g$$

When the cylinder is pushed down further into the liquid the upthrust increases to become $(H + x)A\sigma g$, where x is the displacement from the equilibrium position. Then the net force acting on the cylinder becomes

Restoring force $= LA\rho g - (H + x)A\sigma g$

$$= -xA\sigma g$$

The acceleration $=$ force/mass $= -xA\sigma g/LA\rho$

Hence $\qquad$ acceleration $\propto -x$

The motion is simple harmonic.

Since for simple harmonic motion $a = -\omega^2 x$

$$\omega^2 = \frac{\sigma g}{L\rho}$$

and as $\omega = 2\pi/T$, then

$$T = 2\pi \sqrt{\frac{L\rho}{\sigma g}}$$

This equation can be simplified by using the equilibrium equation where $L\rho = H\sigma$ to give

$$T = 2\pi \sqrt{\frac{H}{g}}$$

Energy

What about the energy of an oscillating mass? Well, the form of the energy is continually changing—kinetic to potential energy and then back again and so on. The potential energy is a maximum when the mass is at one of the extreme points of the oscillation, the kinetic energy is a maximum when the mass is passing through the rest position. When the mass is passing through the rest position all the energy is kinetic energy.

Kinetic energy at this point $= T = \frac{1}{2}mv^2$

where m is the mass and v the velocity of the mass at that point.

But

$$v = -A\omega \sin \omega t$$

Hence

$$T = \frac{1}{2}m(A\omega \sin \omega t)^2$$

At the rest position $\sin \omega t = 1$. Therefore

$$T = \frac{1}{2}m\omega^2 A^2$$

If we ignore any effects of damping then the total energy at any instant must be equal to $\frac{1}{2}m\omega^2 A^2$. At an extreme displacement all the energy is potential energy, hence the potential energy at these points, U, must be equal to $\frac{1}{2}m\omega^2 A^2$. At any

instant the energy is given by

$$T + U = \frac{1}{2}m\omega^2 A^2$$

We can write the equation in terms of frequency, f, as $\omega = 2\pi f$.

$$T + U = \frac{1}{2}m4\pi^2 f^2 A^2 = 2\pi^2 mf^2 A^2$$

An important point here is that the energy is proportional to the square of the amplitude.

Potential energy–distance graphs

For an oscillator, how does the potential energy vary with distance from the rest position? The potential energy could be the energy stored in the springs for the tethered trolley or the energy due to the change in height of a pendulum bob above some datum line. Let us consider the simple pendulum (Fig. 6.13). The potential energy (mgh) is directly proportional to the height of the pendulum bob above some horizontal datum line. In this case we will take the datum line such that the potential energy is zero when the pendulum is at its rest position. Thus a graph can be plotted of potential energy against the distance the bob is displaced from its rest position (s) (Fig. 6.14).

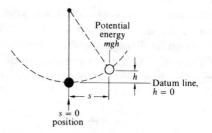

Fig. 6.13

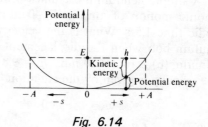

Fig. 6.14

If the maximum amplitude of the pendulum is $+A$ and $-A$ then E is the maximum energy of the bob. When the pendulum bob is at either of the extreme displacements then all the energy E will be potential energy (at $+A$ and $-A$). When $s = 0$ and the bob is at the rest position there is no potential energy and the kinetic energy is E. At any displacement the potential energy plus the kinetic energy is E, thus the potential energy at a particular displacement can be read from the curve and the kinetic energy is energy between the point on the curve and the potential energy = E line.

Though this argument has been given for a simple pendulum it applies to any oscillator

$$\text{Total energy} = PE + KE$$

Resonance

When the pendulum or the mass on the end of the spring was considered, a force was applied to displace the mass from its equilibrium position and then removed. The only force then acting on the mass, which caused motion, was the restoring force. The restoring force varies with time and is proportional to the displacement of the mass from the rest position. What happens if an external force, continually causing displacements, is continually applied to the mass?

When a simple pendulum is oscillating the only force acting on the bob is the restoring force, proportional to the displacement of the bob from its rest position. The frequency of the oscillation of the pendulum is a constant. Now what happens if every time the bob reaches a maximum displacement it is given a push? A force is being applied to the bob at the rate of once every complete oscillation, i.e., at the same frequency as that of the pendulum. When this happens large amplitudes build up. If the frequency of the applied force is different from that of the pendulum, the amplitude produced is not so great. One method of continually applying a force to a pendulum is to suspend it from a support through which the force can be applied. A string stretched between two supports and the pendulum hung from it enables this to be done (Fig. 6.15). The force is supplied by another pendulum with a

Fig. 6.15

larger mass bob attached to the same string. As this oscillates a varying force is applied to the pendulum. The frequency of this applied force can be varied by changing the length of the driver pendulum (the frequency is inversely proportional to the square root of the length). Figure 6.16 shows a typical set of results. When the applied frequency is the same as the natural frequency a large amplitude oscillation is produced. This effect is known as resonance.

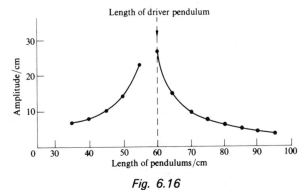

Fig. 6.16

Supplementary material

Vibrations of structures

The resonant frequency of the Empire State Building in New York is $1/8$ Hz (one complete oscillation every 8 s), the new Severn bridge has a (vertical) frequency of about 0.14 Hz (one complete oscillation about every 7 s), your body as a whole has a resonant frequency of about 5 Hz when you are sitting down; all structures have natural frequencies at which they as a whole will resonate and frequencies at which parts of them will resonate. What are the effects of resonance (or even near resonance conditions)?

At resonance the applied frequency is equal to the natural frequency of the structure and the amplitude of oscillation builds up. An increase in amplitude means an increase in both the maximum acceleration and speed. In the case of humans this can result in pain (Fig. 6.17), with other structures damage. The damage may be due to the oscillations triggering off stress movements which would not normally have occurred on their own, e.g., the settling of soil and resulting movement in the foundations of a building. Fracture of a material can be produced by repeated flexing (try it with a strip of card or metal); this is known as fatigue. Oscillations can be excited by machines, the wind, earthquakes, etc.

The following are two examples of structure oscillations which resulted in damage:

(a) In 1940 a suspension bridge across the Tacoma Narrows in the United States collapsed after violent oscillations produced by a 19 m s^{-1} wind (Fig. 6.18) (a steady wind can produce oscillations—think of a fluttering flag, or the reed in a musical instrument).

(b) In January 1954, a BOAC Comet crashed in the Mediterranean, killing 35 people, as a result diagnosed as a high stress concentration at the edge of a countersunk hole near a window, and fatigue producing the resulting rupture.

Not all cases of resonance result in damage, some are just uncomfortable. Figure 6.19 shows the effect of vertical vibrations in a rail-motorcar on a passenger. The main effect is on the

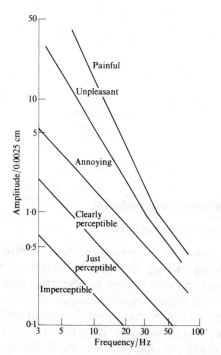

Fig. 6.17   Human sensitivity to vibration

*Fig. 6.18   Torsional oscillations of the Tacoma Narrows Bridge. (*Bulletin 116, University of Washington)

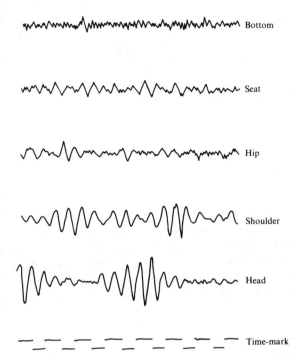

Fig. 6.19 *Vertical vibrations of seat and man in a rail-motorcar. The top two records show car vibration, the lower three show vibration amplitudes of the subject. Time marker, 1 s. (D. Dieckmann.* Ergonomics, **1** *353, 1958)*

passenger's head which keeps bobbing around—not a very comfortable ride.

Further reading

R. E. D. Bishop. *Vibration*, CUP.

Molecular vibration spectra

If we have a mass oscillating at the end of a spring we can calculate the force constant or stiffness of the spring from measurements of the frequency of oscillation and a knowledge of the mass. Suppose the spring and the mass were so small that we could not see when oscillations were occurring and certainly not directly measure the frequency, how could we obtain a value for the frequency of oscillation? If we applied a wide range of different frequency forces then the one at the right frequency would set our mass and spring system into

oscillation, i.e., resonance would occur. When this occurs energy must be absorbed by the mass-spring system. If we can detect the frequency at which energy absorption occurs then we have determined the oscillation frequency.

When white light is incident on a gas, or a liquid, or a solid such as HCl, we find that at a certain frequency in the infrared, 8.658×10^{13} Hz, absorption occurs (Fig. 6.20). The absorbed energy is reradiated in all directions. Absorption also occurs at twice this frequency, three times this frequency, four times this frequency, etc., though each succeeding absorption is weaker. Similar absorption results are produced, at different frequencies, for other diatomic molecules.

Molecule	Strong absorption frequency, /10^{13} Hz
HF	8.721
HCl	8.658
HBr	7.677
HI	6.690
CO	6.429
NO	5.628

Is this absorption of light similar to the energy absorption considered for the mass and spring system? With a diatomic molecule we can consider the two atoms to be at the ends of a bond, rather like two masses attached to the ends of a

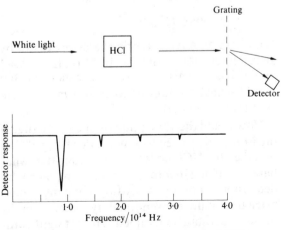

Fig. 6.20 *Absorption spectrum of HCl*

111

spring. If light is some kind of oscillating electrical disturbance then it might drive the atoms into oscillation (Fig. 6.21). White light contains a wide range of frequencies and thus absorption could be expected at the frequencies corresponding to resonance for the molecule.

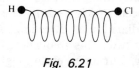

Fig. 6.21

Let us try to calculate the strength of the bond in the HCl molecule. We will make a simplifying assumption that the mass of the chlorine atom is so great compared with that of the hydrogen atom that it remains at rest and only the hydrogen atom oscillates at the end of the bond. If the restoring force acting on the hydrogen atom is proportional to its displacement from its rest position then the oscillation should be simple harmonic. For such a motion

$$\text{Frequency } f = \frac{1}{2\pi}\sqrt{\frac{k}{m}}$$

where m is the mass of the hydrogen atom 1.673×10^{-27} kg. Hence

$$k = 2^2\pi^2f^2m$$

$$= 4\pi^2 \, 8.658^2 \times 10^{26} \times 1.673 \times 10^{-27}$$

$$= 495.0 \text{ N m}^{-1}$$

Is this strong? A typical spring balance extends by about 10 cm for a force of 10 N (balance load about 1 kg). This is a force constant of 100 N m^{-1}—smaller than the force constant for the HCl molecule bond.

How would the absorption frequency change if the isotopes involved in a molecule changed? Let us take the HCl molecule and consider what happens if the hydrogen atom is replaced by deuterium, an isotope of hydrogen having a mass twice that of the conventional hydrogen atom. If the force constant is assumed to be not significantly affected then we have

For hydrogen

$$f_H = \frac{1}{2\pi}\sqrt{\frac{k}{m}}$$

For deuterium

$$f_D = \frac{1}{2\pi}\sqrt{\frac{1}{2m}}$$

Hence

$$f_H = F_D\sqrt{2}$$

The effect of the chlorine atom oscillations has been ignored. Thus we would expect DCl to have an absorption frequency lower than HCl by a factor of about $\sqrt{2}$, i.e., about 6.18×10^{13} Hz. The observed frequency is 6.30×10^{13} Hz.

Problems

1. A body moving with simple harmonic motion has velocity v and acceleration a when the displacement from its mean position is x. Sketch graphs

(i) of a against x, and
(ii) of v against x.

(University of London, Q4,
Paper 2, June 1978)

2. The displacement y of a particle vibrating with simple harmonic motion of angular speed ω is given by

$$y = a \sin \omega t \text{ where } t \text{ is the time}$$

What does a represent?

Sketch a graph of the velocity of the particle as a function of time starting from $t = 0$ s.

A particle of mass 0.25 kg vibrates with a period of 2.0 s. If its greatest displacement is 0.4 m, what is its maximum kinetic energy?

(University of London, Q4,
Paper 2, January 1979)

3. A certain mass, suspended from a spring, performs vertical oscillations of period T when on Earth. If the system were transferred to the Moon, where the acceleration of free fall is one-sixth of that on Earth, what would be the period?

(University of Cambridge, Q1, Paper 1, June 1980)

4. For an object oscillating with simple harmonic motion state when (a) the acceleration, (b) the velocity, (c) the potential energy, (d) the kinetic energy, and (e) the restoring force are a maximum.

5. A light spring is loaded with a mass of 200 g and made to execute vertical oscillations. Figure 6.22 shows a force–extension graph for the spring.

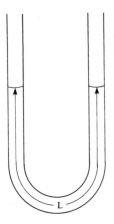

Fig. 6.23

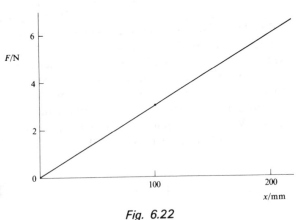

Fig. 6.22

Use it to help

(a) explain why the oscillations are likely to be simple harmonic,
(b) calculate the frequency of oscillation of the 200 g mass where the period, T, of the motion is give by the equation

$$T = 2\pi \sqrt{\frac{x_0}{g}}$$

where x_0 is the static extension which would be produced by the load,
(c) calculate the energy stored in the spring when the mass is at its lowest point, if the amplitude of the oscillation is x_0.

(University of London, Q3, Paper 2, June 1981)

6. Figure 6.23 shows a thread of liquid of length L and density ρ contained in a U-tube. The limbs of the U-tube, each of cross-sectional area

A, are held vertically with the open ends upwards. The level of the liquid in one limb of the tube is depressed a small distance x and then released. Show that the thread of liquid executes simple harmonic motion and derive an expression for its period of oscillation. (Neglect surface tension effects.)

(AEB, Q2, Paper 3, June 1981)

7. (a) (i) Define simple harmonic motion.
(ii) Show that the equation

$$y = a \sin (\omega t + \varepsilon)$$

represents such a motion and explain the meaning of the symbols y, a, ω and ε.
(iii) Draw with respect to a common time axis graphs showing the variation with time t of the displacement, velocity and kinetic energy of a heavy particle that is describing such a motion.
(b) When a metal cylinder of mass 0.2 kg is attached to the lower end of a light helical spring the upper end of which is fixed, the spring extends by 0.16 m. The metal cylinder is then pulled down a further 0.08 m.
(i) Find the force that must be exerted to keep it there, if Hooke's law is obeyed.
(ii) The cylinder is then released. Find the period of vertical oscillations, and the kinetic energy the cylinder possesses when it passes through its mean position.

(Oxford Local Examinations, Q2, Paper I, June 1978)

8. Figure 6.24 shows a mass which can move in a horizontal direction along a channel under the action of the spring shown. Would the motion of the mass along the channel be simple harmonic?

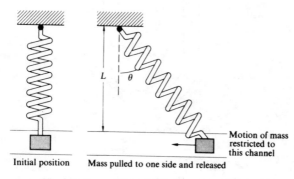

Initial position   Mass pulled to one side and released

Fig. 6.24

9. Figure 6.14 shows a trolley tethered by springs at each end. If the two springs can be assumed to be equal and frictional effects ignored, when the trolley is displaced from its equilibrium position and allowed to oscillate (a) is the motion simple harmonic and (b) if so, on what factors does the frequency of oscillation depend?

10. A mass of 25 kg is suspended from a spring, causing the spring to increase in length by 2.5 mm. The mass is then displaced vertically and released. Estimate the frequency of the resulting vibration, indicating any assumptions made.

The suspension of a car may be represented by a mass–spring system. Explain what is meant by the resonance of such a system when the car traverses an unmade road having a surface of approximately sine waveform.

What measures could be employed to reduce the effects of this resonance?

(University of London, Engineering Science, Q1, Paper 2, June 1981)

11. How would changing the suspension springs of a car, i.e., changing the force constant for the springs, change the behaviour of the car when it goes over a bump in the road?

12. Define simple harmonic motion, and explain what is meant by the amplitude and period of such a motion.

Show that the vertical oscillations of a mass suspended by a light helical spring are simple harmonic, and obtain an expression for the period.

A small mass rests on a scale-pan supported by a spring; the period of vertical oscillations of the scale-pan and mass is 0.5 s. It is observed that when the amplitude of the oscillations exceeds a certain value, the mass leaves the scale-pan. At what point in the motion does the mass leave the scale-pan., and what is the minimum amplitude of the motion for this to happen?

(Southern Universities, Q3, Paper 2, June 1980)

13. The diagram (Fig. 6.25) shows a spring carrying a mass A suspended from a support which may either be held stationary or which may be moved up and down to perform a simple harmonic motion of small constant amplitude. The frequency of motion of the support may be varied. With the support stationary the period of vertical oscillations of mass A is 0.5 s.

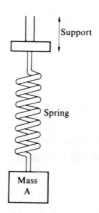

Fig. 6.25

(a) With the support stationary, mass A is replaced by mass B, which has the same volume as mass A but twice the density. Describe the small vertical oscillations of mass B.

(b) Mass B is now replaced by mass A and the frequency of the support is increased step by step up to 5 Hz. Sketch a graph to illustrate the variation of the maximum amplitude of mass

A's vertical oscillations with frequency of the support.

(c) Describe the motion of mass A when the frequency of the support is 2.5 Hz.

(d) Mass A is replaced by mass C (of equal mass but 1/5 density of A) and the frequency again increased in steps up to 5 Hz. Compare the results with those in (b).

(e) One can think of the above system in considering the behaviour of a car when driven over a road with fairly regular bumps or ridges. What makes some cars more comfortable than others to ride in over such a road? How would you expect a 'comfortable' car to behave on sharp corners?

(Oxford and Cambridge Schools Examination Board, Nuffield Advanced Physics, Special paper, 1970)

7 Waves

Progressive waves

When a stone is dropped into still water, waves spread out from the disturbance. We know there is a wave because the water surface is bobbing up and down. Water is not being moved across the surface but energy is. The term *progressive* or *travelling wave* is used for the movement of a disturbance from a source which transfers energy from that source to other places.

There are two basic types of waves: longitudinal and transverse. Longitudinal waves have the displacement of the particles parallel to the direction of motion of the wave energy (Fig. 7.1a). Transverse waves have the displacement perpendicular to the direction of motion of the energy (Fig. 7.1b).

Waves moving in the surface of water are almost transverse waves, the displacement of the water being almost just up and down (the actual motion is elliptical). Electromagnetic waves are transverse waves, the disturbance not being of particles but of electric and magnetic fields. Sound waves are longitudinal waves; when a sound wave passes through air the air molecules are pushed back and forth along the same line as that of the movement of energy.

Displacement–distance graphs

Waves, whether longitudinal or transverse, can be described graphically in terms of a displacement–distance graph. Figure 7.2 shows such a graph. In the case of the transverse wave the displacements are shown in the directions they actually are at some instant of time. For the longitudinal wave

the displacements are again at some instant of time but the actual displacement directions would be along the direction of travel of the wave motion.

Wave terms

To any type of wave motion we can ascribe a frequency, a wavelength, and a velocity. The frequency is the number of waves per second which passes a point in the wave path, or we can think of it as the number of waves produced per second. One wave is taken as being from one crest to the next crest, or one trough to the next trough; this distance is known as the wavelength.

If the frequency is f then f waves of length λ, the wavelength, must pass a point per second. The

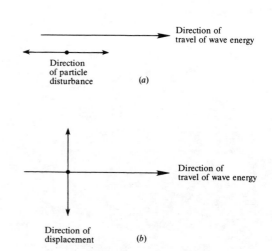

Fig. 7.1   (a) Longitudinal wave. (b) Transverse wave

116

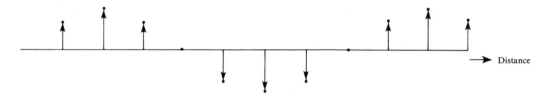

Transverse displacement of particles

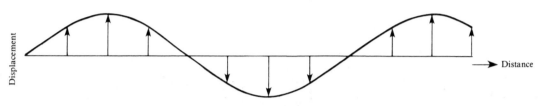

The displacement—distance graph

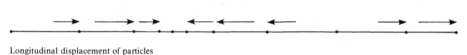

Longitudinal displacement of particles

Fig. 7.2

distance travelled by a wave is thus $f\lambda$ in one second. The wave speed v is given by the distance travelled per second and thus

$$v = f\lambda$$

The unit of frequency is s^{-1}. This is given the name Hertz (Hz). 1 Hz is one cycle per second. If the wavelength is in metres then the velocity is m s^{-1}.

The maximum displacement of a particle from its undisturbed position as a result of the wave is known as the amplitude (Fig. 7.3).

Equation of a sinusoidal progressive wave

If we observed some particle at, say, point A (Fig. 7.3) as the wave travelled past it, then we would see the particle oscillate up and down. If the wave was generated as a result of a vibration with simple harmonic motion (see Chapter 6), then the wave is sinusoidal. This means we can describe the displacement y variation with time t at one point, say A, by the equation

$$y = A \sin \omega t$$

where A is the amplitude and $\omega = 2\pi f, = 2\pi/T$, with f being the frequency and T the time taken for one complete wave to pass.

At some other point in the wave path, say B, the particle displacement would vary with time in the same way as that at B but show a phase lag, i.e., it would happen always a bit later than that at A. B would reach a maximum value of displacement later than A. Thus for B we can write

$$y = A \sin(\omega t - \delta)$$

where δ is the phase lag. If the point at which we considered the displacement had been a distance of λ from A, i.e. point C, then the phase lag would have been 2π, i.e., an entire wave. Thus if we consider a point, such as B, a distance x from A then the phase difference is $(x/\lambda)2\pi$. Hence we can write

$$y = A \sin\left(\omega t - \frac{2\pi x}{\lambda}\right) \qquad (1)$$

117

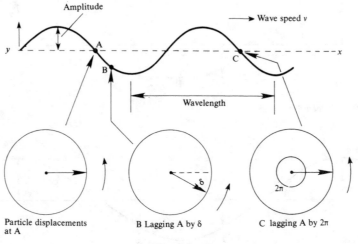

Fig. 7.3

Since $\omega = 2\pi f = 2\pi v/\lambda$, then

$$y = A \sin\left(\frac{2\pi vt}{\lambda} - \frac{2\pi x}{\lambda}\right)$$

$$y = A \sin\frac{2\pi}{\lambda}(vt - x)$$

An alternative way of writing Eq. (1), since $\omega = 2\pi/T$, is

$$Y = A \sin 2\pi\left(\frac{t}{T} - \frac{x}{\lambda}\right)$$

All the above equations represent a wave travelling from left to right with point B further to the right than point A which we are using as a reference point.

If the wave was travelling from right to left with point B still to the right of point A, then we would have the particle displacement at B leading that at A. The equations would thus become

$$y = A \sin\left(\omega t + \frac{2\pi x}{\lambda}\right)$$

$$y = A \sin\frac{2\pi}{\lambda}(vt + x)$$

$$y = A \sin 2\pi\left(\frac{t}{T} + \frac{x}{\lambda}\right)$$

The properties of waves

To get some ideas of the properties of water waves take a look at the waves in your bath water or the sink. A point to notice here is that the direction of the wave motion is at right angles to the line of crests or troughs. Later we will find it convenient to refer to the wavefront; this is the line of a crest, or trough, at some instant. With plane waves the wave fronts would be straight, with circular waves circular.

With plane waves reflected from a straight barrier the angle of incidence is equal to the angle of reflection— just like in optics. Figure 7.4 shows

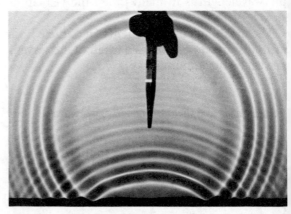

Fig. 7.4 PSSC Physics, *2nd edn, D. C. Heath and Co.*

118

circular waves being reflected from a straight barrier. The angle of incidence is still equal to the angle of reflection and, in addition, we can begin to think in terms of an image source of waves. The image would have to be as far behind the barrier as the object source is in front in order to give the results shown in the photograph. Again this is just like reflection from a plane mirror in light. The same rules apply to both the reflection of light and the reflection of water waves.

Figure 7.5 shows what happens when water waves pass from deep water to shallow water. There is a change in wavelength. The wavelength in the shallow water is less than the wavelength in the deep water. The frequency of waves in both depths of water is the same—it was checked by using a stroboscope to 'stop' the motion; both sections were 'stopped' by the same stroboscope frequency. As the frequency has not changed then there must be a change in velocity of the wave when the water depth changes, the velocity being lower in the shallower water. In the figure the water waves were straight and parallel to the change in water depth step. What happens when the step is at an angle to the wave front? The waves are refracted (see Fig. 7.6). Is there any relationship between the angles of incidence and refraction?

$$\frac{\lambda_1}{PQ} = \sin i; \qquad \frac{\lambda_2}{PQ} = \sin r \quad \text{(Fig. 7.7)}$$

Thus

$$\frac{\sin i}{\sin r} = \frac{\lambda_1}{\lambda_2}$$

But as the wavelengths are directly proportional to the wave velocities

$$\frac{\sin i}{\sin r} = \frac{v_1}{v_2}$$

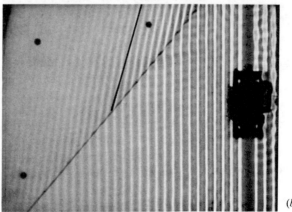

(a)

(b)

Fig. 7.6 PSSC Physics, *2nd edn, D. C. Heath and Co.* (a) Refraction of low-frequency waves. The black marker is placed parallel to the refracted waves. (b) Refraction of high-frequency waves

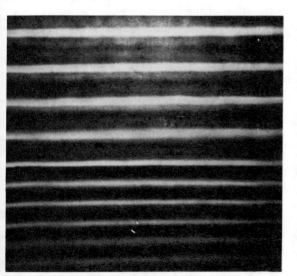

Fig. 7.5 PSSC Physics, *2nd edn, D. C. Heath and Co.* Passage of water waves from deep to shallow water

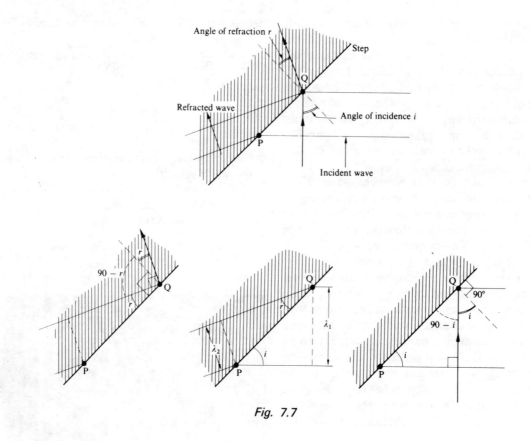

Fig. 7.7

The ratio of the sine of the angle of incidence to the sine of the angle of refraction is a constant, the ratio of the velocities in the two depths. This ratio depends on the frequency of the water waves, as Fig. 7.6 shows. A change in frequency means a change in the angle of refraction, the angle of incidence being kept constant. The different colours of light are refracted by differing amounts—an effect similar to that shown by the water waves.

Figure 7.8 shows what happens when water waves pass through apertures of different widths. When the wavelength is about the same size as the aperture, considerable bending of the wave occurs when it passes through the aperture. This bending is called *diffraction*.

Figure 7.9 shows what happens when the water waves produced by two point sources meet. The waves interfere and produce regions of calm water. This effect is called *interference*. As will be noticed from the two photographs, the effect

changes if the wavelength is changed (or if the separation of the two sources is changed).

To summarize: water waves show reflection, refraction, diffraction, and interference.

Interference of water waves

What happens when two waves meet? Do the waves pass right through each other? Do the waves bounce off each other? Do they cancel out each other and leave no disturbance?

Figure 7.9 shows what happens when two water waves meet. At certain positions the waves from the two sources have cancelled each other and give undisturbed water. It would seem natural to expect that where a wave trough met a wave crest they would cancel. Let us use this as a basis for an attempt at an explanation of the interference pattern. Figure 7.10a shows the waves moving out from a single point source, Fig. 7.10b shows waves from two point sources when we consider no interaction between the waves. If we take into account interaction between the two waves in 7.10b we arrive at the result shown in 7.10c, where regions of undisturbed water (and regions of larger troughs and larger crests) are produced. Figure 7.10d shows diagram 7.10b extended to

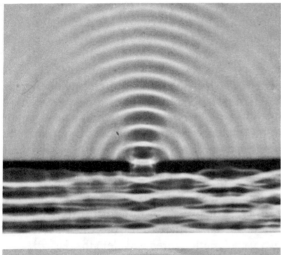

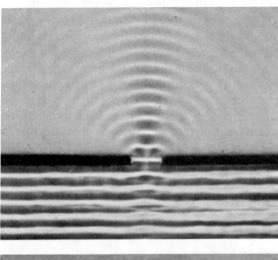

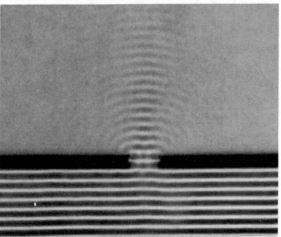

Fig. 7.8 *Three views of water waves of different wavelength passing through the same aperture (PSSC Physics, 2nd edn, D. C. Heath and Co.)*

(a)

(b)

Fig. 7.9 PSSC Physics, *2nd edn, D. C. Heath and Co. Interference pattern from two point sources: (a) separation of two sources about ten times the wavelength; (b) separation about five times the wavelength. (In fact the separation was kept constant and the wavelength changed)*

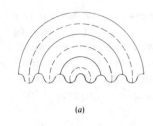

(a)

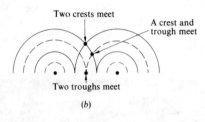

Two crests meet

A crest and trough meet

Two troughs meet

(b)

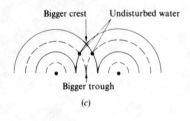

Bigger crest   Undisturbed water

Bigger trough

(c)

cover many more waves. Compare this with the photograph of water waves in Fig. 7.10b; the wavelength and the source separation have been made the same. The diagram agrees with the photograph. The regions of undisturbed water occur when a crest meets a trough—when there is a path difference between the two waves reaching the point of half a wavelength (half a wavelength is the distance between a wave trough and the next crest), or three half wavelengths, or five half wavelengths, or seven half wavelengths (Fig. 7.11), i.e., $(n + \frac{1}{2})\lambda$, where $n = 0, 1, 2, 3, 4$, etc. The regions of maximum disturbance, crest meeting with crest or trough meeting with trough, occur where the path difference is zero, one wavelength, two wavelengths, three wavelengths, i.e., $n\lambda$.

The photograph of the waves from two sources interfering was a picture of the waves at a single instant of time—the wave pattern produced by the water waves travelling out across the surface was frozen. Would the positions of undisturbed water change if we took a photograph at some later time? The answer is no —the undisturbed water positions do not change, provided we do not alter the vibrators producing the waves. The reason for this is that the path differences to any point remain constant— for cancellation of the waves we do not necessarily need a trough to meet a crest, we can have any height of disturbance

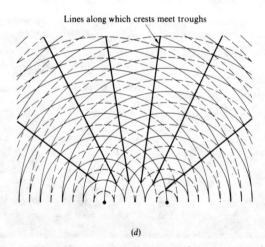

Lines along which crests meet troughs

(d)

Fig. 7.10 Waves spreading out from one point source. (b) Waves from two point sources without interference being considered. (c) The result of the two waves in (b) meeting when we consider interference. (d) Many waves from two point sources, without interference being considered.

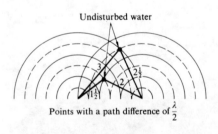

Undisturbed water

Points with a path difference of $\frac{\lambda}{2}$

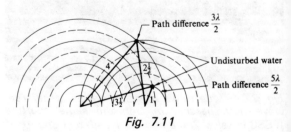

Path difference $\frac{3\lambda}{2}$

Undisturbed water

Path difference $\frac{5\lambda}{2}$

Fig. 7.11

above the water surface cancelled by a corresponding depression below the water surface (Fig. 7.12). Similarly, the maximum displacement positions do not change with time. In such a position the waves from the two sources are always giving displacements in the same direction; with the undisturbed water position the two waves always give displacements which are in opposite directions—whenever one gives a displacement above the surface the other wave gives a corresponding displacement below the surface. The pattern of maximum and minimum displacements remains stationary although it is formed by travelling waves. The interference pattern is sometimes called stationary or standing waves.

Interference patterns are produced whenever waves meet. A simple case is where a wave interferes with its own reflection from some barrier.

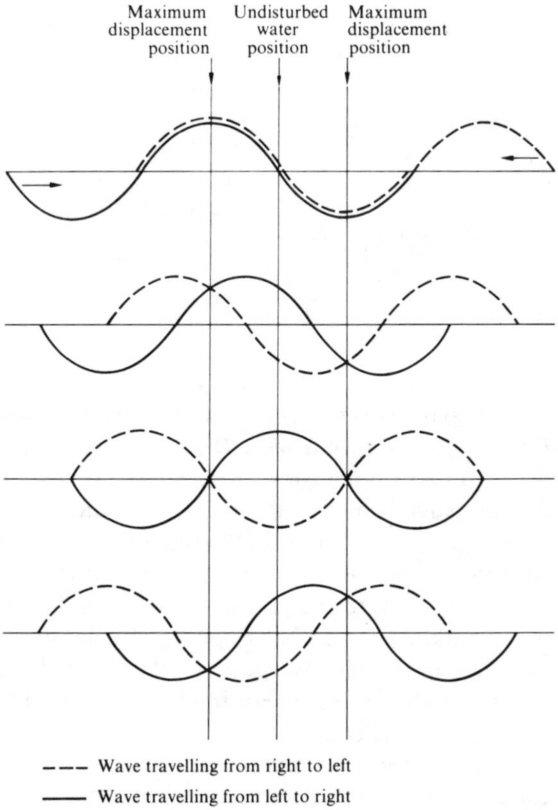

The incident wave moving up to the barrier meets the reflected wave coming back from the barrier.

With plane waves incident on a plane reflector and the wavefronts parallel to the reflector the positions of undisturbed water are a series of lines parallel to the reflector. How far apart are these undisturbed water positions, these destructive interference positions? Consider A and B to be two successive destructive interference positions (Fig. 7.13). For the two waves arriving at A to cancel we must have

$$(W + Y) - (Z + X) = (n + \tfrac{1}{2})\lambda$$

For B to be the next position of cancellation we must have

$$(W + Y + X) - Z = (n + 1 + \tfrac{1}{2})\lambda$$

Subtracting the first equation from this one gives

$$2X = \lambda$$

X, the distance apart of successive destructive interference positions, is equal to half the wavelength.

The principle of superposition

When two water waves meet then an experimental fact is that after the 'collision' the water waves continue in motion with the same shape, speed, and energy as before. The water waves do not interact with each other, the situation being completely different from a collision between two

Maximum displacement position   Undisturbed water position   Maximum displacement position

- - - Wave travelling from right to left

——— Wave travelling from left to right

Fig. 7.12

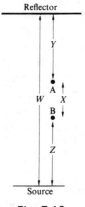

Fig. 7.13

solid objects such as billiard balls. At the point of 'collision' the particle displacement is the sum of the particle displacements that would have occurred for each of the two waves. The only thing we must take account of is the sign of the displacement, i.e., a trough displacement plus a crest displacement gives a different 'sum' displacement than if the displacements due to two crests were added. The term *principle of superposition* is used to describe this summing of displacements.

The principle of superposition states that the net displacement at a particular place and time as a result of a number of waves traversing the same space is the vector sum of the displacements that would have been produced by the individual waves separately.

Diffraction of water waves

Water waves bend round corners—they show diffraction. As Fig. 7.8 shows, the bending is most noticeable with slits when the slit aperture has a width equal to the wavelength of the waves. The bending is not, however, restricted to slits but occurs round any barrier. The diffraction of plane waves through slits does, however, reveal a significant fact—when the slit is about one wavelength wide the resulting wave pattern is just about the same as that which is produced by a point source: the plane wave has been converted into a circular wave. What if the slit is more than one wavelength wide? The same diffraction pattern as of a plane wave passing through a slit can be produced by a line of point wave sources placed in a line extending across the slit. The point sources are all run together, i.e., when one produces a maximum they all do, and with the same frequency as the plane wave. It would appear that a useful way of tackling diffraction problems might be to replace a wavefront by a line of point sources vibrating at the same frequency as that which produced the original wavefront. This method of dealing with problems was invented by Huygens in 1678. Every point on a wavefront can be replaced by point sources of secondary waves.

Waves can bend round objects, the effect being most noticeable when the object has a size of the same order as the wavelength of the waves. When the object is smaller in size than the wavelength it casts no shadow.

Huygens' construction of wavefronts

The term *wavefront* is used for the surface over which the disturbance resulting from some wave source has the same phase at all points. Thus, for example, a point source can be considered to be the centre of spherical wavefronts. If the disturbance is a maximum at one point on the wavefront then it must also be a maximum at all the other points on that wavefront.

Huygens considered that every point on a wavefront acts as a source of secondary waves and the new wavefront some time later can be considered to be the summation of these secondary waves, as illustrated in Fig. 7.14.

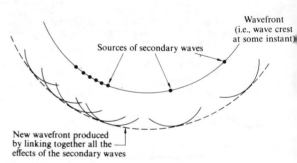

Fig. 7.14

We can use this method to derive a relationship for the reflection of a wave (Fig. 7.15). AC is the wavefront at some instant, for a source so distant that the wavefront is straight. The secondary wave starting at C travels to B in the same time that the secondary wave at A travels to N. As both waves travel in the same medium CB = AN. As the wavefronts, AC and BN, are perpendicular to the rays, this makes the two triangles ACB and ANB identical. Thus the angle of incidence is equal to the angle of reflection.

Similarly we can derive a relationship for refraction (Fig. 7.16). However, we have to assume that the speed of light in a medium such as glass is

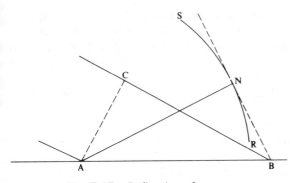

Fig. 7.15 Reflection of a wave

less than that in air in order that the ray of light should bend in the 'right' direction on passing from air to glass, assuming light to be a wave.

The wavefront AC would in the absence of the surface AB move to GB; the portion at C does move to B but the portion at A is slowed down by passing into the medium below the line AB. If the speed of light in this medium is 2/3 of that in air then the arc SNR represents the wave arising from the wave-centre at A, SN = 2CB/3. The line from B tangent to this arc gives the refracted wavefront NB.

$$\frac{CB}{AB} = \sin i$$

$$\frac{AN}{AB} = \sin r$$

Thus

$$\frac{CB}{AN} = \frac{\sin i}{\sin r}$$

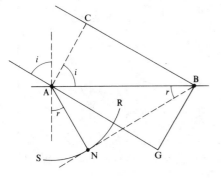

Fig. 7.16 Refraction of a wave

But CB is the distance travelled in air in time t, and AN is the distance travelled in the medium in the same time t. Thus

$$\frac{CB}{AN} = \frac{\text{speed of light in air}}{\text{speed of light in medium}} = \frac{\sin i}{\sin r}$$

Hence

$$\frac{\sin i}{\sin r} = \text{a constant}$$

In a similar way we can consider diffraction and interference.

Standing waves

If one end of a heavy rope or stretched spring is fixed and the other end is moved from side to side, as in Fig. 7.17, then a transverse wave pulse is generated which travels down the spring and becomes reflected from the fixed end. If the side to side movement of the end of the rope or spring is continuous then a continuous wave is produced which travels down the rope and becomes reflected from the fixed end. There is thus a wave travelling down the rope towards the fixed end and a reflected wave travelling in the opposite direction. With continuous wave production we cannot see these two waves as separate entities, what we see is the superposition of them.

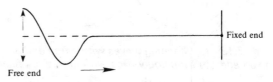

Fixed end

Free end

Fig. 7.17 A transverse wave pulse being sent along a stretched rope

If the frequency of the continuous transverse wave is gradually increased, then at certain frequencies the rope shows one or more loops of large amplitude (Fig. 7.18) with the superposed wave pattern stationary and no apparent motion of waves along the rope. Such wave patterns are

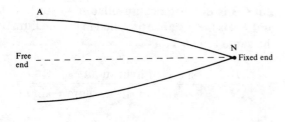

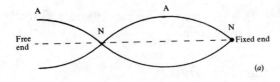

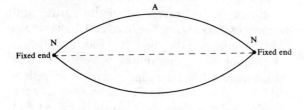

called nodes N, and points of maximum displacement, termed antinodes A. The distance between adjacent nodes, or between adjacent antinodes, is half the wavelength of the progressive wave responsible for the standing wave.

Standing waves result from the superposition of two progressive waves which have the same amplitude and frequency (and hence same wavelength), but oppositely directed velocities of the same size. Figure 7.19 shows this superposition for two sinusoidal waves and how the positions of the resulting nodes and antinodes remain fixed. Each of the parts of Fig. 7.19 shows the standing wave at some instant of time. This is the standing wave that would be seen if the wave was photographed with a short-duration exposure. However, the eye sees a time average and so sees the summation of all the standing wave patterns.

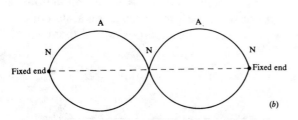

Fig. 7.18 (a) Standing waves with a free end and a fixed end. (b) Standing waves with both ends fixed

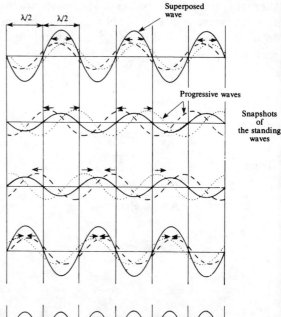

Fig 7.19 Formation of standing waves

called *standing* or *stationary waves*. The condition for standing waves to occur is when the wavelength of the standing waves 'fits' the space provided. This means we have a wavelength which gives waves having zero displacement at fixed ends of ropes and maximum displacements at free ends. Along the standing wave patterns will be fixed points which are points of zero displacement,

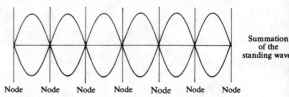

Waves on strings

A transverse wave will travel along a stretched string with a speed v given by

$$v = \sqrt{\frac{T}{\mu}}$$

where T is the tension in the string and μ the string mass per unit length.

When a stretched string is deflected from its equilibrium position and allowed to oscillate, perhaps a guitar player has plucked it or a violin bow pushed it to one side, then a transverse wave travels along the string. The stretched string is, however, fixed at each end and so reflection occurs and a standing wave is produced as a result of the superposition of the initial and reflected waves. A standing wave must have a node at the fixed ends and thus only certain waves can 'fit' between these points (as in Fig. 7.18b). Wavelengths that fit a string of length L are $\lambda = 2L$, this being referred to as the fundamental or first harmonic; $\lambda = L$, the first overtone or second harmonic; $\lambda = \frac{2}{3}L$, the second overtone or third harmonic; $\lambda = \frac{1}{2}L$, the third overtone or fourth harmonic, etc. (In general $\lambda = 2L/n$, where $n = 1$, 2, 3, 4, etc.)

The standing wave pattern that is generated for a particular string depends on the original disturbance which caused the transverse wave. A string can, however, vibrate with several different standing waves and thus the note produced by the string can contain more than one frequency. This is why the same note sounded with a violin has a different sound quality to one on a guitar or some other stringed instrument.

The frequency given by a standing wave is $f = v/\lambda$ and so

$$\text{frequency of fundamental} = \frac{1}{2L}\sqrt{\frac{T}{\mu}}$$

$$\text{frequency of first overtone} = \frac{1}{L}\sqrt{\frac{T}{\mu}}$$

$$\text{frequency of second overtone} = \frac{3}{2L}\sqrt{\frac{T}{\mu}}$$

An equation for superposed waves

Earlier in this chapter an equation for a sinusoidal progressive wave was derived in the form

$$y_1 = A \sin 2\pi\left(\frac{t}{T} - \frac{x}{\lambda}\right)$$

for a wave travelling from left to right and for a wave travelling from right to left

$$y_2 = A \sin 2\pi\left(\frac{t}{T} + \frac{x}{\lambda}\right)$$

We will consider both waves to have the same amplitude, periodic time T (i.e., same frequency) and same wavelength. The standing wave pattern is obtained by superposing two such waves. Hence the displacement of y of the superposed waveform is $(y_1 + y_2)$ and so

$$y = A \sin 2\pi\left(\frac{t}{T} - \frac{x}{\lambda}\right) + A \sin 2\pi\left(\frac{t}{T} + \frac{x}{\lambda}\right)$$

We can simplify this by using the expression

$$\sin A + \sin B = 2 \sin\tfrac{1}{2}(A + B) \cos\tfrac{1}{2}(A - B)$$

Hence

$$y = \left(2A \cos\frac{2\pi x}{\lambda}\right) \sin\frac{2\pi t}{T}$$

The bracketed term does not depend on time but only on position. It shows the variation of amplitude with distance x. When $x = \lambda/4$ or $3\lambda/4$ or $5\lambda/4$, etc., the bracketed term is zero and thus at such positions the amplitude is always zero and at no time is there any displacement—these are the nodes. The distance between adjacent nodes is $\frac{1}{2}\lambda$. Similarly, maximum amplitude positions occur when $x = 0$ or $\lambda/2$ or λ, etc., these being the antinodes. The maximum value of the amplitude is when the cosine term is 1 and so the maximum amplitude is $2A$.

The displacement equation for the standing wave consists of two terms, a location-dependent term which gives the amplitude and a time-dependent term. This latter term indicates that all the particles have the same periodic time, i.e., same frequency. Between the adjacent nodes at $x = \lambda/4$ and $x = 3\lambda/4$ the location-dependent term will be always negative and so all the particles will have the same phase (although they will have different amplitudes, they will all oscillate about their equilibrium position in unison). Between the next pair of adjacent nodes, i.e., $x = 3\lambda/4$ and $x = 5\lambda/4$, the location-dependent term will always be positive and so all the particles will have the same phase. They will, however, all show a phase difference of π with the particles between the previous pair of nodes.

Phase changes on reflection

Transverse waves can be sent along ropes or springs by wagging one end back and forth, as in Fig. 7.17. If the other end of the rope is fixed, then a wave crest on meeting the fixed end becomes reflected as a trough. There has been a phase change of π. This phase change has to occur if the sum of the incident and reflected waves at the fixed end are to give a node—since the end is fixed it cannot be anything else other than a node (Fig. 7.20). If, however, the end is free to move then a wave can still be reflected but now a crest is reflected as a crest, no phase change occurring. This is because the free end is an antinode.

When water waves encounter a boundary, perhaps a change in depth, where on one side the wave speed is different from on the other (if it is a solid boundary, the wave speed of the water in the solid is zero), then the situation is exactly the same as with the transverse wave on the rope. The difference is that we tend to use terms like—the wave is passing from a rarer to a denser medium, a rarer medium being one where the speed is

A comparision of progressive and standing waves

	Progressive	*Stationary*
Amplitude	The same for all particles, A	Varies according to position—zero at nodes to a maximum of $2A$ at antinodes
Waveform	Advances with the speed of the wave	Does not advance, but remains fixed in space
Frequency	All particles vibrate with the same frequency	Except those particles at nodes, which are at rest, all particles vibrate with the same frequency
Phase	The phase angle increases from 0 to 2π within one wavelength	All particles between two adjacent nodes have the same phase; particles in the next segment between nodes have a difference of π
Energy	The wave transfers energy from the source to another place	There is no net movement of energy

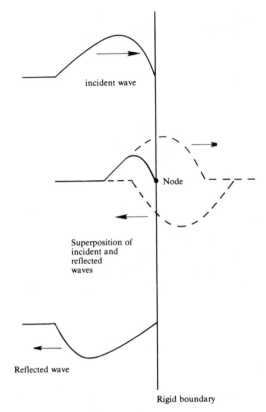

incident wave

Node

Superposition of
incident and
reflected
waves

Reflected wave

Rigid boundary

*Fig. 7.20 Reflection of a transverse wave pulse
with a phase change of π.*

higher than in the denser medium. A wave
encountering a rarer to dense medium boundary
is the same as the wave on the rope meeting a
fixed end —a phase change of π occurs. If,
however, the wave moves from a denser to a rarer
medium, no phase change occurs.

All the above discussion has referred to
transverse waves. Phase changes, however, also
occur with longitudinal waves (see the next
chapter).

Problems

1. Explain how progressive waves can give rise
to stationary waves.

2. Sketch a displacement–distance graph for a
sinusoidal progressive wave and explain what is
represented by the displacements when the wave
is (a) transverse, (b) longitudinal.

3. Using Huygens' principle of secondary
wavelets explain, making use of a diagram, how a
refracted wavefront is formed when a beam of
light, travelling in glass, crosses the glass–air
boundary. Show how the sines of the angles of
incidence and refraction are related to the speeds
of light in air and glass.

(University of London, Q4, Paper 2,
January 1978)

4. A string is stretched between two points a
distance L apart. Sketch the two lowest frequency
modes of transverse vibration of the string, and
write down expressions for their frequencies in
terms of L and of c, the speed of propagation of
transverse waves on the string.

(University of Cambridge, Q3, Paper 1,
June 1980)

5. (a) State how plane progressive waves and
stationary waves differ in respect of

(i) energy transfer
(ii) the amplitude at points along the wave
(iii) the phase differences between points along
the wave.

(b) Describe experiments to investigate how the
frequency, f, of transverse stationary waves in a
stretched string depends on

(i) the length, L, of the string, and
(ii) the tension, T, in the string.

In each case sketch a graph to show how the data
obtained could be suitably processed. State the
relationship which you would expect to verify
from each experiment.

(c) Determine the phase difference between
two points 50 mm apart on a string carrying a progressive wave if the frequency of the wave is 100
Hz and its speed along the string is 20 m s^{-1}.

(University of London, Q10, Paper 2,
June 1982)

6. Describe the differences between stationary
waves and progressive waves. Outline an experimental arrangement to illustrate the formation of
a stationary wave in a string.

Waves, of wavelength λ, from a source, S, reach
a common point, P, by two different routes.

At P the waves are found to have a phase difference of ¾π rad. Show graphically what this

means. What is the minimum path difference between the two routes?

A string fixed at both ends is vibrating in the lowest mode, vibration for which a point a quarter of its length from one end is a point of maximum vibration. The note emitted has a frequency of 100 Hz. What will be the frequency emitted when it vibrates in the next mode such that this point is again a point of maximum vibration?

(University of London, Q10, Paper 2, June 1978)

7. (a) Explain what is meant by the principle of superposition.

(b) Show how a progressive wave travelling in the x-direction is represented by an equation of the form

$$y = a \sin 2\pi \left(ft - \frac{x}{\lambda} \right)$$

(c) Describe the reflection of such a wave incident normally on a boundary

(i) with no change of phase
(ii) with a change of phase π.

Give expressions for the displacements resulting from the superposition of the incident and reflected waves and illustrate your answers with wave diagrams. State an example of a physical situation in which each type of reflection occurs.

(Oxford Local Examinations, Q7, Paper 0, June 1982)

8. A wave at sea is described by the equation

$$h = A \sin (\omega t - kx)$$

in which ω is the angular frequency of the wave, and k is equal to $2\pi/\lambda$, λ being the wavelength. h is the height of the surface measured above the mean level of the water and x is the distance measured in a southerly direction from the leg of an oil rig. The wave direction lies along a south–north line.

(a) Answer the following questions in terms of the symbols used

(i) What is the distance between the maximum and minimum heights of the water on the leg of the oil rig?

(ii) What is the period between the arrival of successive wave crests at the oil rig?

(iii) What is the velocity of the waves relative to the oil rig?

(b) A boat travels in a northerly direction from the oil rig at a speed v. Deduce the period of rise and fall of the boat in terms of the symbols used.

(JMB, Engineering Science, Q4, Paper III, June 1979)

8 Sound

The speed of sound

How does sound travel through air? The fact that sound requires a material medium for its travel can readily be shown; a bell ringing in a vacuum cannot be heard. Air or some other medium is necessary for sound propagation. The experiment with a bell, actually a watch with an alarm, was first made by Boyle in 1660. The production of sound always involves some motion at the source: a bell set in vibration by a blow, the oscillation of a violin string, the thud produced by a falling object, the sound of an explosion. The need for a medium and the movement of part of a sound source led to the idea that sound travels through a medium by virtue of the medium being pushed and pulled, by compression and rarefaction. Ideas like this were held by the Ancient Greeks. That sound takes a finite time to cover a distance, i.e., has a finite speed, has also been known for quite some time. The first measurements of the speed were made at the beginning of the seventeenth century; the methods used were the measurement of the time interval between a sound being produced and its echo coming back by reflection at some distant reflector, and the measurement by an observer some distance from a gun of the time interval between his seeing the flash of the explosion at the gun and hearing the sound of the explosion. The speed of sound in air is about 340 m s^{-1}.

The speed of sound in a solid

Let us consider more closely how the sound wave could travel through a medium. The atoms in a solid can be displaced from their equilibrium positions. If, however, they move, then neighbouring atoms or molecules must experience a force because an atom or molecule has either moved closer to them or further away and disrupted the equilibrium arrangement. Let us represent this by a model, a series of trolleys linked by springs (Fig. 8.1). When one trolley is displaced, along the direction of the line of trolleys, then in time the next trolley will become displaced, then the next one, and so on down the line. Figure 8.2 illustrates this movement of a compression pulse down the line of trolleys. If the end trolley is steadily pushed in with a constant speed u, then in time t it will have moved a distance ut. If the compression travels along the line of trolleys with a speed v, then in this time t it will have moved a distance vt. If x is the distance between trolley centres, then the number of trolleys in this distance vt will be vt/x. The number of springs is equal to the number of trolleys, so the number of springs compressed in time t will be vt/x. As the end trolley was moved in a distance ut and this resulted in vt/x springs being compressed, the average compression of a spring is

$$\frac{ut}{vt/x} = \frac{ux}{v}$$

As the end trolley is being pushed with a constant force at a constant speed, there must be equal and

Fig. 8.1

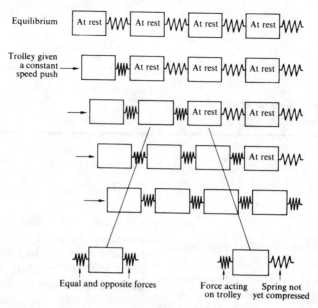

Equilibrium — At rest | At rest | At rest | At rest

Trolley given a constant speed push → At rest | At rest | At rest

Equal and opposite forces

Force acting on trolley — Spring not yet compressed

Fig. 8.2

opposite forces acting on it. Similarly, the next trolley along the line will have equal and opposite forces acting on it when it is moving with constant speed; the springs each side of it are equally compressed. The force acting on a trolley due to a spring being compressed by ux/v will be kux/v if the compression is proportional to the force; k is the force constant (the springs are assumed to obey Hooke's law). A trolley which is just being moved from rest will have this force exerted on one side of it by a compressed spring; the other spring on the other side will not yet have been compressed. The unbalanced force acting on this trolley will be kux/v. During time t this force will have acted on vt/x trolleys and caused them to gain a momentum of mu, where m is the mass of a trolley. The rate of change of momentum is thus $(vt/x)mu$ in time t.

As force = rate of change of momentum

$$\frac{kux}{v} = \frac{vt}{x}\frac{mu}{t}$$

Thus

$$v = x\sqrt{\frac{k}{m}}$$

The speed of the compression pulse thus depends on the spacing of the trolleys, the force constant of the springs and the mass of the trolleys.

Could this equation be applicable to compression waves in a medium? x could be the spacing between the atoms or molecules, m the mass of the atom or molecule, and k the force constant for the bond joining atoms. A material would be three dimensional, Fig. 8.3, and thus our push on the end trolley would be a push on many atoms. However, for each atom there is one spring (bond), along the direction of the push, and the situation could be similar to that of the trolleys.

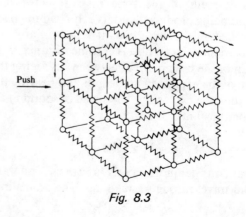

Push

Fig. 8.3

There are, however, in the simple cubic array portrayed in Fig. 8.3, springs (bonds) in a direction at right angles to the push. These would have no effect if the compression acted over the entire face of the solid.

To use our equation to calculate the speed of a compression wave in a material we need to know the force constant of the bond. For a solid with a simple cubic array of atoms we can obtain the force constant in terms of the Young's modulus of the material.

$$\text{Young's modulus, } E = \frac{\text{stress}}{\text{strain}}$$

provided we have a linear stress–strain relationship.

$$\text{Stress} = \frac{\text{force}}{\text{area}}$$

For the piece of solid represented by Fig. 8.3 we have per pair of atoms

$$\text{Stress} = \frac{k\,\Delta x}{x^2}$$

where Δx is the amount of compression.

$$\text{Strain} = \frac{\text{compression}}{\text{length}}$$

$$= \frac{\Delta x}{x}$$

Thus

$$E = \frac{k\,\Delta x}{x^2}\frac{x}{\Delta x}$$

$$E = \frac{k}{x}$$

The speed equation then becomes

$$v = x\sqrt{\frac{Ex}{m}}$$

$$= \sqrt{\frac{E}{m/x^3}}$$

But m/x^3 is the density, for a cubic atom array. Thus

$$v = \sqrt{\frac{\text{Young's modulus}}{\text{density}}}$$

For copper, Young's modulus is 13×10^{10} N m^{-1} and the density 8930 kg m^{-3}. Used in the equation they give a speed of 3800 m s^{-1}. The measured speed is about 3800 m s^{-1}.

The speed of sound in a gas

This seems a reasonable model for a solid but what about a gas? A piece of solid can, like the trolleys and springs model, be pulled or compressed along its length. The motions of our atoms, or trolleys, are along the line of the force. Our masses, atoms or trolleys, were localized. In the case of a gas, or indeed any fluid, we have non-localized masses. We cannot refer to the Young's modulus for a gas, because this is stretching or compressing along a line, but must use the bulk modulus. The bulk modulus is defined as the pressure change divided by the fractional change in volume

$$\text{Bulk modulus} = \frac{\Delta p}{(\Delta V/V)}$$

We can by a re-examination of our derivation of the equation for the trolley model of the solid arrive at an equation for a gas. The result is

$$v = \sqrt{\frac{\text{Bulk modulus}}{\text{density}}}$$

The bulk modulus of a gas is given by

$$\text{Bulk modulus} = \gamma p$$

where γ is the ratio of the specific heat capacities at constant volume and constant pressure and p is the pressure. The above relationship is obtained by considering the relation between pressure and volume during the passage of a longitudinal wave to involve changes which are so rapid that they are governed by the equation $pV^\gamma =$ a constant, the equation for adiabatic changes. Hence

$$v = \sqrt{\frac{\gamma p}{\rho}}$$

This equation might be taken to indicate that the speed depends on pressure. But when the pressure of a gas changes, then so does its density. If the gas is assumed to be an ideal gas, then for 1 kg.

$$pV = \frac{p}{\rho} = RT$$

Hence

$$v = \sqrt{\gamma RT}$$

where R is the specific gas constant and T the temperature on the kelvin scale.

Hence the speed of sound in a gas is

(a) independent of the pressure
(b) proportional to the square root of the temperature on the kelvin scale
(c) dependent on the nature of the gas, this determining the value of the specific gas constant and γ.

In the case of sound travelling in atmospheric conditions, the speed is also affected by changes in humidity, since this changes the value of γ and R, and wind speed. The wind speed has to be added vectorially to the speed of sound in still air to arrive at the speed under windy conditions.

To illustrate the use of the above equation, consider the change in speed that occurs when the air temperature rises from 0°C to 20°C. This is a change from 273 K to 293 K and so the speed changes by a factor

$$v_{20} = (293/273)^{½} v_0$$

$$v_{20} = 1.036 v_0$$

Since the speed of sound is higher in warm air than in cold air, refraction of sound waves can occur when there are temperature gradients in the air. Figure 8.4 illustrates such events.

Echo sounding

Clap your hands in front of a large wall and you can hear an echo—your pulse of sound being reflected

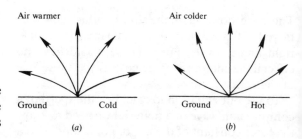

Fig. 8.4 *Sound paths when there is a temperature gradient*

at the wall and, because of the finite speed of sound, being heard a short time interval later. This is the basis of the echo sounder. The time difference between the pulse leaving the transmitter and being received back is directly proportional to the distance of the reflector from the transmitter, if the velocity of sound is constant over the entire sound path.

Figure 8.5 shows the output from an echo sounder on board a ship. The output appears as a chart where horizontal distance along the chart represents horizontal distance traversed by the ship and vertical distances are proportional to the time taken for an echo to be received at the ship. The vertical distances are thus proportional to the vertical distances. The upper trace is of the sea surface, the other traces are echoes. More than one echo is detected at any one depth, owing to

Fig. 8.5 *Echo-sounder chart. A recording of strata in the bed of the river Crouch at Burnham showing faults. (Multiple echoes from sea bed and strata are seen.) (Kelvin Hughes, a division of Smith Industries Ltd)*

the sound pulse travelling down to the sea bottom, being reflected to the sea surface, again reflected and going back down to the sea bed again. The number of echoes detected depends on the hardness of the sea bed. The amount of blur of any one reflection depends on the smoothness of the sea bed. The entire pulse may not be reflected at the sea bed but penetrate and be reflected at a lower rock stratum: some such strata are visible in Fig. 8.5.

One application of the ultrasonic echo principle is in medicine. The depth and thickness of organs in the human body can be determined—useful information when tumerous growths are suspected or when it is necessary to judge the maturation of the embryo during pregnancy.

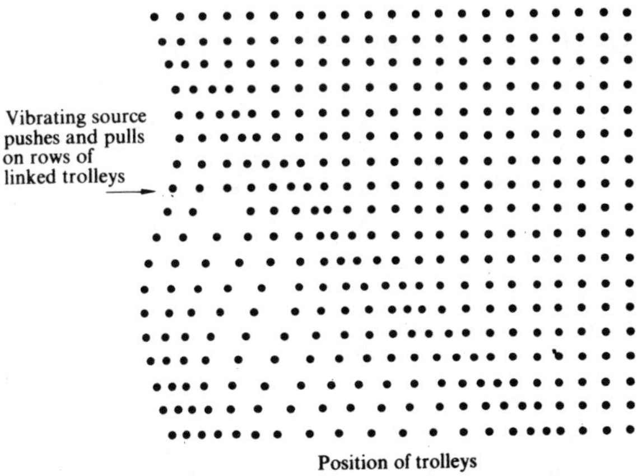

Vibrating source pushes and pulls on rows of linked trolleys →

Position of trolleys

Fig. 8.6

Sound as a pressure wave

If instead of just giving a row of trolleys (Fig. 8.1) a steady push we applied a force which pushed then pulled then pushed then pulled, etc., on the end trolley we would generate a sequence of compressions which would travel along the row of trolleys (Fig. 8.6). At some instant of time we would find trolleys, in one region, grouped closer together, in another region farther apart, than the initial equal distance apart state. We have a series of alternate compressions and rarefactions. In the case of a gas we would have alternate regions of pressure above the normal gas pressure and regions of pressure below the normal (Fig. 8.7a). If we plot the displacement of the trolleys with their positions along the row, a wave pattern is found

(Fig. 8.7b). The distance between successive compressions (or successive rarefactions) is the wavelength. The frequency is the number of waves produced per second, i.e., the number of compressions produced per second.

Waves in air columns

Organ pipes, flutes, recorders, clarinets, etc., all depend on the same basic principle—the air inside a pipe is set into oscillation by a source of sound, perhaps a vibrating reed. A simple experiment to illustrate this effect involves a tuning fork being sounded above the open end of a column of air in a tube (Fig. 8.8). At certain lengths for this air column, a loud sound is heard. The system is

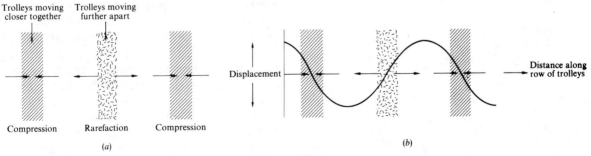

Fig. 8.7

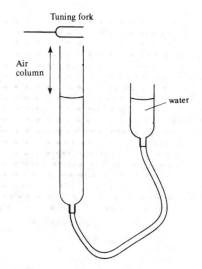

Fig. 8.8 *The resonance tube experiment*

said to show *resonance* at these lengths, hence the name 'resonance tube' for the experiment.

The sound wave produced by the tuning fork travels down the air column to be reflected from the water surface which terminates the column of air. Thus the particle displacement at any point in the air column is determined by the superposition of the incident and reflected waves. Standing waves are set up in the air column. For a closed end the particle displacement must be zero, i.e., there is a node. For an open end there will be an antinode. Figure 8.9 shows standing waves that can be set up in a tube with one closed end and one open end. The largest wavelength is when $L = \frac{1}{4}\lambda$, this being referred to as the fundamental or first harmonic. The next largest wavelength is

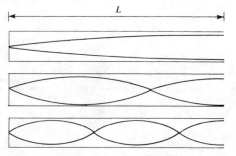

Fig. 8.9 *Resonance in an air column open at one end and closed at the other*

when $L = \frac{3}{4}\lambda$, the first overtone or third harmonic. The next is when $L = \frac{5}{4}\lambda$, the second overtone or fifth harmonic. The term harmonic is used for a note whose frequency is a whole number multiple of the fundamental frequency (of $v/4L$). Hence the first overtone is called the third harmonic, the frequency being $3v/4L$ or 3 × fundamental frequency.

Figure 8.10 shows the standing waves with a tube open at both ends. The fundamental has a wavelength of $2L$, and so a frequency of $v/2L$. The first overtone has a wavelength of L and a frequency of v/L, hence it is the second harmonic. The second overtone has a wavelength of $\frac{2}{3}L$ and so a frequency of $3v/2L$, hence it is the third harmonic.

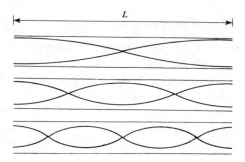

Fig. 8.10 *Resonance in an air column open at both ends*

The above discussion of standing waves has been in terms of the particle displacements. At a fixed end a compression is reflected as a compression, no phase change occurring. Thus, at a fixed end the pressure wave has a maximum value i.e., an antinode. At an open end a compression is reflected as a rarefaction, a phase change of π thus occurring. At an open end the pressure wave amplitude must be zero, i.e., a node, since the open end is at the atmospheric pressure prevailing. For this to occur a compression must be cancelled by a rarefaction, and vice versa; hence the phase change. Figure 8.11 summarises the displacement and pressure standing wave conditions.

The effective length of a vibrating air column is slightly greater than the actual length of the tube containing it. This is because a short length of air outside the open end of a tube is also set into

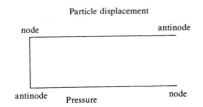

Fig. 8.11 *Standing wave conditions*

vibration. Hence an end correction, of about $0.6 \times$ internal pipe radius, must be added to the length for each open end involved.

A resonance tube can be used to obtain a value for the wavelength of sound in air produced by a tuning fork of known frequency. Hence the speed of sound can be deduced. Using the apparatus shown in Fig. 8.8 the first two resonance positions are found for a particular frequency (corresponding to the upper two diagrams in Fig. 8.9). Hence, for the first resonance condition

$$L_0 + \delta = \tfrac{1}{4}\lambda$$

where δ is the end correction. For the second resonance condition

$$L_1 + \delta = \tfrac{3}{4}\lambda$$

Hence

$$L_1 - L_0 = \tfrac{1}{2}\lambda$$

and so the wavelength can be determined.

The dust tube

Figure 8.12 shows the apparatus known as Kundt's dust tube. This apparatus enables the displacement nodes and antinodes in a gas to be revealed, and hence the wavelength in the gas

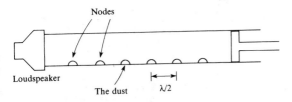

Fig. 8.12 *Kundt's dust tube*

measured. The apparatus consists of a source of sound, often now a loudspeaker but in older forms a brass rod which could be rubbed with a resined cloth until it vibrated, at one end of a horizontal tube. The other end of the tube is closed with a piston which can be moved into the tube to vary its length. Dust, dry lycopodium powder, is placed in the tube and when the length of the tube is 'right' for standing waves the dust settles down into stable patterns, the distance between successive heaps of dust being $\tfrac{1}{2}\lambda$, i.e., the distance between nodes.

Measurement of the speed of sound

A direct method can be used for the speed of sound in air, i.e., measuring the time taken for a sound to cover a measured distance. In a laboratory this could be based on the use of a cathode ray oscilloscope. When the horizontal sweep of the electron beam starts, an electric pulse is produced which can be amplified and fed to a loudspeaker to cause a pulse of sound. A microphone placed some distance away can be used to pick up the sound and feed an electrical signal to the Y-input of the oscilloscope (Fig. 8.13). The result is a blip on the screen. If the microphone is then moved a measured distance further away from the loudspeaker, the position of the blip on the screen moves to a new position. The distance separating these two blip points on the screen can be converted into a time difference using the calibrated time base of the oscilloscope. Hence the speed is the extra distance moved by the microphone divided by the time.

An indirect method involving the measurement of the wavelength of sound in air requires the establishment of standing waves between a loudspeaker and a reflecting screen, Fig. 8.14. Superposition occurs between the waves leaving the speaker and those reflected from the screen. A microphone placed between the loudspeaker and the screen can be used to detect whether a particular position is a node or antinode. One way of obtaining the wavelength is to move the screen to a position where the microphone detects a maximum response. The position of the screen is

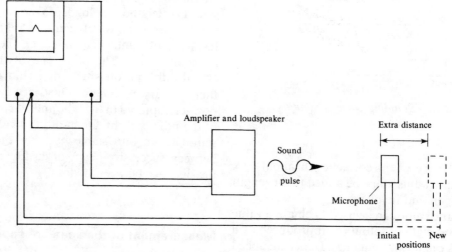

Fig. 8.13 *A direct method for the speed of sound in air*

then noted. The screen is then moved again until the next maximum response is obtained. The distance moved by the screen between these two readings is ½λ. With a known frequency supplied to the loudspeaker, the speed can be calculated, $v = f\lambda$.

The resonance tube and the dust tube experiments, referred to earlier in this chapter, also give an indirect method involving standing waves to obtain a value for the wavelength.

A method that can be used for the measurement of the speed of longitudinal waves in a metal

rod involves determining the time taken for a wave pulse to travel along the length of the rod, be reflected from the far end and then travel back. We can use the analogy of a row of linked trolleys with a solid block, that was used earlier in this chapter, to explain the principles of the method. Figure 8.15 shows four trolleys linked by springs. When they are pushed up against the heavy metal block the timer starts and a compression pulse starts to travel down the row of trolleys. On reaching the free end it reflects as a rarefaction which travels back down the row. On reaching the

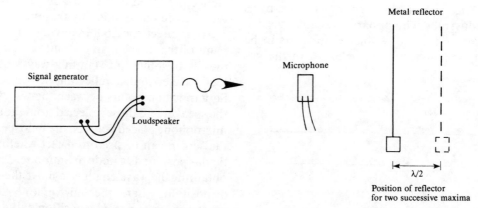

Fig. 8.14 *An indirect method for the speed of sound in air involving standing waves*

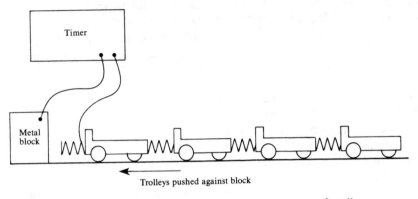

Fig. 8.15 *Timing a longitudinal pulse along a row of trolleys*

block end it pulls the end spring away from the metal block and stops the timer. The timer thus measures the time taken for the longitudinal wave pulse to travel along the row and back again. Figure 8.16 shows the comparable situation for a metal rod. When the hammer hits the end of the metal rod a compression starts to travel down the rod; on reaching the end it is reflected as a rarefaction and when it reaches the hammer end it pulls the rod away from the hammer. During the contact time an electrical circuit can be completed which feeds a signal from a signal generator to an oscilloscope. Thus if the signal generator is set at 25 kHz and the time of contact is such that four complete cycles appear on the oscilloscope screen, then the time of contact is 4 ×

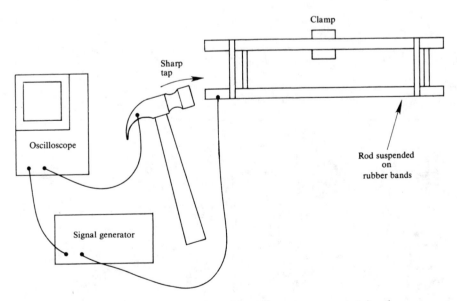

Fig. 8.16 *Timing a longitudinal pulse along a metal rod*

1/25 000 s. The distance travelled in this time is twice the length of the rod. Hence the speed can be calculated.

Beats

When two notes of slightly differing frequencies, but similar amplitudes, are sounded together, the composite sound heard shows periodic rises and falls in loudness. Figure 8.17 shows what happens when two such wave motions are superposed—the amplitude varies in a periodic manner.

The maximum amplitude occurs when the crest of one wave coincides with the crest of the other wave. Zero amplitude occurs when the crest of one wave coincides with the trough of the other. The time elapsing between successive points of maximum and zero amplitudes must be the time taken for the two waves to get out of phase by $\frac{1}{2}\lambda$. Hence the time between successive maxima, or successive zero, amplitudes must be the time

taken for the waves to differ by one wavelength. If this time is T then one sound, frequency f_1, will make $f_1 T$ waves in that time. The other, frequency f_2, will make $f_2 T$ waves. But we must have the difference between these two waves as just one wave. Hence

$$f_2 T - f_1 T = 1$$

$$\frac{1}{T} = f_2 - f_1$$

The beat frequency is the number of times the magnitude of the amplitude reaches a maximum per second. Hence

$$\text{beat frequency} = f_2 - f_1$$

A tuning fork of frequency 520 Hz is sounded at the same time as a violin string is plucked. If the beat frequency heard is 6 Hz, what is the frequency of the violin string? It is not possible to

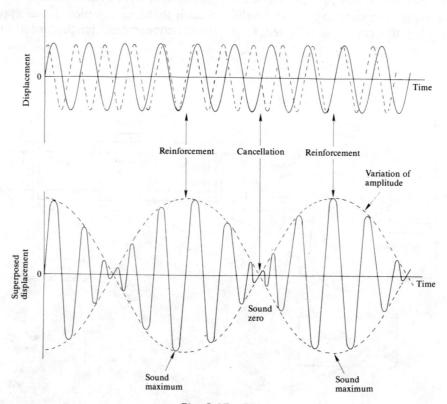

Fig. 8.17 Beats

tell whether the frequency of the violin string is 6 Hz above or below the 520 Hz note, i.e., 526 Hz or 514 Hz. A violinist could determine which was the case by slightly changing the tension of the string. As shown in the previous chapter; reducing the tension would decrease the string frequency. Hence if such a reduction increased the beat frequency, then the string frequency would have been 514 Hz.

The Doppler effect

The Doppler effect is a fairly common every-day occurrence, being concerned with the perceived frequency of a sound by an observer when there is relative motion between the sound source and the observer. Thus the frequency of a car horn is perceived to change as the car approaches and passes you. Similarly, the frequency of the whistle of a train approaching and passing you.

Consider, first, a stationary observer and a moving source of sound. If the source emits sound with a frequency f_s and wave speed c, then the wavelength $\lambda_s = c/f_s$. If the source, and observer, are not moving, then this is the wavelength of the sound perceived by the observer. But if the source is moving towards the observer with a speed v_s, then though f_s waves will be emitted in 1 s with the same speed c, the wave emitted at the beginning of the second will have travelled a distance c but the last wave in the second will only have travelled a distance $(c - v_s)$. Thus f_s waves will have been compressed into a distance of $(c - v_s)$ and so the apparent wavelength λ_0 is $(c - v_s)/f_s$. Hence the observed frequency f_0 is

$$f_0 = \frac{c}{\lambda_0} = \frac{cf_s}{c - v_s}$$

If the source had been moving away from the stationary observer then the waves would have been spread over a greater distance $(c + v_s)$ and so

$$f_0 = \frac{cf_s}{c + v_s}$$

Consider now a moving observer and a stationary source. The source emits waves with a

frequency f_s and speed c. If the observer is moving towards the source with a speed v_0 then the observer will 'gather in' more waves than if he had been stationary. A stationary observer would gather in f_s waves in 1 s. In 1 s, however, the observer will have moved a distance v_0 towards the source and gathered in the extra waves in that distance, i.e., v_0/λ_s. Hence the number of waves gathered in per second, f_0, is

$$f_0 = f_s + \frac{v_0}{\lambda_s}$$

Since $c = f_s\lambda_s$, this equation can be simplified to

$$f_0 = f_s + \frac{v_0 f_s}{c}$$

$$f_0 = f_s\left(1 + \frac{v_0}{c}\right)$$

If the observer had been moving away from the source then fewer waves would have been gathered in per second.

$$f_0 = f_s - \frac{v_0}{\lambda_s}$$

and so

$$f_0 = f_s\left(1 - \frac{v_0}{c}\right)$$

An observer stands by the side of a railway track while a train approaches him at a constant speed of 30 m s^{-1}. If the train is sounding its whistle at a frequency of 500 Hz, what will be the frequencies perceived by the observer as the train (a) approaches, (b) recedes? Take the speed of sound to be 240 m s^{-1}.

As the train approaches then the perceived frequency f_0 is given by

$$f_0 = \frac{cf_s}{c - v_s}$$

$$= \frac{340 \times 500}{340 - 30}$$

$$= 548 \text{ Hz}$$

As the train recedes then the perceived frequency f_0 is given by

$$f_0 = \frac{cf_s}{c + v_s}$$

$$= \frac{340 \times 500}{340 + 30}$$

$$= 459 \text{ Hz}$$

Some terms used in sound

The term *note* is used when there is a periodic waveform which gives pleasant sound. *Noise* is when the sound is not pleasant, the waveform being non-periodic.

Musical notes can be described by *loudness*, *pitch* and *quality*. The human ear responds to pressure variations and loudness assessments depend on the sensitivity of the hearer to the particular note. It is thus a subjective measure. Pitch is also a subjective measure, determining the position of a particular note in the musical scale. This is determined principally by the frequency of the note. A note produced by a musical instrument will generally not be just one single frequency but contain a number of frequencies. It is this mix which determines the quality of a note.

Supplementary material

Ultrasonics in medicine

The term 'ultrasonics' is used for sound with frequencies above 20 kHz, beyond the range of audibility of the human ear. Sources for frequencies at this level are either piezoelectric or magnetostrictive crystals. A piezoelectric crystal has an alternating electric field applied across it (i.e., it is between two plates between which there is an alternating potential difference), the effect of this being to cause the crystal to vibrate and so produce sound. Magnetostrictive crystals exhibit a similar behaviour in a magnetic field.

Because the percentage of ultrasound which is reflected at a boundary depends on the difference in densities of the materials on either side of the boundary, quite small density changes being able to produce significant reflection changes, it can be used like an echo sounder to locate and 'observe' events within the human body. In diagnostic medical work a pulse of ultrasound, produced by a suitable crystal, passes into the body and there suffers reflections from boundaries where density changes occur. The reflections are then picked up by the crystal which operates in the reverse way to when it produced the ultrasound and gives pulses of alternating potential difference for each echo. Then a further pulse is emitted and the process repeated. The echo pulses are fed to a cathode ray oscilloscope and displayed along with the emitting pulse. Hence by use of a calibrated time base the distance of the source of an echo can be determined. The relative size of the echo pulse is a measure of the density change across the reflecting boundary.

Another technique involves the use of a crystal which is moved over the surface of the body. As before, pulses of ultrasound are emitted by the crystal and echoes obtained. However, now the size of the echo pulse is used to control the brightness of the spot on the screen of a cathode ray oscilloscope, the movement of the spot across the screen being determined by the movement of the crystal over the surface of the body. Hence an image of the internal organs in the body can be built up.

Ultrasonics have advantages over X-rays in that, unless very high intensities are used, there are apparently no harmful effects. High intensities can produce large pressure-changes within a very small area and this can cause cavitation, the formation of bubbles of vapour from liquids with these bubbles often collapsing violently. Cell membranes may be ruptured.

The Doppler effect can be used with ultrasound to detect motion within the body, e.g., foetal heart motion. Another application is for the measurement of blood flow rates.

For example, ultrasound of frequency 22 kHz might be used to detect foetal heart motion. If the reflections show a Doppler frequency shift of $+2.84$ Hz and -2.84 Hz and the speed of the sound in human tissues is 1550 m s^{-1}, then we can calculate the velocity of the motion of the heart.

Whenever we have sound from a stationary source reflected by a moving reflector, the easiest way to consider the problem is in terms of the moving image of the source. If the reflector is moving away from the source at a velocity v, then since the reflector moves a distance v in 1 s then the image must move a distance $2v$ and so the image velocity is $2v$. Hence for our stationary observer we have sound being emitted by a moving source with a velocity $2v$. Since

$$f_0 = \frac{cf_s}{c \pm v_s}$$

change in observed frequency $\Delta f = \pm f_0 v_s/c$, the sign depending on whether the source was moving away from or towards the observer. Hence $v_s = 2v = 0.20$ m s^{-1} and so $v = 0.10$ m s^{-1}.

Problems

1. Bats navigate by emitting chirps and judging distance by the time lag between the emission and the returning echo. If a chirp lasts about 2×10^{-3} s with an interval of 7×10^{-2} s between chirps, what is the nearest and furthest distance that a bat can determine? Speed of sound = 340 m s^{-1}.

2. If Young's modulus for a material is 2.0×10^{11} Pa and it has a density of 7.8×10^3 kg m^{-3}, what will be the speed of longitudinal waves in the material?

3. Estimate the force constant for the interatomic forces between the atoms in a block of copper if the speed of a longitudinal wave through copper is 3.8×10^3 m s^{-1}; the interatomic spacing for the copper atoms is 2.5×10^{-10} m and the density of copper is 8930 kg m^{-3}.

4. Estimate the force constant for the interatomic forces between atoms in a block of aluminium if the material has a Young's modulus of 7.0×10^{10} Pa, a relative atomic mass of 27, an interatomic spacing of 2.9×10^{-10} m and the speed of longitudinal waves in aluminium is 5.1×10^3 m s^{-1}.

5. What do you understand by (a) forced vibrations, (b) free vibrations, and (c) resonance?

Illustrate your answer by giving three distinct examples, one for each of (a), (b) and (c).

Explain how a stationary sound wave may be set up in a gas column and how you would demonstrate the presence of nodes and antinodes. State what measurements would be required in order to deduce the speed of sound in air from your demonstration, and show how you would calculate your result.

The speed of sound, c, in an ideal gas is given by the formula $c = \sqrt{(\gamma p/\rho)}$ where p is the pressure, ρ is the density of the gas and γ is a constant. By considering this formula explain the effect of a change in

(i) temperature, and
(ii) pressure, on the speed of sound.

(University of London, Q10, Paper 2, January 1978)

6. Define frequency and explain the term harmonics. How do harmonics determine the quality of a musical note?

It is much easier to hear the sound of a vibrating tuning fork if it is (a) placed in contact with a bench, or (b) held over a certain length of air in a tube. Explain why this is so in both these cases and give two further examples of the phenomenon occurring in (b).

Describe how you would measure the wavelength in the air in a tube of the note emitted by the fork. How would the value obtained be affected by changes in (i) the temperature of the air, and (ii) the pressure of the air?

(University of London, Q10, Paper 2, June 1979)

7. A source of sound of frequency 250 Hz is used with a resonance tube, closed at one end, to measure the speed of sound in air. Strong resonance is obtained at tube lengths of 0.30 m and 0.96 m. Find (a) the speed of sound, (b) the end-correction of the tube.

(University of Cambridge, Q4, Paper 1, December 1979)

8. (a) The equation $y = a \sin 2\pi f(t - x/v)$ which represents a plane progressive wave being propagated with speed v in the positive direction of the x-axis gives the displacement y at time t of a particle from its equilibrium position; this particle is describing simple harmonic motion of

143

frequency f and amplitude a at a distance x from the origin of the coordinates.

Explain what y represents in the case of a longitudinal progressive wave, and show how the oscillations of the particles give rise to a travelling sequence of compressions and rarefactions.

(b) Show how a stationary-wave pattern can be produced. Write down a typical expression for the displacement as a function of x and t of a particle participating in a stationary wave motion.

(c) A cylindrical air-filled pipe is closed at one end and open at the other. Its length is 0.60 m, and the temperature is 15°C.

(i) Show that (starting with the longest) the wavelengths of the stationary-wave patterns that it can support are 2.40 m, 0.80 m, 0.48 m . . ., and add the next member of the sequence. Ignore end corrections.

(ii) Taking the speed of sound in air at 0°C to be 330 m s^{-1}, calculate the corresponding frequencies.

(Oxford Local Examinations, Q9, Paper I, June 1978)

9. (a) The formula for the speed v of sound waves in a gas of density ρ at pressure p is

$$v = \sqrt{\frac{\gamma p}{\rho}}$$

where γ is the ratio of the two principal specific heat capacities.

(i) Show that the speed of sound in any ideal gas is independent of the pressure and proportional to $\sqrt{T}$, where T is the temperature in kelvins.

(ii) Show that, for different gases at the same temperature, the speed of sound is proportional to $\sqrt{(\gamma/M_r)}$, where M_r is the relative molecular mass.

(iii) Discuss briefly the statement that 'sound travels better on a foggy day than on a clear, bright day.'

(iv) Explain why distant sounds are usually more readily audible at night than during the day.

(b) A 'dust tube' 1.8 m long has a fixed plunger at one end and the diaphragm of a variable-frequency sound generator at the other; both ends can be considered as displacement nodes. Taking the speed of sound in air at room temperature to be 340 m s^{-1}, calculate the frequency of the generator when the tube shows three antinodes

(i) if it contains air

(ii) if it contains helium.

(Take the relative molecular mass, M_r, to be 28.8 for air and 4 for helium, and the value of γ to be 1.41 for air and 1.67 for helium.)

(Oxford Local Examinations Board, Q9, Paper I, June 1979)

10. A siren on a building emits sound at a frequency of 1000 Hz. What frequency will be heard by car drivers moving at 20 m s^{-1} (a) towards the siren and (b) away from it? Speed of sound can be taken as 340 m s^{-1}.

11. A train is moving at 35 m s^{-1} and sounding its whistle which has a frequency of 1200 Hz. What is the frequency heard by an observer (a) riding as a passenger on the train, (b) on a bridge overlooking the track when the train is approaching? Take the speed of sound to be 340 m s^{-1}.

12. A source of sound of frequency 1000 Hz is situated near a plane reflecting surface which moves towards the source. If a stationary observer hears beats of frequency 15 Hz, what is the speed of the reflecting surface towards the source? Take the speed of sound to be 340 m s^{-1}.

9 Electromagnetic waves

Interference of light

Interference and diffraction are characteristics of wave motion—has light these characteristics? Two lamps side by side do not seem to give interference patterns, i.e., patches of darkness alternating with light patches; light does not seem to bend round corners but to travel in straight lines and give sharp shadows. With water waves the effects are, however, only noticeable when the two sources are only a matter of a few wavelengths apart or slits or objects are only a few wavelengths wide; perhaps the wavelength of light is very small, or perhaps light is not a wave motion.

Young's experiment

With slits cut with a razor blade or a needle we can observe patterns that look very much like the interference and diffraction patterns produced by water waves. There is, however, one point which is different from water waves—we cannot use two separate sources of light and obtain interference, we must in some way divide the light from one source into two, or more, parts and look for the interference produced between the light from separate parts. The two source interference obtained with water waves can be achieved with light if we put two slits in front of the single source and obtain interference between the light coming from the slits (Fig. 9.1). This experiment is known as Young's experiment as it was first performed by Young in 1803. The maxima (and

minima), i.e., the fringes as they are termed, are farther apart for red light than blue-violet light. This would suggest that light does behave like a wave motion and that the wavelength depends on the colour of the light.

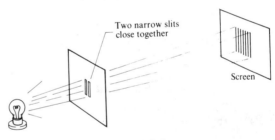

Fig. 9.1

With the two slits there is just one line on the screen for which the light paths from the two slits are equal. This is the central bright fringe, constructive interference occurring. At all other points on the screen there is a path difference between the lengths of the light paths from the two slits. If the path difference is a whole number of wavelengths a bright fringe occurs, if the path difference is an odd number of half wavelengths there is a dark fringe. At any point, for example P in Fig. 9.2, the path difference is $S_2P - S_1P$. Because of the smallness of the wavelength of light the distance D has to be considerably greater than either d or x—we need path differences of the

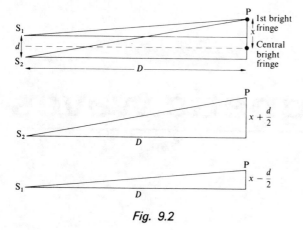

Fig. 9.2

order of the wavelength and small multiples of this.

$$(S_1P)^2 = D^2 + \left(x - \frac{d}{2}\right)^2, \text{ by Pythagoras}$$

$$= D^2 + x^2 - xd + \frac{d^2}{4}$$

$$(S_2P)^2 = D^2 + \left(x + \frac{d}{2}\right)^2$$

$$= D^2 + x^2 + xd + \frac{d^2}{4}$$

$$(S_2P)^2 - (S_1P)^2 = 2xd$$

$$S_2P - S_1P = \frac{2xd}{S_2P + S_1P}$$

But because $D \gg x$ or d

$$S_2P \approx S_1P \approx D$$

Hence path difference $= xd/D = \lambda$, for the first bright fringe. The fringes are equally spaced and $\lambda D/d$ is the spacing between the fringes.

If white light is incident on the two slits then the only position on the screen which will give a bright fringe for all the wavelengths is the centre fringe—no path difference. The central fringe will be white with on either side overlapping fringes for each wavelength in the light.

Consider a Young's double slits experiment with the slits 0.70 mm apart and a distance from the slits to the screen on which the fringes are seen of 0.80 m. If the separation of the fringes is 0.60 mm, what is the wavelength of the monochromatic light used?

$$\lambda = \frac{\text{fringe separation } (x) \times \text{slit separation } (d)}{\text{slits to screen distance } (D)}$$

$$= \frac{0.60 \times 10^{-3} \times 0.70 \times 10^{-3}}{0.80}$$

$$= 5.3 \times 10^{-7} \text{ m}$$

Shifting fringes

With the Young's double slit experiment described by Fig. 9.1 the light from each slit passes through the same medium on its way to the screen. This means that there is a central bright fringe (Fig. 9.2) because the paths from each slit to the central point on the screen are the same, i.e., there is no path difference. However, we can change this by introducing a different material into one of the paths, e.g., a thin piece of glass. The wavelength of light in this medium will be different from that in air and so we need to consider what is referred to as the optical path length rather than the physical path length if we are to determine by how many wavelengths two paths differ.

As indicated in Chapter 7, the refractive index n of a medium in relation to a vacuum (or air as a reasonable approximation) is given by

$$n = \frac{\lambda_a}{\lambda_m}$$

where λ_a is the wavelength in air and λ_m the wavelength in the medium. If the material introduced has a thickness t, then in the absence of it we could have fitted t/λ_a waves in that space but with it we fit t/λ_m. Introducing the material has changed the number of waves fitted into the space by

$$\frac{t}{\lambda_m} - \frac{t}{\lambda_a} = \frac{nt}{\lambda_a} - \frac{t}{\lambda_a} = \frac{(n-1)t}{\lambda_a}$$

The extra path introduced is thus $(n - 1)t$. This

causes the central bright, zero path difference, fringe to shift to a position where this extra path of $(n - 1)t$ is compensated for by an extra physical path length being introduced into the other path, to give a net result of zero optical path difference. This is when

$$\frac{xd}{D} = (n - 1)t$$

The central fringe thus shifts on the screen by a distance x, where

$$x = (n - 1)\frac{tD}{d}$$

Lloyd's mirror

This is essentially the same as the Young's double slit experiment but with the two slits being provided by a single slit and its image in a plane mirror (Fig. 9.3). The light from the slit is incident at an acute angle on a plane glass surface and results in interference fringes in the region where superposition of the direct and reflected light occurs. The effective separation between the slit and its image is twice the distance of the slit from the plane of the reflecting surface.

If the screen on which the fringes are seen is put right up to the reflecting surface, then the fringe at the line where the mirror touches the screen is black. A black fringe indicates that the reflected and direct waves are out of phase by half a wavelength, i.e., π rad. Since at this point there is zero path difference between the direct and reflected waves, this can only mean that there is a phase change of $\frac{1}{2}\lambda$ on reflection.

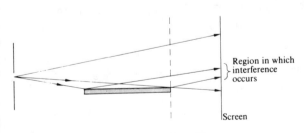

Fig. 9.3 Lloyd's mirror

Thin wedge films

Another way of demonstrating interference with light is to use a thin film to produce a path difference between the light reflected from the top surface of the film and light from the lower surface, as in Fig. 9.4. When the two reflected waves are brought together in the eye or with an optical instrument, superposition occurs.

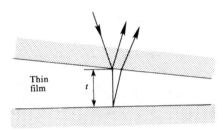

Fig. 9.4 Interference with a thin film

For near normal incidence and films having only a small angle, the physical path difference between the two reflected waves is effectively $2t$. If the thin film has a refractive index n, then the optical path difference is $2nt$ (see earlier in this chapter). For the reflection which takes place at the less to more dense interface (the lower reflection in the figure) a phase change of $\frac{1}{2}\lambda$ occurs. No such phase change takes place at the other reflection, more to less dense interface. The optical path difference, taking account of this phase change, is thus

$$2nt + \frac{1}{2}\lambda$$

Constructive superposition occurs when the optical path difference is a whole number of wavelengths, i.e., 0, 1λ, 2λ, ..., $m\lambda$, m being an integer.

$$2nt + \frac{1}{2}\lambda = m\lambda$$

i.e
$$2nt = (m - \frac{1}{2})\lambda$$

Destructive superposition occurs when the optical path difference is $\lambda/2$, $3\lambda/2$, $5\lambda/2$, ..., $(m + \frac{1}{2})\lambda$.

$$2nt + \frac{1}{2}\lambda = (m + \frac{1}{2})\lambda$$

$$2nt = m\lambda$$

For a wedge-shaped film a series of fringes are produced, each parallel to the line of intersection of the two reflecting surfaces. Where the two surfaces are in contact, i.e., $t = 0$, then there is a dark fringe (because of the phase difference for one of the reflections).

If a wedge-shaped air film has an angle θ as in Fig. 9.5, and we consider two successive bright fringes, then the extra path difference in the film from one fringe to the next must be λ. Since the light traverses the film thickness twice, this means that AB must be $\frac{1}{2}\lambda$. Hence

$$\tan \theta = \frac{\frac{1}{2}\lambda}{s}$$

where s is the horizonal distance between the two fringes. Since θ is very small, this approximates to

$$\theta = \frac{\lambda}{2s}$$

Hence a measurement of the fringe separation for a particular wavelength enables the angle of the air wedge to be determined.

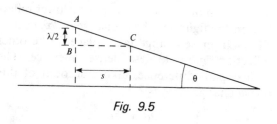

Fig. 9.5

For example, if a wedge-shaped air film is produced between two glass plates illuminated normally by monochromatic light of wavelength 5.8×10^{-7} m and the separation of bright fringes is found to be 0.24 mm, the angle of the wedge is

$$\theta = \frac{5.8 \times 10^{-7}}{2 \times 0.24 \times 10^{-3}}$$

$$= 1.2 \times 10^{-3} \text{ rad}$$

The colours of soap films

The colours of a thin soap film are an example of thin film interference. Where for a particular wavelength the thickness of the film is just right to give destructive interference, then that particular wavelength is not present in the reflected light. The result is that the film assumes the colour of white light minus that wavelength. Thus a vertical soap film which is thicker at the bottom than the top, because of the soap solution draining to the bottom, will show a gradual change in colour from the top down the film. The film when very thin at the top appears black. This is because the optical path difference is due just to the phase change that occurs at one of the reflections, the physical path difference being effectively zero.

Newton's rings

When a convex lens is placed on a flat glass surface a series of concentric interference fringes are produced, these being called Newton's rings. The fringes occur because the light reflected from the inside lower surface of the convex lens interferes with the light reflected at the air-to-flat-glass boundary (Fig. 9.6), the arrangement producing a wedge-shaped air film. The fringes trace out the lines of constant height, bright fringes occurring wherever we have $2nt = (m - \frac{1}{2})\lambda$. The centre of the ring pattern is black, i.e., there is no reflection. This is because though the air film thickness is zero there is a phase change of $\frac{1}{2}\lambda$ occurring at the air-to-flat-glass boundary but not at the other film boundary.

If r_m is the radius of the mth dark fringe (Fig. 9.7) and t_m the thickness of the air film at that point, then if we use the theorem of insecting chords

$$r_m^2 = (2R - t_m)t_m$$

Since t_m is considerably smaller than R, this approximates to

$$r_m^2 = 2Rt_m$$

But the condition for there to be a dark fringe at this point is

$$2t_m + \frac{1}{2}\lambda = (m + \frac{1}{2})\lambda$$

$$2t_m = m\lambda$$

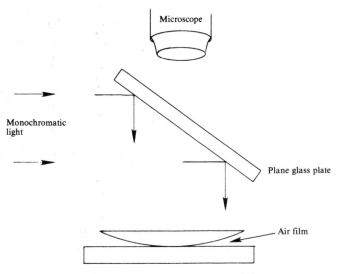

Fig. 9.6   *Experimental arrangement for Newton's rings*

where m is an integer. Hence we can write

$$\frac{2r_{m}^2}{2R} = m\lambda$$

$$r_{m}^2 = R\lambda m$$

Since the actual measurement made on the fringes is of their diameter, $d_m = 2r_m$, then

$$d_{m}^2 = (4R\lambda)m$$

On the basis of measurements of ring diameters using this equation, the number m being counted out from the centre, and a lens of known radius of

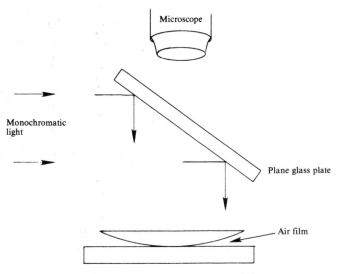

Fig. 9.7

curvature, the wavelength of the light can be determined. Since there is difficulty in counting fringes near the centre of the ring pattern, a number of ring diameters are measured and a graph plotted of d_{m}^2 against m, the slope being $4R\lambda$. If there is an error in the value of m it does not affect the value of the slope but purely the intercept of the straight line graph with the m-axis.

To illustrate the type of calculation involved in obtaining a wavelength from a ring measurement, consider a lens with a radius of curvature of 1.00 m resting on a flat glass plate. If the 10th ring has a diameter of 4.85 mm, then

$$\lambda = \frac{d_{m}^3}{4Rm} = \frac{(4.85 \times 10^{-3})^2}{4 \times 1.00 \times 10}$$

$$= 5.88 \times 10^{-7} \text{ m}$$

Blooming lenses

Surfaces can be made non-reflecting, for one wavelength, by coating them with a thin layer of a transparent material. The thickness of the material must be such that the light reflected from the front surface of the film destructively interferes with

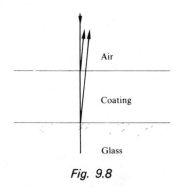

Fig. 9.8

that from the rear surface (Fig. 9.8). This will occur when the material coating the surface has a refractive index intermediate between that of the glass, if a glass surface is being coated, and air. It is assumed that the surface is in air. The first reflection is at an air-to-coating interface, i.e., less to more optically dense, and thus a phase change occurs. The second reflection occurs at the coating-to-glass interface, i.e., less to more optic-ally 'dense', and thus a phase change occurs. The two phase changes are the same and thus destruc-tive interference occurs when the coating thick-ness is $\lambda/4$, a path difference of $\lambda/2$ between the two reflected rays. For the destruction to be complete the two reflected rays must be of equal intensity. This can be achieved by making the ref-ractive index of the coating equal to the square root of the refractive index of the glass.

Camera lenses are coated to reduce the amount of light reflected at the lens surfaces and so give more light transmitted through to the film surface; interference conditions giving zero re-flection give maximum transmission, and vice versa—energy is conserved. The coating is known as 'blooming'. Such lenses have a purplish hue by reflected light because the coating has a thickness which gives destructive interference only for one wavelength and this is chosen near the centre of the visible spectrum; the light being reflected is thus, in the main, the red and the blue.

The conditions for interference

The term interference is used for the superposi-tion of waves from a finite number of coherent

sources. Coherent sources have the same fre-quency and a constant phase difference (if not zero) between them. In addition the waves from the different sources must have roughly the same amplitudes. With transverse waves they must either be unpolarized or have comparable com-ponents in the same plane.

Two separate lamps as light sources will not show interference because of a lack of coherence, the phase difference between them varying in a random manner. For this reason a single source is used and then divided in some way to give effec-tively two identical sources. Young's double slit experiment is said to achieve this by a division of wavefront; thin film interference achieves it by a division of amplitude.

Diffraction of light

Light shows diffraction effects similar to those obtained with water waves. Figure 9.9 shows the diffraction effects from (a) 1 slit, (b) 2 slits, (c) 3 slits, (d) 4 slits, (e) 5 slits and (f) 6 slits, when illuminated with plane waves of a single fre-quency. An immediate point that is noticeable from the photographs is that the positions of the maxima, where more than one slit is involved, do not change as the number of slits increases but the sharpness of the maxima increases. The intensities of all the maxima are governed by the diffraction pattern of the single slit (Fig. 9.10). The fringe maxima all lie within the maxima of the single slit diffraction pattern.

Diffraction at a single slit

Consider first the single slit diffraction pattern. Each point on the wavefront in the slit, width b, can be considered as a source of waves (Fig. 9.11). These waves will interfere. Will there be a maximum, constructive interference, or a mini-mum, destructive interference, in a direction making an angle θ to the axis? For the light coming from the extreme edges of the slit, at this angle θ, there is a path difference of $b \sin \theta$, plane waves are incident on the slit. Light from a point half way along the slit will have a path difference of $(b/2) \sin \theta$ from the light coming from the two

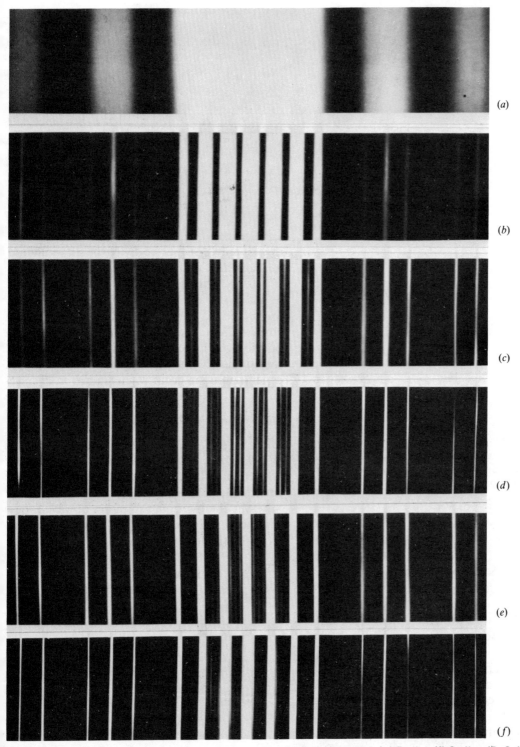

Fig. 9.9 Diffraction at slits: (a) 1 slit, (b) 2 slits, (c) 3 slits, (d) 4 slits, (e) 5 slits, (f) 6 slits. (R. S. Longhurst (1957), Geometrical and Physical Optics, *Longman)*

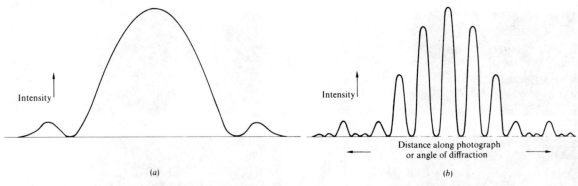

Fig. 9.10 Diffraction pattern (a) single slit (b) two slits

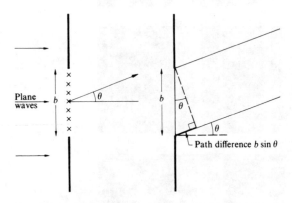

Fig. 9.11 Diffraction at a single slit. (a) Each point marked X represents a secondary source of waves. (b) For the light from secondary sources at each extremity of the slit the path difference is b sin θ

the two halves of a slit we divide the slit width into quarters and find the condition for destructive interference between the light from comparable points in two quarters then we obtain the angle for the second minimum, i.e., $(b/4) \sin \theta = \lambda/2$ or $\sin \theta = 2\lambda/b$. The third destructive interference position can be found by dividing the slit width into sixths, $(b/6) \sin \theta = \lambda/2$ or $\sin \theta = 3\lambda/b$. In general, minima occur when $\sin \pi = m\lambda/b$.

Diffraction at multiple slits

With two slits, each of width b, a distance d apart (Fig 9.12) the problem is much the same as the single slit diffraction. We have to consider the interference, at a particular diffraction angle, due to waves coming from two pieces of wavefront a distance d apart instead of immediately adjacent as in the single slit. The light coming from each

edges of the slit. What happens if $(b/2) \sin \theta = \lambda/2$? Light from half way along the slit will give destructive interference with light from the bottom of the slit. In fact for every point in the bottom half of the slit there is a point in the top half of the slit a distance $(b/2) \sin \theta$ from it. So when $(b/2) \sin \theta = \lambda/2$ there is destructive interference between points in the lower part of the slit and comparable points in the upper half of the slit. There will thus be a central maximum, because it is the same distance from comparable points in the lower and upper parts of the slit, and the first minimum will occur when $\sin \theta = \lambda/b$.

If instead of finding the condition for destructive interference between comparable points in

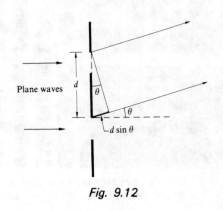

Fig. 9.12

slit will separately give the single slit diffraction pattern and so we can look for interference between the light emerging from the slits in the single slit maxima. For diffraction angles less than those given by $\sin \theta = \lambda/b$ we can get interference between the light coming from the two slits. At angles less than this, destructive interference will occur when $d \sin \theta = m\lambda/2$. Light from the top of the upper slit destructively interferes with that from the top of the lower slit; light from comparable points in the lower slit destructively interferes with light from comparable points in the upper slit. Constructive interference occurs for angles given by $d \sin \theta = m\lambda$; central maximum when $m = 0$, first maximum when $m = 1$, etc. This condition for maxima is equivalent to that obtained for Young's slits, i.e., fringe spacing $\lambda D/d$.

With three slits the same conditions will occur. When there is constructive interference between the light from the top two slits, then at the same angle there will be constructive interference from the middle slit and the lower slit (Fig. 9.13). Thus the first maximum occurs when $d \sin \theta = \lambda$. With two slits there was only one point between this maximum and the central maximum when the light from the two slits cancelled. With three slits, if the path difference between the top two slits is $\lambda/2$ destructive interference occurs between the light from those slits; the third slit will, however, have a path difference of λ from the light coming through the upper slit and thus the intensity will

be reduced but not to zero for $d \sin \theta = \lambda/2$. Destructive interference in fact occurs when $d \sin \theta = \lambda/3$ and when $d \sin \theta = 2\lambda/3$. Between the zero maximum and the first maximum there appears a low intensity maximum, at $\sin \theta = \lambda/(2d)$, and two minima. The effect of this is to give sharper maxima.

Increasing the number of slits does not change the positions of the main maxima, they still occur for $d \sin \theta = \lambda$. Between this maximum and the zero maximum there are, however, many more angles for which destructive interference occurs— the result is very sharp maxima.

The diffraction grating

With very large numbers of slits, the arrangement is generally called a diffraction grating. Very sharp maxima are produced. The condition for maxima with slits, equally spaced with separation d between successive slits, on which plane waves are incident along the normal is

$$d \sin \theta = m\lambda$$

where m has the value 0, 1, 2, 3, 4, etc. The $m = 0$ condition is when $\theta = 0$ and the light from every slit follows the same path length to the maximum. This is called the zero order maximum. When $m = 1$ we have $d \sin \theta = \lambda$; there is a path difference of λ between the path lengths from successive slits. This is called the first order maximum. When $m = 2$ we have the second order maximum, the path difference being 2λ between successive slits.

The angle at which the maxima are formed depends on the wavelength of the light. Thus if white light is incident on the grating, each maximum, with the exception of the zero order, appears as a spectrum. Diffraction gratings are much used in spectroscopy because of this ability to spread light out into a spectrum.

Consider a plane diffraction grating which has 600 slits per millimetre and is illuminated with light of wavelength 5.89×10^{-7} m.

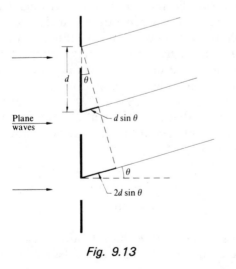

Fig. 9.13

$$d = \frac{1}{600 \times 10^3} \text{ m}$$

153

Hence the first-order maximum occurs when

$$\frac{1}{600 \times 10^3} \sin \theta = 1 \times 5.89 \times 10^{-7}$$

$$\theta = 20.7°$$

The second-order maximum occurs when

$$\frac{1}{600 \times 10^{-3}} \sin \theta = 2 \times 5.89 \times 10^{-7}$$

$$\theta = 45.0°$$

Diffraction by many apertures

We do not need to have slits to show diffraction and interference effects; any shaped aperture will do. Figure 9.14a shows the pattern resulting from

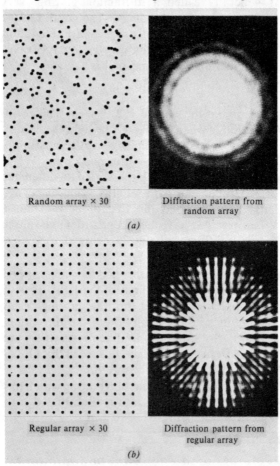

Random array × 30

Diffraction pattern from random array

(a)

Regular array × 30

Diffraction pattern from regular array

(b)

Fig. 9.14 (Harvard Apparatus Limited)

a random array of small circular holes—the pattern is a series of concentric circles. This is the pattern you see if you view a street lamp through a mist—a halo pattern. Figure 9.14b shows the diffraction pattern if the holes are in a regular array. The circular pattern has broken down into discrete maxima.

Resolving power

When light passes through an aperture we obtain a diffraction pattern instead of sharply defined images. The aperture could be the objective lens of a telescope or a microscope. If we have two objects we will obtain two diffraction patterns. How close can these patterns be for us to say that there are two objects and not just one? The patterns will overlap and we will see the combined effect of both. There will not generally be interference between the two lots of diffracted light because they come from different objects or parts of an object. Figure 9.15 shows the diffraction patterns from three point sources produced by lenses of different diameters. As the diameter of the lens increases the resolution improves. Rayleigh suggested a resolution criterion—two sources are resolved if the central maximum from one diffraction pattern falls no nearer than the first minimum of the other pattern. Figure 9.16 shows this position. Looking at the photographs of the point sources makes this seem a reasonable criterion.

For slits the first minimum is at an angle θ given by $\sin \theta = \lambda/b$, where b is the width of the slit. If the light from two objects passes through a slit the minimum angle between their two central maxima at which resolution occurs is thus given by $\sin \theta = \lambda/b$. If circular holes are used instead of slits the angle is given by $\sin \theta = 1.22 \, \lambda/b$. The pupil of the eye has a diameter of about 3 mm and thus for visible light the minimum angle of resolution for the eye is

$$\sin \theta = \frac{1.22 \times 5 \times 10^{-7}}{3 \times 10^{-3}} = 0.000\,20$$

This is about 50 seconds. Optical defects in the eye do not enable this limit to be achieved.

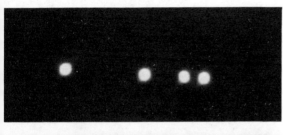

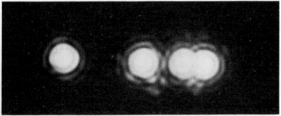

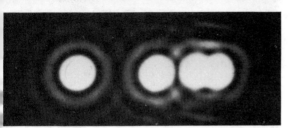

Fig. 9.15 Diffraction pattern from three point sources produced by lenses of different diameters. (F. W. Sears and M. W. Zemansky (1960), College Physics, *3rd edn, Addison-Wesley)*

The Jodrell Bank radiotelescope has a paraboloidal mirror about 80 m in diameter. At a radio wavelength of 0.2 m the minimum angle of resolution is

$$\sin \theta = \frac{1.22 \times 0.2}{80} = 0.003\ 05$$

This large telescope is not as good for resolving radio sources as the eye is for resolving light sources.

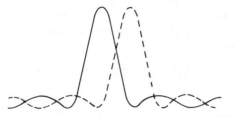

Fig. 9.16 Diffraction patterns due to two sources

Polarization

A transverse wave motion differs from a longitudinal wave motion in that there are many possible directions for the particle displacement with a transverse wave, all at right angles to the wave direction (Fig. 9.17), whereas there is only one possible direction for a longitudinal wave. Light is a transverse wave motion.

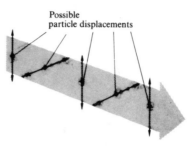

Fig. 9.17 An unpolarized transverse wave

The idea of the transverse wave nature of light arose from experiments with calcite crystals, known as Iceland Spa. Bartholinus reported in 1669 that this crystal exhibited double refraction, i.e., two refracted rays are produced from just one incident ray. One of the refracted rays was found to obey the 'normal' laws of refraction, i.e., the incident ray, the refracted ray and the normal were all in the same plane and the ratio $\sin i/\sin r$ was a constant; the other ray did not and was thus called the 'extraordinary' ray. The explanation of this effect had, however, to wait until early in the 19th century.

Unpolarized light contains all possible particle displacements. Since we can resolve particle displacements into two directions at right angles to each other, it is customary to consider unpolarized light to be two particle displacement components at right angles to each other (Fig. 9.18). When double refraction occurs the initially unpolarized light is divided by the refraction process into two components which are plane polarized at right angles to each other (Fig. 9.19). Plane polarized light contains only one mode of particle displacement.

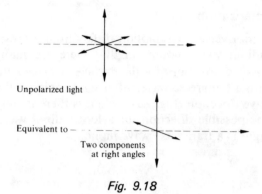

Unpolarized light

Equivalent to

Two components
at right angles

Fig. 9.18

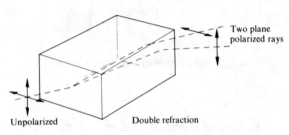

Two plane
polarized rays

Unpolarized

Double refraction

Fig. 9.19   Double refraction

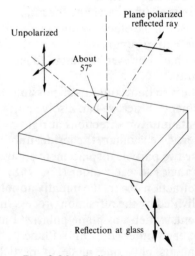

Unpolarized

Plane polarized
reflected ray

About
57°

Reflection at glass

Fig. 9.20   Reflection at glass

When unpolarized light is reflected from a glass, or other dielectric, surface the reflected and transmitted rays are plane polarized for one particular angle of incidence (Fig. 9.20), about 57° for glass. This condition occurs when the angle between the reflected and refracted rays is 90° (Fig. 9.21).

$$\text{refractive index } n = \frac{\sin i}{\sin r}$$

$$= \frac{\sin i}{\sin(90 - i)}$$

$$= \frac{\sin i}{\cos i}$$

$$= \tan i$$

This angle is known as Brewster's angle.

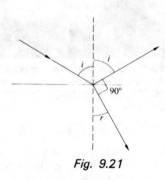

Fig. 9.21

In 1852 Herapath discovered that crystals of iodo-quinine sulphate transmitted just one plane of polarization, absorbing other planes. In 1938 Land, while still an undergraduate at Harvard, used this discovery of Herapath to produce the material now known as 'Polaroid'. Land, instead of trying to produce large crystals of the very fragile iodo-quinine sulphate, made a material with large numbers of small crystals all aligned in the same direction. The manufacturing process is briefly

a sheet of plastic consisting of long hydrocarbon chains is stretched to line up the molecules;

the sheet is dipped in iodine, iodine atoms becoming attached to the hydrocarbon chains;

the result is chains of crystals absorbing all but one plane of polarization.

If unpolarized light is incident on a sheet of 'Polaroid' the transmitted light is plane polarized. If a second sheet of 'Polaroid' is placed in the path of the plane polarized light, then no light is passed if the crystal axes of the second 'Polaroid' are at right angles to those of the first 'Polaroid'. If the crystal axes of the two 'Polaroids' are parallel, light emerges from the second 'Polaroid'. Plane polarized light only passes through a 'Polaroid' if the crystal axes are in the correct direction for that plane (Fig. 9.22).

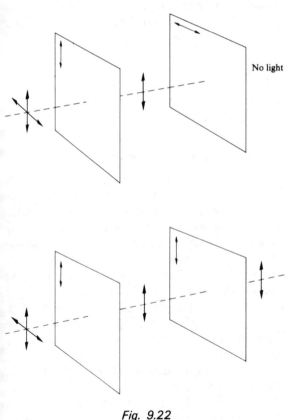

No light

Fig. 9.22

Photoelasticity

A piece of normally transparent material, such as 'Sellotape', placed between a pair of 'Polaroids' or other polarizers and viewed in white light appears coloured. Materials which show this property are those which show double refraction. Some materials are made doubly refracting when subject to stress. In double refraction two refracted rays at different angles of refraction are produced— there must therefore be two refractive indices. This means that the two refracted components travel at different speeds through the material. In passing through the material one ray will get ahead of the other by an amount depending on the difference in refractive indices and the thickness of the material. The second 'Polaroid' brings together the components of the two refracted rays that lie in one direction, and interference occurs between these two components. Thus if the 'path difference' produced by the different speeds is such as to give destructive interference for blue light, then the resulting colour is white minus blue, an orange colour.

'Sellotape' and many of the transparent wrapping materials have their molecules lined up. Plane polarized light incident at an angle to these lines of molecules splits up into two vibrations, along the line of the molecules and at right angles to it. These two rays travel with different speeds. Some of the transparent materials have their molecules all tangled up and do not show this effect until the material is stressed, causing the molecules to line up.

An application of this effect is in polarizing microscopes to heighten the contrast between the different parts of what might otherwise be a colourless specimen. Another application is in stress analysis of structures. Models of the structure are made in a material which becomes doubly refracting under stress. The difference in the two speeds of light in the specimen depends on the amount of stress. Thus the colour seen at a particular point when the specimen is between 'Polaroids' is a measure of the stress at that point. This is known as photoelasticity.

Optical rotation

Certain crystals and certain liquids when put between 'Polaroids' rotate the plane of polarization of light. Quartz and sodium chlorate crystals are typical examples of what are termed optically active crystals. A few millimetres thickness of such crystals will rotate the plane of polarization many degrees. Quartz or sodium chlorate in solution is not optically active—no rotation of the plane of polarization occurs. The rotating or twisting ability of quartz and sodium chlorate must arise from the arrangement of the atoms within the crystal. Spirals (or helices) of copper wire placed in a beam of plane polarized microwaves will rotate the plane of polarization. The spirals should be about 1 cm long, about 0.5 cm diameter and contain about three turns of wire. Right-handed spirals rotate the plane in a right-handed (clockwise) direction, left-handed spirals in a left-handed (anticlockwise) manner. Sodium chlorate and quartz crystals can be obtained in both left-handed and right-handed rotation forms. Perhaps optically active crystals have spiral-shaped conducting paths because of the arrangement of their atoms in the crystal structure.

Certain organic substances show optical rotation when they are in solution. There is no crystal lattice this time to give rotation but only the molecule; the rotation must come from the arrangement of the atoms within the molecule. Copper spheres arranged in an asymmetric way can give rotation of the plane of polarization of microwaves. An asymmetric arrangement of atoms in a molecule can give rotation of the plane of polarization.

The early work on this was done by Pasteur. He knew that tartaric acid obtained from grapes and other fruits was optically active. Tartaric acid in another form called racemic acid was not optically active even though otherwise it had precisely the same chemical and physical properties. Pasteur found that crystals of the tartaric acid obtained from fruit were all asymmetrical in the same way but crystals prepared from racemic acid contained two forms of asymmetrical crystal, one form the same as that of tartaric acid from fruit. Pasteur separated the two forms of crystals and made two solutions. One of the solutions rotated the plane of polarization to the left, the other rotated it to the right. Racemic acid was normally made up of equal numbers of left-handed and right-handed molecules and thus there was no net rotation of the plane of polarization. Tartaric acid molecules can thus exist in two forms, one being a mirror image of the other. In later work Pasteur found that moulds growing in racemic acid destroyed all the tartaric molecules of one form but left the other form untouched. The living organism 'fed' on only one form of asymmetric molecule.

Most organic substances found in living things are optically active; the same substances prepared in the laboratory are generally not active. Living things seem to like asymmetry. Our bodies seem to prefer the left-hand form of asymmetry. The left-hand form of compounds generally affect us more strongly than the right-handed forms. The left-hand form of nicotine occurs in cigarettes made from tobacco plants and has a much greater effect on man than the artificially produced right-hand form of nicotine.

Further reading

M. Gardner (1967) *The Ambidextrous Universe* Penguin.

The scattering of light by particles

How is light affected when reflected by small isolated particles? If we examine the light reflected by, say, the suspension of fine particles produced by putting a drop of milk in water or by looking at the sky we find that the reflected light is partially plane polarized. Try looking at the sky through 'Polaroid' sun glasses—try rotating the glasses. The maximum polarization is found in a direction at right angles to the incident light (Fig. 9.23a). If multiple scattering did not occur the light in this direction would be completely plane polarized.

Light can only consist of transverse oscillations, thus when an unpolarized wave meets a scattering centre the only planes which can be reflected in a direction at right angles to the incident light are just one plane — the other planes would have to be reflected as longitudinal oscillations and this is not possible (Fig. 9.23b).

The degree of scattering of light by small particles is proportional to the fourth power of the frequency of the light. For this reason the scattered light from the sky is blue, blue having a

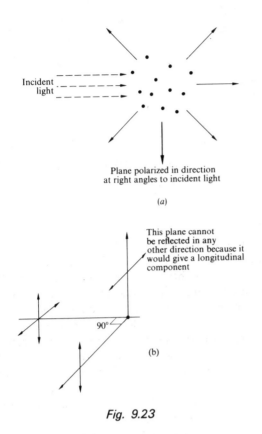

Incident light

Plane polarized in direction
at right angles to incident light

(a)

This plane cannot
be reflected in any
other direction because it
would give a longitudinal
component

90°

(b)

Fig. 9.23

the point in the sky you look at. The scattered blue light is, however, partially polarized, the angle of the polarization depending on the time of day and the point in the sky considered. Bees are able to use this partial polarization for direction finding. The bee has compound eyes, each eye consisting of some 2500 separate eyes, with each having its own lens. Each lens can excite eight vision cells, four being sensitive to light with a plane in one direction and the other four being sensitive to light with a plane at right angles to this direction. This sensitivity to a particular plane of polarization is produced by the substance responsible for converting the light into nerve signals being arranged in tubes, stacked in piles. In each pile all the tubes are stacked in the same direction. Just two sorts of pile exist, the tubes in these piles being at right angles to each other.

Measurement of the speed of light

The first successful measurement of the speed of light was based on data Römer obtained in 1676. He realized that the apparently variable times elapsing between successive passages of one of Jupiter's moons behind the planet could be explained by light having a finite speed. Essentially the problem is—a light flashing at a constant frequency and an observer moving in one instance towards it and in another instance away from it. The apparent frequency of the light will be less than the actual frequency as the earth (observer) moves towards Jupiter (the light) and greater when the earth moves away from Jupiter.

The observer sees the distant light at time T'_1 and again at time T'_2. To him the interval between the two flashes is $T'_2 - T'_1$. However, he realizes that he has moved closer to the source in the interval between his receiving the two flashes. If his speed along the line to the source is v then he reckons that he has moved a distance $v(T'_2 - T'_1)$ in the time interval. Because light travels at a speed c, the observer reckons that his time interval $(T'_2 - T'_1)$ is lower than it would have been if he were stationary by the time taken for the light to travel this distance, i.e., a time of

higher frequency and thus being more scattered than the red. This is true for particles whose size is less than the wavelength of the incident light. Only under this condition can the scattered light be all in phase when reflected. For bigger particles the different parts of the particle will scatter at different times such that path differences are produced which can give rise to destructive interference. Thus for very small particles whose size is less than the wavelength of blue light the predominant colour scattered is blue; for particles whose size is larger than the wavelength of blue light and less than that of red light some blue and a significant amount of red and other colours are scattered; for particles larger than the wavelength of red light the scattering becomes almost independent of wavelength and the scattered light appears white, hence clouds appear white.

When you gaze up at the sky the blue may seem to be much the same whatever the time of day or

159

$(v/c)(T_2' - T_1')$. He therefore reckons that the actual time interval, at the source, must be

$$(T_2' - T_1') + \frac{v}{c}(T_2' - T_1')$$

or

$$t = t'(1 + v/c)$$

t is the observer's estimate of the time interval at the source, t' is his measured time interval.

If the source emits the flashes at a regular rate then we can write the equation in terms of frequencies

$$f' = f(1 + v/c)$$

This is known as the Doppler equation. As an observer moves towards a source emitting a constant frequency light (or sound) the apparent frequency rises.

Romer's data gave a value of about 214 000 km s^{-1} for the speed of light. The idea that light had a finite speed and was not instantaneous was not immediately accepted by all. Universal acceptance of the finite speed did not come until about 1727 when Bradley obtained a similar value by a different method, the aberration of light.

Bradley was the third Astronomer Royal in England and over a period of years had noticed that the positions of some stars appeared to change. He first thought that these changes were due to errors of observation but later noticed that the changes were regular and were related to the time of year when the observation was made. Figure 9.24 shows the apparent movement of the star γ Draconis in the north–south direction, taken from Bradley's paper. Bradley's explanation of the effect was that the apparent direction of the light reaching the earth from a star is altered by the velocity of the earth in its orbit. The observer and his telescope are carried along with the earth in its orbital motion. Think of the light from the star as rain falling on you. If the rain falls vertically and you are still you can stop the rain reaching your head by holding an umbrella over your head. If, however, you run then your umbrella has to be tilted to stop the rain falling on your head (Fig. 9.25a). If in Fig. 9.25b your head moves through a distance AB in the time a

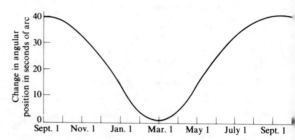

Fig. 9.24 Taken from Bradley, Phil. Trans. Roy. Soc., **35**, 637, 1729

drop of rain covers the distance CB, then the drop at C will hit your head instead of the drop at D. To stop the rain hitting your head your umbrella must be along a line AC instead of AD. To keep the image of a star lined up with the crosswires in a telescope, when the telescope is moving, it must be tilted. Light entering the objective of the telescope moves with a speed c towards the crosswires; the crosswires, however, are moving with a speed v at right angles (near enough if the star is directly overhead) to the light path. If the light takes a time t to travel from the objective to the crosswires, then the crosswires will have moved a distance vt while the light travels a distance ct. The telescope must be tilted at an angle of

$$\tan \alpha = \frac{vt}{ct} = \frac{v}{c} \qquad \text{(Fig. 9.25c).}$$

Bradley found that the angle changed by about 40 seconds for any two points on the earth's orbit six months apart. Figure 9.26 shows the situation from the point of view of the man running in a circular orbit in the rain. The earth 'runs' round its orbit with a speed of about 30 km s^{-1}. Thus we have

$$\tan 20'' = \frac{30}{c}$$

$\tan 20''$ is about 0.001 and thus c is about 300 000 km s^{-1}.

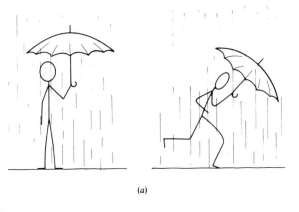

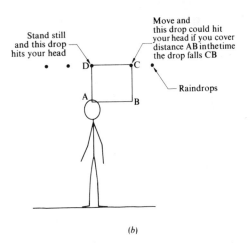

(b)

(a)

Objective

α

ct

Positions of
crosswires

vt

(c)

Fig. 9.25

Fig. 9.26

The first terrestrial method for the speed of light was by Fizeau in 1849 (Fig. 9.27, page 162). Essentially his method consisted in sending a pulse of light to a distant mirror and back again and determining the time taken. A rotating toothed wheel was used to produce brief pulses of light. The pulses then passed to the distant mirror and back again to the toothed wheel. If the wheel had rotated sufficiently the pulse could arrive back in time to hit the next tooth on the wheel and so no light passes onto the eye of the observer. Thus the observer gradually increases the speed of rotation of the toothed wheel until he sees the light is eclipsed. He then knows that in the time taken for the wheel to rotate by the amount from one gap between teeth to the next tooth the light has travelled to the distant mirror and back again. Fizeau's wheel had 720 teeth and it revolved at 12.6 revolutions per second to give the first eclipse position. The distance between the wheel and the distant mirror was 8.6 km. Fizeau's results gave a value for the speed of light of 312 000 km s^{-1}. Improvements in the apparatus and technique led to further results of greater accuracy, a value of 299 901 ± 84 km s^{-1} being obtained by Perrotin, using this method, at the beginning of the twentieth century.

In 1834 Wheatstone suggested an alternative method for determining the time taken for a pulse

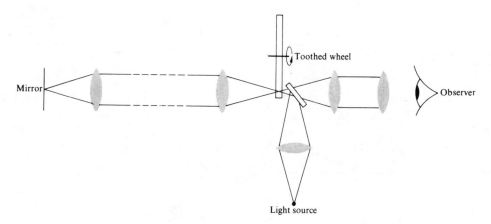

Fig. 9.27 Fizeau's experimental arrangement

of light to traverse a distance. If a beam of light is reflected from a mirror to a distant mirror and then back again, the final image appears at a certain place in the field of view of an eyepiece (Fig. 9.28). If the first mirror rotates, then only pulses of light will be reflected at the right angle to go to the distant mirror. These pulses will be reflected back by the distant mirror and reach the rotating mirror after a short time interval. The result of this will be to displace the image position from the position it occupied when the mirror was stationary. The method was improved by Arago (1850) and Foucault. In 1862 Foucault obtained the value of 298 000 $\pm$ 500 km s^{-1}.

Newcomb in 1880 modified Foucault's method by replacing the rotating plane mirror by a rotating polygon mirror. Instead of looking for the displacement of the image position due to the rotation of the plane mirror during the finite time taken for the light to travel to a distant mirror and back, Newcomb looked for no displacement of the image—one face of his polygon mirror having exactly replaced the previous face during the time taken for the light to go to the distant mirror and back. Michelson, together with Newcomb, made many measurements using polygon mirrors. Four, eight, twelve, and sixteen-sided mirrors were used in their various determinations (Fig. 9.29).

Radio waves

In 1888 Hertz produced a spark between the terminals of the secondary of an induction coil (an induction coil is essentially a transformer in which a large e.m.f. is induced in the secondary turns as a result of applying an interrupted d.c. pulse to the primary instead of a.c.) and a short distance away a spark occurred in a gap in another, isolated loop of wire. Something had passed from the spark gap of the induction coil, the transmitter, to the spark gap of the loop, the receiver (Fig. 9.30). Radio was born.

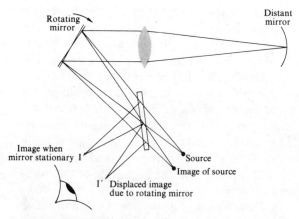

Fig. 9.28 Foucault's experimental arrangement

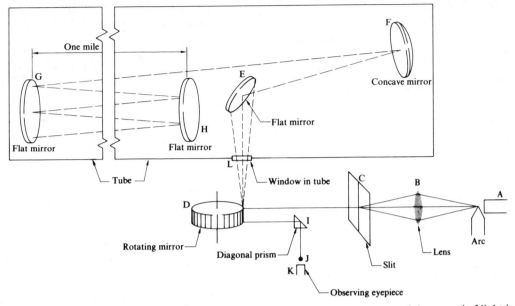

Fig. 9.29   *The arrangement used by Michelson in 1935 for the measurement of the speed of light in an evacuated tube. The mirror D has 32 sides*

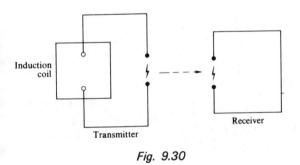

Fig. 9.30

Hertz rapidly determined the properties of this new radiation. The following extracts are taken from his work.

'Rectilinear propagation

If a screen of sheet zinc 2 metres high and 1 metre broad is placed on the straight line joining both mirrors [the source spark gap and the detecting (secondary) spark gap were at the focal points of cylindrical mirrors], and at right angles to the direction of the ray, the secondary sparks disappear completely. An equally complete shadow is thrown by a screen of tinfoil or

gold paper. If an assistant walks across the path of the ray, the secondary spark-gap becomes dark as soon as he intercepts the ray, and again lights up when he leaves the path clear. Insulators do not stop the ray—it passes right through a wooden partition or door. . .

There is no sharp geometical limit to either the ray or the shadows; it is easy to produce phenomena corresponding to diffraction. . . .

Polarization

From the mode in which our ray was produced we can have no doubt whatever that it consists of transverse vibrations and is plane-polarized in the optical sense. We can also prove by experiment that this is the case. If the receiving mirror be rotated about the ray as axis until its focal line, and therefore the secondary conductor also, lies in a horizontal plane, the secondary sparks become more and more feeble, and when the two focal lines are at right angles, no sparks whatever are obtained even if the mirrors are moved close up to one another. . . .

163

I next had made an octagonal frame, 2 metres high and 2 metres broad; across this were stretched copper wires 1 mm thick, the wires being parallel to each other and 3 cm apart. If the two mirrors were now set up with their focal lines parallel, and the wire screen was interposed perpendicularly to the ray and so that the direction of the wires was perpendicular to the direction of the focal lines, the screen practically did not interfere at all with the secondary sparks. But if the screen was set up in such a way that its wires were parallel to the focal lines, it stopped the ray completely. . . .

Reflection

. . . I allowed the ray to pass parallel to the wall of the room in which there was a doorway. In the neighbouring room to which this door led I set up the receiving mirror so that its optic axis passed centrally through the door and intersected the direction of the ray at right angles. If the plane conducting surface was now set up vertically at the point of intersection, and adjusted so as to make angles of 45° with the ray and also with the axis of the receiving mirror, there appeared in the secondary conductor a stream of sparks. . . . When I turned the reflecting surface about 10° out of the correct position the sparks disappeared. Thus the reflection is regular, and the angles of incidence and reflection are equal. . . .

Refraction

In order to find out whether any refraction of the ray takes place in passing from air into another insulating medium, I had a large prism made of so-called hard pitch, a material like asphalt. The base was an isosceles triangle 1.2 metres in the side, and with a refracting angle of 30°. . . . The producing mirror was set up at a distance of 2.6 metres from the prism and facing one of the refracting surfaces, so that the axis of the beam was directed as nearly as possible towards the centre of mass of the prism, and met the refracting surface at an angle of incidence of 25° (On the side of the normal towards the base). Near the refracting edge and also at the opposite side of the prism were placed two conducting screens which prevented the ray from passing by any other path than that through the prism. . . . [The secondary mirror was placed on the emerging side of the prism.] . . . sparks appeared when the mirror (secondary) was moved towards the base of the prism, beginning when the angular deviation . . . was about 11°. The sparking increased in intensity until the deviation amounted to about 22°, and then again decreased. . . . corresponds to a refractive index of 1.69. . . . '

H. Hertz (1888) *Sitzungsber. d. Berl. Akad. d. Wiss.*

Radio waves were thus shown to behave in a similar manner to light or indeed any wave motion. They showed the properties of rectilinear propagation, polarization, reflection, refraction, diffraction, and interference.

The first radio waves were transmitted from an aerial system consisting of two spheres connected by wires to the terminals of an induction coil. It was soon found that the spheres could be replaced by two rods or lengths of wire—the aerial is then known as a dipole. If one of the terminals is connected to the ground only one-half of the dipole is needed; the ground acts as the other half (Fig. 9.31).

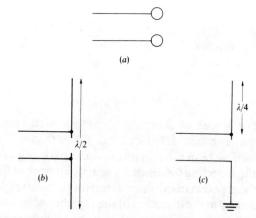

Fig. 9.31 (a) Hertz's aerial system. (b) Dipole. (c) Marconi's quarter wavelength aerial

The production of radio waves

In Hertz's original transmitter, radio emission occurred when sparks passed between two spheres. A high potential difference was maintained between the spheres. The system is a capacitor which is charged by the induction coil. Charging continues until the potential difference between the two spheres has risen high enough for the air to break down and a spark be produced. This discharges the capacitor (Fig. 9.32). But because the aerial system has some inductance the capacitor is being discharged through an inductive circuit and thus oscillations occur. The oscillations are heavily damped. The spark discharges the capacitor because ions are produced in the air and give a conducting path between the two spheres.

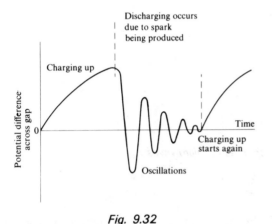

Fig. 9.32

Instead of using an induction coil and relying on a spark to trigger off the oscillations, an oscillating potential difference can be applied to the aerial system. A simple radio transmitter can be a low voltage alternating at, say, 10^9 Hz and applied to an aerial consisting of two conducting rods a few millimetres apart (Fig. 9.33). The high potential difference was only necessary with Hertz's apparatus as a means of discharging the capacitor through the aerial inductance by means of a spark.

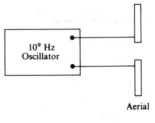

Fig. 9.33

The properties of radio waves

Figure 9.34 shows a series of experiments by which the properties of radio waves with a wavelength of about 3 cm (the term 'microwaves' is generally used) can be shown. As Hertz found, reflection follows the same laws as light. Refraction can be demonstrated using prisms, blocks, lenses, etc. made of paraffin wax. Young's double slit experiment can be duplicated with microwaves, as also can Lloyd's mirror. Standing waves are easily demonstrated with microwaves if the wave is incident on a plane reflector at normal incidence, superposition then occurring between the incident and reflected waves. The result is a series of maxima ½λ apart between source and reflector. Diffraction at a single slit or multiple slits can also be shown.

The microwaves emitted from the source are plane polarized and as the detector, either another horn or an aerial, will only detect waves in one plane of polarization, rotating one by 90° completely reduces the signal strength to zero (as Hertz found). Another way of showing that the waves are transverse is discussed later in this chapter.

Electromagnetic waves

Light and radio waves are part of a group known as electromagnetic waves (Fig. 9.35, page 167). They all have the same speed in a vacuum, all are transverse and all can be described in terms of the regular variation of electric and magnetic fields. Electromagnetic waves can travel through a vacuum, so what is the 'particle' displacement with such waves? The disturbance is a variation with time, at a particular point, of the magnitude

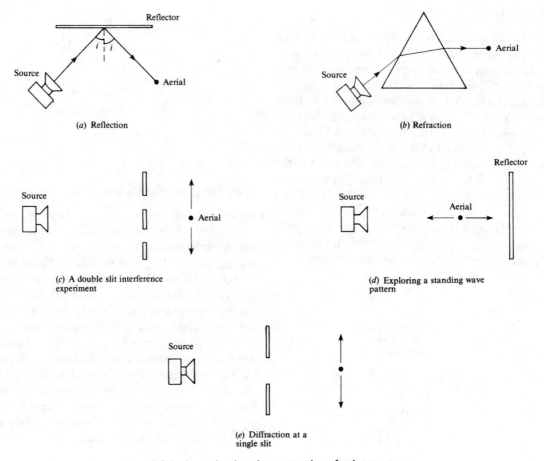

(a) Reflection

(b) Refraction

(c) A double slit interference experiment

(d) Exploring a standing wave pattern

(e) Diffraction at a single slit

Fig. 9.34 *Investigating the properties of microwaves*

of the electric and magnetic fields. Figure 9.36 shows these fields and how they vary with distance for a plane polarized wave.

Polarized electromagnetic waves

The methods mentioned earlier of producing plane polarized light are: double refraction, reflection at a dielectric, and selective absorption. The evidence for the transverse nature of X-rays was first produced by Barkla, in 1906, and involved producing plane polarized X-rays by reflection from carbon. The polarization of radio waves can be shown by what we might call selective emission—the waves are restricted to just one plane by the use of linear aerials for transmission.

If the detecting aerial is at right angles to the transmitting aerial, then no signal is detected; if the detecting aerial is parallel to the transmitting aerial a signal can be detected. A linear aerial emits plane polarized waves. In the case of microwaves selective absorption by a grid of wires can be used to show the transverse nature (Fig. 9.37). During absorption the free electrons in the wires are set into oscillation along the lengths of the wires. The methods used to show the transverse nature of these different waves are similar and suggest that the waves are all similar—part of one family.

Polarization by selective absorption is not just restricted to the microwave region. Similar effects can be achieved in the radio region with wires

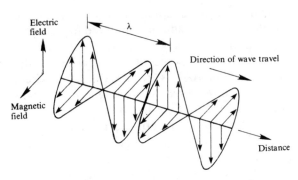

Fig. 9.36   A plane polarized electromagnetic wave

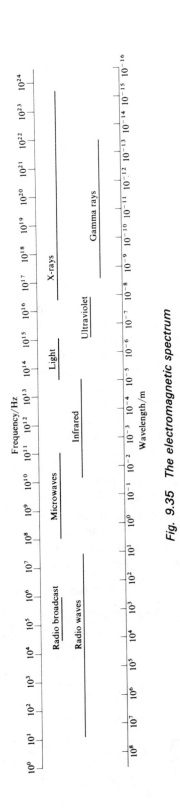

Fig. 9.35   The electromagnetic spectrum

much farther apart. Wires very close together can be used in the visible region to achieve the same effect. Bird and Parrish in 1960 (*J. Opt. Soc. Am.*, **50**, 886, 1960) evaporated gold at a glancing angle onto a plastic diffraction grating. The gold deposited on the sides of ruled grating slits to form parallel conducting wires. The spacing of these 'wires' was about 5×10^{-7} m, about the wavelength of light. The spacing of the wires with

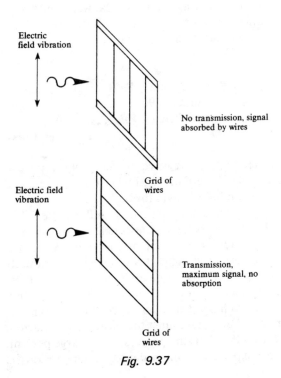

Fig. 9.37

radio or microwave radiation has to be about the wavelength of the radiation involved for selective absorption to be complete when the grid is crossed with the plane of polarization of the radiation. 'Polaroid' is in fact a grid of 'wires'. 'Polaroid' film consists of long hydrocarbon chains to which iodine has been attached. The iodine provides conduction electrons which can move along the hydrocarbon chains but not perpendicular to them.

For historical reasons the plane of polarization of an electromagnetic wire has been taken to be at right angles to the electric field direction.

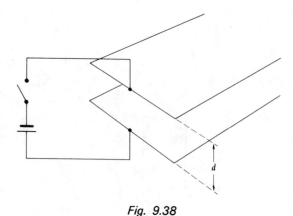

Fig. 9.38

Travelling fields

'Perhaps the most dramatic moment in the development of physics during the 19th century occurred to J. C. Maxwell one day in the 1860's, when he combined the laws of electricity and magnetism with the laws of the behaviour of light. As a result, the properties of light were partly unravelled—that old and subtle stuff that is so important and mysterious that it was felt necessary to arrange a special creation for it when writing Genesis. Maxwell could say, when he was finished with his discovery, "Let there be electricity and magnetism, and there is light!" '

> R. P. Feynman, R. B. Leighton and M. Sands (1963) *The Feynman Lectures on Physics, Vol. 1*, Addison-Wesley, Reading, Mass.

Electromagnetic waves travel through space at a speed of 3×10^8 m s^{-1}. How fast will electric and magnetic fields travel through space?

Consider a long pair of parallel plates (Fig. 9.38) and a battery connected by means of a switch across one end of the pair. When the switch is closed the plates will become gradually charged, starting at the ends nearest the battery. In order that the far ends of the plates shall become charged the charge must flow along the plates. Each plate must therefore carry a current during the charging process. The charge per unit area of plate, i.e., charge density σ, depends on the electric field E:

$$\sigma = \varepsilon_0 E$$

Thus as the charge moves along the plates so must the electric field. An electric field will thus travel along the space between the plates.

Suppose the charge travels along the plates with a speed v, the electric field will travel down the space between the plates with a speed v. In time Δt the charge will have travelled a distance $v\Delta t$ along the plates. If the width of the plates is w, then in time Δt the charge will have spread over an area $wv\,\Delta t$ of a plate. The charge that has spread over this area will thus be $\sigma wv\,\Delta t$.

Current is the rate at which charge moves and so the current along the plates must be σwv. If there is a current then there must be a magnetic field. For a single turn solenoid, these plates can be thought of as that, we have $B = \mu_0 I/w$. The number of turns per metre is $1/w$. Thus we have

$$B = \mu_0 \sigma v$$

Figure 9.39 shows the directions of the electric

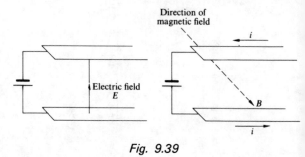

Fig. 9.39

and magnetic fields. They are at right angles to each other. Both are moving down the space between the plates as the charge flows out along the plates.

The electric field between the plates, E, can be introduced in the equation, thus

$$B = \mu_0 \varepsilon_0 E v$$

But as the charge moves out along the plates, giving a current which extends down the plates, so the magnetic field travels along the space between the plates. In a time Δt the magnetic field occupies an extra area $dv\,\Delta t$. If the flux density is B then the extra flux produced in time Δt will be $Bdv\,\Delta t$. The rate of change of magnetic flux is thus Bdv. This rate of increase must be maintained by a voltage V between the plates, where $V = Bdv$. But a voltage V between two plates a distance d apart gives an electric field E, where $E = V/d$. Eliminating V between these two equations gives

$$E = Bv$$

The two equations $B = \mu_0 \varepsilon_0 E v$ and $E = Bv$ can only both hold at the same time if

$$v^2 = \frac{1}{\varepsilon_0 \mu_0}$$

ε_0 has the value $8.854 \times 10^{-12} \text{ C}^2 \text{ N}^{-1} \text{ m}^{-2}$ and μ_0 the value $4\pi \times 10^{-7} \text{ N A}^{-2}$ in air. If we put these values in our equation we find that the speed at which the charge moves down the plates, the speed at which the electric field moves along the gap between the plates, the speed at which the magnetic field moves along between the plates is $3 \times 10^8 \text{ m s}^{-1}$. This is the speed of light.

The electric and magnetic fields are at all points at right angles to the direction of travel of the disturbance—a transverse disturbance.

The speed and the transverse nature of the disturbance both suggest that light might be an electromagnetic wave. Maxwell arrived at similar conclusions.

'... The agreement of the results [the speed of light and the fields] seem to shew that light and magnetism are affections of the same substance, and that light is an electromagnetic disturbance propagated through the field according to electromagnetic laws.... Hence electromagnetic science leads to exactly the same conclusions as optical science with respect to the direction of the disturbances which can be propagated through the field; both affirm the propagation of transverse vibrations, and both give the same velocity of propagation....'

Maxwell (1864) 'A dynamic theory of the electromagnetic field', part VI, *Roy. Soc. Trans.*, **CLV**.

Maxwell considered the behaviour of electric and magnetic fields in empty space and arrived at the same result as we have for fields travelling through the space between two conducting plates. Because of the three-dimensional character of the fields in space, Maxwell's equations are more complex.

Supplementary material

Radio—the miracle of the ages

'It seemed to me at this time that if this radiation could be increased, developed and controlled, it would most certainly be possible to signal across space, for very considerable distances....'

Marconi

B. L. Jacot and D. N. Collier (1935) *Marconi—Master of Space*, Hutchinson

Marconi was referring to his thoughts immediately following Hertz's discovery of radio waves. Hertz had only managed to detect radio radiation a matter of metres from his transmitter. In December 1895 Marconi had a great triumph—he detected radio radiation 10 m away from the transmitter. Soon he was transmitting over a few kilometres; he had found that elevating the aerials increased the range. By 1897 Morse code messages were being sent over many kilometres and Marconi founded 'The Wireless Telegraphy and Signal Company Ltd', later in 1900 to be renamed 'Marconi's Wireless Telegraph Company Ltd', to deal with the installation of radio stations for message transmission. In March 1899 the first message was transmitted across the English Channel, from France to England. On 12 December 1901 the first signals were transmitted across the Atlantic Ocean, from England to Newfoundland. For this transmission Marconi attached his aerials to kites and was by this means able to get his aerials up to a height of about 150 m.

Transmission of signals across the Atlantic was the experiment that should not have worked.

'Despite the opposition which I had received from many quarters, often that of most eminent men, it was still my opinion that electric waves would not be stopped by the curvature of the earth, and therefore could be made to travel any distance, separating any two places on our planet. . . . '

Marconi.

B. L. Jacot and D. N. Collier (1935) *Marconi— Master of Space*, Hutchinson.

Two years later Kennelly and Heaviside advanced the suggestion that the radio signals had been reflected from a layer of ionized particles in the earth's upper atmosphere, the ionosphere, and had not bent round the earth's surface to cross the Atlantic.

The first use of radio waves for the transmission of speech, instead of Morse signals, took place in about 1906. In 1922 the first wireless entertainment station was opened in London (the famous 2LO, London Calling).

Hertz's original transmitter had been the intermittent sparks produced between two spheres by an induction coil. This was capable of transmitting Morse as all that was needed was a key to make the pulse of waves transmitted either long or short. The key was thus used to break the transmission circuit. For the continuous transmission needed for the transmission of speech this was unsatisfactory. A continuous radio wave was necessary so that it could be modulated, i.e., the amplitude of the radio wave was made to change in accord with the fluctuating currents produced from a microphone (Fig. 9.40). At the receiver the wave has to be demodulated, i.e., the speech signal extracted from the radio carrier wave. Crystals were the first method used

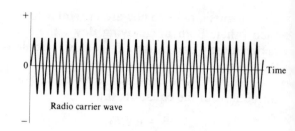

Radio carrier wave

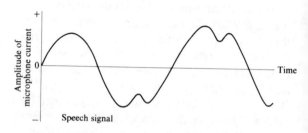

Speech signal

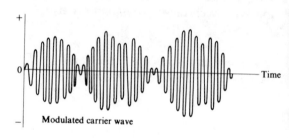

Modulated carrier wave

Fig. 9.40

for demodulating. The crystal behaved as a solid state diode—only positive parts of the signal had a low resistance path (Fig. 9.41). The demodulated signal consists of the positive part of a high-frequency component, the radio carrier wave, and a low-frequency component, the speech wave. These are then picked up by headphones, across which a capacitor has been placed. The capacitor offers a low-reactance path for the radio wave and a high-reactance path for the lower-frequency speech signal. The headphones offer a higher-resistance path for the radio wave and a lower one for the speech signal—the result is that the headphones respond to the speech signal.

The radio signal has a frequency which depends on the capacitance and inductance of the transmitting circuit. By employing an inductor and a variable capacitor in the receiving circuit, tuning

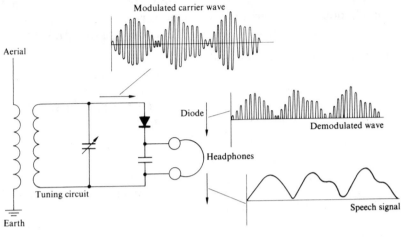

Fig. 9.41

can be employed to make the receiving circuit respond only to the frequency of the transmitted signal. In fact the receiving circuit would respond to a frequency band which would be centred on the transmission frequency. The frequency the circuit responds to is the resonant frequency of the capacitor–inductor circuit.

The advent of valves considerably improved the performance of receivers. Fleming's valve was a diode and thus could be used in place of the crystal. Lee Forest's three-electrode valve, the triode, enabled the signals to be amplified before being received in the headphones, or loudspeaker. In addition, the triode valve could be used with a tuning circuit to give an oscillator for the production of the radio carrier waves.

Figure 9.42 shows a schematic diagram of a simple receiver. The signal is picked up by the aerial, amplified, demodulated, the speech signal is amplified (audio frequency amplifier), and finally the signal is passed to the loudspeaker. Transistors

and junction diodes are nowadays often used for the various stages. These are solid-state equivalents to the triode and diode valves.

Amplitude modulation is not the only way the carrier wave can be made to carry the audio signal. Frequency modulation is used by some stations. Instead of the audio signal being used to control the amplitude of the radio wave it is used to vary the radio wave frequency.

Problems

1. With a Young's double slit experiment the fringe separation was found to be 0.65 mm when the slits to screen distance was 0.80 m and the wavelength of the light used was 5.9×10^{-7} m. What was the separation of the slits?

2. What is the appearance of the fringe pattern observed with Young's double slit experiment when the slits are illuminated by white light?

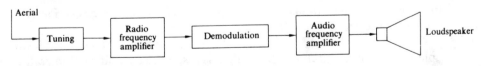

Fig. 9.42   A simple receiver

3. Explain what happens to the fringe patterns observed in a Young's double slit experiment when the following changes are made.

(a) The light illuminating the slits is changed from red to blue.
(b) The slits to screen distance is doubled.
(c) One of the slits is covered up.
(d) Slits with a smaller separation are used.

4. Why do we not see interference effects when the light beams from two car headlamps overlap?

5. Explain the formation of interference fringes when a wedge air film is illuminated by monochromatic light.

6. Explain how Newton's rings can be observed and how measurements made on them can lead to a value for the wavelength of light from a monochromatic source.

7. In a Newton's rings experiment with a convex lens resting on a horizontal flat glass plate, why is the centre of the fringe pattern black? If the lens is carefully vertically raised from the plate, what happens to the fringe pattern?

8. When a plane wavefront of monochromatic light meets a diffraction grating, the diffraction pattern produced is caused by the interference of beams diffracted through the various grating slits. Explain, with the aid of a diagram, exactly where and under what conditions diffraction occurs.

Explain why only beams diffracted in certain directions interfere constructively.

(University of London, Q2, Paper 2, January 1980)

9. (a) What conditions are necessary in order that interference patterns between light from two sources may be observed?

(b) Draw a labelled diagram showing the apparatus required to determine the wavelength of red light using a pair of slits. Indicate approximate values of the dimensions of the apparatus and state a measuring instrument suitable for each measurement required.

How would you use the measured values of the dimensions of the apparatus to estimate the separation of the fringes produced by light of wavelength 500 nm?

What part is played by diffraction in this experiment?

How are the fringes produced in this experiment very different from those produced using a diffraction grating and the same source of light.

(i) When the grating spacing is the same as the slit separation, and
(ii) when the grating spacing is much smaller than the slit separation?

If the red light is replaced by blue light, how do the fringes produced in the experiment differ markedly from those produced using red light?

(University of London, Q11, Paper 2, June 1982)

10. (a) Explain what is meant by (i) interference and (ii) diffraction of waves. Describe experiments by which each of these phenomena may be demonstrated.

(b) The interference of light waves may be used to determine the wavelength of light from a monochromatic source. Describe Young's double slit experiment by which such a determination may be made. The theory of the experiment is not required.

(c) Explain the colours which are produced when a soap film is illuminated with white light. Why might the film appear black just before it breaks?

(d) When a diffraction grating is illuminated by white light at normal incidence the violet in the third-order spectrum may overlap the red in the second-order spectrum. Explain why this happens, giving figures to support your answer.

(AEB, Q11, Paper 3 November 1981)

11. Two optically flat glass plates are in contact along one edge and make a very small angle with each other. They are illuminated normally with yellow light of wavelength 600 nm and blue light of wavelength 450 nm. When viewed from above, the first region where the air wedge appears approximately white is at a distance of 6.0 nm from the line of contact. Explain why this white area occurs and calculate the angle between the two plates.

(University of London, Q3, Paper 2, January 1979)

12. (a) A narrow parallel-sided beam of white light is dispersed by a diffraction grating which is placed perpendicular to the beam, i.e., parallel to

the incident wavefronts. Explain this effect in detail.

(b) Figure 9.43 shows the action, in air, of a plane diffraction grating PQ on a monochromatic beam of light which falls normally on the grating. Figure 9.44 shows the whole arrangement immersed in water, of refractive index 1.33.

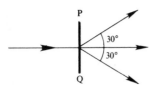

Fig. 9.43

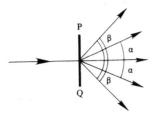

Fig. 9.44

The beam is now diffracted as shown, making angles α (< 30°) and β (> 30°) with the normal. Explain these changes produced by the water.

Give that the grating has 8.0×10^5 lines per metre, calculate

(i) the wavelength of the light in air
(ii) the wavelength of the light in water
(iii) the angle α, and
(iv) the angle β.

(University of London, Q10, Paper 2, June 1981)

13. (a) Show that, for a plane diffraction grating of grating interval s, used at normal incidence, the angle of diffraction, θ, is related to the wavelength, λ, of the light by the equation

$$s \sin \theta = n\lambda$$

where n is an integer. What is the significance of n?

(b) Assuming that you were provided with a spectrometer which had been adjusted correctly and on which a plane diffraction grating was mounted vertically, describe and explain the procedure you would follow to ensure that light falls normally on the grating.

(c) A grating spectrometer is arranged so that light from the collimator falls normally on the grating. When the second-order diffracted image of the slit due to a wavelength λ is viewed on the two sides of the normal to the grating, the readings on the telescope scale are respectively α and β. The slit is first illuminated by sodium light of wavelength 589.3 nm and the values of α and β respectively are found to be 162° 37' and 252° 39'. The sodium source is then replaced by a discharge tube containing a mixture of gases and the values of α and β (still second order) are recorded for three lines as follows:

Line	α	β
1	171° 57'	243° 19'
2	160° 48'	254° 28'
3	155° 41'	259° 35'

Identify the gases in the tube using the data in the table below which shows the wavelengths, in nm, of the lines emitted by various gases.

Carbon dioxide	Hydrogen	Helium	Oxygen
451	410	319	408
483	434	389	441
520	486	447	521
561	656	588	617
608		668	

Show that, whatever the spacing of the grating used, the third-order diffracted image of the shortest wavelength in the spectrum of one of the gases identified will occur at a smaller diffracted angle than the second-order image of the longest wavelength line in that gas's spectrum.

(University of London, Q10, Paper 2, January 1982)

14. (a) Describe in detail how you would determine the wavelength of monochromatic light either by using a diffraction grating or by

some other method based on optical interference.

(b) Explain, without going into detailed calculations, how the 'Newton's rings' pattern observed in reflected monochromatic light is produced, why the centre of the pattern is (or ought to be) dark, and why the pattern seems to be localised in the air film between the lens and the plane glass plate.

(c) White light transmitted normally through a very thin parallel-sided film of mica of thickness t and of refractive index n falls on the slit of a spectrometer, and the continuous spectrum is interrupted by dark lines of which the first three, starting from the violet end of the spectrum, appear at wavelengths 452 nm, 499 nm and 558 nm.

(i) Show that these observations are consistent with the formula $2nt = (p + \frac{1}{2}) \lambda$, where p is an integer and λ is the wavelength at which a dark line is found.

(ii) What are the wavelengths of the two other dark lines that are seen in the visible region of the spectrum?

(Oxford Local Examinations, Q8, Paper I, June 1978)

15. (a) (i) What conditions must be satisfied if two wave-trains are to interfere with each other to produce a stationary interference pattern?

(ii) Explain why it is possible to produce a stationary interference pattern using as sources two separate radio transmitters, but impossible to produce such a pattern using two separate sodium-vapour lamps.

(iii) Draw a labelled diagram of an experimental arrangement to produce and observe circular interference fringes using the light from a sodium-vapour lamp.

(b) Describe how you would use a diffraction grating together with a spectrometer to determine the wavelength of sodium light. Explain how the result would be calculated. Assume that the spectrometer has been correctly set up beforehand, and that the number of lines per metre of the diffraction grating is known.

(c) A distance bright point-source of sodium light is viewed normally through a uniform fine wire-mesh interwoven at right angles.

(i) Describe what is observed.

(ii) Given that the first-order diffracted images lie in a direction making an angle of 0.20° with the normal, calculate the distance between the axes of adjacent wires in the mesh. (Take the wavelength of sodium light to be 589 nm)

(Oxford Local Examinations, Q8, Paper I, June 1982)

16. Explain why colours are produced when a drop of oil falls on a water surface. Why do the colours change, and become more brilliant, as the oil spreads over the surface?

A drop of oil, of volume 0.20 cm³, spreads uniformly on a surface to cover an area of 1.0×10^4 cm². When this oil patch is illuminated normally with light of wavelength 560 nm it appears black. Explain why this is so. Calculate the refractive index of the oil given that it is greater than that of water.

The superposition of two wave motions may result in the formation of (i) a stationary fringe pattern, (ii) beats, (iii) a stationary wave. Describe the experimental arrangements you would use to illustrate each of these phenomena.

(AEB, Q2, Paper S, June 1982)

17. (a) A small source S emits electromagnetic waves of wavelength about 3 cm which can be detected by an aerial A (a straight wire) connected to a meter measuring the intensity of the radiation. Initially the distance SA = d. When the distance between the source and the aerial is increased to 2d, the meter reading falls to one-quarter of its original value. What conclusion can be drawn from this?

What would you expect the meter reading to be if the aerial were moved until SA = 3d?

If the source is rotated through 90° about the line SA, the meter reading falls to zero. Explain briefly the reason for this.

(b) A metal reflecting screen is now placed some distance beyond A with its plane perpendicular to the line SA. It is found that as the screen is moved slowly away from A, alternate maximum and minimum readings are shown on the meter. Explain briefly the reason for this. If the screen is displaced a distance of 8.7 cm between a first and a seventh minimum, calculate the wavelength and the frequency of the wave. (Speed of electromagnetic waves in air = 3.0×10^8 m s^{-1})

(c) The source of the electromagnetic waves used is assumed to be monochromatic. Explain what monochromatic means.

What would you have observed in (b) if the source had emitted simultaneously waves of wavelengths 3 cm and 6 cm, of the same intensity?

(University of London, Q11, Paper 2, June 1980)

18. Give the theory of an experiment to determine the wavelength of yellow light using two narrow slits. Point out any approximations you make.

Why is a third slit usually necessary?

A source S, Fig. 9.45, of continuous waves a distance h from a plane reflector R produces regions of high intensity such as C, C' and C''. Account for this. When the frequency of S is changed slowly, the regions C, C' and C'' move in the direction D as shown. Account for this, and deduce whether the frequency has been increased or decreased.

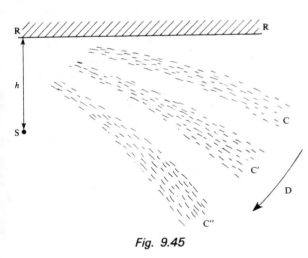

Fig. 9.45

In Appleton's experiment, S was a radio transmitter on the Earth's surface, and R was the Heaviside layer—a reflecting layer in the atmosphere 80 km above the ground. When the wavelength transmitted slowly changed from 200 m to 180 m, a receiver on the ground 120 km away from S observed fluctuations in the received

signal strength. Calculate the number of signal strength maxima observed during this change of frequency.

(University of Cambridge, Q1, Paper 3, June 1979)

19. (a) What do you understand by plane-polarized radiation, and the plane of polarization of electromagnetic radiation?

Explain why the phenomenon of polarization is shown very obviously by radio waves, but is more difficult to demonstrate in the case of visible light. What is the essential difference between 'ordinary' light and plane-polarized light?

(b) Describe how you would produce a beam of plane-polarized light by reflection and how you would show that you have done so. Mention briefly one application of this effect.

(c) The nineteenth-century physicist W. H. Wollaston suggested that the polarization of the light reaching us from a clear blue sky could be used as a means of telling the time. Discuss the physics underlying this idea, and consider whether its accuracy would be likely to approach that of a conventional sundial.

(Oxford Local Examinations, Q9, Paper S, June 1979)

20. The map (Fig. 9.46) shows part of a coastline, with two land-based radio navigation stations A and B. Both stations transmit continuous sinusoidal radio waves with the same amplitude and same wavelength (200 m).

A ship X, exactly midway between A and B, detects a signal whose amplitude is twice that of either station alone.

(a) What can be said about the signals from the two stations?

(b) The ship X travels to a new position by sailing 100 m in the direction shown by the arrow. What signal will it now detect? Explain this.

(c) A ship Y also starts at a position equidistant from A and B and then travels in the direction shown by the arrow. Exactly the same changes to the signal received were observed as in the case of ship X in (b).

Explain whether Y has sailed 100 m, more than 100 m, or less than 100 m.

(Oxford and Cambridge Board, Nuffield, Short answer paper (1971)

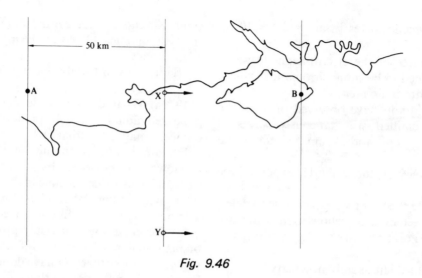

Fig. 9.46

21. A television programme is broadcast at a frequency of 600 MHz with the electric vector vertical. The diagram (Fig. 9.47) is meant to illustrate the waves at a considerable distance from the transmitter.

(a) Make a rough copy of the diagram, add

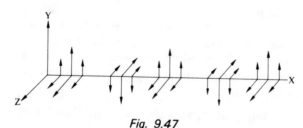

Fig. 9.47

suitable labelling, and explain how it is meant to represent the waves.

(b) Draw another diagram to show what this pulse would look like 5×10^{-10} seconds later ($c = 3 \times 10^8$ m s^{-1}).

(c) Show on another diagram (i) how you would place a short straight wire so as to get the maximum electromotive force induced in it, (ii) how you would place a small loop of wire so as to get the maximum electromotive force induced in it, (iii) where you would place a large metal sheet to increase the e.m.f. in (i).

(d) What features of the diagram indicate that the wave is polarized? How would you decide whether the waves carrying a particular television broadcast were polarized?

(Oxford and Cambridge Board, Nuffield physics I, Options paper, 1970)

10 Optics

The laws of reflection and refraction

The laws of reflection can be stated as:

1. The incident ray, the normal to the surface at the point where the ray meets the surface, and the reflected ray all lie in the same plane.
2. The angle of reflection equals the angle of incidence (Fig. 10.1).

The second law was probably known as far back as the Roman empire, certainly by the second century AD. The first law does not appear to have been stated until about AD 1100.

The laws of refraction can be stated as:

1. The incident ray, the normal to the surface at the point where the ray meets the surface, and the refracted ray all lie in the same plane.
2. For a given pair of media, and light of a given frequency (colour), the sine of the angle of incidence divided by the sine of the angle of refraction is a constant (Fig. 10.2).

The first law was recognized by Alhazen in AD 1100. The second law was not discovered until much later. Kepler in the early seventeenth century tried without success to find the relationship. The law was first discovered by Snell in 1626, hence it is often called Snell's law, though he did not express it in this form. The first expression in terms of sines was given by Descartes. The law was not deduced from any understanding of refraction but merely as a way of fitting the experimental results.

Newton considered light to be small bodies projected at speed through space. On this basis he considered refraction to occur because a refracting surface exerted a normal force on the particles. This changed the normal velocity component but not the horizontal component (Fig. 10.3), hence for the horizontal components

$$v \sin i = v' \sin r$$

$$\frac{\sin i}{\sin r} = \frac{v'}{v}$$

This implies that the speed of light is greater in the refracting medium than in the incident

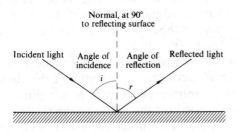

Fig. 10.1

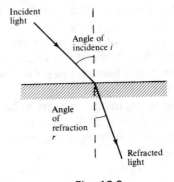

Fig. 10.2

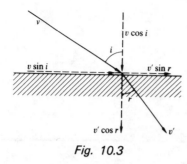

Fig. 10.3

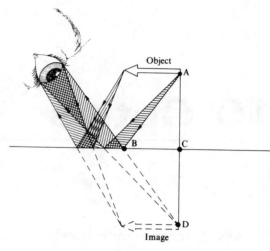

Fig. 10.4

medium, e.g., greater in glass than in air. This was later found to be not the case and a correct derivation of the law was given by Huygens in terms of waves (see Chapter 7):

$$\frac{\sin i}{\sin r} = \frac{\text{speed in incident medium}}{\text{speed in refracting medium}}$$

Optics is concerned with what are called rays. A ray is the path taken by light energy in travelling from a source to a receiver, a straight line in a homogeneous medium. The concept of light as being a wave motion might suggest that, since waves spread round corners and superpose to give interference effects, a consideration of rays would be inappropriate. However, since the wavelength of light is of the order of 10^{-7} m and the objects we consider in optics are generally considerably larger, wave effects are relatively unimportant and can be ignored in most circumstances.

Reflection at a plane mirror

Light coming from the object is reflected by the mirror and so to the eye (Fig. 10.4). The eye sees the object by means of rays of light that are bent by the mirror. We call the object we see an image because we see it by bent rays of light. If we think of light as only travelling in straight lines then the object, or rather its image, appears to be behind the mirror. No light actually passes through mirror to the image. Such an image is called a virtual image.

Because the angle of reflection is equal to the angle of incidence, angle ABC equals angle CBD.

The line of ADC must cut the mirror surface at right angles—a ray of light going along the path AD will be reflected back along the same path and thus appear to come from the image. The triangles ABC and DBC are identical—thus AC equals CD. The image appears to be as far behind the mirror as the object is in front.

Reflection at a spherical mirror

Mirrors do not have to be plane to produce images. The images produced by curved mirrors can, however, be a different size to the object, inverted or the right way up, behind or in front of the mirror. They can be virtual or real. Virtual images occur where the rays of light only appear to converge on them, real images are where the rays actually do pass through the image point.

Objects which are a long way from a spherical mirror, so far that the light reaching the mirror can be considered to be parallel rays, give images at a point called the focus. The distance between the focus and the centre of the mirror is called the focal length (Fig. 10.5).

For a spherical mirror the point known as the centre of curvature is the centre of the circle of which the mirror is an arc; the term radius of curvature is used for the radius of the circle.

Since any line through the centre of curvature must meet the spherical mirror surface at right

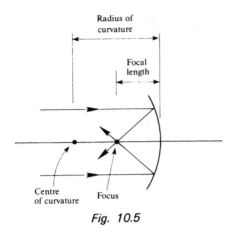

Fig. 10.5

in 1738 (one of Newton's early successors at Cambridge University). The method consists of drawing a number of rays, originating at a point on the object. Such rays after reflection will meet, or appear to meet, at a corresponding point on the image. These are the rules for drawing rays:

1. Each ray is assumed to be independent of other rays.
2. A ray parallel to the axis passes through, or appears to pass through, the focus after reflection.
3. A ray directed through the centre of curvature of a surface returns along the same path after reflection.
4. A ray passing through the focus is after reflection parallel to the axis.

Figure 10.7 (page 180) shows these rays being used to determine image positions for objects at differing distances from spherical mirrors. The table below summarizes the pattern.

angles, then as Fig. 10.6 shows, the laws of reflection must mean that angle ABC equals angle CBF. Because AB is parallel to CP then angle BCF equals angle CBF and so triangle CBF must have CF equal to BF. To a reasonable approximation BF equals PF. Hence the focal length is half the radius of curvature.

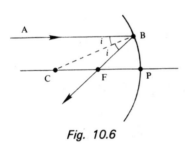

Fig. 10.6

The above applies regardless of whether the spherical mirror presents a concave or convex surface to the incident light.

One way of determining image positions with spherical mirrors is to draw ray diagrams. This is a graphical method, first given by R. Smith

Refractive index

The ratio of the speed of light in a vacuum to that in a material is called the absolute refractive index of that medium. Refraction is generally, however, concerned with light passing across a boundary from one medium to another. In such cases we refer to the relative refractive index as the ratio of the speeds of light in the two media concerned. Whenever light passes across a boundary between two media (or from a vacuum into a medium) the ratio of the sine of the angle of incidence and the sine of the angle of refraction is the relative refractive index between the two media.

$$_an_b = \frac{v_a}{v_b} = \frac{\sin i}{\sin r}$$

	Object distance	Image
Concave mirror	Before F	Erect, magnified, virtual
	Between F and C	Inverted, magnified, real
	Beyond C	Inverted, diminished, real
Convex mirror	All distances	Erect, diminished, virtual

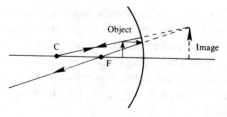

A magnified, virtual image

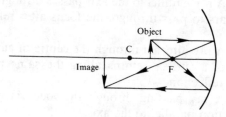

A magnified, real image

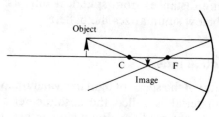

A reduced, real image

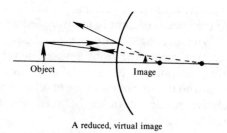

A reduced, virtual image

Fig. 10.7   Images with spherical mirrors

Light paths are reversible. Thus for light passing from, say, air to water (as in Fig. 10.8) we have

$$_an_w = \frac{\sin i}{\sin r}$$

For light passing from water into air we have

$$_wn_a = \frac{\sin i'}{\sin r'}$$

But $i = r'$ and $r = i'$. Hence

$$_an_w = \frac{1}{_wn_a}$$

Another useful relationship can be derived for light passing through a number of media, as in Fig. 10.9.

$$_an_b = \frac{\sin i}{\sin r_1}$$

$$_bn_c = \frac{\sin r_1}{\sin r_2}$$

$$_cn_d = \frac{\sin r_2}{\sin r}$$

Hence

$$_an_b \times {}_bn_c \times {}_cn_d = \frac{\sin i}{\sin r_1} \times \frac{\sin r_1}{\sin r_2} \times \frac{\sin r_2}{\sin r}$$

$$= \frac{\sin i}{\sin r}$$

The above refers to light passing from medium a to b, v_a and v_b being the speeds of light in medium a and medium b respectively, and $_an_b$ being the relative refractive index for the light going from a to b.

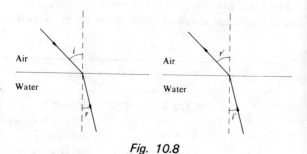

Fig. 10.8

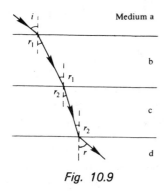

Fig. 10.9

But this is what we would have got if we had only considered the media a and d. Hence

$$_a n_d = {}_a n_b \times {}_b n_c \times {}_c n_d$$

Thus if we need to know the refractive index for light passing from water into glass and we know the refractive indices for air to water to be 1.3 and air to glass to be 1.5, we can obtain the required refractive index as follows:

$$_w n_g = {}_w n_a \times {}_a n_g$$

$$= \frac{1}{_a n_w} \times {}_a n_g$$

$$= \frac{1.5}{1.3} = 1.2$$

A more symmetrical way of writing Snell's law can be obtained by considering light passing from medium a to medium b. Then

$$_a n_b = {}_a n_v \times {}_v n_b$$

$$= \frac{_v n_b}{_v n_a}$$

where v refers to a vacuum. But $_v n_a$ is the absolute refractive index n_a of medium a, $_v n_b$ the absolute refractive index n_b of medium b.

$$_a n_b = \frac{n_b}{n_a}$$

But for light passing from medium a to medium b, the ray in medium a would have an angle to the normal of i_a and in medium b an angle of i_b (i.e.,

the angle of refraction). Thus

$$_a n_b = \frac{n_b}{n_a} = \frac{\sin i_a}{\sin i_b}$$

Hence

$$n_a \sin i_a = n_b \sin i_b$$

Thus if light is incident on a water-glass boundary at an angle of incidence of 30° then, if the absolute refractive index of water is 1.3 and that of glass 1.5

$$1.3 \sin 30° = 1.5 \sin i_g$$

Hence the angle between the ray and the normal in the glass, i_g, is 26°.

Real and apparent depth

Because of refraction the apparent depth of an object immersed in water is less when viewed from above the surface than its real depth (Fig. 10.10).

$$_a n_w = \frac{\sin i}{\sin r}$$

But sin i = AB/BI and sin r = AB/BO, hence

$$_a n_w = \frac{BO}{BI}$$

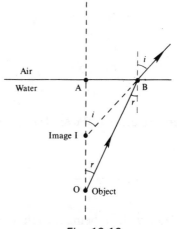

Fig. 10.10

181

If we consider the observer to be viewing the object almost, if not, along the normal, then BO approximates to AO, the real depth of the object, and BI approximates to AI, the apparent depth of the object. Hence

$$_an_w = \frac{\text{real depth}}{\text{apparent depth}}$$

Thus for an object 1.0 m below the surface of a still pond, the refractive index being for air to water 1.3, the apparent depth is 1.0/1.3 = 0.77 m.

Critical angle

When light passes from a dense to a less dense medium, e.g., glass into air, refraction occurs with the angle of refraction being greater than the angle of incidence. Thus as the angle of incidence is increased a particular angle is reached when the angle of refraction is 90°. This angle is known as the critical angle (Fig. 10.11). For angles of incidence greater than the critical angle there is no refraction, all the light being totally reflected within the glass.

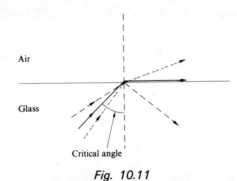

Fig. 10.11

At the critical angle C the angle of refraction is 90°, hence

$$_gn_a = \frac{\sin C}{\sin 90°}$$

But $_gn_a = 1/_an_g$, with $_gn_a$ being the refractive index glass to air and $_an_g$ being the refractive index air to

glass. Hence, since sin 90° = 1

$$_an_g = \frac{1}{\sin C}$$

For glass with a refractive index of 1.5 this means a critical angle of sin C = 1/1.5 and C = 42°.

This effect is made use of in fibre optics when light is 'piped' along a thin solid glass fibre, bouncing from wall to wall (Fig. 10.12). For no light to be lost from the fibre the light must totally internally reflect with no light being refracted out of the glass.

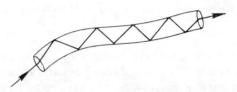

Fig. 10.12   Light passing along a fibre

Another use made of this effect is in optical instruments where a prism is used as a very efficient mirror (Fig. 10.13). Thus light incident normally on one of the shorter sides of a 45° prism meets the diagonal face at an angle of incidence of 45°, and since this is greater than the critical angle of about 42° the light is totally internally reflected.

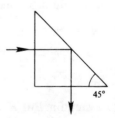

Fig. 10.13   A prism used as a mirror

Refraction by prisms

When light is refracted on passing through a plane surface, it becomes deviated from its original path. With a prism the light then passes onto another surface where the deviation is

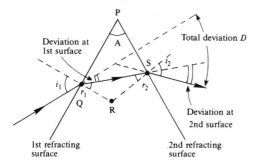

Fig. 10.14   Refraction by a prism

further increased. Figure 10.14 shows a ray passing through a prism. For the refraction at the first surface

angle of deviation at first surface = $i_1 - r_1$

angle of deviation at second surface = $i_2 - r_2$

Total deviation D = sum of the two deviations

$$D = (i_1 - r_1) + (i_2 - r_2) \qquad (1)$$

For the quadrilateral PQRS

angle PQR = angle PSR = 90°

Hence the other two angles in the quadrilateral must add up to 180°.

$$A + \text{angle QRS} = 180°$$

For the triangle QRS all the angles must add up to 180°, thus

$$r_1 + r_2 + \text{angle QRS} = 180°$$

Hence angle QRS = 180° − A = 180° − $(r_1 + r_2)$

and so $\qquad A = r_1 + r_2 \qquad (2)$

Equations (1) and (2) above apply to all prisms and to all conditions. However, there is one version of the equation of special note. When the light passes symmetrically through the prism, i.e., $i_1 = i_2$ and $r_1 = r_2$, then the deviation is a minimum. Equation (1) thus becomes

$$D_{min} = 2(i - r)$$

Equation (2) becomes

$$A = 2r \text{ and so } D_{min} = 2i - A$$

If the refractive index of the prism, relative to the medium in which it is situated, is n, then

$$n = \frac{\sin i}{\sin r}$$

$$n = \frac{\sin [(A + D_{min})/2]}{\sin (A/2)}$$

Measurement of the angle of minimum deviation and the apex angle A of a prism thus enables the refractive index of the prism to be calculated. Figure 10.15 shows how a simple spectrometer can be used for such a measurement.

If in an experiment the apex angle was found to be 59° 55′ and the angle of minimum deviation 40° 50′, then the refractive index was

$$n = \frac{\sin [(50° \ 55′ + 40° \ 50′)/2]}{\sin (59° \ 55′/2)}$$

$$= 1.54$$

Deviation by a small-angle prism

Consider a prism with a small apex angle with light incident at almost normal incidence. Since the sine of a small angle is approximately the same as that angle expressed in radians, we can write for the refraction at the first refracting surface (see Fig. 10.14 for the ray path and symbols used)

$$n = i_1/r_1$$

Angles r_2 and i_2 will also be small, so

$$n = i_2/r_2$$

The deviation D is given by (expression (1) in the previous discussion)

$$D = (i_1 - r_1) + (i_2 - r_2)$$

$$= (nr_1 - r_1) + (nr_2 - r_2)$$

$$= (n - 1)(r_1 + r_2)$$

But, expression (2) shows $A = r_1 + r_2$, hence

$$D = (n - 1)A$$

The deviation produced by a small-angle prism

183

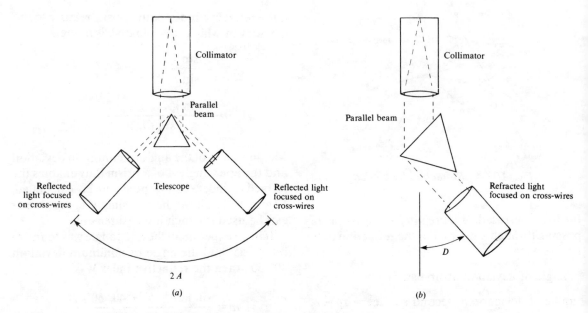

Fig. 10.15   (a) Measurement of apex angle. (b) Measurement of D_{min}; the prism is rotated and the telescope used to track the image until the minimum deviation position is found

is independent of the angle of incidence of the light on the prism, provided it is small. Thus rays with different small angles of incidence are all deviated by the same amount.

Incidently, in using the equation in calculations, if D is in radians then A is in radians, but if D is in degrees then A will be in degrees.

This equation can be considered to be the basic principle of thin lenses. A thin lens can be considered to be made up of small-angled prisms (Fig. 10.16).

Deviation by a thin lens

Figure 10.17 shows the deviation produced for two rays incident on a thin lens. If we consider the lens to be equivalent to a small-angle prism of apex angle A, then the deviation for each of the rays should be the same.

For the first ray the deviation is

$$D = \alpha + \beta$$

$\tan \alpha = h/u$ and $\tan \beta = h/v$. Since the angles are small we can write

$$D = \frac{h}{u} + \frac{h}{v}$$

For the second ray the deviation is

$$D = \gamma$$

$\tan \gamma = h/f$, where f is the focal length (rays parallel to the axis pass through the focus on refraction by a lens). Hence

$$D = \frac{h}{f}$$

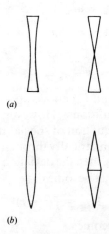

Fig. 10.16   (a) A bi-concave lens as two prisms. (b) A bi-convex lens as two prisms

184

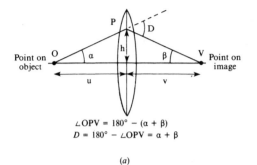

$$\angle OPV = 180° - (\alpha + \beta)$$
$$D = 180° - \angle OPV = \alpha + \beta$$

(a)

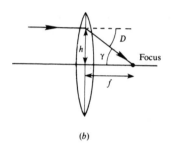

(b)

Fig. 10.17

Thus, since the deviations are equal

$$\frac{h}{f} = \frac{h}{u} + \frac{h}{v}$$

$$\frac{1}{f} = \frac{1}{u} + \frac{1}{v}$$

Terms used with lenses

Parallel light rays, in the case of a convex lens, converge after passing through the lens to a point called the focus. In the case of a concave lens the light after passing through the lens appears to diverge from a point called the focus. Thus the

convex lens has a real focus and the concave lens a virtual focus.

Since light can fall on either surface of a lens, a lens has two focal points, one on each side of the lens.

The principal axis of a lens is the line joining the centres of curvature of the two spherical surfaces. A point on the principal axis and in the centre of the lens is called the optical centre. All distances are measured from this point.

Ray diagrams with thin lenses

Essentially the same rules referred to earlier in this chapter for drawing ray diagrams for spherical mirrors can be used for thin lenses. A number of rays are drawn, originating at a point on the object and meeting at a corresponding point on the image. The rules for drawing the rays are:

1. Each ray is assumed to be independent of other rays.
2. A ray parallel to the axis passes through the focus after refraction.
3. A ray passing through the focus is after refraction parallel to the axis.
4. A ray through the centre of the lens is undeviated.

Figure 10.18 shows such rays with thin lenses. The pattern of results observed with such lens is summarized in the table below.

Sign convention

In this book we will adopt the sign convention called the Real is Positive convention. Whenever a lens convention is used and numbers substituted for symbols, we need to take account of which side of a lens an object, image or focal

	Object distance	Image
Concave lens	All distances	Erect, diminished, virtual
Convex lens	Less than f	Erect, magnified, virtual
	Between f and $2f$	Inverted, magnified, real
	Greater than $2f$	Inverted, diminished, real

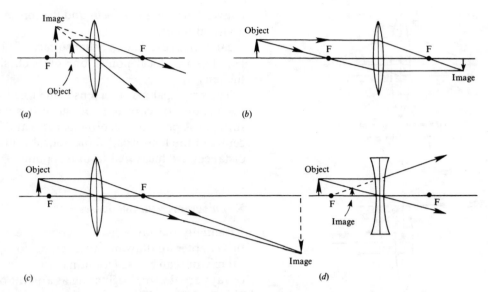

Fig. 10.18   Ray diagrams for thin lenses

point is situated. For this purpose, the convention uses the following rules:

1. All distances are measured from the optic centre of the lens.

2. Distances are taken to be positive if they are distances to real objects, images or focal points. Real ones are where the light actually passes through the points.

3. Distances are taken to be negative if they are distances to virtual objects, images or focal points. Virtual ones are where the light only appears to pass through the points, not actually doing so.

Thus for the situation described by Fig. 10.18a, the object distance is positive, the focal length is positive, but the image distance is, however, negative. For Fig. 10.18d, the object distance is positive, the focal length is negative and the image distance is negative.

The following examples illustrate the use of the lens equation with the real is positive sign convention.

(i) An object is placed 10 cm from a convex lens of focal length 20 cm. What will be the image position?

Object distance $u = +10$ cm, focal length $f = +20$ cm.

$$\frac{1}{f} = \frac{1}{u} + \frac{1}{v}$$

$$\frac{1}{(+20)} = \frac{1}{(+10)} + \frac{1}{v}$$

$$v = -20 \text{ cm}$$

The minus sign means a virtual image, the same side of the lens as the object. Note that no sign should be allocated to any quantity for which a numerical value is not assigned, in this case v. The sign for v emerges from the calculation.

(ii) An object is placed 12 cm from a concave lens of focal length 10 cm. What will be the image position?

Object distance $u = +12$ cm, focal length $f = -10$ cm.

$$\frac{1}{f} = \frac{1}{u} + \frac{1}{v}$$

$$\frac{1}{(-10)} = \frac{1}{(+12)} + \frac{1}{v}$$

$$v = -5.5 \text{ cm}$$

The minus sign means a virtual image, the same side of the lens as the object.

Magnification

The linear magnification of an object is defined as

$$\text{magnification } m = \frac{\text{height of image}}{\text{height of object}}$$

Thus for the situation shown in Fig. 10.19

$$m = \frac{I}{O}$$

But

$$\frac{O}{u} = \frac{I}{v}$$

Hence

$$m = \frac{I}{O} = \frac{v}{u}$$

Thus if an object is placed 20 cm from a convex lens of focal length 10 cm, we can calculate the image distance and the magnification as follows:

$$\text{object distance } u = +20 \text{ cm,}$$
$$\text{focal length } f = +10 \text{cm}$$

$$\frac{1}{f} = \frac{1}{u} + \frac{1}{v}$$

$$\frac{1}{(+10)} = \frac{1}{(+20)} + \frac{1}{v}$$

$$v = +20 \text{ cm}$$

$$m = \frac{v}{u} = \frac{20}{20} = 1$$

The image is the same size as the object.

Fig. 10.19

Dispersion

In the year 1666 Newton took a prism, directed a beam of white light at one refracting surface and observed that the light emerging from the opposite face gave a coloured oblong of light on his wall (Fig. 10.20). Isolating part of that oblong of light and directing it through another prism failed to produce another oblong of coloured light. The conclusion he drew was that white light is a mixture of all the colours and the prism just disperses white light into a spectrum which shows the range of colours. The prism does not colour the light (this being a view prevalent at the time).

The deviation of light on passing through a prism depends on the refractive index. This, however, depends on the frequency of the light, i.e., the colour. Thus light waves of different frequencies are deviated different amounts by a prism and the prism is said to produce dispersion. As Fig. 10.20 shows, red light is deviated less than violet light, this being because for red light the prism has a lower refractive index than for violet light.

It is not only prisms that can be used to produce dispersion, diffraction gratings also do (see previous chapter).

Spectra

If common salt, sodium chloride, is present in a gas flame then the flame has a yellow coloration. If we examine the yellow light with a spectroscope we find that the overall colour is made up by a number of discrete frequencies.

Strong similarities in spectra occur whatever the sodium salt used to give the spectrum. Certain spectrum lines, frequencies, appear to be due to sodium and to occur whatever the compound in which the sodium occurs. The sodium spectrum is different from, say, potassium or indeed any other spectrum. Each element gives out its own spectrum, each has its own fingerprint. Such emission spectra can be used to identify the elements present in a substance.

The spectrum from a hot solid shows a continuous spectrum, a wide range of frequencies being emitted. Such a spectrum is the same for all

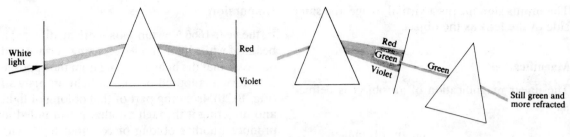

Fig. 10.20

solids at the same temperature, being independent of the identity of the solid.

When light which forms a continuous spectrum is passed through gases the spectrum is found to contain a number of dark lines. These are absorption lines and correspond in position to the frequencies which the gas gives for its emission spectrum. Such absorption lines were first found by Wollaston in 1802 when he examined the spectrum of the sun. Detailed investigation was carried out by Fraunhofer between 1814 and 1824. The sun's spectrum contains a large number of absorption lines due to the continuous spectrum light emitted by the hot solar core having to pass through the hot solar atmospheric gases. These lines are now known as the Fraunhofer lines. Fraunhofer labelled the lines with the letters of the alphabet. The strong yellow sodium lines appear in absorption in the sun's spectrum and are known as the D lines.

An absorption spectrum is produced when light which forms a continuous spectrum is passed through any substance (solid, liquid or gas); with solids and liquid the absorption is generally not as discrete lines but more continuous bands.

The development of the microscope

The following brief outline is intended to show how, over the years, the microscope has developed from a single piece of glass to the complex modern instrument employing many lenses.

The use of a single convex lens as a magnifying glass may possibly date back as far as the Romans, certainly it was known about the year AD 1000. An object placed inside the focal length of a convex lens gives rise to an enlarged virtual image (Fig. 10.21a). The angle subtended by the rays of light, apparently, from the image is greater than

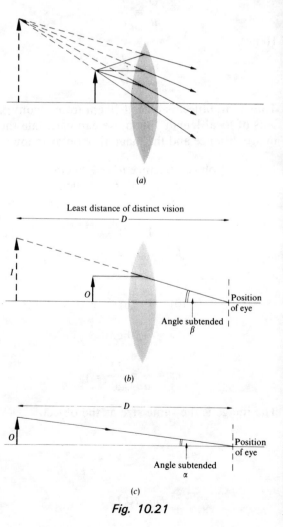

Fig. 10.21

188

the angle the rays would subtend at the eye if no lens were present (Fig. 10.21c). The ratio of these two angles is known as the magnifying power. Without the lens the greatest angle that the object can subtend at the eye is when the object is placed as near to the eye as the eye can give a clear focused image. This distance is known as the least distance of distinct vision and is for the average person about 0.25 m. The virtual image formed by the lens must not be nearer to the eye than this least distance of distinct vision. The bigger the angle subtended at the eye the larger the apparent size of the object. A man 100 m away subtends a much smaller angle than a man 10 m away—at 10 m we may see the buttons on his jacket, at 100 m we may have difficulty in discerning the jacket. A difference in angle subtended at the eye of about one minute of arc is needed if two objects are to appear resolved.

For a single convex lens we have

(Angle subtended at the eye without instrument)
$$= \alpha$$

(Angle subtended at the eye with instrument)
$$= \beta$$

and thus

$$\text{Magnifying power} = \frac{\beta}{\alpha}$$

$$\tan \alpha = \frac{O}{D}$$

$$\tan \beta = \frac{I}{D}$$

where O is the object size, I the image size, and D the least distance of distinct vision.

If the angles are small, often the case, we can make the assumption that the tangent of the angle is approximately the same as the angle. Then

$$\text{Magnifying power} = \frac{I}{D} \times \frac{D}{O} = \frac{I}{O}$$

If the lens is thin, a very doubtful assumption for most single lens magnifiers, we can use the thin lens formula to obtain I and O in terms of the focal length and D

$$\frac{1}{f} = \frac{1}{v} + \frac{1}{u}$$

Hence

$$\frac{v}{u} = \frac{v}{f} - 1$$

and as $I/O = v/u$ we obtain

$$\text{Magnifying power} = \frac{v}{f} - 1$$

If the eye is fairly close to the lens then v is approximately equal to $-D$ and we have

$$\text{Magnifying power} = -\left(\frac{D}{f} + 1\right)$$

or to a reasonable approximation, considering the crudity of our assumptions so far, we can neglect the 1 and consider the magnifying power to be $-D/f$. Large magnifying powers are thus produced with small focal length lenses.

A smaller value of the magnifying power (D/f) is produced if the final image is at infinity instead of the least distance of distinct vision.

Great magnifying power can be achieved if two convex lenses are used. The first such compound microscope was probably produced about the end of the sixteenth century. In such an instrument the first convex lens, known as the objective, produces a real image close to the second lens, known as the eyepiece. This lens acts in the same way as the magnifying glass and gives an enlarged virtual image (Fig. 10.22).

(Angle subtended at the eye without instrument)
$$= \alpha$$

(Angle subtended at the eye with instrument)
$$= \beta$$

$$\text{Magnifying power} = \frac{\beta}{\alpha}$$

$$\tan \alpha = \frac{O}{D}$$

$$\tan \beta = \frac{I}{D}$$

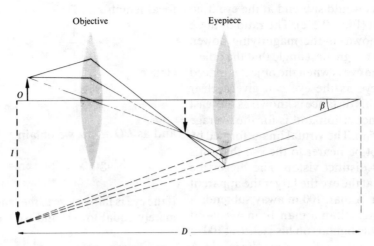

Fig. 10.22 The simple microscope

where I is the size of the final image. Thus for small angles

$$\text{Magnifying power} = \frac{I}{O}$$

If we multiply the top and the bottom of this equation by the same quantity, I', the size of the intermediate image, we obtain

$$\text{Magnifying power} = \frac{I}{I'}\frac{I'}{O}$$

or

$$\binom{\text{Magnifying}}{\text{power}} =$$

$$\binom{\text{magnification}}{\text{of eyepiece}} \times \binom{\text{magnification}}{\text{of objective}}$$

The microscope with the final image produced at the least distance of distinct vision is said to be in normal adjustment.

In order that the entire cone of rays from the intermediate image can be received at the eye, a necessary condition if the image is not to be less bright than the object, the eyepiece lens has to be quite large, larger than the objective. In addition, all the rays passing through the eyepiece must enter the eye. This is most easily achieved if the eye is placed at the position known as the eyepoint (sometimes called the Ramsden circle), a point some considerable distance from the eyepiece (Fig. 10.23). The difficulties in making large eyepiece lenses and the inconvenience in placing the eye some distance from the eyepiece led to the design of eyepieces using more than one lens. Such eyepieces were invented by Huygens and Kepler, in the early seventeenth century (Fig. 10.24). In the Huygens eyepiece the two lenses are about half the sum of the focal lengths of the two lenses apart.

Microscopes built with objective lenses which were just simple convex lenses suffered from severe distortions of the image. The major aberrations were spherical aberration and chromatic aberration. With spherical aberration the rays of light travelling through the outer parts of the lens come to a different focus from that which rays through the inner part of the lens come to (Fig. 10.25a). This is a defect common to all lenses whose surfaces are spherical, i.e., all points on a surface have the same radius of curvature. The effects of this can be reduced by only using the central portion of the lens. With chromatic aberration the different colours of light come to different foci (Fig. 10.25b). This occurs because the glass of the lens has different refractive indices for the different colours of light. The result is that the edges of images are blurred and

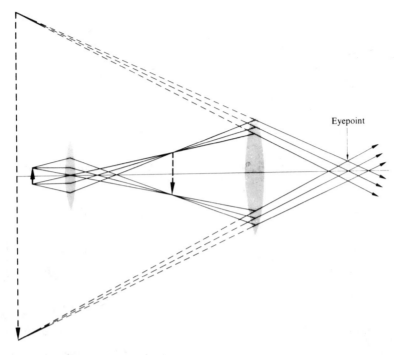

Fig. 10.23   The eyepoint

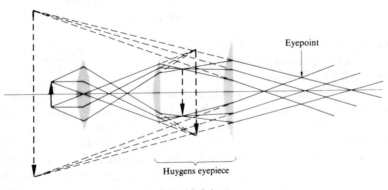

Fig. 10.24

appear coloured. Around about 1740 this problem of chromatic aberration was reduced with the invention of what were called achromatic lenses. Achromatic convex lenses were designed with two components—a convex lens made of crown glass and a concave lens of flint glass (Fig. 10.26). The focal length of the two lenses together for red light can be made equal to the focal length of the combination for blue light. It was the end of the eighteenth century before such lenses could be satisfactorily made and used in microscopes. Even then the achromatic lens could only be achieved for long focal lengths. To achieve high magnifying powers short focal length objective

191

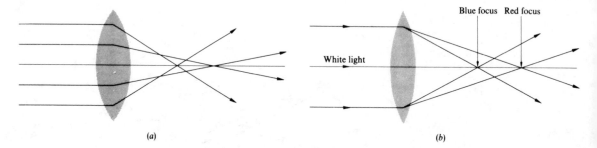

Fig. 10.25 (a) A spherical aberration. (b) Chromatic aberration

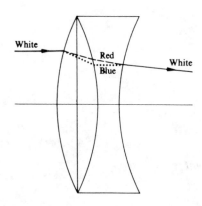

Fig. 10.26 An achromatic lens

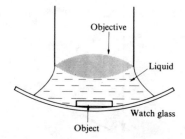

Fig. 10.27 Brewster's immersion lens

lenses were necessary. It was not until about 1830 that short focal length achromatic objective lenses were produced, by using more than one achromatic doublet of lenses. Up to this time empirical methods had been used in combining achromatic lenses. Lister in 1830 showed how to determine theoretically what lenses to use to reduce both chromatic and spherical aberrations to a minimum.

In 1812 Brewster suggested that chromatic aberration could be reduced by immersing the objective lens and the object being examined in a liquid (Fig. 10.27). Effectively this gave a concave liquid lens in contact with the convex objective lens. Such a combination did reduce chromatic aberration but not as effectively as the achromatic doublets made of glasses. About 1850 Amici developed the idea of immersion objectives for a different purpose—to increase the brightness of the image. With a cover glass over the object, the

rays of light entering the objective are limited by total internal reflection at the glass-to-air surface (Fig. 10.28). The critical angle occurs when

$$\frac{\sin C}{\sin 90} = \frac{1}{n}$$

where n is the refractive index from air to glass of the cover glass. Taking n as 3/2 gives a critical angle of about 41° and thus a maximum cone angle of 82° for light rays from the object to enter the objective. In fact this angle would be less due to the air gap between the cover glass and the objective lens. If the air between the cover glass and the objective is replaced by a liquid the critical angle increases.

$$\frac{\sin C}{\sin 90} = \frac{1}{n'}$$

where n' is the refractive index from liquid to glass. For water as the liquid, n' is 3/2 ÷ 4/3 and the critical angle becomes about 64°. This gives a maximum cone angle of about 128°. By using a

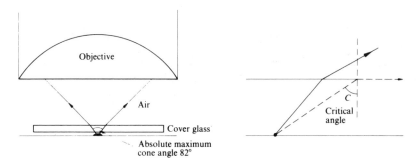

Fig. 10.28

liquid whose refractive index is equal to that of the cover glass the cone angle can be increased even further as the problem of reflection at the glass-to-air, or liquid, surface does not arise. Such immersion lenses were realized about 1870.

Achromatic lenses, either singly or in groups, do not produce images completely free from colour—chromatic aberration is not completely eliminated. In the achromatic lens the red and blue components of the light are brought to the same focus, the other colours do not come to the same focus. This leaves a residual colour of greenish-yellow which shows as a slight coloured border to the image. With the glasses available about 1800 this was the best that could be achieved. It was not until near the end of the nineteenth century that new glasses were produced which enabled better colour correction to be achieved. In the new lenses, known as apochromatic lenses, a number of lenses of different glasses are combined to give the red, the blue, and the green components of light all coming to the same focus.

By the end of the nineteenth century the optics of optical microscopes had reached a state from which little improvement has been made so far this century.

The development of the telescope

The invention of the compound microscope and the telescope are of the same period of time. The first telescope was probably that of Lippershey in about 1609 and consisted of two spectacle lenses separated by a distance equal to the sum of their focal lengths. Figure 10.29 shows the basic arrangement.

$$\text{Magnifying power} = \frac{\beta}{\alpha}$$

$$\tan \alpha = \frac{I'}{f_o}$$

$$\tan \beta = \frac{I'}{f_e}$$

Hence

$$\text{Magnifying power} = \frac{f_o}{f_e}$$

The distance between the objective and eyepiece lenses is $(f_0 + f_e)$. Such a telescope with the final image formed at infinity is said to be in normal adjustment.

For large magnifying powers long focal length objective lenses and short focal length eyepiece lenses are needed. The Yerkes Observatory in the USA has a telescope with an objective of focal length 20 m and an eyepiece of focal length 2.5 cm, giving a magnifying power of about 800.

The circular area AB in figure 10.29 is the smallest area through which all the rays pass and is therefore the optimum position for the observer's eye for maximum image brightness. AB is in fact the image of the objective lens in the eyepiece and is called the eyering.

Newton realized that one of the main factors limiting increases in magnifying powers was the lens aberrations. Careful grinding of the

193

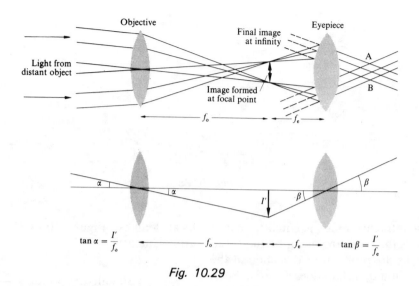

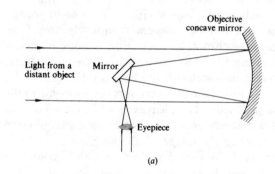

$$\tan \alpha = \frac{I'}{f_o}$$ ← f_o → ← f_e → $\tan \beta = \frac{I'}{f_e}$

Fig. 10.29

lens surfaces enabled him significantly to reduce spherical aberration but he could not reduce chromatic aberration. Seeing no way of reducing this he replaced the objective lens by a concave mirror and invented what is known as the reflecting telescope. Figure 10.30a shows the basic arrangement.

The reflecting telescope at Mount Palomar (Fig. 10.30) has a mirror 5.5 m in diameter. The observer sits with the eyepiece lens near the focal point of the mirror.

Improvements in lens design (see the previous section on microscopes) have enabled further improvements in telescopes to be realized. The biggest instruments are, however, still reflecting instruments.

Spectroscopes

Spectroscopy is the study of the radiation emitted or absorbed by a material, the instruments used being referred to as spectroscopes. Spectroscopy is not restricted to the confines of the visible part of the electromagnetic spectrum. In whatever region of the electromagnetic spectrum we are concerned with, the basic item of a spectroscope is a means of dispersing radiation into its constituent frequencies. The earliest method of doing this was the prism, with the diffraction grating later becoming an important method.

(a)

(b)

Fig. 10.30 (a) A basic reflecting telescope. (b) A 200-inch (5.5-m) Palomar reflecting telescope. The observer is in the prime focus position, the mirror can be seen at the far end of the telescope tube. (Courtesy of the Hale Observatories)

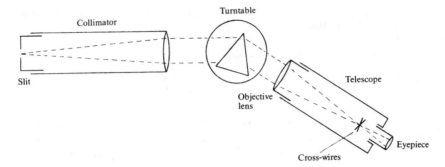

Fig. 10.31   The simple spectrometer

Figure 10.31 shows the constituent parts of the simple spectrometer. Such an instrument can be used with either a prism or a diffraction grating to produce a pure spectrum, i.e., one without overlapping coloured images, and enables it to be observed and measurements made. The instrument consists of three main parts, a collimator, a turntable on which the prism or grating can be mounted, and a telescope.

The sequence of operations used to set up the instrument is as follows:

1. The telescope eyepiece is adjusted so that the cross-wires are in focus.

2. The position of the telescope objective is adjusted so that on looking through the eyepiece a distant object is in focus on the cross-wires. This means that parallel rays of light are being brought to a focus on the cross-wires.

3. The collimator and telescopes are then lined up and the position of the slit relative to the collimator lens adjusted until the slit is in focus on the telescope cross-wires. This means that the collimator must be producing parallel rays of light.

4. The prism or grating is then mounted on the turntable which is levelled.

While modern spectroscopes are not now like the simple spectrometer, the principle of the instrument is still valid. The instrument can also be used for the accurate measurement of the refractive index of a transparent material in the form of a prism.

Probably the simplest spectroscope for use in the visible part of the electromagnetic spectrum involves just a piece of diffraction grating and a slit, Fig. 10.32. The light passing through the grating is diffracted through angles which depend on the wavelength (see previous chapter).

Both the spectroscopes so far described are restricted to the visible part of the spectrum, only slightly overlapping into the ultraviolet and infrared. The restriction occurs because glass, and many materials which are transparent in the visible, is opaque to the far ultraviolet and infrared. One way of overcoming this is to use materials, such as quartz, which are transparent to a wider range of wavelengths. Another way is to use reflection diffraction gratings and spherical mirrors, so that the radiation does not have to pass through any component. Photographic film or photoelectric cells can be used to detect the radiation.

Spectrophotometers are used to determine how the absorption of radiation by a substance varies with wavelength. Radiation from a tungsten lamp is used to give, after being incident on a grating, a

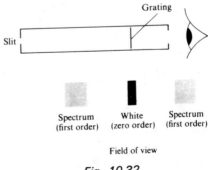

Fig. 10.32

wide band of wavelengths. A different lamp is used for the ultraviolet region, the tungsten lamp being for the visible region. A narrow band of the wavelengths is selected and passed through a cell containing the sample and the radiation transmitted detected by a phototube. The output of the phototube is shown on a meter.

The absorption at a particular wavelength is determined by the molecules present in the sample. The absorption spectrum can thus be used to identify molecules.

The camera

The pinhole camera whereby an image of a distant object is produced on the wall opposite the pinhole (Fig. 10.33) has been known for centuries. It was, however, not until the early nineteenth century that the image could be photographed using the process in which exposure to light affected silver salts. By 1829 the lens camera had been developed, Fig. 10.34 showing the basic principles of a modern lens camera. This uses celluloid film as a base for the photographic emulsion, this first being introduced in 1888. Prior to this the emulsion had inevitably been on glass plates. It was this development which was to lead to the small, light, portable cameras with which we now are so familiar.

The light falling on the photographic emulsion in a camera depends on the amount of light passing through the lens, this being capable of being altered by changing the lens aperture and the time for which the shutter permits light to pass through to the emulsion. The aperture control is in terms of a scale of f-numbers—1.4, 2, 2.8, 4, 5.6, 8, 11, 16, 22 and 32. Reducing the f-number by one setting, e.g., from 11 to 8, doubles the area of the aperture and, at a given shutter speed, the amount of light incident on the photographic emulsion.

The amount of light falling on the image is proportional to the area of the lens aperture. If the aperture has a diameter d then the amount of light is proportional to d^2. The size of the image produced by the camera lens is proportional to its focal length f (see Fig. 10.35), hence the area of the image is proportional to f^2. Thus the brightness of the image is proportional to d^2/f^2. The relative aperture of the lens is defined as d/f, this being expressed on the f-number scale. If the aperture is f-8 then the diameter of the lens is $f/8$, i.e., one-eighth the focal length. The brightness of the image is, however, proportional to the square of the relative aperture, i.e., $1/(f\text{-number})^2$. Hence changing the aperture from f-8 to f-5.6 changes the image brightness from being proportional to $1/8^2$ to $1/5.6^2$, i.e., by a factor of $(1/5.6^2)/(1/8^2) = 2.0$.

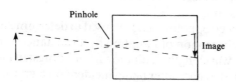

Fig. 10.33   The pinhole camera

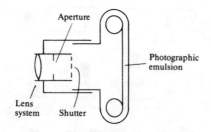

Fig. 10.34   The lens camera

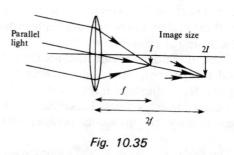

Fig. 10.35

Only an object at one particular object distance will be precisely in focus on the photographic film at a particular film to lens separation (i.e., image distance). The object in focus can, however, be changed by changing the film to lens separation. However, there is a range of object distances which gives images effectively in focus as far as the human eye can detect. This range of object distances is known as the depth of field. The depth of field depends on the size of the lens aperture; the smaller the aperture the greater the depth (Fig. 10.36).

Problems

1. State the conditions under which a beam of light will undergo total internal reflection at the interface between two media of refractive indices n_1 and n_2, where n_2 is greater than n_1.

(University of Cambridge, Q5, Paper 1, November 1979)

2. A ray of light, initially in air, is refracted at a plane glass surface at a gradually increasing angle of incidence, i_1. For each incident angle the value of the angle of refraction, i_2, is measured. What would you plot in order to obtain a straight line graph relating i_1 and i_2? How would you use this graph to determine the refractive index of the glass?

(University of London, Q5, Paper 1, June 1981)

3. A camera has a lens, of focal length 120 mm, which can be moved along its principal axis towards and away from the film. If the camera is to be able to form perfect images of objects from infinite distance down to 1.00 m from the camera, through what distance must it be possible to move the lens?

(University of London, Q3, Paper 2, January 1982)

4. A lamp and a screen are 80 cm apart and a converging lens placed midway between them produces a focused image on the screen.

A thin diverging lens is placed 10 cm from the lamp, between the lamp and the converging lens. When the lamp is moved back so that it is 30 cm from the diverging lens, the focused image reappears on the screen. What is the focal length of the diverging lens?

(University of London, Q3, Paper 2, June 1982)

5. A refracting telescope has an objective of focal length 1.0 m and an eyepiece of focal length 2.0 cm. A real image of the sun, 10 cm in diameter, is formed on a screen 24 cm from the eye-

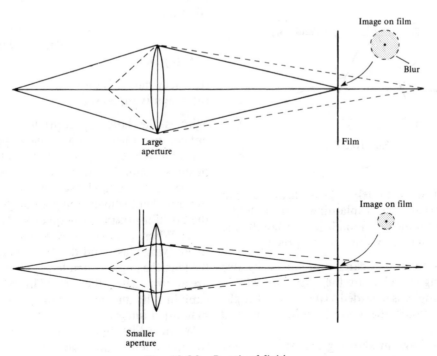

Fig. 10.36 Depth of field

piece. What angle does the sun subtend at the objective?

(University of London, Q3, Paper 2, June 1979)

6. Calculate the position of the eye ring for an astronomical telescope consisting of two thin converging lenses, an objective of focal length 1.0 m and an eyepiece of focal length 20 mm, placed 1.02 m apart.

Explain the advantages of placing the eye at the eye ring position when using the telescope.

(University of London, Q2, Paper 2, June 1983)

7. (a) Describe briefly how you would measure the deviation of a beam of monochromatic light by a prism using a spectrometer. (A full ray diagram is not required but sketches showing the prism positions should be given. Details of the initial adjustments are not required.)

(b) Figure 10.37 which is not to scale, shows a ray of monochromatic light entering and leaving a glass prism of refracting angle A. The graph in Fig. 10.38 shows how the deviation, D, of the ray varies with the incident angle, i_1. Show that $D = (i_2 + i_2) - A$.

Using Fig. 10.38

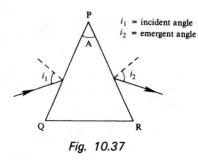

Fig. 10.37

(i) Estimate as accurately as possible the value of A for the prism used, explaining your method.
(ii) Show that the deviation is least when the ray passes symmetrically through the prism.

A deviation of 42° can be produced by two incident angles. What are they? Explain why, if one of the angles is regarded as the incident angle, the other equals the corresponding emergent angle.

Sketch a diagram showing the path of a ray which enters face PQ and leaves face PR with the

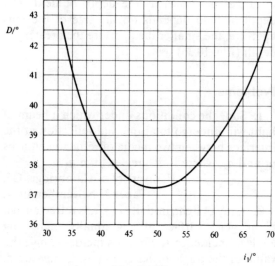

Fig. 10.38

deviation a maximum. If this maximum deviation is 58°, what is the angle of incidence on face PQ?

(c) Prisms are widely used to produce deviations in light beams but they suffer a major disadvantage. By means of a suitable diagram explain what this is.

(University of London, Q11, Paper 2, January 1980)

8. (a) Define

(i) linear magnification and
(ii) magnifying power.

Why is the latter appropriate in considering optical instruments such as telescopes?

(b) Draw a ray diagram to illustrate the action of an astronomical telescope consisting of two convex (converging) lenses, the instrument being in normal adjustment. On your diagram indicate the positions of the principal foci of the lenses.

(c) When a single convex lens is used as a magnifying glass, and the eye is placed close to the lens, the angle subtended by object and image are approximately the same. This being the case, explain why the magnifying glass produces a magnified image.

When white light is refracted on passing through a lens it undergoes dispersion and each colour produces a separate image. Why, then, is a series of coloured images not observed when the eye is placed close to a magnifying glass?

(d) A camera is set at f-5.6, 1/120 s. If the aperture is changed to f-16 to what value should the exposure time be set to achieve the same exposure? What other effect would the change of aperture have?

(AEB, QB12, Paper 3, June 1982)

9. Explain the term angular magnification as related to an optical instrument.

Describe, with the aid of a ray diagram, the structure and action of an astronomical telescope. Derive an expression for its angular magnification when used so that the final image is at infinity. With such an instrument what is the best position for the observer's eye? Why is this the best position?

Even if the lenses in such an instrument are perfect it may not be possible to produce clear separate images of two points which are close together. Explain why this is so. Keeping the focal lengths of the lenses the same, what could be changed in order to make the separation of the images more possible?

(University of London, Q11, Paper 2, June 1978)

10. (a) An astronomical telescope, consisting of two, thin, converging lenses, is set up in normal adjustment in order to view a distance object.

(i) Show, by means of a labelled ray diagram, how a magnified image is formed by the instrument. The diagram should show the paths through the telescope of three rays from a non-axial point on the object.
(ii) Indicate the position of the eye-ring (exit pupil) and explain its formation.
(iii) Define the magnifying power of the instrument.

(b) A parallel beam of monochromatic light, incident normally on a very small circular aperture and filling it completely, falls on a plane surface placed approximately one metre behind and parallel to the plane of the aperture.

(i) Sketch the graph which shows the intensity of the light falling on the surface as a function of the radial distance from the normal to the surface which passes through the centre of the aperture.

(ii) Hence explain the criterion which is used to obtain the resolving power of an astronomical telescope.
(iii) What is the effect on the resolving power of reducing the diameter of the aperture by half?

(c) An observer, with the aid of an astronomical telescope, can just resolve two stars which have an angular separation of two seconds of arc. If the observer's unaided eye has a resolving power of two minutes of arc, calculate the magnifying power of the instrument.

(JMB, Q1, Paper I Section (2), June 1979)

11. (a) A thin converging lens can be used to form a real image or a virtual image of a small extended object at right angles to its principal axis. State how the nature of the image, and also the magnification (defined as length of image/length of object) depend on the position of the object relative to the principal focus on the object side.

(b) Defining the magnifying power of a simple magnifying glass to be

$$\frac{\text{angle subtended at the eye by image in its actual situation}}{\text{angle subtended at the unaided eye by object if it were placed at the eye's near point}}$$

show that the magnifying power of a magnifying glass of focal length f can range from d/f when the image is formed at infinity to $(1 + d/f)$ when the image is formed at the near-point distance d.

(c) A compound microscope consists of two thin lenses, an objective of focal length 20 mm and an eyepiece of focal length 50 mm, placed 220 mm apart. If the final image is viewed at infinity, calculate the distance of the object from the objective and also the magnifying power of the system when it is used by a man whose near-point distance is 250 mm.

(d) Draw a ray-trace diagram (not to scale) illustrating the passage of light through the microscope, showing rays starting from a non-axial point on the object.

(Oxford Local Examinations Board, Q7, Paper I, June 1979)

12. (a) A converging (convex) lens collects light coming from a point on its principal axis and brings this light together again at another point on the principal axis. Draw

(i) a wavefront diagram, and
(ii) a ray diagram to illustrate this fact.

What is the relationship between the rays and the wavefronts?

(b) Some road signs consist of small transparent spheres embedded in a silvered background. What should be the refractive index of the material of the sphere if a beam of light incident at a small angle of incidence is to be reflected back in a direction parallel to the incident beam?

Other reflector warning devices consist of two reflecting surfaces placed at right angles to one another. Explain how these cause an incident beam of light to be reflected back along a parallel path for all angles of incidence.

(c) Explain what is meant by an f-number as applied to a camera. A camera is marked with the following f-numbers: 8, 11, 16, 22. How are these numbers related and how do they affect the exposure? Explain, with the aid of a diagram, how a change in the f-number affects the range of distances of objects from the camera which appear to be satisfactorily in focus.

(AEB, Q11, Paper 3, June 1981)

Part 3
Electricity and Fields

11 Electric circuits

Current and voltage

We may look at an electrical circuit and say—the current is 5 A, the battery has an e.m.f. of 6 V, the potential difference across that resistor is 3 V. What do these terms mean?

Current is the term used to describe the rate of movement of charge past some point.

$$I = \frac{dO}{dt}$$

If 5 coulombs of charge pass a point in a circuit every second we call the current 5 coulombs per second, or 5 amps.

What causes the current? A battery could be the reason. We say the battery supplies an electromotive force, i.e., an e.m.f. A battery is a device in which by chemical action one electrode, or terminal, becomes positively charged and the other negatively charged. When an external connection is made between the two battery terminals charge flows, i.e., there is a current through the connecting wire, and the chemical reaction in the battery endeavours to maintain the charge separation. In the battery is some mechanism which moves charge carriers in an opposite direction to which they move round the external circuit. The e.m.f. can be defined as the energy used to produce a separation of one coulomb of charge. The unit of e.m.f. is the volt. When the battery terminals are connected by an external circuit this energy is available to drive charge round the circuit. Thus the e.m.f. could be defined as the energy available to drive one coulomb of charge round a circuit. This last definition requires some modification—all the energy used to produce the charge separation will not be available to drive the charge round an external circuit as some energy will be dissipated within the battery, driving the current through the battery's own internal resistance, when a current flows. Thus the modified definition becomes— the e.m.f. is the energy available to drive one coulomb round a circuit when no current is being taken.

The energy needed to drive one coulomb through a circuit component such as a resistor is called the voltage or potential difference, V.

$$V = \frac{\text{energy}}{\text{charge}}$$

The unit of V is volts if energy is in joules and charge in coulombs. A voltmeter placed in parallel with the resistor is a means of measuring the energy per coulomb needed. Many voltmeters are current-measuring instruments and depend on the fact that there is a linear relationship between the current flowing through the voltmeter coil (resistor) and the potential difference across the coil.

The energy dissipated by a charge q passing through a circuit component is the same as the energy needed to drive the charge through the component

$$\text{Energy dissipated} = Vq$$

where V is the potential difference across the component. If the energy dissipated in time $t = Vq$, then the energy dissipated per second $= Vq/t$.

This is known as the power—rate of energy dissipation.

$$\text{Power} = \frac{Vq}{t} = VI \quad \text{as} \quad I = \frac{q}{t}$$

The unit of power is the watt. In the above equation this is when V is in volts and I in amps.

Measurements of the power due to a current passing through a coil can be used to give a measure of the potential difference without the use of a voltmeter. If the coil is mounted inside a metal cylinder the rise in temperature of the cylinder per second can be measured, for a known current. The energy needed to produce this temperature change can be estimated if the same temperature change is produced by the expenditure of a measured amount of mechanical energy.

Resistance

The ratio of the potential difference across a resistor to the current I is called the resistance R.

$$R = \frac{V}{I}$$

When I is in amps, V in volts, then R is in ohms (Ω).

For some materials, some circuit components, R is a constant independent of the value of the potential difference across it. This means that if the potential difference is doubled then the current is doubled. This relationship is generally called Ohm's law, being expressed as:

Provided physical conditions, e.g., temperature, do not change then, regardless of the value of the applied potential difference, the current is proportional to the potential difference.

Circuit components that obey Ohm's law over a wide range of potential difference, e.g., components generally consisting of just lengths of pure metals or alloys, are said to be ohmic. However, there are many non-ohmic components, e.g., electrolytes, diodes and gases.

Figure 11.1 shows graphs of potential difference against current, such graphs being called the electrical characteristics, for some ohmic and non-ohmic components.

Variation of resistance with temperature

The resistance of a material varies with temperature. For metals and alloys at temperatures in the region of room temperature, the variation with temperature can generally be expressed as

$$R_0(1 + \alpha\theta)$$

where R_0 is the resistance at $0°C$, R_θ the resistance at a temperature θ, and α is a constant for the material concerned, being known as the temperature coefficient of resistance.

Copper has a temperature coefficient of resistance of $4.0 \times 10^{-3} \text{ K}^{-1}$ and so if we have a coil of copper wire with a resistance of 50.0Ω at $0°C$, at $30°C$ the resistance will be

$$R_\theta = 50.0(1 + 4.0 \times 10^{-3} \times 30)$$
$$= 56.0 \Omega$$

Definitions

Current is defined as the rate of flow of charge through a given cross-section, the unit being the ampere.

The *ampere* is that constant current which, if maintained in two straight parallel conductors of infinite length, of negligible circular cross-section, and placed 1 m apart in a vacuum, causes each to exert a force of 2×10^{-7} N on one metre length of the other (see Chapter 14).

The unit of charge is the *coulomb* and is defined as the charge passing through a given cross-section when a steady current of 1 A flows for 1 s.

The *potential difference* between two points is the work done in moving unit charge between those points (see Chapter 13), the unit being the volt.

The *volt* is that potential difference existing between two points when 1 J of work has to be done to move 1 C between them.

The *resistance* of a device is defined as the

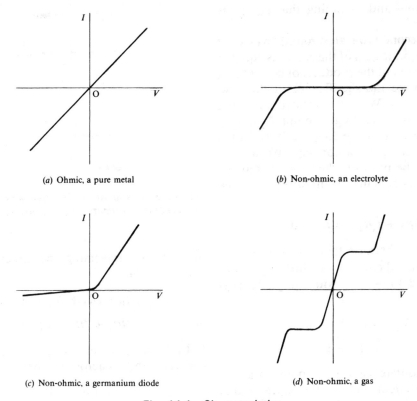

(a) Ohmic, a pure metal

(b) Non-ohmic, an electrolyte

(c) Non-ohmic, a germanium diode

(d) Non-ohmic, a gas

Fig. 11.1 Characteristics

potential difference across it divided by the current through it, the unit being the ohm.

A device has a *resistance of 1 Ω* when a potential difference of 1 V across it occurs with a current of 1 A through it.

Electrical circuits

Figure 11.2 shows a simple circuit junction with meters measuring the current flowing into the junction and out of it. A simple rule emerges from examination of the meter readings,

$$I_1 = I_2 + I_3$$

The current entering the junction is equal to the current leaving the junction. This rule is known as Kirchoff's first law. It is often put in the form: the algebraic sum of the currents at a junction is zero (the term algebraic meaning we must take into account the current directions, thus $I_1 - I_2 - I_3 = 0$).

All the first law really states is that the rate at which charge enters a junction is equal to the rate at which charge leaves the junction. This is what we would expect if charge does not accumulate

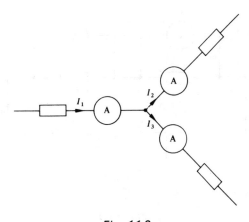

Fig. 11.2

205

at the junction—and assuming that charge is conserved.

Kirchoff's second law states: round any closed circuit the algebraic sum of the e.m.f.s is equal to the algebraic sum of the products of current and resistance. To see the significance of this law, consider Fig. 11.3. We will consider traversing the circuit loop by starting at point A moving along the top part of the loop to B and then returning to A along the bottom part. We take the *IR* product to be positive when we are moving through a component in the same direction as the current. Thus

$$I_1R_1 + I_1R_2 - I_2R_3 = 0$$

The sum is zero because there is no source of e.m.f. in this closed circuit loop. Since $V_1 = I_1R_1$, $V_2 = I_1R_2$ and $V_3 = I_2R_3$, what this tells us is that

$$V_1 + V_2 - V_3 = 0$$
$$V_1 + V_2 = V_3$$

The potential difference between points A and B via the upper circuit loop is the same as that between the points via the lower circuit loop.

The sign convention used for e.m.f.s (ε) and the *IR* products is shown in Fig. 11.4; movement round a circuit in the direction of the current is taken as being positive, in a direction opposite to the current as negative. Consider the use of the second law with the circuit in Fig. 11.5. Starting

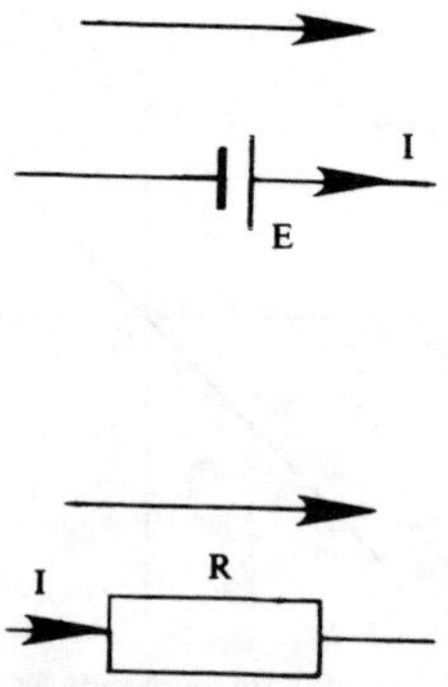

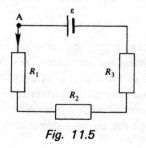

Fig. 11.4 E and IR are positive when traversed in the directions indicated by the arrows

from A and traversing the circuit loop anti-clockwise, then

$$IR_1 + IR_2 + IR_3 - \varepsilon = 0$$

or

$$IR_1 + IR_2 + IR_3 = \varepsilon$$

If V_1 is the potential difference across R_1, V_2 across R_2 and V_3 across R_3, then

$$V_1 + V_2 + V_3 = \varepsilon$$

Resistors in series and in parallel

Consider three resistors of resistance R_1, R_2 and R_3 in series (Fig. 11.6a). The same current must flow through each of them. The potential difference between points A and B must, however, be the sum of the potential differences, i.e., the *IR* products, across each resistor. Hence

$$V = IR_1 + IR_2 + IR_3$$

If the three resistors were to be replaced by a single resistor of resistance R having the same

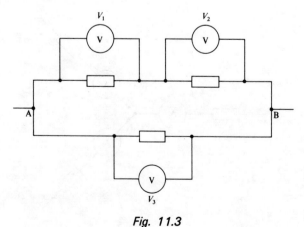

Fig. 11.3

Fig. 11.5

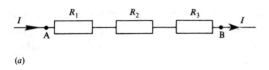

(a)

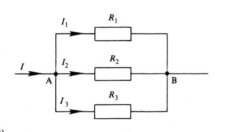

(b)

Fig. 11.6 (a) Resistors in series. (b) Resistors in parallel

effect on the circuit, then there must be a potential difference of V across it when a current I flows through it, i.e., $V = IR$.

Hence

$$IR = IR_1 + IR_2 + IR_3$$

$$R = R_1 + R_2 + R_3$$

The combined resistance of resistors in series is the sum of their resistances.

Consider three resistors of resistance R_1, R_2 and R_3 in parallel (Fig. 11.6b). Using Kirchoff's first law, we must have

$$I = I_1 + I_2 + I_3$$

The potential difference V between points A and B will be the same for each of the resistors. Hence

$$V = I_1R_1 = I_2R_2 = I_3R_3$$

Thus

$$I = \frac{V}{R_1} + \frac{V}{R_2} + \frac{V}{R_3}$$

If the three resistors were replaced by a single resistor of resistance R having the same effect on the circuit, then there must be a potential difference V across it when a current I flows through

ELECTRIC CIRCUITS

it, i.e., $V = IR$. Hence

$$\frac{V}{R} = \frac{V}{R_1} + \frac{V}{R_2} + \frac{V}{R_3}$$

$$\frac{1}{R} = \frac{1}{R_1} + \frac{1}{R_2} + \frac{1}{R_3}$$

Thus if a 10 Ω resistor was in parallel with a 20 Ω resistor, the resistance of the combination is given by

$$\frac{1}{R} = \frac{1}{10} + \frac{1}{20}$$

$$R = 6.7 \ \Omega$$

Figure 11.7 illustrates a slightly more complex circuit. The parallel arm of the circuit with the 6 Ω and 12 Ω can be replaced by a resistor of 6 + 12 = 18 Ω. We now have 18 Ω in parallel with 24 Ω. This can be replaced by a resistor of resistance R where

$$\frac{1}{R} = \frac{1}{18} + \frac{1}{24}$$

$$R = 10.3 \ \Omega$$

This is in series with the 10 Ω resistor, so the entire circuit can be replaced with a 10 + 10.3 = 20.3 Ω resistor.

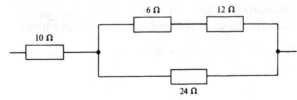

Fig. 11.7

Electromotive force and internal resistance

Figure 11.8a shows a circuit by which the potential difference across a cell is monitored, using a high resistance voltmeter, when different currents are taken by virtue of the resistive load being

207

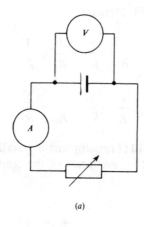

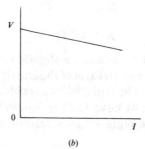

(a)

(b)

Fig. 11.8

varied. Figure 11.8b shows the result. The potential difference between the terminals of the cell drops as the current taken from it increases.

We can explain this effect by considering the cell to consist of a source of e.m.f. ε in series with a resistor of resistance r, this being the internal resistance of the cell (Fig. 11.9). Hence, for the circuit, the total resistance is $(R + r)$ and hence

$$\varepsilon = I(R + r)$$

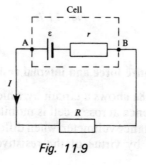

Fig. 11.9

The potential difference between the terminals of the cell, V, is the potential difference between points A and B, i.e., that across the external resistance R. Hence $V = IR$ and so

$$\varepsilon = V + Ir$$
$$V = \varepsilon - Ir$$

This is the equation of the graph in Fig. 11.8b, the intercept with the $V = 0$ axis being the e.m.f. ε and the slope of the graph $-r$, the internal resistance.

If a battery with an e.m.f. of 1.50 V and internal resistance 1.0 Ω supplies a circuit with a current of 0.20 A, then the potential difference between the terminals of the battery is

$$V = 1.50 - 0.20 \times 1.0$$
$$= 1.30 \text{ V}$$

Cells in series and parallel

When cells are in series the total e.m.f. is the algebraic sum of the individual e.m.f.s, and the total internal resistance is the sum of the individual internal resistances. In calculating the total e.m.f. there is a need to consider which way round the cell is connected in the circuit, in calculating the total internal resistance it does not matter which way round the cell is connected.

When a number of identical cells, each with e.m.f. ε, are in parallel with all positive terminals connected together and all negative terminals connected together, then the total e.m.f. is just ε. The total internal resistance r is obtained using

$$\frac{1}{r} = \frac{1}{r_1} + \frac{1}{r_2} + \frac{1}{r_3} \text{ etc.}$$

where r_1, r_2 and r_3 are the internal resistances of the cells. The effect of such a parallel arrangement is to give the same e.m.f. but reduce the effective internal resistance.

Electrical measurements

Changing the range of a meter

The moving coil instrument is basically a micro-ammeter or milliammeter. However, by the use of shunts, resistors in parallel with the instrument, or multipliers, resistors in series with the instrument, it can be converted into a meter to measure amps or volts (Fig. 11.10).

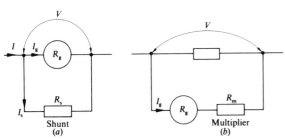

Fig. 11.10   A moving-coil meter as (a) an ammeter, (b) a voltmeter

As an ammeter:

$$I = I_g + I_s$$

where I is the current to be measured, I_g is the current indicated by the meter, and I_s is the current passing through the shunt. The shunt takes a constant fraction of the current, leaving only a small fraction to be detected by the meter. The fraction taken depends on the resistances of the meter R_g and the shunt R_s

$$V = I_g R_g = I_s R_s$$

Thus

$$\frac{I_g}{I_s} = \frac{R_s}{R_g}$$

and therefore

$$I = I_g + \frac{R_g}{R_s} I_g = \left(1 + \frac{R_g}{R_s}\right) I_g$$

The resistance of the shunt is less than the resistance of the meter. To convert a microammeter, say full-scale deflection 100 μA, to an ammeter, say full-scale deflection 10 A, we must have

$$10 = \left(1 + \frac{R_g}{R_s}\right) 100 \times 10^{-6}$$

or approximately

$$\frac{R_g}{R_s} = 10^5$$

If the meter has a resistance of 100 Ω the shunt will need to have a resistance of 10^{-3} Ω.

As a voltmeter:

$$V = I_g(R_g + R_m)$$

For a 100 μA meter of resistance 100 Ω to be converted to read 10 V at full-scale deflection, we must have

$$10 = 100 \times 10^{-6}(100 + R_m)$$

$$R_m = 999\,00\ \Omega$$

Multipliers have high resistances. In both the case of the shunt and the multiplier it is assumed that the resistors and the meter obey Ohm's law.

Meter resistance

The resistance of a voltmeter affects the voltage reading given by the instrument when it is placed across a circuit component (Fig. 11.11). The potential difference across a resistor, resistance R, is IR when no voltmeter is in parallel with the resistor. When the voltmeter is in parallel with the resistor the potential difference drops to $I_R R$ as some current flows through the voltmeter; I_R is the current through the resistor.

$$I = I_R + I_V$$

$$V = I_R R = I_V R_V$$

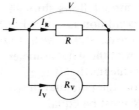

Fig. 11.11

Thus

$$I = I_R \left(1 + \frac{R}{R_V} \right)$$

$$IR = I_R R \left(1 + \frac{R}{R_V} \right)$$

p.d. with no voltmeter
$$= \text{(p.d. with meter)} \left(1 + \frac{R}{R_V} \right)$$

The p.d. with the voltmeter approaches the value without the voltmeter when R_V becomes considerably greater than R. Thus the higher the voltmeter resistance the more 'correct' the value.

Measurement of resistance

The measurement of the p.d. across a resistor and the current flowing through it gives a value for the resistance. If moving coil instruments are used the accuracy of the result is limited owing to the limited accuracy with which such meters can be read. Also, putting a voltmeter in parallel with a resistor means that an ammeter measures the current through the parallel arrangement and so the resistance value computed is that of the combination.

In 1843 Sir Charles Wheatstone gave a lecture, published in the same year in *Philosophical Transactions*, **133**, 323, in which he described what has since become known as Wheatstone's bridge. In fact it had previously been discovered and published by S. H. Christie in 1833 (*Phil. Trans.*, **123**, 95); Wheatstone did acknowledge the earlier work. The bridge compares resistances and is capable of high accuracy because the meter used in the circuit has only to indicate whether the current is zero or not (it is called a null method). Figure 11.12 shows the basic form of the bridge.

When no current flows through the galvanometer—this condition is arrived at by adjusting the values of the resistors—we have zero potential difference across the galvanometer, i.e., between B and D. This means that B and D are at the same potential. Thus the potential drops across P and that across R must be equal

$$\text{p.d. across } P = \text{p.d. across } R$$

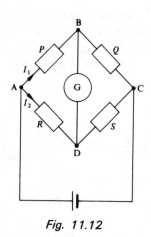

Fig. 11.12

Similarly
$$\text{p.d. across } Q = \text{p.d. across } S$$

The current through P must be equal to the current through Q as no current flows through the galvanometer. Similarly the current through R must equal that through S. Hence using the above equations

$$I_1 P = I_2 R$$
$$I_1 Q = I_2 S$$

and thus

$$\frac{P}{Q} = \frac{R}{S}$$

Knowing the ratio R/S and the value of Q, the value of P can be found. The accuracy of this result depends on the accuracy of these resistance values and the accuracy with which the zero current condition can be determined.

The potentiometer

1841 saw the invention by Poggendorff of the potentiometer. This is a method of comparing potential differences by balancing one potential difference against another. A battery connected across a tapped resistor, see Fig. 11.13, enables a variable potential difference to be obtained between the tapping point and one end of the resistor. The resistor may be of the form of a strip

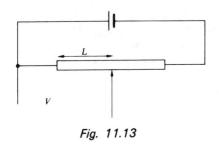

Fig. 11.13

of carbon or a wire along which a sliding contact, the tapping point, can move. If the resistor is perfectly uniform along its length, the distance the tapping point is from one end is proportional to the p.d. between the tapping point and that end.

$$V \propto L$$

This can then be balanced against another potential difference.

Figure 11.14a shows the circuit used for the comparison of the e.m.f.s of cells. The sliding contact is moved along the resistor until there is no current detected by the galvanometer. When this occurs

$$\varepsilon \propto L$$

The cell is then replaced with a standard cell and a new no-current position of the contact found.

$$\varepsilon_s \propto L_s$$

Hence

$$\frac{\varepsilon}{\varepsilon_s} = \frac{L}{L_s}$$

Two measurements of length, or angle in the case of the slider moving round a circular track, and a knowledge of the e.m.f. of one cell thus enable an e.m.f. to be measured.

It is the cell e.m.f. that is being determined, not the potential difference between the cell terminals, because no current is taken from the cell at the balance condition.

The potentiometer can be used to determine the potential difference across a resistor, that of P in Fig. 11.14b, by comparing its balance length with that of a standard cell. Resistances can be compared (Figs 11.14b and 11.14c) if the p.d. across one resistor is compared with that across another resistor, when the same current flows through each resistor

$$\frac{V_P}{V_Q} = \frac{L_P}{L_Q}$$

As the same current flows through each resistor

$$\frac{P}{Q} = \frac{L_P}{L_Q}$$

The potentiometer can be used to determine the current I in a circuit, for example that in the

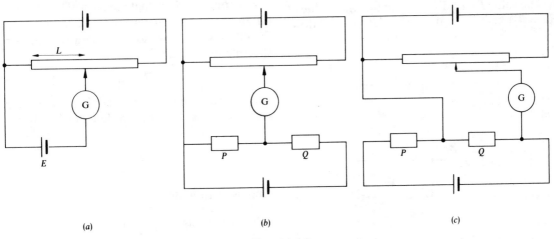

(a)   (b)   (c)

Fig. 11.14

lower circuit of Fig. 11.14b, by determining the potential difference V across a known resistor of resistance R through which the current is flowing. The potential difference is obtained by comparing it with a cell of known e.m.f. ε. If the 'balance' lengths of potentiometer wire are respectively L_V and L_ε, then

$$\frac{V}{\varepsilon} = \frac{L_V}{L_\varepsilon}$$

and since $V = IR$, then

$$I = \frac{L_V \varepsilon}{RL_\varepsilon}$$

The longer the potentiometer wire the smaller can be the potential difference per unit length of wire and hence the smaller the potential difference which can be determined. One way of effectively extending the length of the wire is to put a resistance in series with the wire. Figure 11.15 shows such a circuit being used for the measurement of a very small e.m.f., that from a thermocouple (of the order of millivolts). The potential difference V_D is applied across a resistance of $(R_1 + R_2 + r)$, where r is the resistance of the potentiometer wire. Thus the potential difference per ohm of potentiometer wire can be adjusted by changing the value of $(R_1 + R_2)$. These are adjusted until a balance length L_t is obtained with the thermocouple. The potentiometer is then calibrated by connecting a standard cell ε across R_1. The value R_1 is adjusted, but the total value of $(R_1 + R_2)$ kept constant, until zero current flows through the galvanometer. The potential difference per ohm is then ε/R_1. Hence as the potentiometer wire has a total resistance r, the potential difference across its full length L is $r\varepsilon/R_1$ and so the potential difference per unit length is $r\varepsilon/LR_1$. Hence the e.m.f. of the thermocouple is $L_t r\varepsilon/LR_1$.

The accuracy of a potentiometer is limited by the degree of uniformity of the slide wire, the precision with which the no-current condition can be determined and the accuracy with which the balance length of wire can be measured. However, with quite simple apparatus, greater accuracy can be achieved than is feasible with moving coil instruments for measurement of potential difference.

Currents in matter

Suppose we take samples of a wide variety of substances in a wide variety of shapes and sizes and we measure the current passing through them and the potential difference across them when we connect a battery. We would end up with vast tables of current and voltage for each material and each shape. We could then, by using our tables, work out the effect of putting a piece of material in a d.c. circuit. There is a simpler way of tackling the problem—we can look for simple relationships which can be used, perhaps approximately, to describe the effects of changing the material and the shape.

Experiments show that the ratio of the potential difference to the current, i.e., the resistance, is directly proportional to the length of a uniform specimen of a material

$$R \propto L$$

and is inversely proportional to the cross-sectional area of a uniform length of material

$$R \propto \frac{1}{A}$$

Thus we can write

$$R \propto \frac{L}{A}$$

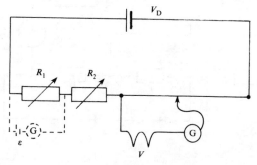

Fig. 11.15 *Measurement of small a e.m.f.*

and if we introduce a constant ρ

$$R = \frac{\rho L}{A}$$

The value of ρ, called the resistivity, depends on the nature of the material. It has the unit of Ω m (ohm metre).

This relationship can be deduced if we assume that charge is conserved and the current entering a wire must equal the current leaving the wire. Suppose we consider two equal lengths, equal cross-sectional area, of the same material. If we have the same current in each length we expect the same potential difference across each length. Suppose we now put the two lengths together to give a wire of double the length, between the ends we must have, for the same current double the potential difference (Fig. 11.16a). The ratio V/I has been doubled by doubling the length of a wire. The resistance R is thus proportional to the length. Suppose we now put the two wires together to give one wire of double the cross-sectional area (Fig. 11.16b). For the same potential difference we have double the current. Thus doubling the area gives half the value for the ratio V/I, the resistance is inversely proportional to the area.

The reciprocal of resistance is called conductance and the reciprocal of resistivity the conductivity. Metals have, at room temperature, resistivities of the order of 10^{-8} to 10^{-7} ohm m, insulators have resistivities of the order of 10^{12}

ohm m—about 10^{20} times greater than that of a metal. Roughly mid way between these we have resistivities of the order of 10^2 ohm m; materials with resistivities in this region are called semi-conductors. In general, the resistivity of pure metals increases with an increase in temperature, that of semiconductors and insulators decreases with an increase in temperature.

Thus as manganin has a resistivity of 4.4×10^{-7} Ω m at about room temperature, a 50 cm length of manganin wire with a diameter of 1.0 mm will have a resistance of

$$R = \frac{\rho L}{A}$$

$$= \frac{4.4 \times 10^{-7} \times 50 \times 10^{-2}}{\frac{1}{4}\pi \times (1.0 \times 10^{-3})^2}$$

$$= 0.28\ \Omega$$

Energy band model for conduction

An explanation of the conductivity of solids is given by an energy band model. Isolated atoms have discrete energy levels (see Chapter 18), however when atoms are packed together in a solid the outer energy levels become broadened into bands. At absolute zero the electrons in a solid occupy the lowest available energy states. An increase in temperature, however, means that

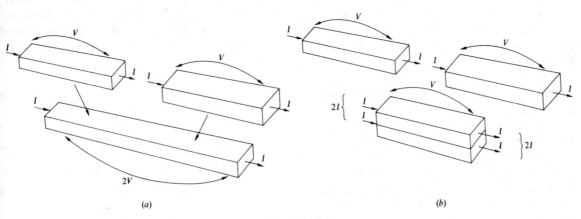

(a)   (b)

Fig. 11.16

some might have enough energy to move to higher energy levels.

At absolute zero the outermost electrons of an atom are packed into what is called the valency band. The next higher band is called the conduction band and at absolute zero is empty of electrons. A good conductor has overlapping valency and conduction bands (Fig. 11.17a). At room temperature some of the valency electrons will have moved into this conduction band. This means that electrons can 'accept' small amounts of energy and participate in the conduction process.

Insulators have valency and conduction bands separated by quite a large energy gap (Fig. 11.17b). The valency band is full of electrons and the conduction band empty. The gap between the bands is, however, too large for electrons, even at room temperature, to jump the gap and so there are no charge carriers available for electrical conduction.

With a semiconductor (Fig. 11.17c), at absolute zero the valency band is full and the conduction band empty. However, the gap between the bands is small enough for some electrons to have jumped the gap by room temperature. These escaping electrons leave vacancies, termed holes, in the valency band. Thus electrical conduction can take place by movements of the electrons in the conduction band and electrons in the valency band moving into the holes, the effect being as though the holes were moving. In a pure semiconductor there are as many 'free' electrons as holes and so there is an equal contribution to electrical conduction by both. Such semiconductors are said to be intrinsic. Increasing the temperature increases the number of electrons jumping the energy gap and so the number of charge carriers available for conduction increases.

The electrical conductivity of semiconductors can be very markedly increased by the introduction of very small amounts of impurity atoms. Germanium and silicon are semiconductors; each of their atoms has four valency electrons. Antimony, arsenic and phosphorus atoms each have five valency electrons. When small amounts of such materials are introduced into, say, germanium only four of the electrons are needed for bonding and so the fifth one is easily detached.

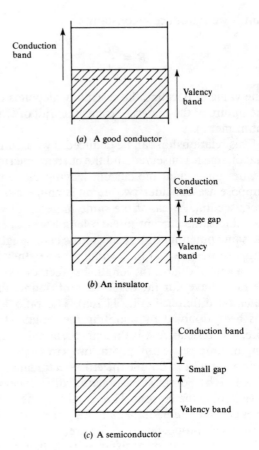

(a) A good conductor

(b) An insulator

(c) A semiconductor

Fig. 11.17 Energy bands

The result is that such a material has more electrons available for conduction than holes (Fig. 11.18). It is said to be n-type (the n standing for negative since the major part of the conduction is by negative charge movement). Aluminium, boron and indium atoms have three valency electrons. Thus when small amounts of these materials

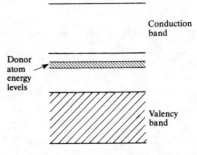

Fig. 11.18 n-type semiconductor

are introduced into germanium extra holes are donated (Fig. 11.19). The result is that the majority charge carriers for conduction are holes, not electrons in the conduction band. Such materials are called p-type (the p standing for positive since a hole in the presence of an electric field moves in the opposite direction to an electron and so behaves like a positive particle). The introduction of impurities into germanium, or silicon, is called doping and the resulting semiconductors are called extrinsic.

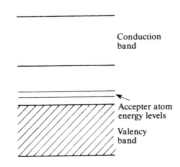

Fig. 11.19   p-type semiconductor

An electron 'gas' model for conductors

A simple model that can be adopted for conduction in good conductors involves considering there to be free electrons which drift through the conductor under the action of an applied potential difference. The term electron 'gas' is used for these free electrons because they are considered to behave rather like gas molecules in simple kinetic theory. In the absence of an applied potential difference these electrons move about in a random manner, with speeds determined by the temperature. Each electron moves in a straight line at constant speed until it comes close enough to an atom for a 'collision' to occur. The collision is considered to be elastic and the electron after the collision will have a new speed and direction. When a potential difference is applied the electrons are all acted on by forces which superimpose on their random motion a steady drift velocity along the potential gradient.

This model of conduction was developed by Drude late in the nineteenth century. But what is the evidence for free electrons? When a current flows in a metal there is a complete absence of any discernible movement of chemically identifiable material—thus the atoms cannot be moving and cannot give the current. The charge carrier must therefore be 'something' which is not identified with a particular atom. The high conductivity of metals also suggests that the charge carriers must be free since they move under the action of very small potential differences. The obvious conclusion—electrons.

This model is in accord with the energy band picture for a good conductor in which valency electrons are free to move because of the overlap of the valency and conduction energy bands.

The movement of charge through conductors

Suppose we have a conductor of cross-sectional area A carrying a current I (Fig. 11.20). Also we suppose that there are n charge carriers per unit volume, each carrying a charge q and each moving with a drift velocity v along the conductor. In time t a charge carrier would cover a distance vt. In time t all the charge carriers in a volume Avt will have crossed through an area WXYZ. Thus the charge passing through the area in time t is $Avtnq$. Current is the rate of movement of charge, thus

$$I = Avnq$$

How big is v? If we consider a copper wire of cross-sectional area 1 mm², i.e., 10^{-6} m², and assume that each copper atom donates one electron for

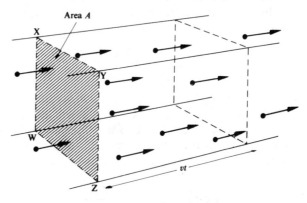

Fig. 11.20

conduction purposes, n will be 8.5×10^{28} per m³.

(Relative atomic mass of copper 63.6, density 8930 kg m⁻³, 6×10^{23} atoms per mole. Volume of 1 mole of copper $63.6 \times 10^{-3}/8930$.)

For a current of 1 A, we have

$$v = \frac{1}{10^{-6} \times 8.5 \times 10^{28} \times 1.6 \times 10^{-19}}$$

$$v = 0.74 \times 10^{-3} \text{ m s}^{-1}$$

or about 0.7 mm s⁻¹. On our theory the charge carriers are moving very slowly. (The high speed with which a lamp comes on when you press the electric light switch can be explained in terms of the high speed with which an electric field travels through the circuit.)

Charge movement and Ohm's law

The energy needed to move a charged particle, charge q, along the length of a wire, length L, is Vq. V is the potential difference between the ends of this wire. This energy must be equal to FL, where F is the force component acting along the length of the wire.

$$FL = Vq$$

The acceleration of the charged particle will be

$$a = \frac{F}{m} = \frac{Vq}{mL}$$

where m is the mass of the charged particle. Suppose the particle accelerates from rest. In time t the particle will have acquired a velocity v where

$$v = at = \frac{Vqt}{mL}$$

If t is the time over which the particle accelerates before colliding with some atom, v will be the maximum velocity. It is assumed that after the collision the particle has no velocity in this force direction. The average velocity will be ½v.

$$\text{Average velocity} = \frac{Vqt}{2mL}$$

But $I = Avnq$, thus by eliminating the velocity term (the v in the current expression is the average velocity) we have

$$\frac{I}{Anq} = \frac{Vqt}{2mL}$$

$$I = \left(\frac{A}{L}\right)\left(\frac{nq^2t}{2m}\right)V$$

We assume here that all the electrons have the same value of t, regardless of the value of V. This is only a reasonable approximation if the velocity change produced by the p.d. is very small compared with the random velocity. Then the random velocity determines the time between collisions and this depends only on the temperature. In this case the terms in brackets are constant, at a particular temperature, and thus I is proportional to V. This is Ohm's law. Thus we have the resistance R given by

$$R = \frac{L}{A}\frac{2m}{nq^2t}$$

But

$$R = \frac{L}{A}\rho$$

where ρ is the resistivity. Thus

$$\rho = \frac{2m}{nq^2t}$$

For copper: ρ is about 1.6×10^{-8} Ω m, n about 8.5×10^{28} m⁻³, the mass of an electron, m, about 9.1×10^{-31} kg, q 1.6×10^{-19} C. Thus we obtain for t a value of about 5×10^{-14} s. With the electrons having random velocities of the order of 3×10^5 m s⁻¹, the electrons will travel about 15×10^{-9} m between collisions. This means electrons travelling about 100 atom lengths before suffering a collision. This seems highly improbable in the densely packed structure of a metal. We must consider the electron as a wave and its progress along a wire as the passage of a wave past scattering centres if we are to develop a better explanation.

Charge movement and temperature

If we have a potential difference V across a resistor of resistance R when there is a current I, then $R = V/I$. Since $I = Avnq$, then

$$R = \frac{V}{Avnq}$$

Resistivity $\rho = RA/L$, hence

$$\rho = \frac{V}{vnqL}$$

V/L is the potential gradient (the electric field strength—see Chapter 13).

$$\rho = \frac{1}{vnq} \times \text{(potential gradient)}$$

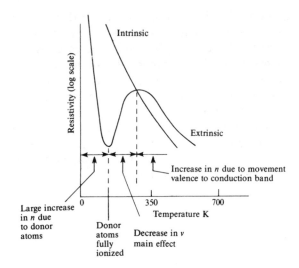

Fig. 11.21

For metals the resistivity increases when the temperature increases. The above equation thus suggests that $1/(vnq)$ must increase, i.e., vnq decreases. Since for electrons q is constant, this means either v or n must decrease. There is evidence, the Hall effect (see Chapter 14), that there is no significant change of n with temperature for metals. Thus v must decrease when the temperature increases.

We can explain this reduction in drift velocity by considering an increase in temperature to cause an increase in the amplitude of the vibrations of the metal ions and so the electrons travel shorter distances between collisions with the metal ions.

Figure 11.21 shows how the resistivity of intrinsic and extrinsic semiconductors tends to vary with temperature. With a pure semiconductor (intrinsic) the resistivity decreases almost exponentially with temperature. This decrease in resistivity with an increase in temperature can be explained by an increase in the number of charge carriers per unit volume of material; more electrons in the valency band cross to the conduction band. With an intrinsic semiconductor this means an equal increase in the number of electrons in the conduction band and holes in the valency band.

With an extrinsic semiconductor, i.e., a doped semiconductor, when the temperature is increased from absolute zero then in the case of, say, a n-type material the resistivity decreases as more electrons cross into the conduction band—the material thus showing a similar property to that of an intrinsic semiconductor. At higher temperatures, however, most of the impurity atoms end up having donated their electrons and thus there is less movement of electrons into the conduction band. The material then begins to behave more like a metal and the resistivity now increases with temperature. This increase is because the thermal vibration of the ions increases; also the impurity atoms act as significant scattering centres for the electrons, and this becomes a more significant factor than any increase in the number of charge carriers. This is often the case at about room temperature, see Fig. 11.21. At even higher temperatures, however, the number of electrons jumping from the valency band to the conduction band begins to be a more dominant factor than the decrease in drift velocity due to scattering from ions. The extrinsic material then begins to behave like an intrinsic material.

Conduction by ions

If a potential difference is applied between two inert (perhaps carbon) electrodes immersed, but not touching, in very pure water (Fig. 11.22) there is only a very minute current. If, however, a small

217

amount of sodium chloride, or some other 'salt', is dropped in the water there is a large increase in current. We can explain this increase by an increase in the number of charge carriers. Sodium chloride breaks up into its separate ions when it is put into water and these provide charge carriers additional to the few ions that are already present in the water. In fact we believe that the sodium chloride is already in the form of ions in the crystal and that the effect of the water is to pull the ions apart from each other.

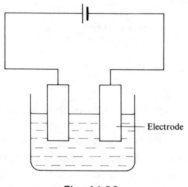

Electrode

Fig. 11.22

Sodium chloride in the crystal form gives only very small currents when a potential difference is applied across a block of the material; the ions are not free to move. Sodium chloride is a good insulator.

Faraday's laws of electrolysis

Liquids which conduct electricity are called electrolytes; such liquids might be solutions like sodium chloride in water or molten solids. The process of passing the current through an electrolyte and the accompanying chemical reactions is called electrolysis. The conductors dipping into the electrolyte and which connect it to a d.c. source are called electrodes, the one connected to the positive side of the supply being called the anode and the one to the negative side the cathode. When, for example, sodium chloride is dissolved in water it breaks up into two ions, a positive ion Na^+ and a negative ion Cl^-. With a potential difference between the electrodes, as in

Fig. 11.22, the positive ion moves towards the cathode and the negative ion towards the anode. It is this movement of ions which constitutes the current through the electrolyte.

Copper sulphate dissolved in water gives rise to positive copper ions and negative sulphate ions. When a potential difference is applied between two electrodes immersed in copper sulphate solution, the copper ions move towards the cathode and the sulphate ions towards the anode. The result is a deposit of copper on the cathode when a current is passing through the electrolyte. Experiments show that the mass m of copper deposited is proportional to the time t for which a current flows and the size of the current I, i.e.

$$m \propto It$$

But current is the rate of movement of charge, hence It is the quantity of charge passing through the electrolyte. This is expressed as Faraday's first law:

The mass of a material liberated in electrolysis is proportional to the quantity of charge passing through the electrolyte.

One mole of copper has a mass of 63.6 g. A charge of $2 \times 96\,500$ C is required to liberate this amount of copper.

If such electrolysis experiments are carried out with other electrolytes it turns out that the amount of charge needed to liberate one mole is a simple multiple of 96 500 C. Thus if hydrogen is liberated, $1 \times 96\,500$ C are required. Faraday's second law can be expressed as:

The quantity of charge required to liberate one mole of substance is a simple multiple of 96 500 C (this number is called the Faraday constant).

The reason for this simple multiple factor is that some ions carry only one package of charge while others (e.g., oxygen) carry two or more packages. The size of the package is the charge carried by the electron. Since one mole contains 6.02×10^{23} particles (the Avogadro constant) then 63.6 g of copper will have been deposited by 6.02×10^{23} copper ions. $2 \times 96\,500$ C is needed to deposit the copper. Hence the charge carried by each ion is $2 \times 96\,500/6.02 \times 10^{23} = 2 \times 1.6 \times 10^{-19}$ C.

The equation for the mass liberated in electrolysis can thus be evolved as follows:

96 500 C liberates the relative atomic mass

1 C liberates $\dfrac{\text{relative atomic mass}}{96\,500}$

Q C liberates $Q \times \dfrac{\text{relative atomic mass}}{96\,500}$

Thus mass liberated $m =$

$$Q \times \frac{\text{relative atomic mass}}{96\,500}$$

The term electrochemical equivalent z is used for the relative atomic mass/96 500. Hence

$$m = zQ = zIt$$

If the electrochemical equivalent for copper is 3.29×10^{-7} kg C^{-1}, what mass of copper will be deposited when a current of 2.0 A is passed for 100 s through a copper sulphate electrolyte? If we use the above equation, then

$$m = 3.29 \times 10^{-7} \times 2.0 \times 100$$

$$= 6.58 \times 10^{-5} \text{ kg}$$

Problems

1. (a) Explain what is meant by the electromotive force and the terminal potential difference of a battery.

(b) A bulb is used in a torch which is powered by two identical cells in series each of e.m.f. 1.5 V. The bulb then dissipates power at the rate of 625 mW and the p.d. across the bulb is 2.5 V. Calculate

(i) the internal resistance of each cell and
(ii) the energy dissipated in each cell in one minute.

(JMB, Q9, Paper II, June 1979)

2. A moving coil meter has a resistance of 25 Ω and indicates full-scale deflection when a current of 4.0 mA flows through it. How could this meter be converted to a milliammeter having a full-scale deflection for a current of 50 mA?

(University of London, Q6, Paper 2, June 1980)

3. A galvanometer of resistance 40 Ω requires a current of 10 mA to give a full-scale deflection. A shunt is put in position to convert it to a meter reading up to 1.0 A full-scale deflection. A resistance bobbin, intended to convert the galvanometer to one reading up to 1.0 V full-scale deflection, is now attached to the instrument but the shunt is inadvertently left in position. By considering the potential difference across the bobbin and the meter, calculate the voltage which would produce full-scale deflection of the meter.

(University of London, Q6, Paper 2, June 1978)

4. A moving coil ammeter at 0°C has a resistance of 5 Ω and gives a full-scale deflection for a current of 15 mA. What value of shunt resistance is required so that it reads 1.50 A at 0°C? What circuit current will give a full-scale deflection of the instrument if the temperature of the shunt rises to 25°C while the instrument remains at 0°C? (Temperature coefficient of resistance of material of shunt = 4.0×10^{-3} K^{-1}, i.e., the resistance of the shunt increases by 0.04% of its resistance at 0°C for every degree rise in its temperature.)

(AEB, Q5, Paper 3, June 1981)

5. Define electrical resistivity and state the unit in which it is measured.

Explain carefully why, in an experiment to measure the resistivity of polythene (a very poor electrical conductor), it would be advantageous to use

(a) a large but thin sheet of polythene,
(b) a high voltage supply.

(University of London, Q6, Paper 2, June 1981)

6. (a) Explain what is meant by

(i) the electrical resistance of a conductor, and
(ii) the resistivity of the material of a conductor.

(b) The graphs, Fig. 11.23, show how the current varies with applied potential difference across

(i) a 12-V, 36-W filament lamp, and
(ii) a metre length of nichrome wire of cross-section 0.08 mm^2. Using the graphs, find the ratio of the values of the electrical resistance of the filament lamp to the nichrome wire (1) when the potential difference across them is 12 V, and (2) when the potential difference across them is 0.5 V.

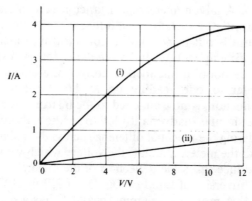

Fig. 11.23

How does the resistance of the filament lamp change as the current increases? Suggest a physical explanation for this change.

(c) The resistivity of copper is about 1.8×10^{-8} Ω m at 20°C. Show, using the information given in (b) above, that the resistivity of nichrome is approximately 60 times this value. Explain why, in a domestic circuit containing an electric fire element and connecting cable, only the element becomes appreciably hot.

(University of London, Q13, Paper 2, January 1979)

7. (a) Define resistivity, and temperature co-efficient of resistance.

(b) Outline briefly how you would measure the temperature coefficient of resistance of copper in the laboratory.

(c) The temperature at which the tungsten filament of a 12 V 36 W lamp operates is 1750°C. Taking the temperature coefficient of tungsten to be 6×10^{-3} K^{-1}, find the resistance of the filament at room temperature, 20°C.

(d) The table gives readings for two filament lamps A and B of different ratings.

Current, I in A	0	0.05	0.10	0.15	0.20
p.d. across lamp A, V_A in V	0	0.40	1.1	2.8	6.5
p.d. across lamp B, V_B in V	0	1.25	2.6	5.0	9.1

(i) On the same graph, with I as y-axis, draw the graph of I against V for each lamp.
(ii) The two lamps A and B are connected in parallel. Find and tabulate the corresponding values of the current I and the p.d. V across the lamps up to 6 V and draw the I-V graph (on the same graph as (i)).

(Oxford Local Examinations, Q10, Paper I, June 1979)

8. A closed box has three terminals A, B and C. Inside the box are known to be combinations of some or all of resistors X, Y and Z arranged in one of the ways shown in Fig. 11.24a to f.

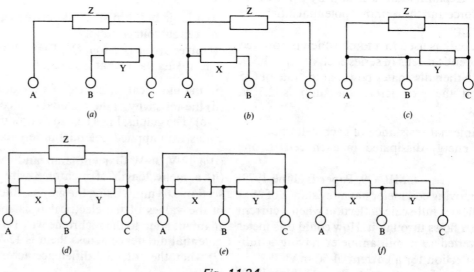

Fig. 11.24

ELECTRIC CIRCUITS

(a) An accumulator, of negligible internal resistance, and a 15-Ω resistor are connected to the terminals A and C of the box. The potential differences between various points are measured by a potentiometer and are shown in Fig. 11.25.

(i) Draw a labelled diagram of a potentiometer showing how it would be connected to measure the potential difference across the 15-Ω resistor in Fig. 11.25.

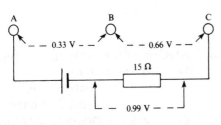

Fig. 11.25

(ii) What advantages does a potentiometer have over a moving coil voltmeter for measuring potential differences?
(iii) From the measurements in Fig. 11.25 explain why only two of the circuits in Fig. 11.24a to f are possible arrangements.
(b) The cell and resistor are now connected as in Fig. 11.26.

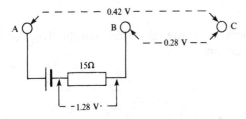

Fig. 11.26

(iv) Deduce which of the two circuits identified in (iii) is the correct arrangement, explaining your reasoning.
(v) Deduce the resistance of those resistors used in the box.

(University of London, Q13, Paper 2, January 1984)

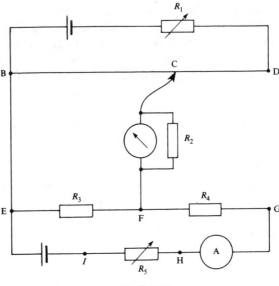

Fig. 11.27

9. (a) Figure 11.27 shows a potentiometer circuit arranged to compare the values of two low resistance resistors.

(i) Which resistors are to be compared?
(ii) What are the functions of the remaining three resistors?
(iii) During the experiment what connection changes would need to be made?
(iv) When the circuit was initially set up the galvanometer was found to be deflected in the same direction wherever along the wire BD the sliding contact C was placed. Suggest two possible reasons for this.
(v) For the purpose of this experiment explain whether or not it is necessary to calibrate the potentiometer with a standard cell.
(b) A potentiometer may be regarded as equivalent to a voltmeter. Illustrate this by drawing the basic potentiometer circuit, marking the points which correspond to the positive and negative terminals of the equivalent voltmeter. Describe how this basic circuit may be developed in order to measure the internal resistance of a cell. How may the observations be displayed in the form of a straight line graph and how could the internal resistance be found from this graph?

(University of London, Q13, Paper 2, January 1980)

10. (a) Define the volt and the ohm.

Water in a barrel may be released at a variable rate by an adjustable tap at the bottom. If this system is compared to an electric circuit what in the system would be analogous to (a) the potential difference, (b) the charge flowing, (c) the current, and (d) the resistance, in the circuit?

Give two examples, illustrated by appropriate graphs, of conductors or components which do not obey Ohm's law.

(b) Circuits (i) and (ii) in Fig. 11.28 may be used to measure the resistance of the resistor, R. If both meters are of the moving coil type, explain why in each case the value of R obtained would not be correct.

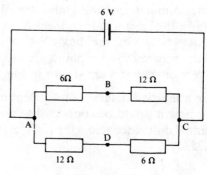

Fig. 11.29

in branch ADC in order to make the potential difference between B and D zero?

(University of London, Q13, Paper 2, January 1981)

11. (a) Show that the electric current I associated with n electrons per unit volume moving with average drift velocity v along a uniform bar of length L and cross-sectional area A, as in Fig. 11.30, is given by

$$I = hAve \qquad (1)$$

where e is the electronic charge.

Show that if V is the potential difference between the end of the same conducting bar then Ohm's law leads to the relation

$$\sigma = \frac{neLv}{V} \qquad (2)$$

where σ is the electrical conductivity of the specimen.

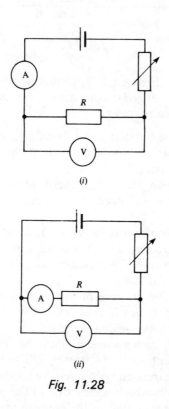

(i)

(ii)

Fig. 11.28

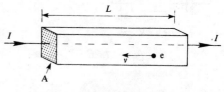

A

Fig. 11.30

What alternative method would you use to obtain a better value for R? (No circuit details are required.)

(c) In the circuit shown in Fig. 11.29 what is the potential difference between the points B and D? What resistor could you add to the 12-Ω resistor

(b) The number of electrons in a bar of pure silicon, an intrinsic semiconductor, equals the number of holes. Explain the term hole and describe the mechanism of current flow based on the movement of holes.

The graph in Fig. 11.31 shows how the electrical conductivity of a specimen of n-type silicon varies with temperature.

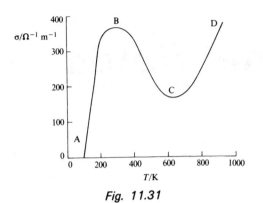

Fig. 11.31

State and explain the effect of n-type impurity on

(i) the number of conduction electrons per unit volume, and
(ii) The number of holes per unit volume.

With reference to (2) above and to the graph in Fig. 11.31, account for the general rise or fall of the electrical conductivity of n-type silicon within the temperature ranges

(iii) below 250 K,
(iv) above 250 K but below 650 K, and
(v) above 650 K.

(c) An electrolytic cell holds 600 cm³ of copper sulphate solution which contains 12 g of copper ions. Parallel copper electrodes are suspended 3 cm apart in the solution. Each has an area of 100 cm² in the solution and facing the other electrode. A steady current of 2.00 A flows through the solution for 20 minutes. Calculate

(vi) the mass of copper deposited on the cathode,
(vii) the volume of electrolyte which initially held that mass of copper, and
(viii) an average value for the speed of a copper ion. (Electrochemical equivalent of copper = 3.29 × 10⁻⁷ kg C⁻¹)

(University of London, Q14, Paper 2, January 1985)

12. (a) What are the reasons for believing

(i) that a sample of pure metal contains a large number of free electrons which permeate the metal as an 'electron gas',
(ii) that the electric current through such a metal is transported by these electrons?

(b) (i) Assuming that, when an electric field E is applied between the ends of a wire, it accelerates each electron for an average time τ after which the electron is scattered by another collision with a positive ion, obtain an expression for the drift velocity u of the electrons.
(ii) A wire of cross-sectional area A and length L has a potential difference V between its ends. If the number of conduction electrons per unit volume is n, obtain expressions for the current I through the wire, its resistance, and the resistivity of its material.
(iii) For copper, given that $n = 10^{29}$ m⁻³ and that the value of τ at 300 K is 10^{-14} s, estimate the resistivity of copper at this temperature.
(iv) Why would you expect the resistivity of copper to increase as the temperature rises?
(Take the electronic charge e to be 1.60×10^{-19} C and the electronic mass m_e to be 9.11×10^{-31} kg)

(Oxford Local Examinations, Q10, Paper 0, June 1981)

12 Gravitational fields

Gravitational forces

The first manned landing on the moon, Apollo 11, took place on 17th July 1969. The following is part of the record of the return flight to earth. All the times are in British Summer Time.

At 5.57 am Apollo 11 left moon orbit.
At 12.36 pm Apollo 11 was 37 750 km from the moon.
Velocity was 1327.8 m s^{-1}.
At 3.32 pm Apollo 11 was 47 835 km from the moon heading towards home at 1301.9 m s^{-1}.
At 4.32 pm Apollo 11 was 52 579 km from the moon travelling at a speed of 1296.6 m s^{-1}.
At 6.02 pm Apollo was 59 668 km from the moon and travelling at a speed of 1290.9 m s^{-1}.
At 8.36 pm there was one minute to go until the fifth mid-course correction. This would give a change of velocity retrograde of 1.4 m s^{-1}. The reason for this manoeuvre was to control the angle of the flight path of Apollo at re-entry.
On the next day.

At 7.50 pm Apollo 11 was 197 002 km from the earth and velocity was 1682.4 m s^{-1}.
On the succeeding day.
At 5.36 during re-entry blackout the velocity was 1087.1 m s^{-1}.
At 5.50 pm the spacecraft splashed down successfully.

Apart from the one rocket burn for the mid-course correction, only a small velocity change, the spacecraft was freely travelling from the moon to earth. Yet the velocity first decreases as the craft moves away from the moon and then builds up a very high value on re-entry to the earth's atmosphere (Fig. 12.1). What force produces these velocity changes?

The only forces acting on the spacecraft are the gravitational attractions between the craft and both the earth and the moon. If you, standing on the earth's surface, release a stone it falls to the earth—there is a force of attraction on it due to the presence of the earth. The spacecraft slows down on leaving the moon because the force acting on it due to the moon is greater than that due to the earth. After a distance of about 60 000 km from the moon the force on the craft due to the earth must be about equal to the force due to the moon because the velocity is almost constant. From that point on the craft accelerates towards the earth due to the force of attraction between it and the earth becoming greater than that between it and the moon. This explanation of the velocity-distance graph seems feasible—we have, however, to reckon with a gravitational force of attraction which varies with the separation between two bodies.

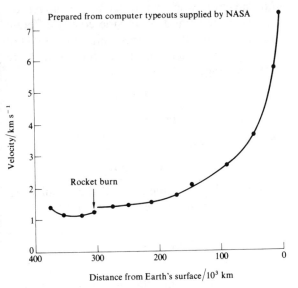

Rocket burn

Distance from Earth's surface/10^3 km

Fig. 12.1

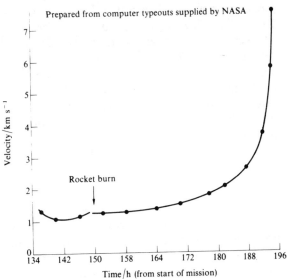

Rocket burn

Time/h (from start of mission)

Fig. 12.2

We can use our data to calculate the resultant force acting on the craft at different distances from the earth, or moon.

$$\text{Force} = ma$$

Thus

$$\text{Force} = m \text{ (slope of velocity–time graph)}$$

where m is the mass of the spacecraft.

Taking values of the slope from the velocity-time graph (Fig. 12.2) results in Fig. 12.3 showing how the acceleration, and thus the force, varies with distance from the earth. An examination of this graph shows that, roughly, the acceleration decreases by a factor of four when the distance decreases by a factor of two for distance values out to about 200×10^3 km. This means that the force acting on the spacecraft varies as the reciprocal of the distance squared. Closer examination of the data shows that this is the case when the distance is measured from the centre of the earth and not the surface.

$$\text{Force} \propto \frac{1}{r^2}$$

The moon also exerts a force on the craft and thus the net force is the difference between the

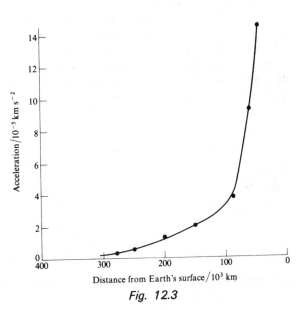

Distance from Earth's surface/10^3 km

Fig. 12.3

225

force due to the earth and that due to the moon. This force due to the moon only becomes apparent at distances greater than about 200×10^3 km. At about 350×10^3 km the two forces are approximately opposite and equal and there is virtually no acceleration. Beyond that distance the force due to the moon is greater than that due to the earth (Fig. 12.4). At the equal force point we must have

$$\frac{C_e}{r_e^2} = \frac{C_m}{r_m^2}$$

where C_e and C_m are the constants of proportionality for the forces due to the earth and the moon, r_e and r_m are the distances to the equal forces point from the centres of the earth and the moon.

$$r_e = 350 \times 10^3 + 6 \times 10^3 \text{ km}$$

$$r_m = 38 \times 10^3 + 2 \times 10^3 \text{ km}$$

Hence we have

$$\frac{C_e}{C_m} = 79$$

But the ratio of the earth's mass to that of the moon is about 81—a coincidence?

Consider a more down-to-earth example, a stone has a weight mg. The force of attraction on the stone, due to the earth, is mg. The force is directly proportional to the mass of the stone. As to every action there is a reaction we must expect that there is a force on the earth due to the stone—its value must be directly proportional to the mass M of the earth (there would seem to be no reason why the earth should be considered any different from the stone). If we changed either the mass of the stone or the mass of the earth then the force should change.

$$\text{Force} \propto m$$

$$\text{Force} \propto M$$

Thus we can write

$$\text{Force} \propto mM$$

Taking this argument and the results we obtained from the space flight we have

$$\text{Force} \propto \frac{m_1 m_2}{r^2}$$

where m_1 and m_2 are the two point masses, a distance r apart, which produce a force on each other. We can write the equation as

$$\text{Force} = G \frac{m_1 m_2}{r^2}$$

where G is a constant, called the universal constant of gravitation. Its value is 6.67×10^{-11} N m² kg⁻².

This relation was first arrived at by Newton. The sequence of Newton's argument can be summarized as follows:

Kepler had already established, experimentally, that the time, T, taken for one complete orbit of the sun is related to the radius, R, of the orbit by

$$T^2 \propto R^3$$

The force, F, necessary to cause a planet to move in a circular orbit about the sun is given by

$$F = m \frac{v^2}{R}$$

where m is the mass of the planet, v its speed in orbit.

But

$$v = \frac{2\pi R}{T}$$

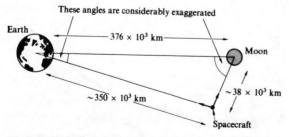

These angles are considerably exaggerated

Earth

376 × 10³ km

Moon

~350 × 10³ km

~38 × 10³ km

Spacecraft

Fig. 12.4 Position of a spacecraft when there is virtually no net force on the craft

Thus

$$F = \frac{4\pi^2 mR}{T^2}$$

To satisfy the relationship found by Kepler we must have

$$F \propto \frac{1}{R^2}$$

In this way the inverse square law for gravitation can be arrived at. The arguments for the mass terms proceed in the way the arguments for the stone were conducted.

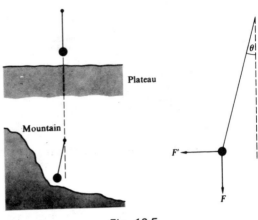

Fig. 12.5

Further reading

G. Gamow (1962) *Gravity*, Heinemann Science Study Series, No. 17.

Inertial and gravitational mass

No distinction has been made in this text between inertial and gravitational mass. Inertial mass is the mass defined in terms of the acceleration produced by a force, perhaps that produced by a stretched spring. Gravitational mass is the mass defined by the force of attraction between objects. Both can be defined independently. But it turns out that the gravitational mass is always proportional to the inertial mass. This equivalence is the basis of Einstein's general theory of gravitation.

Measurement of G

There have been many experiments to determine G, the universal constant of gravitation. Some of the earlier experiments were concerned with the measurement of the deviation of a pendulum bob line from the vertical due to the presence of a large mass such as a mountain (Fig. 12.5). The force on the bob due to the mountain is

$$F' = \frac{GM'm}{r^2}$$

where M' is the mass of the mountain and r is the distance of its centre of mass from the pendulum

bob. m is the mass of the bob. The force on the bob due to the earth is mg.

$$F = mg$$

where g is the acceleration due to gravity.

$$\frac{F'}{F} = \frac{GM'}{r^2 g}$$

But

$$\frac{F'}{F} = \tan \theta$$

Hence

$$G = \frac{r^2 g \tan \theta}{M'}$$

A difficulty of this experiment is the determination of the mass of the mountain and the distance of its centre of mass from the bob.

Later experiments generally involved masses in a laboratory. In essence these consisted of a light rod carrying a small metal sphere at each end, the rod being suspended by a fine fibre. When two other spheres are brought close to the suspended ones (Fig. 12.6) the gravitational forces cause the rod to rotate slightly. This can be detected by the movement of a light beam reflected from a mirror attached to the suspension wire. The rod rotates until the torque resulting from the gravitational forces is in equilibrium with the

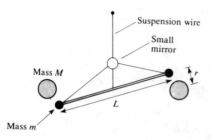

Fig. 12.6 The principles of Cavendish's torsion balance

torque produced by twisting the suspension wire, i.e.

$$\frac{GMm}{r^2} L = c\theta$$

where θ is the angular rotation of the beam and c a constant for the suspension wire. This can be found with a separate experiment. Because the gravitational forces are so small the experiment is beset with many problems.

Action at a distance

What is the origin of gravitational forces? Is there any mechanism we can suggest? At present the answer is—we do not know.

'So far I have accounted for the phenomena presented to us by the heavens and the sea by means of the force of gravity. . . . But hitherto I have not been able to discover the cause of those properties from phenomena, and I frame no hypotheses. . . . To us it is enough that gravity does really exist, and act according to the laws which we have explained, and abundantly serves to account for all the motions of the celestial bodies and of our sea.'

Newton, *Principia.*

'Many mechanisms for gravitation have been suggested. It is interesting to consider one of these, which many people have thought of from time to time. At first, one is quite excited and happy when he "discovers" it, but he soon finds that it is not correct. It was first discovered about 1750. Suppose there were many particles moving in space at a very high speed in all directions and being only slightly absorbed in going through matter. When they are absorbed, they give an impulse to the earth. However, since there are as many going one way as another, the impulses all balance. But when the sun is nearby, the particles coming toward the earth through the sun are partially absorbed, so fewer of them are coming from the sun than are coming from the other side. Therefore, the earth feels a net impulse towards the sun and it does not take one long to see that it is inversely as the square of the distance—because of the variation of the solid angle that the sun subtends as we vary the distance. What is wrong with the machinery? It involves some new consequences which are not true. This particular idea has the following trouble: the earth, in moving around the sun, would impinge on more particles which are coming from its forward side than from its hind side (when you run in the rain, the rain in your face is stronger than that on the back of your head!). Therefore there would be more impulse given the earth from the front, and the earth would feel a resistance to motion and would be slowing up in its orbit. One can calculate how long it would take for the earth to stop as a result of this resistance, and it would not take long enough for the earth to still be in its orbit, so this mechanism does not work. No machinery has ever been invented that "explains" gravity without also predicting some other phenomenon that does not exist.'

R. B. Feynman, R. P. Leighton and M. Sands (1963) *The Feynman Lectures on Physics*, Vol. 1 Addison-Wesley, Reading, Mass.

The mechanism by which one body attracts another over great distances—the mechanism of gravity—posed great problems in Newton's time (and still does). Matter has some property of attracting other matter. Action over a distance between bodies was felt to require the exchange of something, but nothing could be discerned.

Newton produced equations which enabled predictions about the motion of matter to be made but he did not produce any 'mechanism' responsible for his equations. In this chapter we look at the equations without knowledge of the mechanism.

One piece of matter does affect another piece of matter and we can arrive at laws, based on observations of matter, which can be used to describe the effects of such an interaction. A useful concept—a useful language—by which we can describe such interactions is that of fields. Around one piece of matter we construct (mathematically) a field—a region of influence—and say that this is produced by our piece of matter. When another piece of matter comes within that field we have a force acting on the matter due to its interaction with the field.

' "If we pick up a stone and then let it go, why does it fall to the ground?" The usual answer to this question is: "Because it is attracted by the earth." Modern physics formulates the answer rather differently.

The action of the earth on the stone takes place indirectly. The earth produces in its surroundings a gravitational field, which acts on the stone and produces its motion of fall.'

A. Einstein (1920) *The Theory of Relativity*, 3rd ed., transl. R. W. Lawson, Methuen.

The concept of a field is not just restricted to gravitation but is useful in electricity and magnetism. A charged particle can be thought of as producing an electric field and if another charged particle is placed in the field an interaction occurs between the particle and the field.

The field concept is abstract; many physicists have tried to devise some 'machinery' to avoid this abstraction, but it is a useful concept enabling considerable simplifications to be made.

Gravitational fields

Two pieces of matter attract each other with a force which varies inversely with the square of their distance apart (d) and directly in proportion to the masses of the two bodies (m and M).

$$F = \frac{GMm}{d^2}$$

G is the constant of proportionality, known as the universal constant of gravitation. The experimentally determined value of this constant is $6.67 \times 10^{-11} \, \text{m}^3 \, \text{kg}^{-1} \, \text{s}^{-1}$.

Suppose we take a mass m and place it near a mass M, it experiences a force F. If we put another mass m' at the same distance from M then the force is F' where

$$\frac{F'}{F} = \frac{m'}{m}$$

It does not matter what position we choose to put our masses, m and m', the ratio of the forces is the same (provided both are put in turn at the same point). Thus if $m' = 2m$ then $F' = 2F$. Thus if I measure the force on a 2 kg mass at a particular point above the earth's surface I will measure twice the force that I would have measured with a 1 kg mass. Thus if I took a 1 kg mass to every point in space and measured the forces at these points all I would need to do to find the force on another mass would be tc multiply the force value by the mass. This value of force per unit mass is called the gravitational field strength.

$$\text{Gravitational field strength} = \frac{\text{force}}{\text{mass}}$$

At the surface of the earth the force on a 1 kg mass is about 9.8 N and thus the gravitational field strength is 9.8 N kg^{-1}. This is identical in magnitude with the acceleration due to gravity, in m s^{-2}, at the point concerned. The gravitational field strength is always equal to the acceleration due to gravity at the point concerned.

By putting a 1 kg mass at different positions near another mass we can plot the contour lines of gravitational field strength. These lines tell us what the force would be if we put a 1 kg mass at particular points. These contour lines are said to give a map of the gravitational field. Is the field there when we have no test mass at the point concerned? The field is not radiated by a mass but is only a measure of the force that would occur when a mass is put in the vicinity of another mass.

Gravitational field strength

For a point mass (!) M, the force on a 1 kg mass a distance, d, away is

$$F = G \frac{M \times 1}{d^2}$$

The gravitational field strength is the force acting on unit mass and thus we have

Gravitational field strength $g = \dfrac{GM}{d^2}$

The direction of the field is the direction of the force. The gravitational field strength thus varies as the inverse square of the distance of the point concerned from the point mass.

What if we do not consider point masses but masses of finite size, say spheres? Do we measure the distance d from the surface of the mass M or the centre? Figure 12.7 shows a situation where we calculate the field strength at a point P close to the surface of a sphere. We can consider the sphere to be made up of a large number of small masses. These masses will be different distances from P and the forces experienced by a test mass placed at P will not all be in the same direction. To find the field strength at P we need to sum all the forces due to all these small masses. The direction of the field at P will be the direction of the resultant force. The result of such a summation is that the sphere behaves as though all its mass M was concentrated in a point at its centre, when distances greater than the sphere radius are considered.

Field maps

The gravitational field strength varies as the reciprocal of the square of the distance from the centre of a sphere and the field at all points is in a direction pointing to the centre of the sphere. Figure 12.8 shows how both the field strength magnitude and direction can be represented by diagrams for the earth. The direction lines are often called 'lines of force'.

The figure has assumed a perfectly spherical earth. This is not quite true. The departure from the sphere is, however, not large enough significantly to alter the results of Fig. 12.8 which shows the field on a relatively coarse scale. On a more local scale, irregularities in the earth's field are used to establish the presence of underground deposits of coal or salt, etc. Figure 12.9 shows

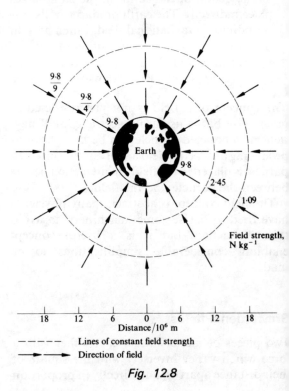

Fig. 12.8

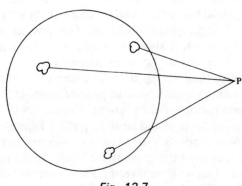

Fig. 12.7

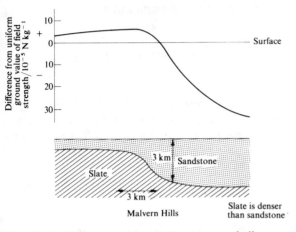

Fig. 12.9 *Field strength variations over rock discontinuity (A. H. Cook and V. Saunders (1969) Gravity and the earth, Wykeham Publications (London) Ltd)*

some typical field values. The irregularities arise because of local variations in the earth density.

The top of a mountain is farther from the centre of the earth than sea level and as the value of the field strength varies as the reciprocal of the square of the distance from the earth's centre we would expect the field strength to be lower at the top of the mountain.

$$\frac{\text{Field strength at height } h}{\text{Field strength at sea level}} = \frac{R^2}{(R + h)^2}$$

R is the radius of the earth, i.e., the distance of sea level from the centre of the earth. A mountain of height 1 km would give a difference in field strength between the top and the base of about 3×10^{-3} N kg^{-1}.

The masses of planets

What is the mass of the earth? We can estimate this by the use of our gravitation equation.

Consider a mass m, perhaps a stone, near the earth's surface. The force on the mass will be

$$F = mg$$

where g is the gravitational field strength (accel-

eration due to gravity). But the force must also be

$$F = G\frac{mM}{R^2}$$

where M is the mass of the earth, R the radius of the earth. Thus

$$mg = G\frac{mM}{R^2}$$

$$M = \frac{gR^2}{G}$$

$$= \frac{9.8 \times (6.4 \times 10^6)^2}{6.7 \times 10^{-11}}$$

$$= 6.0 \times 10^{24} \text{ kg}$$

What is the mass of another planet, say Saturn? The innermost of Saturn's satellites, Mimas, revolves in an almost circular orbit around Saturn. The time for one orbit is about 23 hours and the radius of the orbit is about 187 000 km.

The force acting on the satellite to keep it moving in a circular path must be

$$F = \frac{mv^2}{r}$$

where r is the radius of the orbit, m the mass of the satellite, and v its speed in orbit. But

$$F = G\frac{mM}{r^2}$$

where M is the mass of Saturn. Thus

$$\frac{mv^2}{r} = G\frac{mM}{R^2}$$

$$M = \frac{v^2 r}{G}$$

But the time to complete an orbit, T, is related to v.

$$v = \frac{2\pi r}{T}$$

231

Hence

$$M = \frac{4\pi^2 r^3}{GT^2}$$

Using our data gives for the mass M of Saturn 5.6×10^{26} kg.

This method can be used to determine the mass of any planet, or star, around which another mass rotates. We could have used the rotation of the moon around the earth to give us the mass of the earth.

Gravitational potential

If we move a mass m away from another mass M then energy must be supplied to move it against the force of attraction.

Energy needed to move m in a direction	=	force component in that direction	×	distance moved along that direction

But the gravitational field strength at a point is force/mass. If the distance moved ΔR is very small so that we can assume that the field strength does not change

Energy = field strength × mass × distance

$$= gm \, \Delta R$$

This energy must be supplied to the mass to move it through this distance—if the mass moves back to its original position then it will give up this amount of energy, perhaps as kinetic energy. The new position has thus an energy associated with it when the mass is present—this is known as potential energy.

The potential energy per unit mass is called the potential. The potential difference between the two points a distance ΔR apart is thus $g\Delta R$.

If the field is not constant over the distance the mass is moved then we must consider the movement of the mass in a large number of small steps—the field strength being considered constant over the distance of each step (Fig. 12.10a)

Potential difference $= g_1 \, \Delta R + g_2 \, \Delta R + g_3 \, \Delta R$

$+ \, g_4 \, \Delta R + g_5 \, \Delta R + g_6 \, \Delta R + g_7 \Delta R$

We can write this summation as

$$\text{Potential difference} = \int_{R_1}^{R_2} g \, dR$$

If we have a graph showing how the field strength changes with distance the summation is the area under the graph between R_1 and R_2 (Fig. 12.10).

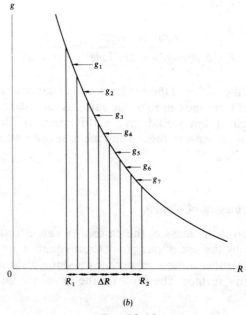

(a)

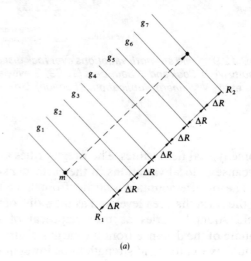

(b)

Fig. 12.10

The integral can be written as

$$\text{Potential difference} = \int_{R_1}^{R_2} \frac{GM}{R^2}\, dR$$

$$= \left[-\frac{GM}{R} \right]_{R_1}^{R_2}$$

$$= \frac{GM}{R_1} - \frac{GM}{R_2}$$

It is customary to measure potential differences between infinity, our zero, and a particular point if we want to specify the absolute potential at the point. Thus if we fetch a mass from infinity we have $R_1 = \infty$ and thus

$$\text{Potential} = -\frac{GM}{R_2}$$

where R_2 is the distance from the centre of mass M at the point we are considering. For a spherical mass the potential varies as the reciprocal of the distance. We can plot lines of constant potential around a spherical mass—they are called equipotentials (Fig. 12.11). The minus sign in the

equation means that the potential increases, i.e., becomes more positive, as the distance increases. This sign is a result of our convention of taking the potential to be zero at infinity.

The field strength is the potential gradient. Rewriting the integral in differential form shows this.

$$\text{Potential difference} = \int_{R_1}^{R_2} g\, dR$$

$$dV = g\, dR$$

$$g = \frac{dV}{dR}$$

Tearing mass away from the earth

Between the earth and all the objects on it (and away from it) there is a force of attraction due to gravity. To move an object away from the earth requires energy—a force is required to move through a distance.

The force of attraction, due to gravity, between two masses m and M a distance r apart is

$$F = G\frac{mM}{r^2}$$

where G is a constant, 6.67×10^{-11} m^3 kg^{-1} s^{-2}.

Let us consider moving a 1 kg mass away from the surface of the earth. The mass of the earth is 6×10^{24} kg. Thus we have

$$F = \frac{3.8 \times 10^{14}}{r^2}$$

and can plot a graph showing how the force varies with distance. r is measured from the centre of the earth to the centre of the 1 kg mass. The radius of the earth is 6371 km and thus we could use the formula to calculate the force on a 1 kg mass at the earth's surface—but this we know, it is the weight of the 1 kg mass, i.e., 9.8 N. At twice the earth's radius the force will be 9.8/4; the force varies as $1/r^2$. Figure 12.12 shows the resulting graph.

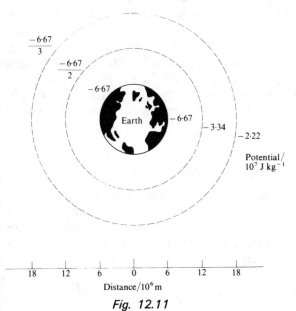

Fig. 12.11

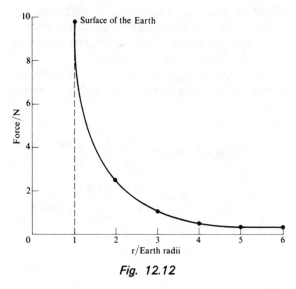

Fig. 12.12

The energy needed to tear our mass away from the earth is the area under the graph, between the value of r equal to the earth's radius and infinite radius (only at infinity has the mass completely escaped). The area is, by rough estimate, 5.2×10^7 J from $r = 1$ to $r = 6$ earth radii. As beyond $r = 6$ earth radii will contribute some area, it would be a reasonable approximation to say that the energy needed for the escape of 1 kg is about 6×10^7 J.

How big is this? A 1 kg mass would have to have a kinetic energy of 6×10^7 J on leaving the earth's surface if it is just to reach infinity. This means a velocity of about 10^4 m s^{-1}. This known as the escape velocity.

The area could have been obtained by integration.

$$\text{Energy} = \int_{r = 6371 \times 10^3}^{r = \infty} \frac{3.8 \times 10^{14}}{r^2} \, dr$$

$$= 5.97 \times 10^7 \text{ J}$$

Escape velocity

Since the potential energy of a mass m at the surface of the earth, mass M and radius R, is $m \times$ gravitational potential at the surface, then

$$\text{Potential energy} = \frac{GMm}{R}$$

To move the mass to infinity we must supply a kinetic energy $\frac{1}{2}mv^2$ which is at least equal to the potential energy. Hence escape velocity v is given by

$$v = \sqrt{\left(\frac{2GM}{R} \right)}$$

Notice that the escape velocity is the same for all masses leaving the earth's surface. The equation can be simplified as we know the force at the earth's surface in terms of the acceleration due to gravity g.

$$mg = \frac{GMm}{R^2}$$

Thus escape velocity v is given by

$$v = \sqrt{(2gR)}$$

This is 11.2×10^3 m s^{-1} at the earth's surface.

All spacecraft going to other planets or the moon must reach a velocity of this order. In the Apollo 11 shot which landed the first men on the moon, the sequence of events which got the crew on their way to the moon was: first stage rocket brings velocity up to 2.4×10^3 m s^{-1}, second stage brings velocity up to 6.7×10^3 m s^{-1}, third stage puts the spacecraft in an earth orbit before bringing the velocity up to 10.7×10^3 m s^{-1} (the velocity not to escape the earth but to get as far as the moon).

Energy and satellite motion

Consider a satellite of mass m orbiting a planet of mass M at a radial distance r, then the satellite will have a potential energy of Vm, where V is the potential at this radial distance from the planet. Hence

$$\text{Potential energy} = -\frac{GMm}{r}$$

The satellite will also possess kinetic energy, $\frac{1}{2}mv^2$. Since the centripetal force acting on the satellite is GMm/r^2, we have

$$\frac{mv^2}{r} = \frac{GMm}{r^2}$$

Hence

$$\text{Kinetic energy} = \frac{GMm}{2r}$$

The magnitude of the kinetic energy is half that of the potential energy. However, the potential energy is negative, the kinetic energy being positive. Hence the total energy of the satellite is

$$-\frac{GMm}{r} + \frac{GMm}{2r} = -\frac{GMm}{2r}$$

Figure 12.13 shows how the potential, kinetic and total energies vary with radial distance out from the planet.

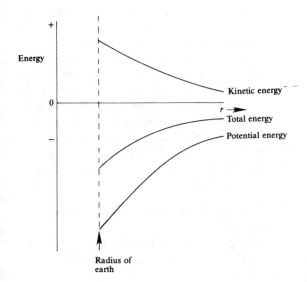

Fig. 12.13   Energies of satellite motion

Supplementary material

The discovery of Neptune

The earth, or indeed any planet, in orbit round the sun is acted on by forces due not only to the gravitational force of the sun but those of all the other planets. These other forces cause a planet to deviate from the elliptical path it would follow if it alone was orbiting the sun. These effects are called perturbations.

When Copernicus produced his model of the universe only six planets were known: Mercury, Venus, Earth, Mars, Jupiter, and Saturn. The invention of the telescope (see Chapter 10) led to the discovery of Jupiter's moons by Galileo in 1610 and in the same year Saturn's rings. In 1781 telescope observations revealed the existence of a new planet—Uranus. It was shown to be a planet because the size of its image in the telescope changed when different magnifying power telescopes were used; the image size does not change when stars are observed (they are so far away that they behave as points). The planet was discovered by W. Herschel. His observations, coupled with those on old star maps where it was recorded as a star, enabled its orbit to be plotted.

The orbit, however, did not precisely fit the ellipse shape, even when perturbations due to the presence of Jupiter and Saturn were allowed for. Figure 12.14a shows the unexplained deviations of

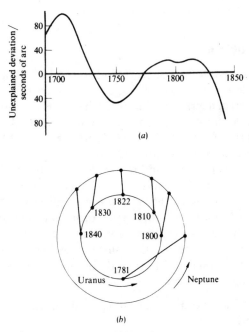

Fig. 12.14

Uranus's orbit from that expected. The solution to the problem was proposed, independently, by J. C. Adams and U. J. Le Verrier—there was another planet farther out than Uranus and this produced the unexplained deviation. They both theoretically worked out the position that the new planet should occupy—it was found close to the predicted position and called Neptune. Figure 12.14b shows how its position changes relative to that of Uranus—compare this figure with the maximum and minimum deviations of Uranus in Fig. 12.14a. In the period immediately prior to 1822 Neptune's pull speeded up Uranus, after that its pull slowed Uranus down.

Irregularities in the orbit of Neptune led in 1930 to the discovery of the planet Pluto by C. Tombargh. Pluto is much smaller than the other outer planets and has an orbit which is not in the same plane as all the other planets. It is thought that it might be an escaped moon of Neptune.

The planet Mercury also shows unexplained perturbations. Le Verrier estimated from these deviations the position of a new planet, which he called Vulcan, between Mercury and the sun. No such planet has been found. An explanation of the deviation was supplied by Einstein replacing Newton's gravitational theory by a new theory—the general theory of relativity.

Problems

1. Explorer 38, a radio-astronomy research satellite of mass 200 kg, circles the earth in an orbit of average radius $3R/2$ where R is the radius of the earth. Assuming the gravitational pull on a mass of 1 kg at the earth's surface to be 10 N, calculate the pull on the satellite.

(University of London, Q5, Paper 2, June 1979)

2. A preliminary stage of spacecraft Apollo 11's journey to the moon was to place it in an Earth parking orbit. This orbit was circular, maintaining an almost constant distance of 189 km from the Earth's surface. Assuming the gravitational field strength in this orbit is 9.4 $N\,kg^{-1}$, calculate

(a) the speed of the spacecraft in this orbit, and

(b) the time to complete one orbit.

(Radius of the earth = 6370 km)

(University of London, Q4, Paper 2 January 1981)

3. (a) State Newton's law of gravitation and derive the dimensions of the gravitational constant G.

(b) If a planet is assumed to move around the sun in a circular orbit of radius r with periodic time T, derive an expression for T in terms of r and other relevant quantities.

(JMB, Q1, Paper II, June 1978)

4. The Earth is elliptical with polar and equatorial radii equal to 6.357×10^6 m and 6.378×10^6 m respectively. Determine the difference, Δg, in the values of the acceleration of free fall at a pole and at the equator due to this difference in radii. What other factors affect Δg?

(Mass of Earth = 5.957×10^{24} kg, Gravitational constant, $G = 6.670 \times 10^{-11}$ N m^2 kg^{-2})

(University of London, Q5, Paper 2, January 1980)

5. (a) Give an account of one method of measuring the value of the gravitational constant, G, explaining how the result is calculated from the observations made.

(b) Kepler's third law of planetary motion, as simplified by taking the orbits to be circles round the Sun, states that if r denotes the radius of the orbit of a particular planet and T denotes the period in which that planet describes its orbit, then r^3/T^2 has the same value for all the planets.

The orbits of the Earth and of Jupiter are very nearly circular with radii of 150×10^9 m and 778×10^9 m respectively, while Jupiter's period round the Sun is 11.8 years.

(i) Show that these figures are consistent with Kepler's third law.

(ii) Taking the value of the gravitational constant, G, to be 6.67×10^{-11} n m^2 kg^{-2}, estimate the mass of the Sun.

(Oxford Local Examinations, Q1, Paper I June 1978)

6. (a) (i) State Newton's law of gravitation.

(ii) Describe an experiment by which the gravitational constant G may be determined.

(b) A space station of mass m is in a circular orbit at a height h above the Earth's surface. In terms of these quantities together with the radius r

of the Earth and the acceleration due to gravity g_0 at the Earth's surface, derive expressions for the space station's:

(i) potential energy;
(ii) kinetic energy;
(iii) total energy.

The space station descends from a height of 300 km to 299 km in one orbit. If $m = 8.0 \times 10^4$ kg, $r = 6400$ km and $g_0 = 9.8$ m s^{-2}, calculate:

(iv) the energy lost by the space station;
(v) the retarding force acting on it.

(Oxford Local Examinations, Q3, Paper I, June 1981)

7. What do you understand by the intensity of gravity (gravitational field strength) and the gravitational potential at a point in the Earth's gravitational field? How are they related?

Taking the Earth to be a uniform sphere of radius 6400 km, and the value of g at the surface to be 10 m s^{-2}, calculate the total energy needed to raise a satellite of mass 2000 kg to a height of 800 km above the ground and to set it into circular orbit at that altitude.

Explain briefly how the satellite is set into orbit once the intended altitude has been reached, and also what would happen if this procedure failed to come into action.

(Oxford Local Examinations, Q2, Paper II, Summer 1977)

8. The gravitational field strength, g_0, on the surface of the Earth is 9.81 N kg^{-1}. Explain what this means.

Using Newton's law of gravitation show that

$$gr^2 = \text{constant}$$

where g is the gravitational field strength at a distance r from the centre of the Earth ($r > r_0$, where r_0 is the radius of the Earth).

The gravitational field strength at the surface of the moon is 1.67 N kg^{-1}. At what point on a line from the Earth to the moon will the net gravitational field strength due to the Earth and the moon be zero? Sketch a rough graph showing how this net gravitational field strength varies along the line between the surface of the Earth and the surface of the moon.

(b) The gravitational potential on the surface of the Earth is -63 MJ kg^{-1}. Explain what this means. If the gravitational potential on the surface of the moon is -3 MJ kg^{-1}, what is the gravitational potential difference between the surface of the Earth and the surface of the moon?

The moon's surface is at a higher gravitational potential than the Earth's surface, yet in returning to the Earth from the moon, a spacecraft needs to use its rocket engine initially to propel it towards the Earth. Why is this?

(Distance from the centre of the Earth to the centre of the moon = 400 000 km, radius of the Earth = 6400 km, radius of the moon = 1740 km.

(University of London, Q11, Paper 2, January 1982)

9. (a) Define the gravitational constant, G, and describe one method of measuring its value in the laboratory.

(b) The diameter of Mars is 6760 km, its average density is 3945 kg m^{-3}, and its period of rotation about its axis is 24.6 hours.

Stating the assumptions that you make, estimate the radius of the synchronous circular orbit described by a spacecraft travelling round Mars. (Take the value of G to be 6.67×10^{-11} N m^2 kg^{-2})

(c) The 1975 Viking spacecraft described an elliptical orbit, its closest distance from the centre of Mars being 4900 km, and its greatest distance 36 000 km. Find the ratio of the angular velocities in these two positions and explain your calculations.

(Oxford Local Examinations, Q1, Paper S, June 1979)

10. (a) Explain what is meant by the gravitational constant G.

(b) The Earth may be taken to be a uniform sphere of mass M and radius r. In terms of these quantities and G, derive expressions for:

(i) the acceleration due to gravity g at the Earth's surface;
(ii) the period T of a satellite in a circular orbit at a height h above the Earth's surface;
(iii) the escape velocity v at the Earth's surface.

(c) A neutron star has a mass of 2.0×10^{30} kg and a diameter of 20 km.

(i) What is the mean density of the star?

(ii) Calculate the gravitational field strength at the surface.

(iii) What would be the theoretical maximum height of a cylindrical granite column which could support its own weight without crushing when exposed to a gravitational field of this magnitude?

(iv) What do your answers suggest about the composition at an atomic level of the materials at the surface of a neutron star?

(Take the gravitational constant G to be 6.7×10^{-11} N m^2 kg^{-2}, the density of the granite to be 2700 kg m^{-3} and its crushing strength to be 3.6×10^6 N m^{-2})

(Oxford Local Examinations, Q2, Paper I, June 1982)

13 Electric fields

Electrical forces

If you rub a plastic comb (or pen or other similar object) against a wool material it becomes charged. This shows by the comb attracting small pieces of paper or other light objects. We call this attractive force an electrical force. Such forces have been known for many centuries. It was not, however, until about 1730 that it was realized that electrical forces were not always attractive forces but could be repulsive.

'... there are two distinct electricities, very different from each other: one of these I call vitreous electricity; the other, resinous electricity. The first is that of (rubbed) glass, rock crystal, precious stones, hair of animals, wool, and many other bodies. The second is that of (rubbed) amber, copal, gum lac, silk, thread, paper, and a vast number of other substances.

The characteristic of these electricities is that a body of, say, the vitreous electricity repels all such as are of the same electricity; and on the contrary, attracts all those of the resinous electricity. . . .'

C. F. de C. Dufay (1733–4) *Phil. Trans.*, **38**, 258.

The rubbed plastic comb has to be put fairly close to objects to pick them up; the repulsion, or attraction, between two charged objects is much more noticeable when they are close together—the conclusion from these observations is that the electric force depends on the distance away from the charged object. What is the relationship linking force and distance?

Though the answer to this question had, by analogy with gravitation, been earlier guessed by J. Priestley in 1767, it was Coulomb in 1785 who first experimentally obtained the answer.

'. . . It follows from these trials that the repulsive force which two balls exert on each other when they are electrified with the same kind of electricity is inversely proportional to the square of the distance (between the centres of the balls).'

C. A. Coulomb (1785) *Mémoires de l'Académie Royale des Sciences.*

Coulomb obtained his experimental results by the use of a torsion balance. In this a charged ball was situated near to a second similarly charged ball. The second ball was attached to the end of an insulator rod which itself was horizontally suspended by a wire attached to its midpoint (Fig. 13.1). The other end of the wire was fixed. The force of repulsion between the spheres caused the wire to twist. In an earlier experiment Coulomb had found the torque necessary to twist the wire through different angles and so was able to determine the force of repulsion.

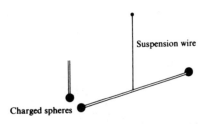

Fig. 13.1 Schematic diagram of Coulomb's torsion balance

We can repeat Coulomb's experiment in the laboratory with simpler apparatus. Two graphite-coated pith or expanded polystyrene balls, one on the end of an insulator rod and the other suspended by two insulator threads, can be used (Fig. 13.2). Coulomb used pith balls, because they are very light. When the pith ball on the rod is brought up to the similarly charged suspended ball, deflection of the suspended ball occurs. This deflection can be easily measured by casting shadows of the balls onto a distant screen. The deflection is proportional to the force (for small deflections). You can readily check this by 'deflecting' a suspended weight with a spring balance (Fig. 13.3). The deflection is proportional to the force reading given by the spring balance. The result—the force is inversely proportional to the square of the distance between the centres of the balls

$$F \propto \frac{1}{r^2}$$

The force also depends on the amount of charge carried by the balls. If at a constant distance between the two balls we reduce the charge on one of the balls by a factor of two we find that the force is reduced by a factor of two. The reduction of the charge by a factor of two can be produced by putting in contact with the charged ball an equal size but uncharged ball. The charge then becomes equally shared between the two. If the charge on both balls is reduced by a factor of two then the force is reduced by a factor of four. More results all show that the force is directly proportional to the product of the charges on both balls.

$$F \propto q_1 q_2$$

The relation thus becomes

$$F \propto \frac{q_1 q_2}{r^2}$$

The constant of proportionality is taken as $1/4\pi\varepsilon_0$.

$$F \propto \frac{q_1 q_2}{4\pi\varepsilon_0 r^2}$$

The constant of proportionality is written in this form for reasons which can only become apparent from a study of electric and magnetic fields. The value of the constant is, however, an established fact arrived at from experiment. ε_0 has the value of $8.85 \times 10^{-12} \ C^2 \ N^{-1} \ m^{-2}$.

The equation is often known as Coulomb's law.

Electric fields

Suppose we take a charged particle and place it near another charged particle, it experiences a force. With all the points in the space around a charge we can associate a force—the force that a test charge would experience if placed there. We can imagine that there is a field of force surrounding the charge and assign to each point a field strength, the field strength being the force per unit charge. The direction of the electric field is taken as the direction of the force on a positive charge.

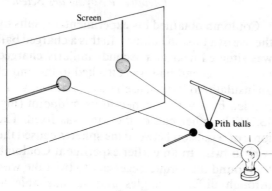

Screen

Pith balls

Fig. 13.2

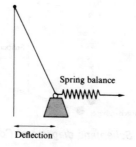

Spring balance

Deflection

Fig. 13.3

$$\text{Electrical field strength} = E = \frac{\text{force}}{\text{charge}}$$

The directions of the electric field can be plotted in the space around the charge to give a field map. The lines marking these directions are known as lines of force (Fig. 13.4).

Electric field patterns can be 'seen' if charged conductors are in an insulating liquid and grass seed is sprinkled on the surface of the liquid. The grass seed lines up along the direction of the field.

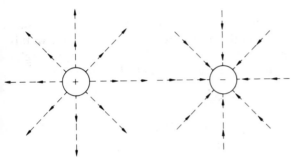

Fig. 13.4   Electric field patterns

Electric field strength between parallel plates

A case which is of particular interest is the one involving two parallel plates. The electric field is everywhere between the plates at right angles to the plates. Indeed for any conducting surface the electric field is always at right angles to the surface. If the field were not at right angles there would be a component of the field parallel to the conducting surface—this would cause electrons to move within the surface and hence a current flow. This current would continue until the electrons have so arranged themselves that the electric field is at right angles to the surface. The parallel plate arrangement is a capacitor and we would normally charge the plates by connecting a potential difference between the plates. This would result in one plate having a positive charge and the other a negative charge. The two charges would have the same magnitude. The charges would, however, be spread over the plates—two 'carpets' of charge facing each other.

A voltmeter connected between the two parallel plates gives a reading V when there is an electric field between the plates. When $V = 0$ there is no field. The voltmeter reading tells us the energy transformed when a unit charge moves between the plates.

$$\text{Energy} = Vq$$

There is nothing in this equation which suggests that it matters between which two points on the plates the charge moves. The field beween the plates is uniform. This can be tested by putting a charged oil drop between the plates (the Millikan experiment)—the drop experiences the same force, the same acceleration is measured, wherever the drop is between the plates. Some peculiarities occur near the edges but the greater part of the volume between the plates has the same field strength. The energy transformed by moving a charge between the plates must be the product of the force acting on it and the distance through which it is moved.

$$\text{Energy} = Fd$$

where d is the separation of the plates and F the force acting on the charge due to the electric field. Hence

$$Fd = Vq$$

or as $E = F/q$ we must have, for the field strength between the plates,

$$E = \frac{F}{q} = \frac{V}{d}$$

The units of E can be N kg^{-1} or V m^{-1}. E is the potential gradient. Our definitions (Fig. 13.5) of the directions of the field and the potential gradient are such as to require us to write $E = -(\text{potential gradient})$.

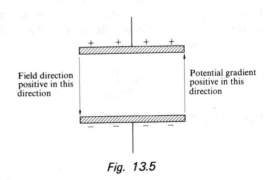

Field direction positive in this direction

Potential gradient positive in this direction

Fig. 13.5

Thus if the potential difference between two parallel plates is 5000 V and they are 10 mm apart, the electric field strength between them is

$$5000/10 \times 10^{-3} = 5.0 \times 10^5 \, \text{V m}^{-1} \text{ or N kg}^{-1}$$

Electric field strength for a point charge

At a distance r from a point charge Q the force on a test charge q will be

$$F = \frac{Qq}{4\pi\varepsilon_0 r^2}$$

and thus as $E = F/q$ we have

$$E = \frac{Q}{4\pi\varepsilon_0 r^2}$$

The electric field strength varies as the reciprocal of the square of the distance from the charge.

The Coulomb's law equation and the electric field concept have implicit in them the idea that electric charge is additive in its effect. Doubling the charge at one point doubles the force on another charge, i.e., doubles the field at the point where the second charge is situated. But also the force acting on the second charge due to the first one is not influenced by the presence of another, third, charge. Coulomb's law can be used to calculate the interaction force for any pair of charges, regardless of whether other charges are present. We can calculate the force on one charge due to the presence of say two other charges by calculating the force due to each charge separately and then finding the vector sum.

Consider two charges, A with +3 C and B with −2 C (Fig. 13.6) and the field produced by them at a point P. P is 4 m from A and 3 m from B. A and B are 5 m apart. To calculate the field we consider the force on a +1 C charge placed at P. The field at P due to A will be

$$E_A = \frac{3}{4\pi\varepsilon_0 4^2}$$

The field at P due to B will be

$$E_B = \frac{2}{4\pi\varepsilon_0 3^2}$$

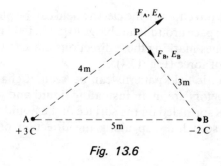

Fig. 13.6

To find the resultant field at P we must take into account the directions of these two fields. In this particular case the two fields are at right angles and thus the resultant field E is given by

$$E^2 = E_A^2 + E_B^2$$

$$E^2 = \frac{1}{4\pi\varepsilon_0} \sqrt{\left[\left(\frac{3}{16}\right)^2 + \left(-\frac{2}{9}\right)^2\right]}$$

$$E = \frac{0.5}{4\pi\varepsilon_0}$$

The tangent of the angle between this resultant and the E_B direction is given by

$$\tan\theta = \frac{E_A}{E_B}$$

Electric field strength for a charged sphere

The electric field strength a distance r from the centre of a charged sphere of radius a can be obtained, for $r \geqslant a$, by considering the charge to be effectively located as a point charge at the centre of the sphere. This can be shown in the same way mentioned in Chapter 12 for the gravitational field strength due to a spherical mass.

For all points within a charged sphere there is no electric field strength. Thus for

$$r < a \qquad E = 0$$

$$r \geqslant a \qquad E = \frac{Q}{4\pi\varepsilon_0 r}$$

Potential due to a point charge

Consider the energy change involved in fetching a charged particle from infinity up to a distance r from another charged particle. The force between the two charged particles (assumed to be points) can be written as

$$F = \frac{K}{r^2}$$

where r is the distance between the particles and K a constant, $q_1 q_2 / 4\pi\varepsilon_0$. Figure 13.7 shows a graph of F against r.

Area between	(very approx.)
$r = \infty$ and $r = 10$	0.040 K
10 9	0.020 K
9 8	0.024 K
8 7	0.028 K
7 6	0.036 K
6 5	0.040 K
5 4	0.052 K
4 3	0.088 K
3 2	0.176 K
2 1	0.480 K

Thus the total areas up to particular r values are

r	∞	9	8	7	6	5	4	3	2	1
Area × K	0	0.060	0.084	0.112	0.148	0.188	0.240	0.338	0.504	0.984

Thus the energy needed to fetch a charge from infinity up to $r = 1$ is about 0.984 K or 1 K. The energy in fact varies as $1/r$ as a graph of the above energies against $1/r$ shows (Fig. 13.8). The results fit an equation

$$\text{Potential energy} = \frac{K}{r}$$

According to this equation the potential energy falls as r increases. For an attractive force this is not correct. Decreasing r decreases the potential energy. Think of the potential energy of a mass above the earth's surface—the higher it is above the surface the greater the potential energy. We can make our equation fit this behaviour by writing it as

$$\text{Potential energy} = -\frac{K}{r} = -\frac{q_1 q_2}{4\pi\varepsilon_0 r}$$

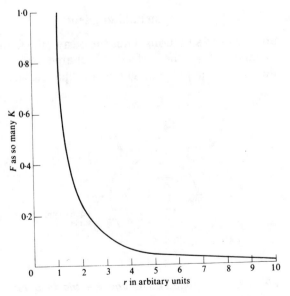

Fig. 13.7

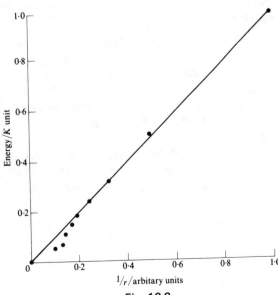

Fig. 13.8

243

Now the smaller r becomes the more negative the potential energy becomes.

This result could have been obtained by integration.

$$\text{Potential energy} = \int_{\infty}^{r} F \, dr = \int_{\infty}^{r} \frac{K}{r^2} \, dr = -\frac{K}{r}$$

Thus at points in space around a charged object we can associate certain potential energies as being the energies needed to put a charge at those points. If we double the charge we put at a point we double the energy needed; the force between two charges is directly proportional to the sizes of the charges. It is convenient to talk of the potential energy per unit charge for a point—this is called the potential

$$\text{Potential } V = \frac{\text{potential energy}}{\text{charge}}$$

Hence the potential V at a distance r from a point charge Q is given by

$$V = -\frac{Q}{4\pi\varepsilon_0 r}$$

Potential due to an insulated conducting sphere

The potential a distance r from the centre of an insulated conducting sphere with a charge Q and of radius a is, for $r > a$ the same as that given by a point charge Q located at the centre of the sphere. This is assuming that the sphere is isolated and its potential not affected by the proximity of other objects.

Because the sphere is made of a conducting material, every point on both the surface of and within the sphere will be at the same potential. Thus

$$r \leqslant a \quad V = -\frac{Q}{4\pi\varepsilon_2 a}$$

$$r > a \quad V = -\frac{Q}{4\pi\varepsilon_0 r}$$

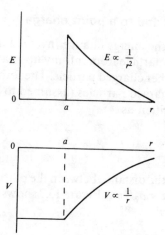

Fig. 13.9 E and V for an insulated conducting sphere

Figure 13.9 shows how both the electric field and potential vary with distance for an insulated, isolated, conducting sphere. The electric field direction is always radial (see Fig. 13.4) with the surfaces of constant potential, called equipotential surfaces, being spherical and centred on the sphere centre. Thus the equipotential surfaces are always at right angles to the electric field (Fig. 13.10).

The equation derived earlier for the charged parallel plates that

$$E = -(\text{potential gradient})$$

applies to all situations. Thus the greater the field strength at, say, the surface of a charged sphere the greater the potential gradient at that surface.

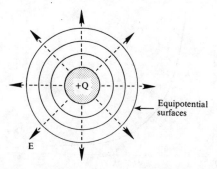

Fig. 13.10 Equipotentials and electric field for a charged sphere

The potential of a conducting surface is not determined by just its own charge unless that body is isolated, no other objects being close. Thus, for instance, bringing an earthed conducting sphere near to a charged sphere will change the potential on the surface of the charged sphere. The earthed conducting sphere will be at zero potential and thus to maintain the same potential gradient, i.e., same electric field strength at the surface of the charged sphere, the potential of that sphere must change.

Capacitors

When a potential difference is applied across a pair of insulated parallel plates, as in Fig. 13.11a, they become charged, one plate positively and the other negatively. We can show that this is happening by monitoring the current to or from each plate. The current decreases with the time, eventually becoming zero. But at any instant, the current is towards one plate and away from the other. This tells us that charge is flowing onto one plate and off the other. Since the currents are always the same size, this means that the size of the charges on the two plates is the same.

The parallel plate arrangement is called a

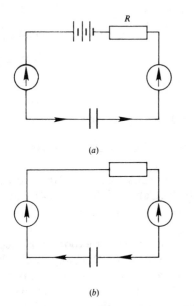

(a)

(b)

Fig. 13.11   (a) Charging a capacitor. (b) Discharging the capacitor

capacitor and in the above situation we are said to be charging the capacitor. The capacitor is said to be fully charged when the charging current has decreased to zero.

We can show that there is charge on the capacitor plates by taking a charged capacitor and connecting it as shown in Fig. 13.11b. We again detect current as the charge on each plate decreases to zero. This discharge current is in the opposite direction to the charging current. The discharge current decreases with time to become eventually zero when the capacitor is fully discharged.

During the charging, if V is the d.c. supply voltage and I the current, then we must have for the circuit shown in Fig. 13.11a (counting the resistance of the meters as included within the circuit resistance R)

$$V = V_R + V_C$$

where V_R is the potential drop across the resistor and V_C that across the capacitor. But $V_R = IR$, hence

$$V = IR + V_C$$

Thus when initially the current in the charging circuit is high the potential difference across the capacitor is low. When the current decreases then V_C increases until eventually when the current is zero $V_C = V$.

During the charging, the current decreases with time to become eventually zero, the charge and potential difference increase with time to a maximum value when the current is zero. At any instant the ratio of the charge on a capacitor plate to the potential difference between the plates is a constant, being called the capacitance C.

The above arguments apply not only to parallel plates but to any insulated conductor. When a charge is given to an insulated conductor its potential changes; it also has capacitance. Thus our general definition of capacitance is: if a charge Q given to an insulated conductor changes its potential by V then the capacitance C of that conductor is

$$C = \frac{Q}{V}$$

When Q is in coulombs and V in volts then C has the unit of coulomb volt^{-1}, this being given the name of farad (F).

The discharge of a capacitor

A capacitor is charged and then allowed to discharge through a resistor. How does the current through the resistor change with time during the discharge? How does the charge on a capacitor plate change with time during the discharge? Suppose we charge a 1000 μF (i.e., 10^{-3} F) capacitor by putting 10 V across it. The charge on a capacitor plate will be

$$Q = CV = 10^{-3} \times 10 = 10^{-2} = 0.01 \text{ coulomb}$$

When we discharge it the current (Fig. 13.12) is initially 1 mA (i.e., 10^{-3} A). So in one second the charge lost from the capacitor plate is given by

$$I = \frac{\Delta Q}{\Delta t}$$

and thus charge lost $\Delta Q = 10^{-3} \times 1 = 10^{-3}$ coulomb. The charge left on the plate after one second is therefore $0.01 - 0.001 = 0.009$ coulomb. The change in charge is in any time interval Δt given by $-I\Delta t$. The minus sign is because there is a drop in charge and we must subtract our change from the total charge.

$$\Delta Q = -I\,\Delta t$$

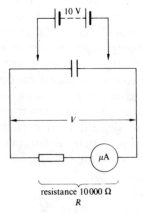

Fig. 13.12

But $V = IR$, hence we can write

$$\Delta Q = -\frac{V}{R}\,\Delta t$$

The potential difference V across the capacitor is related to the charge on a capacitor plate by

$$V = \frac{Q}{C}$$

hence

$$\Delta Q = -\frac{Q}{CR}\,\Delta t$$

The rate of change of charge on a capacitor plate is directly proportional to the charge on the plate. In our example with a resistance of 10 000 Ω and a capacitance of 10^{-3} F the change in charge per second is

$$\Delta Q \text{ per second} = -0.1\,Q$$

At time $t = 0$, $Q = 0.01$ C.
At time $t = 1$ s

$$\Delta Q = -0.1 \times 0.01 = -0.001 \text{ C}$$

Thus after 1 s the charge will be $0.01 - 0.001 = 0.009$ C.
At time $t = 2$ s

$$\Delta Q = -0.1 \times 0.009 = -0.0009 \text{ C.}$$

Thus after 2 s the charge will be $0.009 - 0.0009 = 0.0081$ C.
At time $t = 3$ s

$$\Delta Q = -0.1 \times 0.0081 = -0.000\,81 \text{ C.}$$

Thus after 3 s the charge will be $0.0081 - 0.000\,81 = 0.007\,29$ C.

After 4 s the charge will be 0.006 561 C, after 5 s 0.005 904 9 C, after 6 s 0.005 314 41 C, etc. Figure 13.13 shows a graph of the charge variation with time.

The graph shows an exponential decrease of the charge with time. One way of checking that this is the case is to see whether it is a constant ratio graph (see Chapter 0). The ratio of values of Q at times separated by the same interval Δt is a constant. At $t = 0$ s, $Q_0 = 0.01$ C; at $t = 1$ s, $Q_1 = $

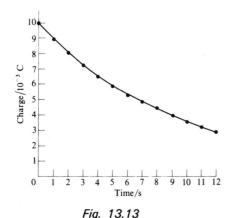

Fig. 13.13

0.009 C; at $t = 2$ s, $Q_2 = 0.009$ C. Thus

$$\frac{Q_1}{Q_0} = \frac{0.009}{0.01} = \frac{Q_2}{Q_1} = \frac{0.0081}{0.0009} = 0.90$$

This is a direct consequence of the form of our rate of change of charge equation. Since $\Delta Q = Q_1 - Q_0$, we could write the equation as

$$Q_1 - Q_0 = -\frac{Q_0}{CR} \Delta t$$

$$\frac{Q_1}{Q_0} = 1 - \frac{\Delta t}{CR} = \text{a constant}$$

Such an exponential variation of charge with time can be written as

$$Q = Q_0 e^{-t/RC}$$

However the equation is written there is an important term, RC, which determines the size of the ratio Q_1/Q_0 and controls the rate of discharge. The bigger the value of RC the smaller the ratio Q_1/Q_0 and hence the faster the rate of discharge. This term RC is called the time constant of the circuit.

The units of the time constant are seconds. R has the unit V/A, C has the unit C/V = A s/V and so RC has the unit (V/A) × (A s/V) = s.

After a time interval equal to $1RC$ then the charge remaining on the capacitor is

$$Q = Q_0 e^{-1RC/RC} = Q_0 e^{-1} = 0.37 Q_0$$

The percentage of charge left on the capacitor plates is 37 per cent. After $2RC$

$$Q = Q_0 e^{-2RC/RC} = Q_0 e^{-2} = 0.135 Q_0$$

The percentage of charge left on the capacitor plates is thus 13.5 per cent. After $3RC$ the percentage is 5.0 per cent, after $4RC$ it is 1.8 per cent, after $5RC$ it is 0.7 per cent, and after $6RC$ it is 0.25 per cent.

Charge and discharge equations

During charging of a capacitor (Fig. 13.11a) we have

$$V = IR + V_C \tag{1}$$

$$V = R\frac{dQ}{dt} + \frac{Q}{C}$$

This differential equation has the solution

$$Q = VC(1 - e^{-t/RC}) \tag{2}$$

or, since VC is the maximum value of the charge Q_m

$$Q = Q_m(1 - e^{-t/RC}) \tag{3}$$

It follows that since the charging current $I = dQ/dt$, so

$$I = \frac{V}{R} e^{-t/RC} \tag{4}$$

Since V/R is the maximum value of the current I_m

$$I = I_m e^{-t/RC} \tag{5}$$

Since the potential difference across a capacitor $V_C = Q/C$, then Eq. (2) gives

$$V_C = V(1 - e^{-t/RC}) \tag{6}$$

Graphs of the above equations are shown in Fig. 13.14a.

During discharging of a capacitor (Fig. 13.11b) we have for Eq. (1), since $V = 0$

$$0 = IR + V_C$$

$$0 = R\frac{dQ}{dt} + \frac{Q}{C}$$

247

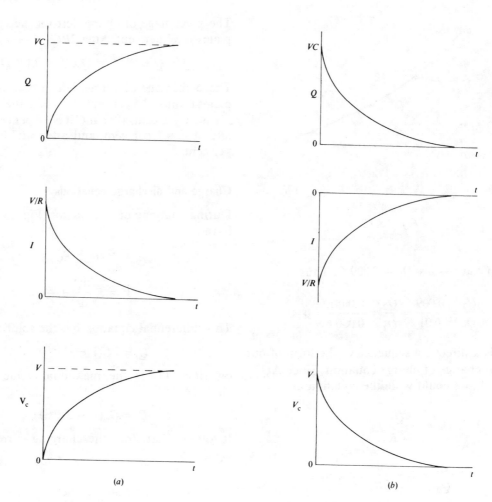

Fig. 13.14 Charging a capacitor. (b) Discharging a capacitor

This differential equation has the solution

$$Q = Q_0 e^{-t/RC} \qquad (7)$$

where Q_0 is the initial charge. Since during discharge $I = dQ/dt$

$$I = -\frac{Q_0}{RC} e^{-t/RC} \qquad (8)$$

Since $V_C = Q/C$, then Eq. (7) gives

$$V_C = \frac{Q_0}{C} e^{-t/RC} \qquad (9)$$

In both Eq. (8) and Eq. (9) $Q_0/C = V$, the p.d. across the fully charged capacitor. Graphs of the above equations are shown in Fig. 13.14b.

Capacitors in series and parallel

Consider three capacitors connected in series, Fig. 13.15. The size of the charges on all the capacitor plates must be the same, since for those plates connected together all that has happened is that charge has flowed off one plate and onto the other. The potential difference V across all the capacitors must be

$$V = V_1 + V_2 + V_3$$

But $V_1 = Q/C_1$, $V_2 = Q/C_2$ and $V_3 = Q/C_3$, hence

$$V = \frac{Q}{C_1} + \frac{Q}{C_2} + \frac{Q}{C_3}$$

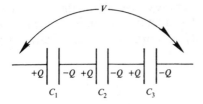

Fig. 13.15 Capacitors in series

We could replace the three capacitors by a single capacitor C, where capacitance $C = Q/V$, hence

$$\frac{1}{C} = \frac{1}{C_1} + \frac{1}{C_2} + \frac{1}{C_3}$$

For capacitors in parallel, Fig. 13.16, the potential differences across all the capacitors must be the same. The total charge Q spread across all the capacitors must equal the sum of the charges on each, i.e.

$$Q = Q_1 + Q_2 + Q_3$$

But $Q_1 = C_1V$, $Q_2 = C_2V$ and $Q_3 = C_3V$, hence

$$Q = C_1V + C_2V + C_3V$$

We could replace the three capacitors by a single capacitor C, of capacitance $C = Q/V$, hence

$$C = C_1 + C_2 + C_3$$

To illustrate the use of the above equations and principles, consider the following problems.

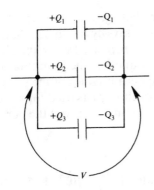

Fig. 13.16 Capacitors in parallel

(i) What is the capacitance of an arrangement involving a 2 µF capacitor in series with a 8 µF capacitor?

$$\frac{1}{C} = \frac{1}{2} + \frac{1}{8}$$

$$C = 1.6 \ \mu F$$

(ii) What is the capacitance of an arrangement involving a 2 µF capacitor in parallel with an 8 µF capacitor?

$$C = 2 + 8 = 10 \ \mu F$$

(iii) An 8 µF capacitor is fully charged by an applied potential difference of 24 V. The capacitor is then disconnected from the supply and connected across an uncharged 16 µF capacitor. What are the charges on the two capacitors and the potential difference across each?

The initial charge on the 8 µF capacitor is $Q = CV = 8 \times 10^{-6} \times 24 = 192 \times 10^{-6}$ C. When the two capacitors are connected together the charge is spread over the two capacitors.

$$192 \times 10^{-6} = Q_1 + Q_2$$

$$= C_1V + C_2V$$

$$= 24 \times 10^{-6}V$$

Hence $\qquad V = 8$ V

Thus $Q_1 = C_1V = 8 \times 10^{-6} \times 8 = 64 \times 10^{-6}$ V and $Q_2 = C_2V = 16 \times 10^{-6} \times 8 = 128 \times 10^{-6}$ C.

Energy stored in a capacitor

Energy is needed to move a charge through a potential difference. To charge a capacitor we bring charges and put them on one of its plates. For the first charge brought up no energy is needed as the potential of the plate is zero (we assume the plate is initially uncharged). As we keep on putting charges on the plate so its potential increases and so for each new charge brought up we have to supply more energy to get the charge up the potential gradient: the gradient keeps on growing steeper. We can think of the charge on the plate exerting bigger and bigger repulsive forces on the new charge being brought up, the forces grow because of the increase of charge on the plate.

If at some instant the potential on the plate is V and we bring up a new charge ΔQ then the energy needed will be $V \Delta Q$. This is in fact the area under a graph of V against Q (Fig. 13.17) which corresponds to the potential and size of ΔQ. The total energy used in charging up the capacitor to a potential V will be the area under the V against Q graph from zero potential to V. The area is $\frac{1}{2}VQ$.

$$\text{Energy} = \tfrac{1}{2}VQ$$

As $Q = CV$ we can write this as

$$\text{Energy} = \tfrac{1}{2}CV^2$$

If we charge a capacitor up to 4 V we supply 16 times the energy we did when charging it up to 1 V. When we discharge a capacitor the energy used in putting the charge onto the capacitor plates is released. Capacitors are convenient ways of storing energy. In an electric flashgun used in photography we charge a capacitor up by slowly supplying energy and then release it, all in one quick lump, by discharging it through the flashbulb.

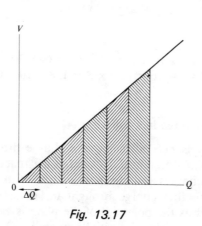

Fig. 13.17

The parallel plate capacitor

What are the factors that determine the capacitance of a parallel plate capacitor? Experimentally this can be investigated, using perhaps the reed switch method described later. If the plate areas facing each other are constant and the medium between the plates unchanging, then the capacitance C is inversely proportional to the distance d between the plates.

$$C \propto \frac{1}{d}$$

The area of the plates facing each other can be varied by varying the degree of overlap of the plates. With a constant separation and medium between the plates the capacitance is directly proportional to the plate area A.

$$C \propto A$$

The capacitance is also affected by the medium between the plates. Thus if a sheet of polythene is slid between the plates and replaces air, then the capacitance is found to be increased.

We can combine these factors in a single equation

$$C \propto \frac{A}{d}$$

In air, or rather more strictly a vacuum

$$C = \varepsilon_0 \frac{A}{d}$$

where ε_0 is a constant called the permittivity of free space. If we use some other medium between the plates then

$$C = \varepsilon_r \varepsilon_0 \frac{A}{d}$$

where ε_r is called the relative permittivity and is the factor which says by how much the capacitance of a capacitor is increased when the air (vacuum) is replaced by another medium. Plastics tend to have relative permittivities of the order of 2 to 3. The term permittivity ε is used for the product of the relative permittivity ε_r and the permittivity of free space ε_0.

$$\varepsilon = \varepsilon_r \varepsilon_0$$

ε_0 has the value 8.85×10^{-12} F m^{-1} (or C^2 N^{-1} m^{-2}).

The following are some of the types of problems involving the equation for the capacitance of the parallel plate capacitor.

(i) What is the capacitance of a parallel plate capacitor having plates 0.40 m square, separated by 1.0 mm of a medium of relative permittivity 4.0?

$$C = \varepsilon_r\varepsilon_0 \frac{A}{d}$$

$$= \frac{4.0 \times 8.85 \times 10^{-12} \times 0.40^2}{1.0 \times 10^{-3}}$$

$$= 5.7 \times 10^{-9} \text{ F}$$

(ii) A battery is connected to a parallel plate capacitor with air between the plates. If the separation of the plates is doubled while the battery is still connected, how does the charge on the plates and the energy stored by the capacitor change?

$$Q = CV = \varepsilon_0 \frac{AV}{d}$$

With V, A and ε_0 constant then $Q \propto 1/d$. Hence doubling d halves Q.

$$\text{Energy stored} = \tfrac{1}{2}VQ$$

Hence, since V is constant and Q halved, the energy stored is halved.

(iii) A battery is used to charge a parallel plate air capacitor. The battery is then disconnected and then the separation of the plates doubled. How does the potential difference between the plates and the energy stored by the capacitor change?

$$V = \frac{Q}{C} = \frac{Qd}{\varepsilon_0 A}$$

Since Q, A and ε_0 remain constant then $V \propto d$ and so doubling d doubles the potential difference V.

$$\text{Energy stored} = \tfrac{1}{2}VQ$$

Hence, since Q is constant and V doubled, the energy stored is doubled.

Charge density

For a parallel plate capacitor

$$C = \varepsilon \frac{A}{d}$$

But $C = Q/V$ and so

$$\frac{Q}{V} = \varepsilon \frac{A}{d}$$

$$\frac{V}{d} = \frac{Q}{A} \times \frac{1}{\varepsilon}$$

But $V/d = E$, the electric field strength between the plates. Q/A is the charge per unit area of the plates and is called the charge density σ. Hence

$$E = \frac{\sigma}{\varepsilon}$$

This equation is also valid for other situations, giving the relationship between the electric field and the charge density close to the surface of any charged conductor.

The above equation has here been derived from a consideration of the equation of the capacitance for a parallel plate capacitor, which in turn was derived from experimental results. The constant ε is the same one that was introduced in the first section of this chapter for Coulomb's law. We could have started with Coulomb's law and derived the above equation, by considering each plate to have a 'carpet' of point charges and summing the effects of all of them on a test charge placed between the plates. Hence we could have derived, from this Coulomb law start, the equation for the parallel plate capacitor.

Relative permittivity

The effect of some medium, referred to as the dielectric, other than a vacuum between capacitor plates is to increase the capacitance. How can we explain this? When a charged rod, perhaps a plastic pen which has been rubbed against your coat, is brought near to a small piece of paper (dry) the paper adheres to the rod. We say that charges have been induced in the paper—one end of the paper becoming positive and the other negative. Perhaps when we put an insulator between charged plates charges become induced on it. Figure 13.18 shows the possible effect. The plates produce a field E, the charges on the dielectric produce a field $-E'$ and the resultant field is $E - E'$. As the field between the plates is reduced, the net charge density at the plates is reduced by the presence of the dielectric. Thus an applied potential difference between the plates produces a lower electric field and effectively a lower charge density than it would if there was a vacuum between the plates. The dielectric has increased the capacitance.

Bringing a dielectric or a conducting object near a capacitor, whether it be a parallel plate arrangement or just an isolated object, changes its capacitance and hence the electric field. Some fishes produce electric fields around themselves and sense the disturbance of the field produced by objects in their vicinity. Field changes as low as 10^{-6} V m^{-1} can be detected.

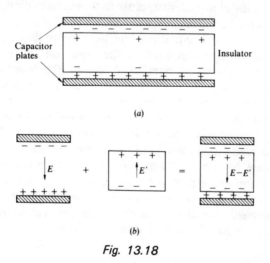

(a)

(b)

Fig. 13.18

Capacitance of an isolated sphere

If a charged conducting, but isolated, sphere of radius r has a charge Q, then the potential V at the surface of the sphere is

$$V = -\frac{Q}{4\pi\varepsilon_0 r}$$

But the capacitance of the sphere is $C = Q/V$, hence

$$C = 4\pi\varepsilon_0 r$$

Types of capacitors

The parallel plate air capacitor is not a very practical capacitor since even when made very large it can only give capacitances of the order of 10^{-9} F. There are many forms of what is essentially the parallel plate capacitor but using materials other than air as the dielectric. In the paper or polyester capacitor (Fig. 13.19a) the parallel plates are sheets of aluminium foil which are kept apart and insulated from each other by sheets of waxed paper or polyester film, these being the dielectric. The entire assembly is rolled up in a tight roll, so enabling large area plates to be used in a very compact space. Capacitances of the order of 50

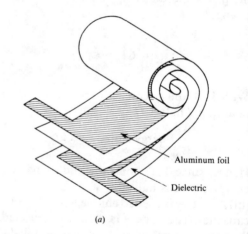

(a)

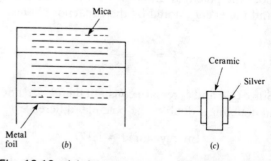

Fig. 13.19 (a) A polyester type of capacitor. (b) A mica capacitor. (c) A disc ceramic capacitor

252

pF (10^{-12} F) to a few microfarads (10^{-6} F) are produced this way.

Mica capacitors, with capacitances of the order of 10^{-9} F, are made by depositing silver onto both sides of thin sheets of mica or by putting the mica between sheets of aluminium foil (Fig. 13.19b).

Ceramic capacitors can be made in many forms but generally involve silver being deposited on both sides of a thin sheet of ceramic. Capacitances of the order of 10 pF to 1μF can be produced with very small size capacitors (Fig. 13.19c).

With the above types of capacitor it does not matter which of the plates is connected to the positive side of the supply and which to the negative. However, with electrolytic capacitors they can only be used when connected the right way round in a circuit. The electrolytic capacitor consists of two strips of aluminium foil separated by a strip of paper soaked in an aluminium borate solution. When they are made, a current is passed through the aluminium borate solution and causes a thin layer of aluminium oxide to form on the aluminium; this layer then becomes the dielectric. Capacitances ranging from a microfarad to many thousands of microfarads can be produced.

Measurement of capacitance

A simple method of measuring capacitance in school or college laboratories involves the use of a reed switch. This is used to alternately charge and discharge the capacitor. Figure 13.20 shows the basic principles. The reed switch is made to switch back and forth at a frequency f by an input to the switch from a signal generator operating at this frequency. The result is that the capacitor is charged at f times a second to the potential difference V, i.e., a charge $Q = CV$. This charge is discharged f times per second through a galvanometer. At sufficiently high frequencies the meter registers a steady current I. But I is rate of movement of charge and this $I = CV/(1/f) = fCV$. Thus a measurement of the current I, the potential difference V and a knowledge of the frequency, f enables C to be calculated.

A condition of the above experiment is that the frequency should be such as to allow sufficient time for the capacitor to both become fully charged and fully discharged.

The above experiment can be used to obtain a value of ε_0 if a parallel plate air capacitor is used. Since $C = \varepsilon_0 A/d$, measurements of C, A and d enable ε_0 to be determined.

Another method that can be used for the comparison of capacitances involves the use of the ballistic galvanometer. A ballistic galvanometer is one specially adapted for the measurement of charge by damping being made as small as possible. This means that the charge can be passed through the galvanometer coil in a time which is less than about a quarter of the periodic time of oscillations of the coil. The result of this is that the deflection of the galvanometer is proportional to the charge. When used for the com-

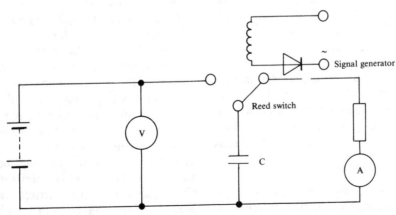

Fig. 13.20 Reed switch method of measuring capacitance

parison of capacitances, each capacitor is in turn charged to the same potential difference and then discharged through the galvanometer coil. Since the deflection θ of the galvanometer coil is proportional to charge Q, then:

$$Q_1 = C_1V = k\theta_1$$

$$Q_2 = C_2V = k\theta_2$$

$$\frac{C_1}{C_2} = \frac{\theta_1}{\theta_2}$$

Supplementary material

Lightning and sparks

Small sparks can be observed when some charged objects discharge. The effect is most pronounced when conditions are dry. Newton observed a spark when he brought a needle close to a piece of amber or resin which had been rubbed against a silk cloth. Lightning is a discharge on a much grander scale. That clouds carry charge, was first shown, it is said, by Franklin's experiment in which he flew a kite up into a thundercloud. Rain made his kite string conducting and charge flowed down his kite string. A knuckle of his hand placed close to the end of the wet kite string produced a spark between his hand and the string.

What is the cause of such sparks, the small ones and lightning?

A charged capacitor will not maintain its charge indefinitely—the charge slowly leaks away. This is due to the ions that are always present in normal air. These ions are in the main produced by cosmic radiation. Thus if we think of two parallel charged capacitor plates the ions will move between the plates, the positive ions moving to the negative plate and the negative ions to the positive plate. The plates are charged and thus there is a potential difference between the plates and so an electric field. This accelerates the ions.

$$\tfrac{1}{2}mv^2 = Vq$$

v is the velocity acquired by an ion of mass m and charge q moving through a potential difference V. The greater the potential difference V the larger

we would expect the kinetic energy to be. There is, however, air between the plates and the ions will collide with air molecules many times in their movement between plates. The vital factor is thus deciding the kinetic energy that can be acquired by an ion between collisions and is therefore the potential difference per unit length of ion path. The greater the value of this the greater the energy of an ion immediately prior to a collision. The potential difference per unit length has been already met—it is the electric field.

$$E = \frac{V}{d}$$

If the kinetic energy acquired by an ion is large enough it can ionize an air molecule when they collide. The energy needed for this will be about 10 electron volts, i.e., about 10^{-18} J. For air molecules moving about among air molecules at atmospheric pressure and normal room temperature the mean disance between collisions is about 5×10^{-7} m. An ionized air molecule could be expected to have the same mean distance between collisions. Electrons are considerably smaller than ionized air molecules and thus collide less with air molecules; their mean distance between collisions would be about 2×10^{-6} m. Thus the ions or electrons must acquire an energy equivalent to being accelerated through 10 volts in a distance ranging from 5×10^{-7} to 2×10^{-6} m. For capacitor plates 1 cm apart this would mean a voltage of 2×10^5 V for ionized air molecules to produce ionization and 5×10^4 V for electrons to produce ionization.

In dry air, at atmospheric pressure and normal room temperature, with plates 1 cm apart a spark will jump between the plates when they have a potential difference between them of 3×10^4 V. This is of the same order as our calculated value for electrons to produce ionization.

When ionization occurs there is an increase in the number of ions and electrons, these in turn become accelerated and produce more ions and electrons, these in turn produce more. Thus when ionization starts there is a very rapid build-up in the number of charge carriers which can cause leakage of the charge from the capacitor plates. The effect is known as an avalanche and the voltage at which it occurs as the breakdown voltage. All these ions provide a conducting path of low resistance between the two plates. The resistance thus suddenly drops from a very high value (air is a reasonable insulator) to almost a short circuit. The effect of this is for the charge on the plates to become very quickly discharged along the leakage path provided by the ions. It is this surge which appears as the spark. The ions and electrons rushing between the plates excite many air molecules and visible light is produced.

The presence of water droplets considerably reduces the breakdown voltage: water molecules act as small dipoles. Drops about 1 mm radius reduce the breakdown voltage to about 10 000 V for a 1 cm path. Bigger drops reduce the breakdown value even more.

The discharge of charge occurs more readily from an object which has points or sharp edges than one that is perfectly smooth. Lightning conductors are points for this very reason. Newton put a needle close to his charged piece of amber and obtained a spark—leakage of the charge from the amber occurred rapidly when the needle was brought close. For a charged conducting sphere we can think of all the charge Q as being at the centre, the potential at the surface of the sphere, radius R, is thus

$$V = \frac{Q}{4\pi\varepsilon_0 R}$$

Suppose we have two spheres connected together by a conducting wire. Both spheres will have surfaces at the same potential because they are connected together. If the second sphere has a radius r then the charge q must be given by

$$V = \frac{Q}{4\pi\varepsilon_0 R} = \frac{q}{4\pi\varepsilon_0 r}$$

$$\frac{Q}{R} = \frac{q}{r}$$

The electric field at the surface for the first sphere is given by

$$E = \frac{Q}{4\pi\varepsilon_0 R^2}$$

$4\pi R^2$ is the surface area of a sphere. For the second sphere we have

$$E' = \frac{q}{4\pi\varepsilon_0 R}$$

The ratio of the electric field is thus

$$\frac{E}{E'} = \frac{Qr^2}{R^2 q}$$

But we have $Q/R = q/r$, hence

$$\frac{E}{E'} = \frac{r}{R}$$

If R is bigger than r we have the result that the field is greatest near the smaller radius sphere. The fields are inversely proportional to the radii. A point has a small radius and thus near a point the field will be much greater than near a flat or larger radius of curvature surface. It is thus easier for discharge to occur from points because for the same potential as any other surface they have larger fields in their vicinity.

Charges are produced on sheet insulators running over rollers. Dust particles are attracted to charged surfaces—think of how you probably sometime have rubbed a plastic pen or comb against your jacket and used it to pick up small pieces of paper. The dust particles become dipoles in the field of the charged surface. If the charges are produced on fabrics running over rollers in a factory then this dust can mark the fabric. There are two main methods of reducing this effect—both involve providing a leakage path for the charge to escape from the fabric by supplying ions. One method uses a radioactive source to ionize the air in the vicinity, other methods employ points placed close to the fabric. Sometimes fine wires are used.

The earth as a whole carries a negative charge and thus near the earth's surface there is an electric field. The electric field can be measured; in fine weather its value is about $130\,\mathrm{N\,C^{-1}}$. Hence the charge density will be given by $E = \sigma/\varepsilon_0$ as

$$\sigma = 130 \times 8.85 \times 10^{-12}$$

$$= 1.2 \times 10^{-9}\ \mathrm{C\ m^{-2}}$$

As the earth has a surface area of 5.1×10^{14} m², this would mean a total charge of 6.1×10^5 C, about half a million coulombs. The charge is negative. Thunderclouds are generally positive in the upper part of the cloud and negative in the lower part. Balloons or aircraft flying through the clouds give this information—Franklin with his kite was able to determine the sign of the charge in the base of thunderclouds. The base of a thundercloud is, however, more negative than the immediate ground area under the cloud. We have effectively a parallel plate capacitor, the base of the cloud being one plate and the surface of the earth the other plate. The base of the cloud will be about 2 km above the surface of the earth. The breakdown voltage for wet air is about 10 000 volts per centimetre of path ($E = 10^6$ N C⁻¹). Thus for breakdown of the air between the cloud and the earth we would need about 2×10^9 V.

The sequences occurring in a lightning flash can be followed by high speed photography. The avalanche of ionization moves out from the cloud with a speed about 1/6 that of light. This gives a moving spot of light which progresses down to the earth. It does not move down to the earth in one uninterrupted step but comes down in a series of steps with short pauses between steps. This is called the step leader—it is not the main lightning flash. The progress of the step leader to the ground is irregular. When the step leader reaches the ground the negative charge in the base of the cloud is rapidly discharged to the earth. This discharge gives the bright lightning flash, and the corresponding thunder. The lightning, however, travels from the ground up to the cloud: it is known as the return stroke. The light is produced when the charges can move rapidly and it is those charges in the step leader near to the ground which first move rapidly. When they shoot into the ground then those higher up the leader can move rapidly—then those higher up, and so on up to the cloud. After a short interval of time a further leader comes down the path of ions left by the first leader and again there is a return stroke. Near pointed or tall objects on the earth there will be higher electric fields and so the step leader is more likely to strike them than the flat ground. The high electric field will already have produced some ions and thus there is a lower resistance path for the step leader in their vicinity. Lightning conductors on tall buildings provide a lower resistance path to earth than the fabric of the building and thus the discharge current, perhaps of the order of 10^4 A, bypasses the building.

Lightning is the means by which the earth acquires its negative charge. During fine weather the earth is steadily loosing charge, lightning replenishes it.

Problems

1. Two point charges Q_1 and Q_2 are situated as shown in Fig. 13.21. Q_1 is a positive charge and Q_2 is a negative charge; the magnitude of Q_1 is greater than Q_2. A third point charge, which is positive, is now placed in such a position, X, that it experiences no resultant electrostatic force due to Q_1 and Q_2. Explain carefully why X must lie on the line AB which passes through Q_1 and Q_2.

Copy the diagram and indicate clearly in which section of the line AB the point X must lie. Give reasons for your answer.

Explain why the position X would be unchanged if the magnitude or the sign of the third charge were altered.

(University of London, Q7,
Paper 2, January 1982)

2. How do (a) the magnitude of the gravitational field, and (b) the magnitude of the electrostatic field, vary with distance from a point mass and a point charge respectively?

Sketch a graph illustrating the variation of electrostatic field strength, E, with distance, r, from the centre of a uniformly solid metal sphere of radius r_0 which is positively charged.

$$A \text{————————} \bullet \text{————————} \bullet \text{————} B$$
$$\qquad\qquad Q_1 \qquad\qquad\qquad Q_2$$

Fig. 13.21

Explain the shape of your graph

(i) for $r > r_0$ and

(ii) for $r < r_0$.

(University of London, Q5,
Paper 2, January 1981)

3. A simple model for a thundercloud is a charge of -40 C at a height of 5 km and a charge of $+40$ C at a height of 10 km. What would be the electric field strength on the ground directly under the cloud due to such charges?

4. Write down expressions for the electric field E at the surface and the potential V of an isolated spherical conductor of radius R carrying a charge q.

If air ionises in an electric field greater than 3.0×10^6 V m^{-1}, what is the maximum operating potential of a Van de Graaff generator with a spherical dome of radius 6.0 cm?

(University of Cambridge, Q7,
Paper 1, June 1980)

5. The capacitance of a certain variable capacitor may be varied between the limits of 1×10^{-10} F and 5×10^{-10} F by turning a knob attached to the movable plates. The capacitor is set to 5×10^{-10} F, and is charged by connecting it to a battery of e.m.f. 200 V.

(a) What is the charge on the plates?
The battery is then disconnected and the capacitance changed to 1×10^{-10} F.

(b) Assuming that no charge is lost from the plates, what is now the potential difference between them?

(c) How much mechanical work is done against electrical forces in changing the capacitance?

(University of Cambridge, Q9,
Paper 1, June 1979)

6. A student is provided with two square plates of glass of uniform thickness, each about 1.0 m^2 in area, and some thin aluminium foil, and is asked to construct a parallel plate air capacitor. Explain briefly how this should be done and list any additional items of equipment needed.

How should the plates be arranged to obtain the highest possible value of capacitance?

Estimate the highest capacitance value that could be achieved with this apparatus in practice.

(permittivity of air $= 9 \times 10^{-12}$ F m^{-1})

In order to further increase the capacitance the student is given a sheet of PVC of thickness 0.2 mm with which to separate the glass plates. If the relative permittivity of PVC is 4, calculate by what factor the capacitance of the student's capacitor would be increased.

Describe, with the aid of a labelled circuit diagram, how you would compare experimentally the capacitance in these two cases.

(University of London, Q14,
Paper 2, January 1979)

7. (a) An isolated metal plate is charged negatively. Explain how and why its potential would be modified by the presence of an earthed metal plate brought near to it. When the plates are separated the energy stored in the system increases. Explain why this is so and explain where the increase in energy comes from.

(b) Describe, giving the relevant theory, how you would determine experimentally the capacitance of a capacitor.

(c) A capacitor of capacitance 4.0 µF is charged to a potential of 100 V and a second capacitor of capacitance 2.0 µF is charged to a potential of 200 V. The two capacitors are now connected in parallel with like charged plates together. Calculate

(i) the energy stored in each capacitor initially,
(ii) the total charge stored when the capacitors are connected,
(iii) the capacitance of the system when the capacitors are connected,
(iv) the p.d. across the system, after connection,
(v) the energy now stored in the system.

Why has the energy changed from the total energy stored initially?

(AEB, Q13, Paper, 3, June 1981)

8. (a) (i) Define capacitance.
(ii) Obtain an expression for the energy stored in a charged capacitor, and show that when a capacitor is charged from a battery through a resistor half the energy drawn from the battery is given to the capacitor, while half is converted as heating in the resistor.

(b) Figure 13.2 represents a very large capacitor C $(2.2 \times 10^{-3}$ F), a resistor R (20 kΩ) and a 24 V d.c.

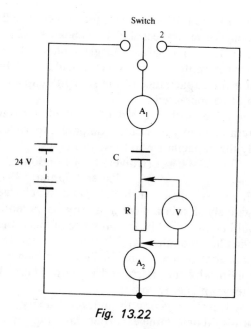

Switch

24 V

A₁

C

R   V

A₂

Fig. 13.22

supply. The meters A_1 and A_2 are centre-zero microammeters and V is a centre-zero voltmeter.

State, without giving detailed calculations, what you would expect to observe on each of the meters:

(i) on closing the switch to position 1 and leaving it closed;

(ii) on then opening the switch again, and leaving it open;

(iii) on then closing the switch to position 2 and leaving it closed.

In stage (iii), find the energy initially stored in C; and also the rate of energy conversion in R 20 s after the switch was closed.

(Oxford Local Examination Q11, Paper I, June 1978)

9. (a) Establish a relationship between the electric field intensity E and the electric potential V at a point in an electric field.

(b) A conducting sphere A of radius a is hung from an insulating thread and charged to a potential V_0. Draw sketch-graphs to show the variation with distance r measured from the centre of the sphere (at points both inside and outside the sphere) of:

(i) the electric field intensity E;

(ii) the electric potential V.

A second sphere B, similar to A but initially uncharged, is suspended on an insulating thread close to (but not touching) A.

(iii) Explain why A and B attract each other.
(iv) How would this force of attraction change if B was suspended by a conducting thread connected to earth?

(c) In a model Van de Graaf generator a conducting sphere of diameter 120 mm in air is charged electrostatically to a potential of 2.5×10^5 V.
Calculate:

(i) the stored charge;
(ii) the stored energy;
(iii) the electric field intensity at the surface of the sphere.

What factors would limit the potential to which the sphere could be charged?
(Take the permittivity of air to be 8.8×10^{-12} F m^{-1})

(Oxford Local Examinations, Q10, Paper I, June 1982)

10. (a) Describe a method for measuring the relative permittivity of a material. Your account should include a labelled circuit diagram, brief details of the procedure and the method used to calculate the results.

(b) In the circuit, Fig. 13.23, the capacitor C is first fully charged by using the two-way switch K. The capacitor C is then discharged through the resistor R. The graph shows how the current in the resistor R changes with time. Use the graph to help you answer the following questions.

Calculate the resistance R. (The resistance of the microammeter can be neglected.) Find an approximate value for the charge on the capacitor plates at the beginning of the discharging process and hence calculate

(i) the energy stored by the capacitor at the beginning of the discharge process, and
(ii) the capacitance C.

(University of London, Q15, Paper 2, June 1985)

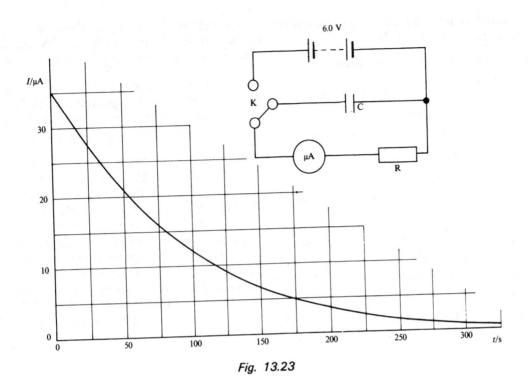

Fig. 13.23

11. Figure 13.24a shows a section through a type of microphone called a 'capacitor microphone'. Figure 13.24b is a circuit which shows how the microphone may be connected for use.

(The output from the microphone could be taken from terminals B and C, which would be connected to a suitable amplifier.)

(a) If the switch S were closed for a few seconds,

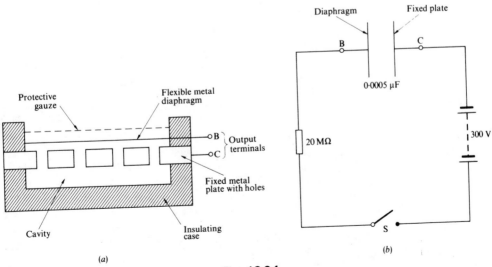

Fig. 13.24

then opened again, and the diaphragm then pushed slightly inwards, explain:

(i) what would happen to the capacitance of the microphone.

(ii) what would happen to the p.d. between B and C.

(b) Explain what would now happen if, with the diaphragm still pushed in, the switch S were closed.

(c) Why is the instrument constructed so that the diaphragm is as close to the first plate as possible?

(d) What is the time constant of this circuit?

(e) Assuming that switch S is closed, state the changes of p.d. between B and C that you would expect to occur if a compression wave moved the diaphragm inwards in a time:

(i) which was short compared with the time constant of the circuit—say in about 10^{-5} second.

(ii) which was long compared with the time constant of the circuit—say in about 1 second.

(f) Two sources of sound, one having a frequency of 10 000 Hz, the other of 50 Hz, are each found to produce the same amplitude of mechanical vibration in the diaphragm:

(i) Why is the amplitude of the resulting variations of p.d. across BC smaller for the 50 Hz vibrations than for the 10 000 Hz vibrations?

(ii) Explain what change you could make in the circuit to bring the amplitude of the electrical output from the microphone, when responding to the 50 Hz note, to approach more closely than produced by the 10 000 Hz note.

(Oxford and Cambridge Schools Examination Board, *Nuffield Advanced Physics*, Long answer paper, 1970)

14 Magnetic fields

Force on current-carrying conductor

Iron filings sprinkled round a permanent magnet or round a wire carrying a current show the 'existence' of what is called a magnetic field. We say there is a field because without there being any contact between either the magnet or the current-carrying wire and the iron filings, forces act on the filings, forcing them into patterns.

Consider two parallel and perfectly free wires—when there is no current in the wires there seems to be no noticeable force acting on the wires due to the presence of each other. The wires must contain both positive and negative charges and as the electrical forces between the two wires seem to cancel out there must be equal numbers of positive and negative charges in each wire. If, however, the charges are made to move, i.e., currents flow, forces are experienced by the wires. Moving charges in each wire give forces where previously no forces were apparent. We call these forces magnetic forces.

Motion of charge leads to a current and an associated magnetic field. Without motion there is no magnetic field. For a charge at rest there is only the electric field—the magnetic field appears when the charge begins to move.

The strength of an electric field is measured in terms of the force experienced by a charge, the strength of a gravitational field is in terms of the force experienced by a mass, the strength of a magnetic field we define in terms of the force on a current-carrying element of wire.

Figure 14.1 shows a simple 'current balance' which can be used to investigate the effects of magnetic fields on current-carrying conductors.

The deflection of the balance, and hence the force acting on the balance wire, is found to depend on the length of the current-carrying wire which is in the magnetic field. Doubling the length of the wire in the field doubles the force. The force is also directly proportional to the current in the wire. If we take the direction of the magnetic field as given by the direction in which the iron filings line up, then the magnetic field must be at right angles to the wire for the greatest effect. Thus the strength of the magnetic field can be expressed in terms of F/IL, where F is the force acting on a length of wire L carrying a current I. The term flux

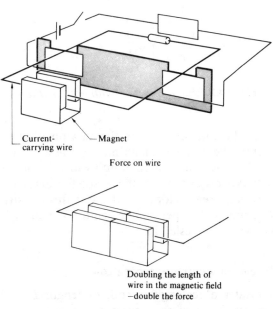

Current-carrying wire — Magnet

Force on wire

Doubling the length of wire in the magnetic field —double the force

Fig. 14.1   A current balance

density, B, is used for this quantity—the reason for this we will meet shortly.

$$B = \frac{F}{IL}$$

B is the component of the flux density at right angles to both the forces and the current. The force on the wire is at right angles to both the current and the magnetic flux component. A simple rule for these directions is known as the left-hand rule: hold your left hand with your second finger at right angles to the palm of your hand with your thumb in the plane of your hand but at right angles to the first finger; the first finger then gives the field direction, the second finger the current (opposite to electron flow) direction and the thumb the force direction (Fig. 14.2). Figure 14.3 shows the accepted directions of some fields, the direction being that of the force on a north pole.

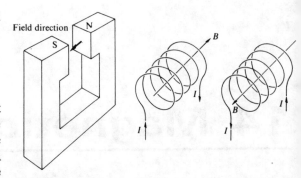

Fig. 14.3 Field directions, the anticlockwise current end of the solenoid behaving as a north pole, the clockwise as a south pole

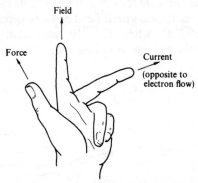

Fig. 14.2 Force direction with left-hand rule

magnetic field of flux density B (Fig. 14.4). If we apply the left-hand rule to find the force directions on the sides of the coil, the forces on PQ and SR combine to give zero resultant force since they are opposite and equal on the same line of action. The forces on sides PS and QR constitute a couple. The torque acting on the coil is thus

$$T = F \times b \cos \phi$$

$$= BIL \times b \cos \phi$$

But Lb = area of the coil face A, hence

$$T = BIA \cos \phi$$

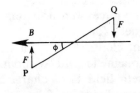

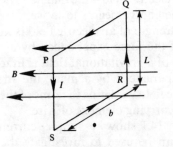

Fig. 14.4 Torque on a coil in a magnetic field

As the unit of force is the newton, that of current the ampere, length metres, the unit of B will be $\text{N A}^{-1} \text{ m}^{-1}$. Another unit which is used is webers per square metre; the reason for this is tied in with the reason for using the term flux density. The unit weber per square metre (Wb m^{-2}) is known as the tesla (T).

Torque on a current-carrying coil

Consider a rectangular coil, of length L and breadth b, carrying a current I in a uniform

The above has assumed a coil with just one wire. If there are N wires, then

$$T = NIAB \cos \phi$$

The moving coil galvanometer

Figure 14.5 shows the basic form of the moving coil galvanometer, a current-carrying coil able to rotate in the narrow air gap between a cylindrical iron core and the curved pole pieces of a permanent magnet. The design of the magnetic field is such that it is always at right angles to the plane of the coil. Thus the torque on the coil is

$$T = NIAB$$

The coil rotates under the action of this torque. It, however, rotates against a spring or twists a suspension wire, this supplying a restoring torque which is proportional to the angle θ through which the coil rotates.

$$\text{Restoring torque} = c\theta$$

where c is a constant for the spring or suspension wire. When the coil is in equilibrium

$$c\theta = NIAB$$

$$\theta = \left(\frac{NAB}{c} \right) I$$

The deflection is proportional to the current.

The current sensitivity is defined as θ/I, hence

$$\text{current sensitivity} = \frac{NAB}{c}$$

A high sensitivity is thus achieved by (a) a large magnetic field, (b) a large area coil with a large number of turns, (c) a small value of c for the restoring system.

The voltage sensitivity is defined as θ/V, hence

$$\text{voltage sensitivity} = \frac{\theta}{IR} = \frac{NAB}{cR}$$

A high voltage sensitivity thus requires the same conditions as the high current sensitivity, but in addition the coil must have a low resistance.

Force on moving charges

A current is charges moving, current being defined as the rate of movement of charge past a point.

$$I = \frac{\Delta Q}{\Delta t}$$

where ΔQ is the charge passing point X in time Δt (Fig. 14.6). In time Δt the charge that passed X at the beginning of this time interval will have travelled a distance $v \Delta t$, where v is the velocity of the charges. The length of the beam of charges produced in time Δt is thus $v\Delta t$. If this beam of charge is in a magnetic field then the force experienced will be

$$F = BIL$$

$$F = B \frac{\Delta Q}{\Delta t} v \Delta t$$

$$F = Bv \Delta Q$$

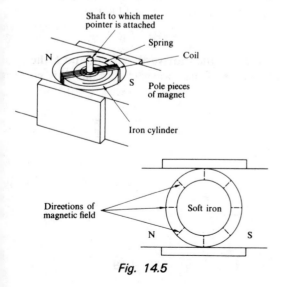

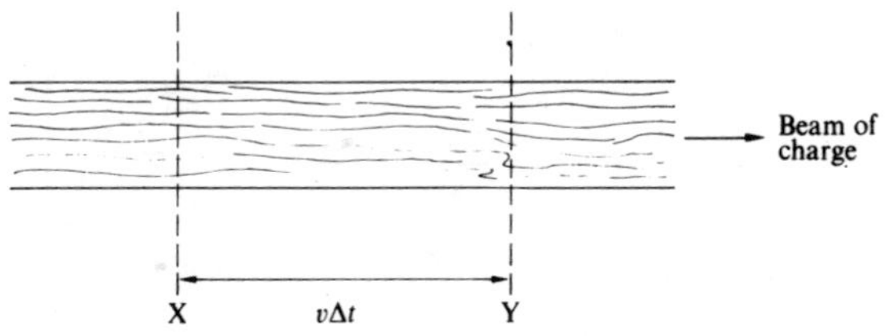

Shaft to which meter pointer is attached

Spring

Coil

N

S   Pole pieces of magnet

Iron cylinder

Directions of magnetic field

Soft iron

N   S

Fig. 14.5

Beam of charge

X $v\Delta t$ Y

Fig. 14.6

The charge ΔQ is made up of N charges each carrying a charge q, hence

$$F = BvNq$$

This is the force on N charges, the force on one charge will thus be

$$F = Bvq$$

Hall effect

Suppose we have a current passing through a slab of material, as in Fig. 14.7. If we apply a magnetic field normal to the surface of this material, the charge carriers giving the current should experience a force

$$F = Bqv$$

This force will cause negative charge to drift to one edge of the slab and positive charge to the opposite edge. This separation of charge will produce an electric field. This field will give another force acting on the charged particles, in the opposite direction to the force produced by the magnetic field.

$$F = Eq$$

The charge separation will grow until the force due to the electric field becomes equal to the force exerted by the magnetic field.

$$Eq = Bqv$$

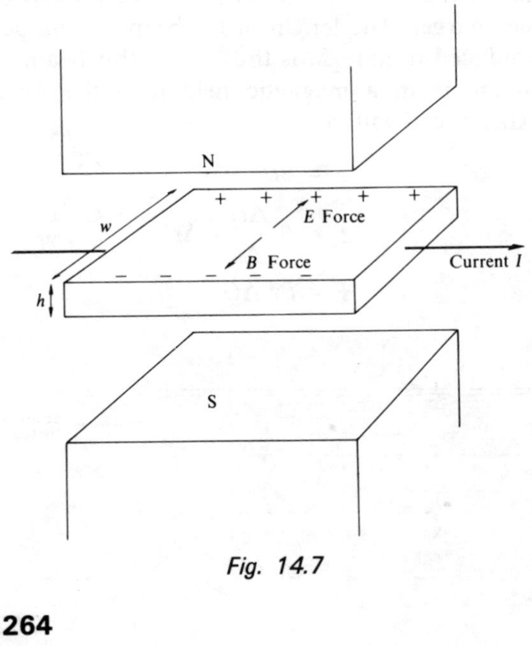

Because there is an electric field there will be a potential difference between the opposite edges of the slab.

$$E = \frac{V}{w}$$

Thus

$$V = Bvw$$

But

$$I = nAqv \quad \text{(see Chapter 11)}$$

where n is the number of charge carriers per unit volume, A is the cross-sectional area, and I the current.

$$A = wh$$

Thus

$$I = nwhqv$$

and

$$V = Bw\,\frac{I}{nwhq}$$

$$V = \frac{BI}{nhq}$$

This potential difference occurs when no current is drawn off the slab in a transverse direction, i.e., the charge separation is not affected. When a current is drawn off, Fig. 14.8, then

$$V = I'R$$

where I' is the transverse current and R the total resistance of the transverse circuit. This current

Fig. 14.7

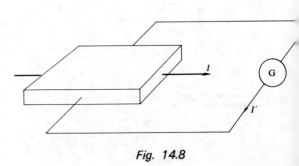

Fig. 14.8

can be measured. For the same material and current I we have

$$I' \propto B$$

We can thus use such a slab for the measurement of magnetic flux densities. The slab is known as a Hall probe and is generally made of a semiconductor material, for this purpose.

We can use the measurements, with known magnetic flux density, for the measurement of the number of charge carriers per unit volume in a material.

For example, the following data refers to silver. $B = 0.1\,\mathrm{N A^{-1}\,m^{-1}}$, $I = 18\,\mathrm{A}$, $h = 0.1\,\mathrm{mm}$, $V = 1.6 \times 10^{-6}\,\mathrm{V}$. This give for n, if we take q as 1.6×10^{-19} C, a value of $6.9 \times 10^{28}\,\mathrm{m^{-3}}$.

The density of silver is $10\,500\,\mathrm{kg\,m^{-3}}$, its atomic mass $107.87\,\mathrm{g}$. In $107.87 \times 10^{-3}\,\mathrm{kg}$ there will be 6×10^{23} atoms. This mass has a volume of $107.87 \times 10^{-3}/10\,500\,\mathrm{m^3}$. Thus the number of atoms per unit volume is

$$6 \times 10^{23} \times \frac{10\,500}{107.87 \times 10^{-3}} = 5.9 \times 10^{28}\,\mathrm{m^{-3}}$$

The number of charge carriers in silver would thus seem to be about one per atom, each charge carrier having the charge of an electron.

Hall effect measurements with germanium show that the number of charge carriers increases rapidly as the temperature is increased and that the number of charge carriers is only a very small fraction of the number of germanium atoms, about one charge carrier per million germanium atoms. This is typical of semiconductors. Metals have roughly equal numbers of charge carriers and atoms.

Magnetic fields produced by currents

Exploration of the field inside a solenoid shows that the field within the greater part of the internal volume is a constant. It only departs from the constant value near the ends. The magnetic field is at virtually all points parallel to the axis of the solenoid, the exceptions again being near the ends. The field can be measured by means of a current balance, a search coil, or a Hall probe. (Details of all these appear in this chapter.)

On what factors does the magnetic field inside a solenoid depend? We can do experiments to find out. The results—the magnetic flux density, B, is directly proportional to the current carried by the solenoid:

$$B \propto I$$

B is independent of the cross-sectional area of the solenoid; B is independent of the length of the solenoid provided the number of turns of wire per unit length is constant; B is directly proportional to the number of turns of wire per unit length (n)

$$B \propto n$$

B is independent of the nature of the wire or its cross-section provided the current is constant; B is independent of the shape of the solenoid. B seems to depend on just two quantities, the current and the number of turns per unit length

$$B \propto nI$$

As B, n, and I can be measured we can arrive at a value for the constant of proportionality μ_0. This constant has been called 'the magnetic space constant' or 'permeability of free space'.

$$B = \mu_0 nI$$

The experimentally determined value for μ_0 is $4\pi \times 10^{-7}\,\mathrm{N A^{-2}}$. The reason for putting the constant in this form is that it is more general than just a constant relating the flux density B to the current and number of turns per metre for a solenoid. n is assumed to be in turns per metre and I in amperes.

If we explore the magnetic field near a long straight current-carrying wire we find—at a particular distance from the wire B is directly proportional to the current I carried by the wire

$$B \propto I$$

B varies as the reciprocal of the distance r from the wire

$$B \propto \frac{1}{r}$$

B is independent of the cross-section of the wire,

its material or shape, provided the current is constant. The directions of B are in circles, centred on the wire, which lie in planes at right angles to the wire (Fig. 14.9).

$$B \propto \frac{I}{r}$$

In the same way as for the solenoid we can experimentally determine the value of the constant of proportionality.

$$B = k \frac{I}{r}$$

$$k = 2 \times 10^{-7} \text{ N A}^{-2}$$

which gives us

$$k = \frac{\mu_0}{2\pi}$$

Thus we have

$$B = \frac{\mu_0 I}{2\pi r}$$

We do not, however, have to rely on experiment to show the relationship between k and μ_0. A solenoid is only a lot of parallel wires. If we sum the effects due to each single wire in a solenoid we end up with the solenoid formula.

In the discussion of the solenoid it was assumed that the core of the solenoid only contained air. If, however, it had been, say, a ferrous material the flux density in that material would be $(B_0 + B_m)$, where B_0 is the flux density due to the current in the solenoid wires and B_m that due to the magnetization of the core material.

Ampère's circuital law

The flux density at a radial distance r from an infinitely long straight conductor is given by

$$B = \frac{\mu_0 I}{2\pi r}$$

This flux density is in a direction tangential to the circle of radius r (the circle is the line of force, Fig. 14.9). Since the circumference of this circle is $2\pi r$, we have the flux density multiplied by the length of the loop enclosing the conductor is equal to $\mu_0 I$.

$$B \times (2\pi r) = \mu_0 I$$

For a given current the product $B \times (2\pi r)$ is a constant for all circular loops enclosing the conductor. This product is a special case of what is called the line integral round the loop of B, the symbol $\oint$ being used to indicate this. Hence

$$\oint B \, \mathrm{d}L = \mu_0 I$$

This law holds for any closed path around any configuration of current-carrying conductors and is called Ampère's circuital law.

The unit of current

The flux density B a distance r from a long straight wire is

$$B = \frac{\mu_0 I}{2\pi r}$$

If at this distance we place another long straight wire, everywhere at right angles to B, a force will act on this wire when a current passes through it.

$$F = BIL$$

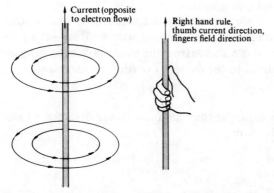

Fig. 14.9 Direction of field near a long wire

Current (opposite to electron flow)

Right hand rule, thumb current direction, fingers field direction

Thus if the current in both the wires is the same

$$F = \frac{\mu_0 I}{2\pi r} IL$$

$$= I^2 \frac{\mu_0 L}{2\pi r} = I^2 \times 2 \times 10^{-7} \frac{L}{r}$$

The force depends on the square of the current, the value of μ_0, and the geometrical arrangement of the wires, i.e., r and L. Whether the force is repulsion or attraction will depend on the directions of the current (Fig. 14.10). Measurement of this force using a current balance forms the basis of the ampere definition.

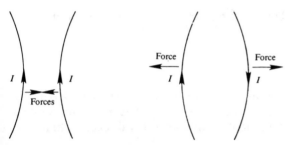

Fig. 14.10   Forces between two parallel current-carrying wires

The definition of the ampere is that constant current which if maintained in two straight parallel conductors of infinite length, of negligible circular cross-section, and placed 1 metre apart in a vacuum, would produce between these conductors a force equal to 2×10^{-7} N per metre length.

It is our definition of the ampere which determines the value of μ_0; the ampere is the primary unit. The values of the constants we have obtained in this section on magnetic fields have been fixed by our fixing the unit of current. Fixing the current unit not only fixes the value of μ_0 but also the value of ε_0. μ_0 and ε_0 are related by the equation

$$\text{Speed of light} = \frac{1}{\sqrt{(\mu_0 \varepsilon_0)}}$$

Electromagnetic induction

'Two hundred and three feet [about 65 m] of copper wire in one length were coiled round a large block of wood; other two hundred and three feet of similar wire were interposed as a spiral between the turns of the first coil, and metallic contact everywhere prevented by twine. One of these helices was connected with a galvanometer, and the other with a battery of one hundred pairs of plates four inches [10 cm] square, with double coppers, and well charged. When the contact was made, there was a sudden and very slight effect at the galvanometer, and there was a sudden and very slight effect when the contact with the battery was broken. But while the voltaic current was continuing to pass through the one helix, no galvanometrical appearances nor any effect like induction upon the other helix could be perceived. . . . '

M. Faraday (1831)
Experimental Researches in Electricity,
First series, Item 10.

When a current in one coil of wire changes a current can be observed in another isolated coil of wire. The current is only produced when there is a changing current in the first coil. Currents produce magnetic fields; thus changing magnetic fields can produce currents. This work of Faraday was the beginning of that part of physics known as electromagnetic induction. It was to have profound effects on the life of man through the many changes in technology that resulted from it.

Figure 14.11 shows how we could demonstrate electromagnetic induction by moving a wire through a magnetic field. We could, alternatively have moved the magnetic field past the stationary wire. The magnetic field is shown as being given by a permanent magnet, but we could have used current-carrying conductors.

An equation for the induced e.m.f.

Consider the vertical part of the wire, PQ, which is moving in the field (Fig. 14.12). Suppose it is moving with a velocity v. The wire contains electrons which are being dragged in the wire through

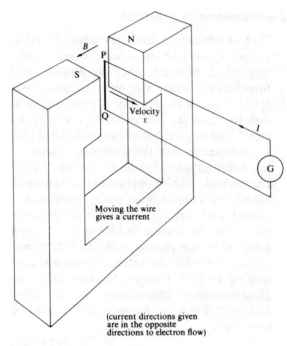

Moving the wire gives a current

(current directions given are in the opposite directions to electron flow)

Fig. 14.11

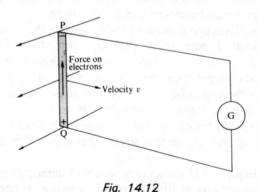

Fig. 14.12

a magnetic field. Charges moving in a magnetic field experience a force if there is a field component at right angles to their motion

$$F = Bqv$$

The electrons in the wire PQ should therefore be acted on by a force, the direction of the force being towards P. The force on an electron, charge e, is

$$F = Bev$$

This will cause the electrons to move along the wire. The result of this will be to produce an electric field E, which will produce an opposing force on the electrons

$$F = Ee$$

The field is produced by a potential difference V between the ends P and Q of the wire distance, L

$$E = \frac{V}{L}$$

Thus

$$F = \frac{Ve}{L}$$

The net force acting on an electron is thus

$$Bev - \frac{Ve}{L}$$

It is this force which is responsible for driving the current round the circuit. The maximum value of the potential difference V will occur when

$$Bev = \frac{Ve}{L}$$

This gives for V

$$V = BLv$$

The maximum potential difference occurs when there is no current taken by the circuit. The higher the resistance of a voltmeter connected across the ends of the wire the nearer will be the measured potential difference to the value given by this equation. This potential difference with no current drain is called the electromotive force (e.m.f.), symbol ε

$$\varepsilon = BLv$$

The e.m.f. is thus proportional to the magnetic flux density component normal to the wire, the length of the wire, and the velocity with which the wire sweeps through the field.

In a time t the distance moved by the wire PQ is vt (Fig. 14.13). The area A of field swept out by the

268

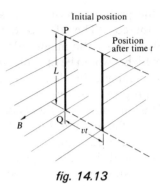

Initial position

P

Position after time t

L

B

Q

vt

fig. 14.13

wire in time t is Lvt, the area being at right angles to the field. Thus

$$\varepsilon = B\frac{Lvt}{t} = \frac{BA}{t}$$

The quantity BA is called the flux, ϕ.

$$\varepsilon = \frac{\phi}{t}$$

The e.m.f. is thus proportional to the amount of flux the wire sweeps through, links, in time t.

B is generally called the flux density because it is the flux per unit area. The unit of flux is the weber and hence B has the units webers per square metre (now called the tesla T).

$$B = \frac{\phi}{A}$$

The induced e.m.f. is zero if there is no change in magnetic flux linked by the circuit. Thus if the coil is moving in a magnetic field such that there is no change in the magnetic flux linked then there is no e.m.f. The vital factor is the rate of change of magnetic flux linked by the circuit. To emphasize this our equation is generally written as

$$\varepsilon = \frac{d\phi}{dt}$$

If, as in Fig. 14.11, the wire PQ is connected to a circuit external to the magnetic field and a current

I flows, then

$$\varepsilon = IR = \frac{d\phi}{dt}$$

The current, however, produces a magnetic field. The direction of this magnetic field is such as to reduce the rate of change of flux. For this reason our equation for induced e.m.f. is generally written as

$$\varepsilon = -\frac{d\phi}{dt}$$

If there are N conductors instead of just one

$$\varepsilon = -N\frac{d\phi}{dt}$$

The laws of electromagnetic induction

Faraday's first law. When the magnetic flux linking a circuit is changing, an e.m.f. is induced in the circuit.

Faraday's second law. The magnitude of the induced e.m.f. is proportional to the rate of change of flux-linkage.

Lenz's law. The direction of any induced current is such that its effect would oppose the change in magnetic flux which gave rise to it

$$\varepsilon = -N\frac{d\phi}{dt}$$

The above equation is sometimes known as Neumann's equation.

The flux linked by a circuit ϕ is the product of the area of the circuit and, if the flux density is constant over the area, the flux density component at right angles to the area.

Fleming's right-hand rule (Fig. 14.14) can be used to summarize the various directions involved in electromagnetic induction. If the thumb and first two fingers of the right hand are extended so that they are at right angles to one another, then the direction of the field is given by the first finger, and the induced e.m.f. by the second finger when the thumb indicates the direction of the motion.

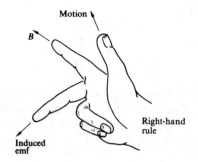

Fig. 14.14   Fleming's right-hand rule

Flux linking

Figure 14.15 shows some arrangements in which loops of wire move in magnetic fields. In (a) the flux linked by the loop is changing (the flux is passing through the shaded area) and thus an e.m.f. is induced. In (b) although the loop is moving in a magnetic field there is no change in the flux linked by the loop; the flux linked remains a constant. There is therefore no induced e.m.f. In (c) the loop is rotating. The flux through the loop is changing because the flux is the product of the area and the component of the flux density at right angles to the area; the component is changing. In (d) there is no flux linked by the loop and thus no induced e.m.f. In (e) there is flux linked and moving the loop changes the flux linked—hence an e.m.f. is induced. In (f) the area of the loop in the magnetic field is not changing but the magnetic field is. The magnetic field is proportional to the current in the solenoid and as this is alternating current we have an alternating flux density. There is thus an alternating flux linked by the loop, hence an e.m.f. is induced.

The transformer

Transformers can be used to step up or down a current, or step up or down a voltage. Thus an electric model railway system may need 12 V a.c. to operate it. By using a suitable transformer we can take the mains voltage of 240 V and step it down to 12 V. Essentially a transformer consists of two coils, called the primary and the secondary coils, wound on an iron core. Figure 14.16 shows a simplified arrangement. Alternating current applied to the primary produces an alternating flux within the core. The effect of the iron is to considerably increase the magnitude of the flux above that which it would be in a solenoid with an air core. The magnetic flux density produced by a solenoid is proportional to the current in that solenoid. Thus the magnetic flux is proportional to the current in the solenod (Fig. 14.17). The flux oscillates in magnitude and direction, one way along the axis and then the opposite way, in a manner exactly similar to the alternating current supplied to the primary coil. An e.m.f. will be induced in the secondary coil—it is a series of loops of wire and each loop will have an e.m.f. induced in it. As they are in series they add up to give an e.m.f. for the coil as a whole. The induced e.m.f. is directly proportional to the rate of change of flux in the coil. When the rate of change of flux is zero the secondary e.m.f. is zero—this occurs when the flux and hence the primary current is a maximum or a minimum. The rate of change of flux is a maximum when the flux and hence primary current is zero. The e.m.f. in the secondary coil is thus 90° out of phase with the current in the primary coil. Both, however, have the same frequency.

The amount of flux linked by the secondary coil is directly proportional to the number of coil turns of the secondary. Doubling the number of secondary coil turns will double the induced secondary e.m.f.

$$\varepsilon_s = -N_s \frac{d\phi}{dt}$$

For two coils within which there is a changing magnetic flux—we have only considered that there will be an induced e.m.f. in the secondary coil. There must, however, be an induced e.m.f. in the primary coil as well as the one in the secondary coil.

$$\varepsilon_p = -N_p \frac{d\phi}{dt}$$

Thus

$$\frac{\varepsilon_p}{\varepsilon_s} = \frac{N_p}{N_s}$$

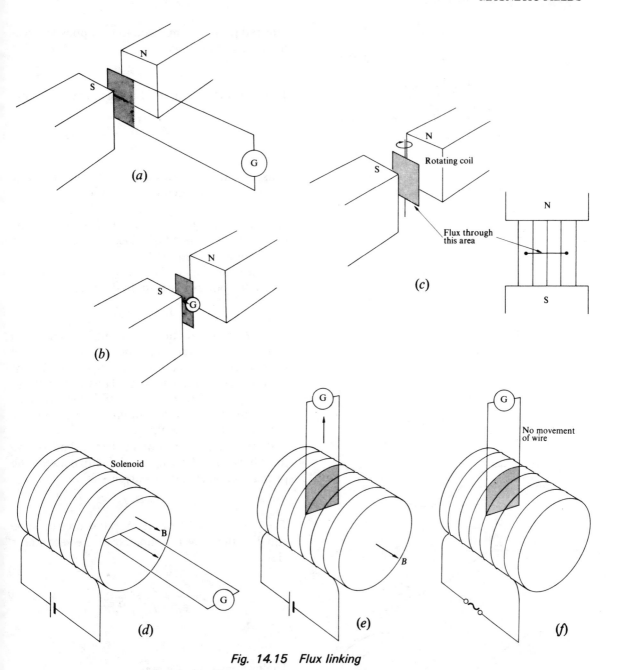

Fig. 14.15   Flux linking

The ratio of the induced e.m.f.s is the same as the ratio of turns numbers.

The induced primary e.m.f. is 90° out of phase with the magnetizing current supplied by the input source. If no current is taken from the secondary and we assume conservation of electrical energy, e.g., no temperature changes produced, then no energy is taken from the secondary and none is dissipated in the primary. This can only be the case if the input e.m.f. is equal to the

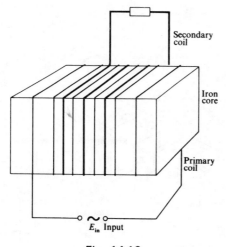

Fig. 14.16

induced primary e.m.f. and in the opposite direction, i.e., out of phase.

$$\varepsilon_{in} - \varepsilon_p = 0$$

Thus for this condition of no secondary current

$$\frac{\varepsilon_{in}}{\varepsilon_s} = \frac{N_p}{N_s}$$

This condition is approximately true for large resistance in the secondary circuit.

Thus if we have an input of 240 V a.c. and require an output of 12 V a.c. across a high resistance load, a turns ratio of 240:12 or 20:1, primary to secondary is required.

If the secondary coil passes a current through a resistance power is being dissipated.

$$\text{Power} = \varepsilon_s I_s$$

where I_s is the secondary current. The energy to supply this power must be provided by the primary circuit, i.e., taken from the input. Thus ε_{in} must become larger than ε_p. Thus in the above example, a 20:1 turns ratio would give less than 12 V output for a 240 V input if the secondary current was significant.

If we have conservation of electrical energy we must have the following relationship between the primary and secondary currents

$$\varepsilon_{in} I_p = \varepsilon_s I_s$$

The power drawn from the input source must be equal to the power dissipated in the secondary. Hence

$$\frac{\varepsilon_{in}}{\varepsilon_s} = \frac{I_s}{I_p} \approx \frac{N_p}{N_s}$$

The transmission of power

The mains voltage in Britain is nominally 240 V. The voltage is alternating. The power is transmitted from the generator to your home area at voltages of either 400 kV or 132 kV through what is called the 'grid'. The power lines carrying these voltages are to be seen strung between pylons which straggle the country. The generator produces

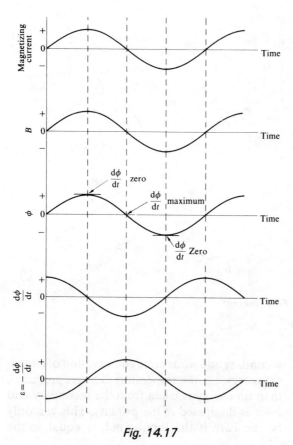

Fig. 14.17

the power at a voltage of about 10 to 20 kV. The step-up of the voltage from the generator to that of the pylon wires is done with a transformer, the step-down from the voltage of the pylon wires to that of the area supply and then down again to that of your mains supply is again done with transformers. Why the high voltage for transmission?

The power lost by passing a current along a power cable, or indeed any wire, is proportional to the square of the current.

$$\text{Power loss} \propto I^2$$

For a fixed power input, the current along a line is inversely proportional to the potential difference between the ends of the wire.

$$I \propto \frac{1}{V}$$

Thus

$$\text{power loss} \propto \frac{1}{V^2}$$

For a 400 kV power line the power lost is $\frac{1}{16}$ that of a power line operating at 100 KV. A 400 kV line loses only 1 part in 4 million of that of 200 V line would lose. Operating at a high voltage reduces the power loss. If we wanted to transmit power at a low voltage we would need much thicker cables, and hence more pylons to take the load, in order to reduce the power loss.

For the same power loss at all voltages, how must the resistance of a cable be changed for the different transmission voltages? For a constant current, i.e., constant power loss, we have

$$R \propto V$$

Thus the resistance per kilometre for a 400 kV line can be four times that of a line operating at 100 kV and still give the same power loss. As the resistance of a cable is inversely proportional to the cross-sectional area of that cable

$$R \propto \frac{1}{A}$$

the cross-sectional area of the 400 kV line need

only be ¼ that of the 100 kV line. A 400 kV line has a cross-sectional area of 2.6×10^{-4} m^2, a diameter of about 2 cm. Thus the cross-sectional area of a 100 kV line would need to be 10.4×10^{-4} m^2, a diameter of about 4 cm. A line operating at 200 V would need a cross-sectional area of 0.52 m^2, a diameter of about 90 cm.

We have pylons straggling across the countryside carrying the power because we use high voltages. The high voltages are necessary to keep the energy losses down to an acceptable value. With the 400 kV lines used in Britain the energy loss is about 0.02 per cent for each kilometre, If we put the cables underground there is the difficulty of dissipating the heat that this energy loss produces. With the cables in the air, cooling is by the air flowing over them; in the ground cooling can only occur by the flow of heat through the soil—soil is a bad conductor of heat. Thus underground cables have to be thicker in order to keep the energy loss low enough for the cable temperature to keep within acceptable limits. Also there is the problem of electrical insulation when the cables are in the ground, perhaps wet ground which may be a reasonable conductor of electricity. The cost of underground cables has been estimated to be about ten times greater that that for overhead cables. If you dislike the sight of pylons, do you want to pay the higher cost for electricity?

Inductance

Mutual inductance

Consider two coils wound on the same former. If we put alternating current in the first coil, the primary, an alternating e.m.f. is induced in the second coil. The flux density produced by the current I_p in the primary coil is in air

$$B = \mu_0 \frac{N_p}{l} I_p$$

where l is the length of the primary coil and N_p the total number of turns on that coil. If we assume that this is the flux density in the secondary coil

273

then the flux linked by the secondary coil will be

$$\phi = N_s BA$$

where N_s is the total number of secondary turns, A the cross-sectional area of the secondary coil. Thus

$$\phi = N_s \mu_0 \frac{N_p}{l} I_p A$$

The e.m.f. induced in the secondary coil is equal to the rate of change of flux linked by the coil

$$\varepsilon_s = -\frac{d\phi}{dt}$$

$$\varepsilon_s = -\frac{d}{dt} \left(N_s \mu_0 \frac{N_p}{l} I_p A \right)$$

The only quantity in the brackets which is varying with time is I_p, hence

$$\varepsilon_s = -\left(N_s \mu_0 \frac{N_p}{l} A \right) \frac{dI_p}{dt}$$

or

$$\varepsilon_s = -M \frac{dI_p}{dt}$$

where M is a constant for a particular pair of coils. M is called the mutual inductance. The unit of M is called the henry (H). M is 1 H when the rate of change of current is 1 A s^{-1} and the induced e.m.f. 1 V.

An alternative way of defining mutual inductance M, which is still compatible with the above equation is

$$MI_p = N_s \phi_s$$

Self-inductance

When a current in a wire or coil changes then its magnetic field changes. However, this flux links the coil or circuit producing it and so an induced e.m.f. is produced. This effect is known as self-inductance.

The flux ϕ produced by a coil of N turns, length l and area A, is $\phi = NBA$, with B for the coil being $\mu_0 NI/l$. Hence

$$\phi = \frac{N^2 \mu_0 A I}{l}$$

The e.m.f. induced, ε, is

$$\varepsilon = -\frac{d\phi}{dt} = -\frac{N^2 \mu_0 A}{l} \times \frac{dI}{dt}$$

$$\varepsilon = -L \frac{dI}{dt}$$

where L is a constant known as the self-inductance (or often just the inductance).

An alternative way of defining self-inductance L, which is still compatible with the above equation, is

$$LI = N\phi$$

Because this induced e.m.f. opposes the change in current (hence the minus sign in the equation) it is sometimes called the 'back e.m.f.'. Thus if a battery, e.m.f. ε, is connected to a resistor of resistance R in series with an inductor of inductance L

$$\varepsilon - \text{back e.m.f.} = IR$$

$$\varepsilon - L \frac{dI}{dt} = IR \qquad (1)$$

The result of this is that when the current is switched on and starts to grow, the back e.m.f. slows down the growth. Thus the presence of inductance in a circuit increases the time taken for the current to rise from zero to its steady value.

The differential equation (1) above has the solution

$$I = \frac{\varepsilon}{R} (1 - e^{-t/(L/R)})$$

The maximum value of the current is ε/R. The quantity L/R is known as the time constant. When $t = L/R$ the current is smaller than its maximum, final value by $1/e$ or 37 per cent.

When the e.m.f. to the inductor is switched off, the current does not abruptly drop to a zero value but decays exponentially with time. Thus if we consider Eq. (1) with ε = 0, we have

$$- L \frac{\mathrm{d}I}{\mathrm{d}t} = IR$$

This differential equation has the solution

$$I = \frac{\varepsilon}{R} \, \mathrm{e}^{-t/(L/R)}$$

In a time equal to 1L/R the current decays to 1/e or 37 per cent of its maximum value (ε/R).

Eddy currents

What happens when a metal plate, e.g., an aluminium plate, moves into a magnetic field? (see Fig. 14.18). The plate slows down on entering the field. Why? An e.m.f. is induced in the plate—this means a force acts on the 'free' electrons within the plate owing to its moving in a magnetic field—and because there is a possible low resistance path currents flow in the plate. Closed loops of currents are produced (Fig. 14.19). These produce magnetic fields which oppose the field producing them. The current acts in such a way as to oppose the change in flux through the plate. Thus if, as in this case, the flux linked by the plate is increasing then the current produces a field in a direction which tries to reduce this increase in flux. If the plate is moving out of the field, the eddy currents are in such a direction as to oppose the flux change—in this case the flux linkage is being reduced so the field produced is in the same direction as the magnet's field, to stop the flux linked becoming smaller. The eddy currents in this case have the effect of opposing the motion out of the field. To sum up, eddy currents are in such a direction as to oppose motion into a field or out of a field, i.e., they oppose motion relative to the field. If we move a magnet past an aluminium plate, the plate will endeavour to follow; the eddy

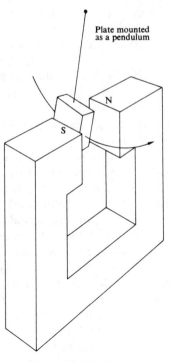

Fig. 14.18

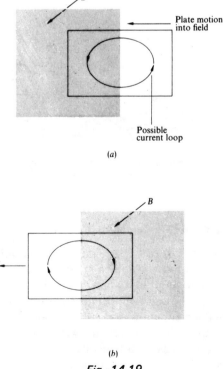

(a)

(b)

Fig. 14.19

currents oppose relative motion between the field and the plate.

If we have a metal plate stationary in a constant magnetic field there is no changing magnetic flux and thus no eddy currents. If, however, the magnetic field is changing there is changing flux linked by the plate and thus eddy currents. The core of a transformer will have eddy currents induced in it when a.c. is supplied to the primary coil.

One effect of currents flowing in a metal sheet is to produce an increase in temperature. Transformer cores get hot. The size of these eddy currents depends on the size of the induced e.m.f., the nature of the material, and its shape. The lower the resistance of the material the larger the eddy currents. If the material is in small segments less current flows. Each segment links less flux than the material in bulk and thus the e.m.f. produced is less. In addition the resistance is higher. Transformer cores are laminated (Fig. 14.20) in order to reduce the size and effects of eddy currents. Reducing the size of eddy currents reduces both the temperature rise and the 'wastage' of energy.

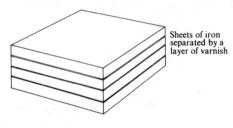

Sheets of iron separated by a layer of varnish

Fig. 14.20 A laminated core

Damping of galvanometers

Use is made of eddy currents for the damping of the coils of moving coil galvanometers. If such a coil had no damping, when a current was passed through it the coil would deflect and then proceed to oscillate for quite some time about the final deflection. This is necessary when the galvanometer is to be used ballistically, i.e., when the first deflection is to be proportional to the charge

passed through the coil, but very inconvenient if a steady current reading is required. Damping can be achieved by winding the coil on a metal frame. The eddy currents set up in this frame produce magnetic fields which oppose the motion producing them and so damp down the motion. When oscillation is just prevented the meter is said to be critically damped and its movement is deadbeat.

Another method used for the damping of moving coil galvanometer coils uses the fact that eddy currents will be set up in the coil wires themselves when they move in the magnetic field if the coil is short-circuited or there is a shunt. The smaller the resistance of the shunt the greater the eddy currents and so the greater the damping.

Motors and generators

A pivoted current-carrying coil in a magnetic field can experience forces which will cause it to rotate (Fig. 14.21). With the coil VWXY, all the wires experience forces. It is, however, only the forces on the wires VY and WX which can cause the coil to rotate. In diagram (b) the forces are causing the coil to rotate in an anti-clockwise direction, in (c) the forces are not causing rotation, in (d) they produce a clockwise rotation, in (e) a clockwise rotation. With the arrangement shown the coil will rotate to the vertical position and there stop. If it overshoots this position there is a force returning it to that position. The coil can be made to rotate continuously if the current is reversed every time the coil reaches the vertical position. All the forces will then be acting to cause rotation in the same direction. Figure 14.22 shows an arrangement, known as a commutator, by which this reversal of current can be achieved. The wires from the coil are connected to split rings which rotate with the coil. Contact with the current source is made by these split rings being in contact with fixed brushes. As the coil rotates these brushes make contact with the rings, changing the rings they are in contact with every time the coil passes through the vertical. This is the basis of the d.c. motor.

This arrangement will produce an alternating current if the coil is rotated in the magnetic field.

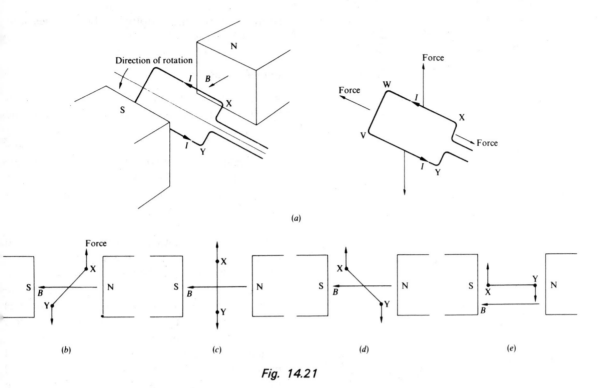

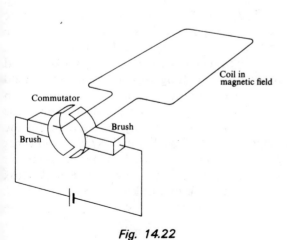

(a)

(b)   *(c)*   *(d)*   *(e)*

Fig. 14.21

The flux linked by the coil keeps changing. If the coil is connected to simple slip rings, not split, the alternating e.m.f. can be used to produce an alternating current in a circuit (Fig. 14.23)

$$\varepsilon = -\frac{d\phi}{dt}$$

Fig. 14.22

But

$$\phi = NBA \sin \theta$$

You can either think of the area through which the flux passes being $A \sin \theta$ and the flux density B or consider the area to be A and the flux density component at right angles to the area $B \sin \theta$. Hence

$$\varepsilon = -\frac{d}{dt}(NBA \sin \theta)$$

$$\varepsilon = -NBA\frac{d}{dt}(\sin 2\pi ft)$$

where f is the frequency of rotation of the coil.

$$\varepsilon = -NBA \, 2\pi f \cos 2\pi ft$$

Figure 14.23c shows a graph of the variation of e.m.f. and flux with time. The value of the maximum e.m.f. is thus $2\pi fBAN$, i.e., when the cosine is +1 or −1. The greater the flux density, the coil area, the number of coil turns, and the

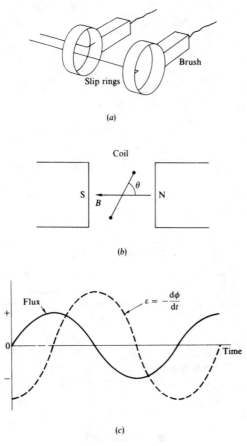

(a)

(b)

$$\varepsilon = -\frac{d\phi}{dt}$$

(c)

Fig. 14.23

frequency of rotation the greater the e.m.f. This is the basis of an alternating current generator.

Series and shunt wound motors

Both the above accounts, of the motor and the generator, are considerably simplified accounts. Modern motors and generators do not consist of just a single coil rotating between the poles of a permanent magnet. The magnetic field is provided by coils wound on a laminated core of magnetic material. In what is called the series wound motor these coils, known as the field coils, are in series with the rotating coil, the armature coil, and so the same current passes through both. With the shunt wound motor the field and armature coils are in parallel. Most modern motors tend to be compound wound, employing both series and shunt windings.

Induction motor

A difficulty with the d.c. motor is the need to use a split ring commutator to periodically reverse the current to the armature coil in order to keep the coil rotating. In the induction motor no connections are made to the armature and so a considerable simplification occurs. The induction motor depends for its rotation on the fact that a conductor will follow a moving magnetic field (see the section on eddy currents).

Figure 14.24 shows a section of an induction motor. The rotating part is the 'squirrel-cage' (Fig. 14.24g). This is a number of conducting bars of copper or aluminium connected together at the ends by conducting rings. The whole rotor is generally sunk into slots in a laminated iron cylinder. The cylinder is attached to the shaft which is to rotate. The magnetic field is provided by two sets of coils, opposite pairs being connected in series. Each of these pairs is supplied with an alternating current—there is, however, a phase difference between the currents of 90° (Fig. 14.24f). The effect of this is to give a rotating field. The resulting induced currents in the rotor drag the rotor after the field.

The homopolar generator

The homopolar generator consists of a metal disc rotating between the poles of a magnet (Fig. 14.25). Connections are made to the axle of the disc and a point on its circumference. If we imagine the disc to be rather like a bicycle wheel, then when such a wheel rotates the spokes would repeatedly be cutting through the magnetic field and an e.m.f. would be induced. The disc has an e.m.f. induced because the radius of the disc between the contacts at any instant is cutting the magnetic field. If the disc makes f revolutions per second and has a radius r, then the area swept out per second by a radius is $\pi r^2 f$. If B is the flux density then the flux linked per second is $\pi r^2 f B$. Hence the induced e.m.f. is

$$\varepsilon = \pi^2 f B$$

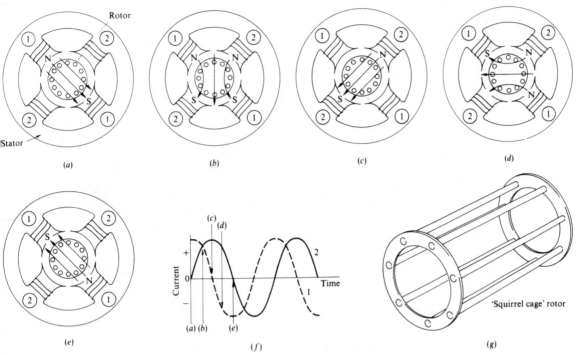

Fig. 14.24 The induction motor

The induced e.m.f. is always in the same direction, i.e., the generator does not produce an alternating e.m.f. Such generators can, however, only be used to produce a small e.m.f., but the current can be large.

Measurements of flux density

A number of methods are commonly used for the measurement of flux density. A current balance

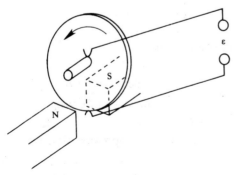

Fig. 14.25 The homopolar generator

can be used to determine the component of flux density that is at right angles to the balance wire and in the horizontal plane (Fig. 14.26a). The flux density component $B = F/IL$, where F is the force on the balance wire, I the current in it and L the length.

A smaller, more sensitive, device is the search coil (Fig. 14.26b). This is a small coil of wire. When the magnetic flux linked by the coil changes, an e.m.f. is induced in it. One way the coil can be used is to place it in a magnetic field, the flux density component being at right angles to the plane of the coil, and then suddenly remove the coil to a region of negligible flux density. With this arrangement the coil is connected to a ballistic galvanometer. Such a galvanometer has a suspension for its coil which gives a large periodic time for its oscillations, so large that the pulse of current given to it by moving the search coil is all over before the galvanometer coil has shown any significant deflection. When this occurs the galvanometer coil deflection θ is proportional to the charge Q passing through it, i.e., $\theta = bQ$, where b is a constant called the charge sensitivity.

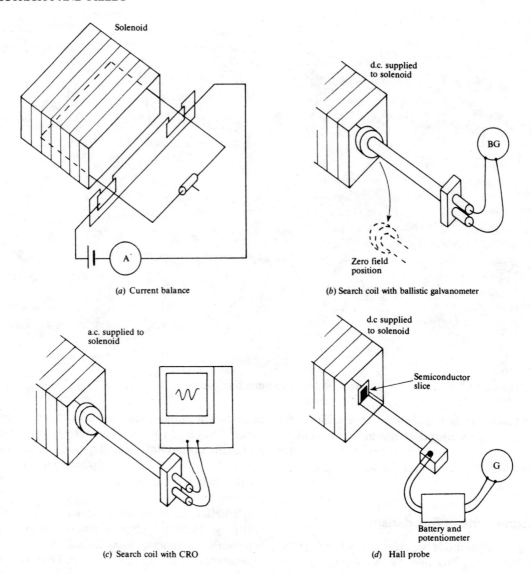

(a) Current balance

(b) Search coil with ballistic galvanometer

(c) Search coil with CRO

(d) Hall probe

Fig. 14.26 *Methods for measuring flux density*

Induced e.m.f. = −(rate of change of flux linked)

$$\varepsilon = - NA \frac{(\text{change in } B)}{(\text{duration of change})}$$

where N is the number of turns on the search coil and A its area. This e.m.f. causes a current I to flow through the galvanometer circuit. If this has a resistance R, then

$$I = - \frac{NA}{R} \frac{(\text{change in } B)}{(\text{duration of change})}$$

But to a reasonable approximation we can say that

$$Q = I \times (\text{duration of change})$$

Hence

$$Q = - \frac{NA}{R} \text{ (change in } B)$$

$$\theta = - \frac{bNA}{R} \text{ (change in } B)$$

$$\theta \propto \text{ (change in } B)$$

For a given search coil the galvanometer scale can be directly calibrated in term of flux density.

An alternative way of using the search coil is to connect it to the Y-input of a cathode ray oscilloscope. In this situation the magnetic flux density being measured might be that in a solenoid, the solenoid, however, being supplied with alternating current. This means that the flux density is continually changing and an e.m.f. is induced in the search coil without it having to be moved (Fig. 4.26c). We thus have

$$B = B_m \sin 2\pi f t$$

where B_m is the maximum value of the flux density and f the frequency of the variation. Hence

$$\frac{dB}{dt} = 2\pi f B_{max} \cos 2\pi f t$$

and so

$$\text{induced e.m.f. } \varepsilon = -2\pi f NA B_m \cos 2\pi f t$$

The induced e.m.f. varies with time, the maximum value ε_m, however, occurring when the cosine term equals 1. Hence

$$\varepsilon_m = -2\pi f NA B_m$$

$$\varepsilon_m \propto B_m$$

The maximum value of the induced e.m.f. which can be determined from the screen of the oscilloscope is proportional to the maximum value of the flux density.

Another method for measuring flux density is the Hall probe (Fig. 14.26d). This is a thin slice of a semiconducting material across which a Hall voltage is produced when there is a magnetic field at right angles to it (see earlier in this chapter).

The probe is generally connected to a galvanometer via a circuit box which includes a battery and a potentiometer. The potentiometer is adjusted so that the galvanometer indicates zero current when the probe is not in the magnetic field. When the probe is in the field the galvanometer current is directly proportional to the magnetic flux density component at right angles to the slice.

Problems

1. What is the force per unit length on each of two long parallel wires 20 cm apart in which currents of 2.0 A and 1.5 A flow in opposite directions? ($\mu_0 = 4\pi \times 10^{-7}$ H m^{-1})

(University of London, Q6, Paper 2, January 1981)

2. Two parallel wires have currents passing through them which are in the same direction. Draw a diagram showing the directions of the currents and of the forces on the wires.

Alternating currents are now passed through the wires. Explain what forces would act if the currents were (a) in phase, and (b) out of phase by π rad.

(University of London, Q6, Paper 2, January 1978)

3. If a straight wire carrying a current is subject to a uniform magnetic field acting perpendicular to the wire, a potential difference will be produced across the diameter of the wire.

(a) Draw a diagram showing the direction of the force (due to the magnetic field) which acts on a free electron which is moving with the drift velocity. (Indicate clearly the directions of the drift velocity and the magnetic field.)

(b) Hence explain how the potential difference across the diameter of the wire arises.

(University of London, Q5, Paper 2, January 1984)

4. A long uniformly-wound solenoid is placed with its axis vertical and its ends are connected to the Y plates of a cathode ray oscilloscope with a suitable time base. A short bar magnet with its axis vertical is placed well above the solenoid, and is dropped so that it falls through the solenoid and finishes well below it. Sketch the

trace you would expect to see on the oscilloscope and explain its shape.

(University of London, Q7, Paper 2, January 1978)

5. Explain in terms of the laws of electromagnetic induction why a 'back e.m.f.' is developed in a coil when an alternating potential difference is applied across it.

(University of London, Q6, Paper 2, January 1979)

6. An aluminium disc is rotating freely about an axis through its centre perpendicular to its surface. Explain why it is quickly brought to rest when a strong U-shaped magnet is brought up so that the rim of the disc passes between its poles. Describe a possible practical application to which this effect might be put.

(AEB, Q6, Paper 3, November 1981)

7. (a) A long straight conductor is situated in a uniform magnetic field of flux density B and makes an angle θ with the direction of B. If the conductor carries a current I, write down an expression for the force on a length L of the conductor and draw a diagram showing its direction relative to the current and field directions. Show how the equation could be used to define a unit of magnetic flux density.

(b) The coil of a moving coil ammeter designed to measure steady currents is wound on a conducting frame. State and explain the function of such a frame.

(JMB, 6, Paper II, June 1978)

8. Define self-inductance.

A 12-V battery of negligible internal resistance is connected in series with a coil of resistance 1.0 Ω and inductance L. When switched on the current in the circuit grows from zero. When the current is 10 A the ratio of growth of the current is 500 A s^{-1}. What is the value of L?

(University of London, Q7, Paper 2, June 1983)

9. Explain the origin of the Hall effect. Include a diagram showing clearly the directions of the Hall voltage and other relevant quantities for a specimen in which electron conduction predominates.

A slice of indium antimonide is 2.5 mm thick and carries a current of 150 mA. A magnetic field of flux density 0.5 T, correctly applied, produces a maximum Hall voltage of 8.75 mV between the edges of the slice. Calculate the number of free charge carriers per unit volume, assuming that they each have a charge of -1.6×10^{-19} C. Explain your calculation clearly.

What can you conclude from the observation that the Hall voltage in different conductors can be positive, negative or zero?

(University of Cambridge, Q5, Paper 3, June 1980)

10. (a) A moving coil meter possesses a square coil mounted between the poles of a strong permanent magnet. The torque on the coil is 4.2×10^{-9} N m when the current is 100 μA.

(i) The meter is designed so that whatever the deflection of the coil, the magnetic flux density is always parallel to the plane of the coil. Explain, with the aid of a labelled diagram how this is achieved.

(ii) The restoring springs bring the coil to rest after it has turned through a certain angle. If the restoring couple per unit angular displacement applied by the springs is 3.0×10^{-9} N m per radian, through what angle, in radian, will the coil turn when a current of 100 μA flows?

(iii) Explain what is meant by the current sensitivity of such a meter. If the pointer on the instrument is 7.0 cm long, what length of arc on the scale would correspond to a change in current of 2 μA?

(iv) The instrument indicates full-scale deflection for a current of 100 μA. What current produces full-scale deflection if the number of turns in the coil is doubled?

Increasing the number of turns also increases the resistance of the coil. Explain whether or not this change affects the sensitivity of the meter.

(b) A moving coil meter has a resistance of 1000 Ω and gives a full-scale deflection for a current of 100 μA.

(i) What value resistor would be required to convert it to an ammeter reading up to 1.00 A? Draw a circuit diagram showing where the resistor would be connected. What form might this resistor have?

(ii) Draw a diagram showing the additional circuitry needed for the moving coil meter to be adapted to measure alternating currents. Mark clearly on the diagram the connecting points for the meter and for the a.c. supply.

What is the relationship between the steady current registered by the meter and the current from the a.c. supply?

(University of London, Q14,
Paper 2, June 1985)

11. (a) Define magnetic flux (ϕ) and magnetic flux density (B).

The unit of magnetic flux, named the weber Wb, is also expressed as the volt second, V s, and in terms of SI base units as kg m^2 s^{-2} A^{-1}. Write down the corresponding expressions for the tesla T, the unit of magnetic flux density.

(b) A 'long' air-cored solenoid of length 0.80 m has 4000 turns, and carries a current of 5 A. Inside the solenoid, as in Fig. 14.27, a copper disc of area 1.2×10^{-3} m^2 is arranged so that it can rotate in its own plane about a thin axle perpendicular to that plane.

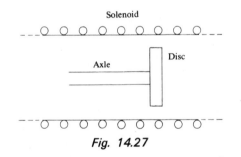

Fig. 14.27

Calculate:

(i) the flux density along the axis of the solenoid;
(ii) the flux linked with the disc, assuming that the flux density is uniform within the solenoid;
(iii) the e.m.f. induced between the rim and the axle of the disc when it rotates at 30 revolutions per second.

Describe how you would attempt to measure this e.m.f. (The value of μ_0 is $4\pi \times 10^{-7}$ H m^{-1})

(Oxford Local Examinations, Q12,
Paper I, June 1979)

12. (a) Magnetic fields can be described in terms of field lines (lines of force). Use this concept to distinguish between magnetic flux density (magnetic induction) and magnetic flux.

(b) A coil of cross-sectional area 0.0016 m^2 and length 50 cm, having 400 turns, is to be used to produce a uniform magnetic field of value 1.51 mT. It is calculated that this can be done if there is a current of 1.5 A in the coil.

(i) State where the magnetic field will be uniform.
(ii) Show how the value of the current is calculated.
(iii) Calculate the total flux through the coil for this current value.
(Permeability of free space, $\mu_0 = 4\pi \times 10^{-7}$ H m^{-1})

(c) A coil of 8 turns is now wound around the centre portion of the above coil and its ends are connected to the Y plates of a cathode ray oscilloscope. A 50 Hz alternating current is passed through the 400 turn coil.

(i) Explain briefly why an e.m.f. will be induced in the 8 turn coil.
(ii) Explain, how, with the time base switched off, you would use the oscilloscope to measure the e.m.f. induced in the coil.
(iii) If the waveform of the 50 Hz alternating current is as shown in Fig. 14.28.

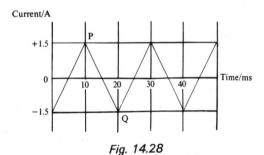

Fig. 14.28

(1) calculate the change in the flux linkage through the 8 turn coil during the time interval between the points P and Q on the diagram; also calculate the induced e.m.f. during this time interval.
(2) Sketch a graph showing how the induced e.m.f. varies with time over two cycles of current change, beginning at $t = 0$ and using the same time scale as above.

(University of London, Q14,
Paper 2, January 1982)

13. Faraday's Law of Induction says that the electromotive force induced in a circuit is proportional to the rate at which the flux linking the circuit is changing.

A student is investigating the flux in an iron rod standing in a coil carrying alternating current [Fig. 14.29].(The magnetic field is sketched at an instant when the current is at a maximum.)

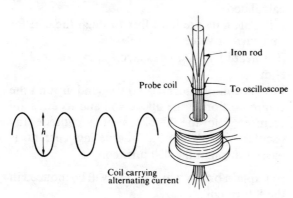

Fig. 14.29

He uses a probe coil which surrounds the iron rod, as shown, and connects this coil to an oscilloscope to display the induced voltage in the probe coil. With the coil in the position shown, he obtains the trace illustrated and measures the height h.

State and explain the effect or lack of effect on the oscilloscope trace of the following changes. Each change is made separately and starts from the original arrangement shown above. Give quantitative information wherever you can.

(a) Doubling the number of turns in the probe coil.

(b) Using, in the same place, a probe coil whose area is twice as big.

(c) Raising the probe coil to the top of the rod.

(d) Doubling the frequency of the supply to the magnetizing coil, keeping the current the same.

(Oxford and Cambridge Schools Examination Board, Nuffield Advanced Physics, Short answer paper, 1971)

15 Circuits and systems

Alternating current

When a direct current, d.c., is passed through a resistor power is dissipated.

$$\text{Power} = IV$$

If Ohm's law is obeyed, $V = IR$, and we can write

$$\text{Power} = I^2R$$

or

$$\text{Power} = \frac{V^2}{R}$$

What is the power dissipated when an alternating current, a.c., passes through a resistor? The power dissipated at any instant will be that due to the values of I and V at those instants. Suppose we have an alternating current where the voltage, and the current, vary as sin θ, where θ is some function of time, say $V = V_{max} \sin θ$. Figure 15.1a shows how the voltage varies with time. We can find how the power varies with time by taking the square of the sine curve.

$$\text{Power} = \frac{V^2_{max}}{R} \sin^2 θ$$

Figure 15.1b shows the square of the sine curve. The average power dissipated will be the average value of $\sin^2 θ$ multiplied by V^2_{max}/R. The average value of $\sin^2 θ$ is half the maximum value. (The $\sin^2 θ$ curve is symmetrical about the 0.5 line.) Thus the average power is

$$\text{Average power} = \frac{V^2_{max}}{2R}$$

If we compare this average power equation with the power equation for d.c. we can see that for the same power dissipation in the same resistor we must have

$$V^2_{d.c.} = \frac{V^2_{max}}{2}$$

$$V_{d.c.} = \frac{V_{max}}{\sqrt{2}}$$

The value of the d.c. voltage which gives the same power dissipation as that given by the a.c. is called the r.m.s. or root mean square voltage.

$$V_{r.m.s.} = \frac{V_{max}}{\sqrt{2}}$$

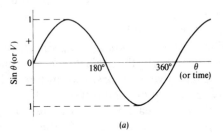

(a)

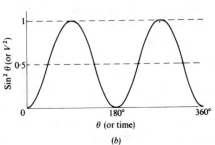

(b)

Fig. 15.1

In a similar way we can arrive at the root mean square current.

$$I_{\text{r.m.s.}} = \frac{I_{\text{max}}}{\sqrt{2}}$$

Thus a root mean square current of 4 A will have a maximum value of 5.6 A, a root mean square voltage of 240 V will have a maximum of 336 V.

Alternating current (a.c.) meters

Alternating currents and potential differences can be measured by moving coil instruments if they are used with a rectifying circuit. This may be a half-wave rectifier or a full-wave rectifier. In the case of a half-wave rectifier it is essentially just a diode in series with the instrument. The reading given by such an instrument is the average of the half-wave pulses, I_m/π. When used with a full-wave rectifier, the instrument could be, for example, the load resistor in the bridge rectifier circuit of Fig. 15.26; the reading given is $2I_m/\pi$.

Vector representation

We can represent any sinusoidal quantity by the projection onto a fixed line of a rotating vector, rotation generally being taken in an anticlockwise direction.

Thus if we consider a potential difference described by the equation $V_1 = V_m \sin \omega t$, then we can represent this by the projection of the rotating vector, angular velocity ω, shown in Fig. 15.2a. If we have another potential difference V_2 which is not in phase and reaches its maximum value, say, a quarter of a cycle ahead of V_1 then it can be represented by the rotating vector shown in Fig. 15.2b. In this case we talk of V_2 leading V_1 by a quarter of a cycle, i.e., $\pi/2$.

Suppose we have V_1 as the potential difference across one circuit component and V_2 across another component in series with it. We can find the potential difference across the pair of components by taking the vector sum of V_1 and V_2. Thus, as Fig. 15.2c shows, we can add the vectors by using the parallelogram law (see Chapter 0)

and these then give a resultant vector which gives the projection we could have obtained by adding the two sinusoidal graphs, Fig. 15.2a and b, together.

The projection of the vector sum of two vectors is the same as the sum of the projections of the two vectors.

Resistor in an a.c. circuit

If we apply an alternating potential difference $V = V_m \sin \omega t$ to a circuit containing only resistance, then the current is given by

$$I = \frac{V}{R} = \frac{V_m}{R} \sin \omega t$$

The maximum current I_m occurs when the sine term has a value 1, i.e., $I_m = V_m/R$, and so

$$I = I_m \sin \omega t$$

The current and potential difference are in phase for a resistor.

Capacitor in an a.c. circuit

In a d.c. circuit a capacitor only gives a current when the supply is switched on and when it is switched off, i.e., during charging and discharging. In an a.c. circuit we can think of the capacitor being continually charged, then discharged, then charged, then discharged, and so on. The result is that we continue to have a current in the circuit, an alternating current.

Consider a simple circuit of an a.c. supply being connected directly across a capacitor, and assume there is no resistance in the circuit. If the a.c. is sinusoidal, then

$$V = V_m \sin \omega t$$

where V is the p.d. applied across the capacitor at some instant, V_m its maximum value and $\omega = 2\pi f$, where f is the frequency of the supply. At some instant the charge Q on the capacitor, capacitance C, is given by $Q = CV$, hence

$$Q = CV_m \sin \omega t$$

The current in the circuit is the rate at which this

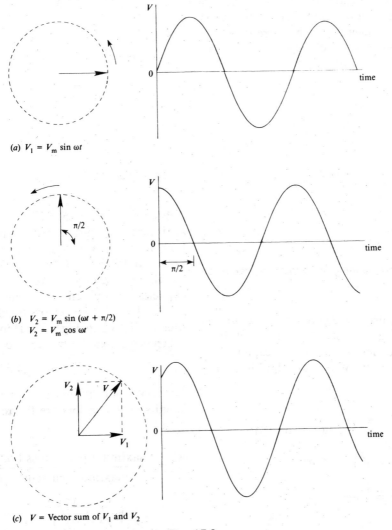

(a) $V_1 = V_m \sin \omega t$

(b) $V_2 = V_m \sin (\omega t + \pi/2)$
$V_2 = V_m \cos \omega t$

(c) V = Vector sum of V_1 and V_2

Fig. 15.2

charge is changing

$$I = \frac{dQ}{dt} = \frac{d(CV_m \sin \omega t)}{dt}$$

$$I = \omega C V_m \cos \omega t$$

The maximum value of this current will occur when the cosine term has the value of 1, hence

$$I_m = \omega C V_m$$

The ratio V_m/I_m is called the capacitative reactance of the capacitor (X_C), hence

$$X_C = \frac{V_m}{I_m} = \frac{1}{\omega C}$$

Reactance has the unit of ohm. It should be noted that the maximum values of the current and potential difference are not occurring at the same instant of time.

The equations for the current 'through' the capacitor and the potential difference across it can thus be stated as

$$I = I_m \cos \omega t \text{ and } V = V_m \sin \omega t$$

The current and potential difference are not in phase, the current leading the potential difference by 90° or $\pi/2$. This means that the current reaches its maximum one-quarter of a cycle ahead of the potential difference (Fig. 15.3).

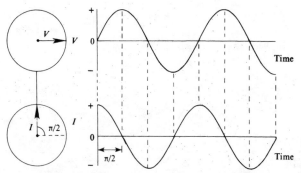

Fig. 15.3 *Current leading potential difference by* $\pi/2$

To illustrate a use of the above, consider an a.c. source supplying a sinusoidal voltage of 10 V r.m.s. at a frequency of 50 Hz to a capacitor of capacitance 2.0 μF. What will be the r.m.s. current?

$$X_C = \frac{1}{2\pi f C} = \frac{1}{2\pi \times 50 \times 2.0 \times 10^{-6}}$$

$$= 1.6 \times 10^3 \ \Omega$$

$$X_C = \frac{V_m}{I_m} = \frac{V_{r.m.s.}}{I_{r.m.s.}}$$

Hence

$$I_{r.m.s.} = \frac{10}{1.6 \times 10^3} = 6.3 \ \text{mA}$$

If the frequency of the voltage source is increased to 500 Hz, the reactance decreases to 160 Ω and the current increases to 63 mA. The higher the frequency the lower the reactance. Figure 15.4 shows how the reactance changes with frequency.

Capacitor and resistor in a.c. circuit

Consider a circuit supplied with a sinusoidal alternating voltage and which consists of a

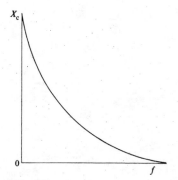

Fig 15.4 *Variation of* X_C *with frequency*

resistor in series with a capacitor. Because they are in series the current must be the same through both at any instant we consider. For a resistor the potential difference V_R across the resistor will be in phase with the current; however, for the capacitor the potential difference V_C lags the current by $\pi/2$. The vectors for this situation are thus as shown in Fig. 15.5. Hence the potential difference across the two components is given by

$$V^2 = V_R^2 + V_C^2$$

The potential difference values used for the lengths of the vectors are the maximum values, hence

$$Z = \frac{\text{maximum p.d. across both components}}{\text{maximum current through both}}$$

$$= \sqrt{\left(\frac{V_R^2}{I_m^2} + \frac{V_C^2}{I_m^2}\right)}$$

But $R = V_R/I_m$ and $X_C = V_C/I_m$, hence

$$Z = \sqrt{(R^2 + X_C^2)}$$

The symbol Z is used for the circuit impedance, the quantity relating the maximum potential difference and the maximum current in the circuit and having the unit of ohm.

The sum p.d. V lags the current by angle ϕ (see Fig. 15.5), where

$$\tan \theta = \frac{V_C}{V_R} = \frac{I_m X_C}{I_m R} = \frac{X_C}{R}$$

To illustrate the above, consider a 2.0 μF

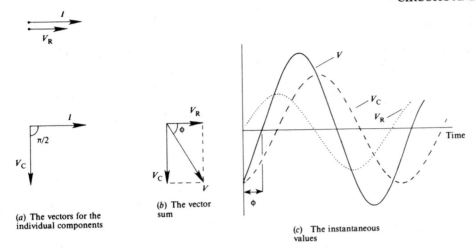

(a) The vectors for the individual components

(b) The vector sum

(c) The instantaneous values

Fig. 15.5   R and C in series

capacitor in series with a 100 Ω resistor and supplied with an alternating voltage of 12 V r.m.s. at 200 Hz.

$$X_C = \frac{1}{2\pi fC} = \frac{1}{2\pi \times 200 \times 2.0 \times 10^{-6}}$$

$$= 398 \ \Omega$$

Hence

$$Z = \sqrt{(100^2 + 398^2)} = 410 \ \Omega$$

Since

$$Z = \frac{V_m}{I_m} = \frac{V_{r.m.s.}}{I_{r.m.s.}}$$

then

$$I_{r.m.s.} = \frac{12}{410} = 29.3 \text{ mA}$$

Inductor in an a.c. circuit

Consider an a.c. circuit supplied with a sinusoidal alternating voltage $V_m \sin \omega t$ and containing just an inductor of inductance L. A back e.m.f. of $-L \ dI/dt$ will be produced by the inductor. Thus the total e.m.f. in the circuit is

$$V_m \sin \omega t - L \frac{dI}{dt}$$

If there had been any resistance in the circuit then this e.m.f. would have been equal to IR, but since we are assuming R to be zero then we must have the total e.m.f. to be zero. Hence

$$L \frac{dI}{dt} = V_m \sin \omega t$$

The current I at time t is thus given by

$$\int_0^I dI = \int_0^t \frac{V_m}{L} \sin \omega t \ dt$$

$$I = -\frac{V_m}{\omega L} \cos \omega t$$

The current will be a maximum when the cosine term equals 1, hence

$$I_m = \frac{V_m}{\omega L}$$

$$X_L = \frac{V_m}{I_m} = \omega L$$

where X_L is the inductive reactance, unit the ohm. It should be noted that the maximum values of the current and potential difference are not occurring at the same instant of time.

The equations for the current through the inductor and the potential difference across it can

289

thus be stated as

$$I = -I_{m} \cos \omega t \text{ and } V = V_{m} \sin \omega t$$

The current and potential difference are not in phase, the current lagging the potential difference by 90° or $\pi/2$. This means that the current reaches its maximum value one-quarter of a cycle later than the potential difference (Fig. 15.6).

Thus if we have an alternating voltage of 12 V r.m.s. at 50 Hz applied across an inductor of inductance 200 mH, then the reactance is

$$X_{L} = 2\pi fL = 2\pi \times 50 \times 0.200 = 63\,\Omega$$

$$X_{L} = \frac{V_{m}}{I_{m}} = \frac{V_{r.m.s.}}{I_{r.m.s.}}$$

Hence

$$I_{r.m.s.} = \frac{12}{63} = 0.19 \text{ A}$$

If the frequency of the alternating voltage is increased to 500 Hz, the reactance increases to 630 Ω and the current decreases to 0.019 A. The higher the frequency the higher the reactance. Figure 15.7 shows how the reactance varies with frequency.

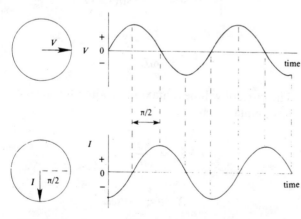

Fig. 15.6 *Current lagging potential difference by $\pi/2$*

Inductor and resistor in a.c. circuit

Consider a circuit supplied with a sinusoidal alternating voltage and which consists of a

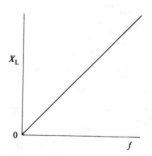

Fig. 15.7 *Variation of X_{L} with frequency*

resistor in series with an inductor. Because they are in series the current must be the same through both at any instant we consider. For a resistor the potential V_{R} across the resistor will be in phase with the current; however, for the inductor the potential difference leads the current by $\pi/2$. The vectors for this situation are thus as shown in Fig. 15.8. Hence the potential difference across the two components is given by

$$V^{2} = V_{R}^{2} + V_{L}^{2}$$

The potential difference values used for the lengths of the vectors are the maximum values, hence

$$Z = \frac{\text{maximum p.d. across both components}}{\text{maximum current through both}}$$

$$= \sqrt{\left(\frac{V_{R}^{2}}{I_{m}^{2}} + \frac{V_{L}^{2}}{I_{m}^{2}}\right)}$$

But $R = V_{R}/I_{m}$ and $X_{L} = V_{L}/I_{m}$, hence

$$Z = \sqrt{(R^{2} + X_{L}^{2})}$$

The symbol Z is used for the circuit impedance, the quantity relating the maximum potential difference and the maximum current in the circuit and having the unit of ohm.

The sum p.d. V leads the current by angle ϕ (see Fig. 15.8), where

$$\tan \phi = \frac{V_{L}}{V_{R}} = \frac{I_{m}X_{L}}{I_{m}R} = \frac{X_{L}}{R}$$

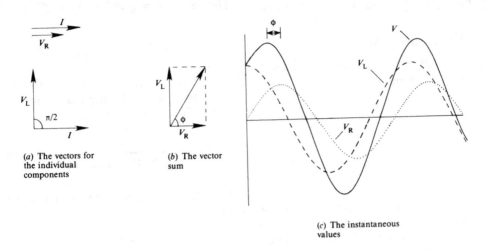

(a) The vectors for the individual components

(b) The vector sum

(c) The instantaneous values

Fig. 15.8   R and L in series

To illustrate the above, consider a 500 mH inductor in series with a 60 Ω resistor and supplied with an alternating voltage of 20 V r.m.s. at 100 Hz.

$$X_L = 2\pi f L = 2\pi \times 100 \times 0.500 = 314 \ \Omega$$

Hence $Z = \sqrt{(60^2 + 314^2)} = 320 \ \Omega$

Since

$$Z = \frac{V_m}{I_m} = \frac{V_{r.m.s.}}{I_{r.m.s.}}$$

then

$$I_{r.m.s.} = \frac{20}{320} = 63 \ \text{mA}$$

An inductor is generally just a coil of wire with either an air core or one of magnetic material. Thus such a coil has invariably both inductance and resistance and behaves as though it is a pure inductance, with no resistance, in series with a resistor having no inductance.

The *RCL* series circuit

Consider a circuit where we have a resistor, a capacitor and an inductor in series and connected to a sinusoidal alternating voltage. The current through all the components must be the same since they are in series. The potential difference across the resistor will be in phase with the current, that across the capacitor will lag the current by π/2 while that for the inductor will lead by π/2. Figure 15.9 shows the vectors for these potential differences and their summation.

$$V^2 = V_R^2 + (V_L - V_C)^2$$

Hence since the circuit impedance Z is the maximum potential difference divided by the maximum current

$$Z = \sqrt{\left(\frac{V_R^2}{I_m^2} + \left(\frac{V_L}{I_m} - \frac{V_C}{I_m}\right)^2\right)}$$

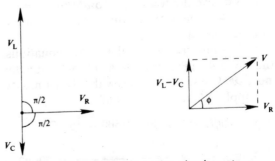

Fig. 15.9   The RCL series circuit vectors

291

But $R = V_R/I_m$, $X_L = V_L/I_m$ and $X_C = V_C/I_m$, hence

$$Z = \sqrt{(R^2 + (X_L - X_C)^2)}$$

The impedance will have a minimum value of R when $X_L = X_C$, i.e., when

$$2\pi f L = \frac{1}{2\pi f C}$$

$$f = \frac{1}{2\pi\sqrt{(LC)}}$$

When the impedance is a minimum then the current must be a maximum. Figure 15.10 shows how the current varies with frequency for different values of resistance. The condition of maximum current, i.e., minimum impedance, is called current resonance.

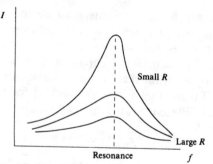

Fig. 15.10   Current in the RCL series circuit

The sum p.d. V leads the current by angle ϕ (see Fig. 15.9) where

$$\tan \phi = \frac{(V_L - V_C)}{V_R R} = \frac{(X_L - X_C)}{R}$$

When we have the resonance condition $X_L = X_C$ and so $\phi = 0$, the potential difference is in phase with the current.

To illustrate the use of the above equations, consider a 4.0 µF capacitor, a 500 mH inductor and a 200 Ω resistor in series with a 12 V r.m.s. 50 Hz supply. What is the current?

$$X_L = 2\pi f L = 2\pi \times 50 \times 0.500 = 157 \ \Omega$$

$$X_C = \frac{1}{2\pi f C} = \frac{1}{2\pi \times 50 \times 4.0 \times 10^{-6}} = 796 \ \Omega$$

Hence $Z = \sqrt{(R^2 + (X_C - X_L)^2)} = 670 \ \Omega$

$$I_{r.m.s.} = \frac{V_{r.m.s.}}{Z} = \frac{12}{796} = 18 \text{ mA}$$

What is the resonant frequency for the above components, and if the applied voltage is still 12 V what is the current at resonance?

$$f = \frac{1}{2\pi\sqrt{(0.500 \times 4.0 \times 10^{-6})}} = 113 \text{ Hz}$$

At resonance the impedance is just R, i.e. 200 Ω, and so

$$I_{r.m.s.} = \frac{V_{r.m.s.}}{Z} = \frac{12}{200} = 60 \text{ mA}$$

The CL parallel circuit

Consider a circuit which has a capacitor in parallel with an inductor (Fig. 15.11a). Such a circuit is used as the tuning part of a radio (Fig. 15.11b). The potential difference across the capacitor is the same as that across the inductor (we are assuming there is no resistance in either arm of the circuit). The current through the capacitor leads this potential difference by $\pi/2$,

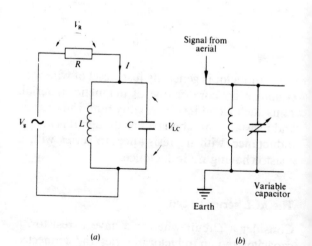

(a)   (b)

Fig. 15.11   CL parallel circuits

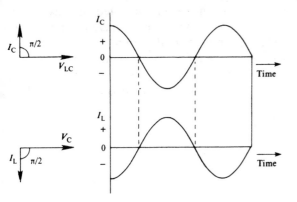

Fig. 15.12   Out of phase currents

while that through the inductor lags it by $\pi/2$ (Fig. 15.12). Thus the current I entering the parallel arrangement is

$$I = I_C - I_L$$

$$= \frac{V_{LC}}{X_C} - \frac{V_{LC}}{X_L}$$

When $X_C = X_L$ then $I = 0$. There is thus zero current taken from the a.c. supply at this condition. There are, however, obviously currents in the parallel arrangement. What is happening is that when the current is going one way in the capacitor arm it is going the other way in the inductor arm; the current is thus circulating back and forth between the capacitor and inductor (Fig. 15.13). This condition is said to be resonance and the fre-

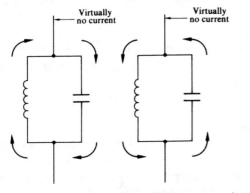

Fig. 15.13   Current directions in a resonant circuit

quency at which this occurs is given by

$$X_C = X_L$$

$$\frac{1}{2\pi f C} = 2\pi f L$$

$$f = \frac{1}{2\pi \sqrt{(LC)}}$$

We can now explain why the parallel CL circuit is used as the tuner in a radio. For the potential differences in Fig. 15.11a circuit, we have

$$V = V_R + V_{LC}$$

But $V = IR$ and since at resonance I is effectively zero, we must have the entire potential difference across the LC circuit. At all other frequencies there is a significant current through R and hence V_{LC} is much smaller. Thus only for one frequency do we have a high potential difference across the radio circuit.

Power in a.c. circuit

With a resistor the instantaneous power dissipation is given by $P = VI = V^2/R$. The average power dissipation is thus the square of the average potential difference divided by the resistance. Hence

$$\text{average power} = \frac{V_{\text{r.m.s.}}^2}{R} = V_{\text{r.m.s.}} I_{\text{r.m.s.}}$$

With a capacitor the instantaneous power dissipation is given by

$$P = VI = (V_m \sin \omega t)(I_m \cos \omega t).$$

Hence average power =

$$V_m \times \text{average value of}$$
$$(\sin \omega t)(\cos \omega t)$$

Since $2 \sin \theta \cos \phi = \sin(\theta + \phi) + \sin(\theta - \phi)$, then $(\sin \omega t)(\cos \omega t) = \frac{1}{2} \sin 2\omega t$. But since the average value of a sine function is zero, this means that the average power is zero.

How can the average power be zero? Power is drawn from the a.c. source during one-half of the cycle and the energy stored in the capacitor. During the next half-cycle the capacitor returns this energy. The net result over a complete cycle is zero power taken from the source.

With an inductor the instantaneous power dissipation is given by

$$P = VI = (V_m \sin \omega t)(-I_m \cos \omega t).$$

Hence average power =

$$-V_m I_m \times \text{average value of} \\ (\sin \omega t)(\cos \omega t)$$

As with the capacitor, the average value of this term is zero and so the average power dissipated is zero. During one-half of the cycle, power is drawn from the source and the energy stored in the magnetic field of the inductor. During the next half-cycle the inductor returns this energy. The net result over a complete cycle is zero power taken from the source.

When we have a series circuit involving resistance and a capacitor and/or an inductor, the average power dissipated is only that due to power dissipation in the resistor.

Pulses in a *CR* circuit

What happens when we pass electrical pulses through circuits containing resistors, capacitors, and inductors? Consider a generator which produces square pulses and the results when such pulses are fed into circuits containing these different elements. With a resistor, Fig. 15.14, the oscilloscope trace has the same shape as when the

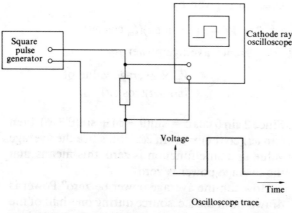

Fig. 15.14 Square pulses in a circuit containing only resistance

294

output from the generator is fed directly to the oscilloscope. If, however, we have a capacitor as well as the resistor in the circuit and examine the p.d. across the capacitor as a function of time, we find a change in the shape of the pulse (Fig. 15.15). The pulse across the resistor is also changed.

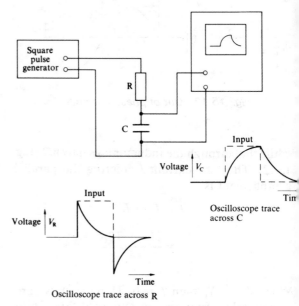

Fig. 15.15 Square pulses in a CR circuit

We can explain the form of these pulses by considering the rise in the voltage pulse of the generator charging up the capacitor and the drop in the generator voltage pulse as discharging the capacitor. The potential difference across the capacitor plates is directly proportional to the charge on the plates ($Q = CV$) and thus the oscilloscope trace given by the oscilloscope when connected across the capacitor shows the charge and discharge process. The sum of the voltages across the resistor and across the capacitor gives the voltage supplied by the generator (Fig. 15.16).

The product of the capacitance C and the resistance R is known as the time constant of the circuit.

Figure 15.17 shows how the pulse shapes differ for different time constants. With a small time constant the pulse across the resistor consists of two sharp voltage spikes, the pulse across the

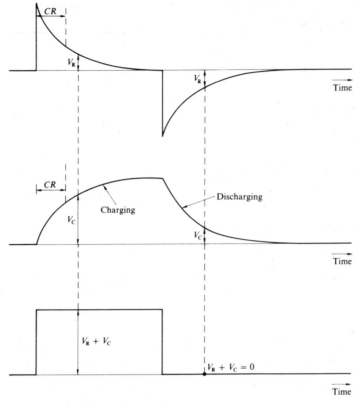

Fig. 15.16   Pulses in a CR circuit

capacitor consists of only a slight change from the generator pulse. The pulse across the resistor is, if Ohm's law is obeyed, proportional to the circuit current.

$$V_R = RI$$

But

$$I = \frac{dQ}{dt}$$

Thus

$$V_R = R \frac{dQ}{dt}$$

But

$$Q = CV_C$$

Thus

$$V_R = RC \frac{dV_C}{dt}$$

The pulse seen on the oscilloscope when it is connected across the resistor is the differential of the pulse seen when the oscilloscope is connected across the capacitor. With a small value of CR the pulse across the capacitor is almost the same as that given by the generator. Thus with a small time constant the output pulse across the resistor is approximately equal to the differential, i.e., the gradient, of the generator pulse. Such a circuit is known as a differentiating circuit.

With a large time constant the pulse across the resistor is almost the same shape as that supplied by the generator, that across the capacitor is almost a steady rise with time followed by a steady fall.

$$\frac{dV_C}{dT} = \frac{1}{RC} V_R$$

$$V_C = \frac{1}{RC} \int V_R \, dt$$

295

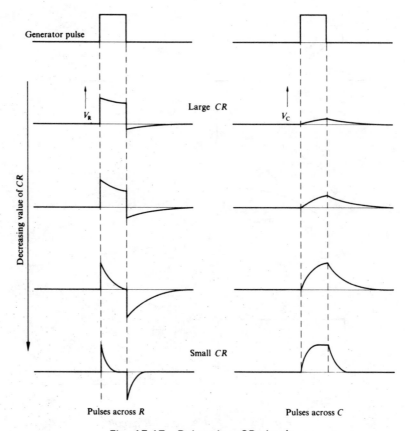

Fig. 15.17 Pulses in a CR circuit

V_C is the integral of the variation with time of V_R. As with a large time constant V_R varies with time in almost the same way as the generator pulse, the output across the capacitor is roughly the integral, i.e., the area under the voltage–time curve, of the generator pulse. Such a circuit is known as an integrating circuit. With the pulse the integration is about the mean voltage level of the pulse, see Fig. 15.18.

The time constant for this circuit is L/R, where L is the value of the inductance. If L is in henries and R in ohms, the time constant is in seconds. Figure 15.20 shows the effects on the pulse of using different time constants. For a large time constant

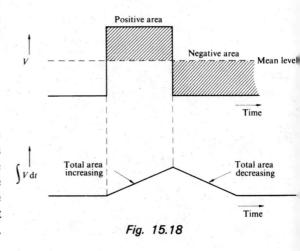

Pulses in an LR circuit

Figure 15.19 shows what happens when a square pulse is fed into a circuit with an inductor in series with a resistor. The sum of the voltages across the resistor and across the inductor gives the voltage supplied by the generator. The voltage across the resistor shows that the current in the circuit first grows with time and then decays exponentially.

Fig. 15.18

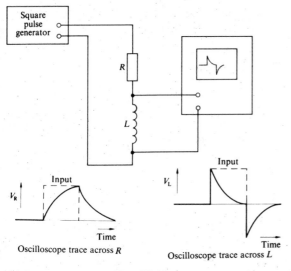

Oscilloscope trace across R   Oscilloscope trace across L

Fig. 15.19

the voltage across the resistor rises almost linearly with time and then decays almost linearly, the voltage across the inductor is almost the same as that supplied by the generator. With a small time constant the voltage across the inductor is in the form of two sharp spikes, that across the resistor is almost the same as that supplied by the generator.

The diode valve

In 1883 Edison while studying the blackening which occurred inside the early electric lamps sealed an extra electrode in the lamp. Figure 15.21 shows the basic arrangement, a heated filament to give the light and another electrode. He found that if this extra electrode was made positive a

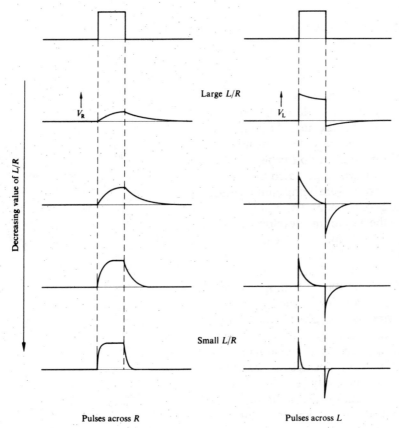

Pulses across R   Pulses across L

Fig. 15.20

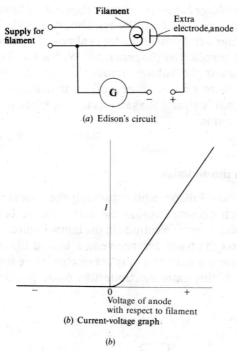

(a) Edison's circuit

I

0

Voltage of anode
with respect to filament

(b) Current-voltage graph

(b)

Fig. 15.21   The diode value

current flowed, if it was negative no current flowed. We now call this effect thermionic emission and consider that the heated filament is emitting electrons. Edison, however, saw no use for the effect and investigated no further.

It was J. J. Thomson who elucidated the effect by showing that electrons were being emitted and by his investigations of the nature and properties of electrons paved the way for the development of electronic valves (see Chapter 18 for details of Thomson's work).

The diode valve can be claimed as the invention of J. A. Fleming in 1904. Fleming was an associate of Marconi and concerned with the development of 'wireless' (see Chapter 9). In this work he saw the need for a device to rectify high frequency alternating current, i.e., to convert currents alternating from positive to negative values to currents having only positive values. The diode valve, essentially the light bulb of Edison with the extra electrode, does this. Current can only flow in one direction through such a

valve—when the extra electrode (called the anode) is positive with respect to the filament.

The p–n junction diode

In a p-type material we have mobile holes, in n-type material mobile electrons. When a junction between such materials is formed diffusion of holes and electrons occurs across the junction (Fig. 15.22). The holes and electrons combine with the result that the layer of material on either

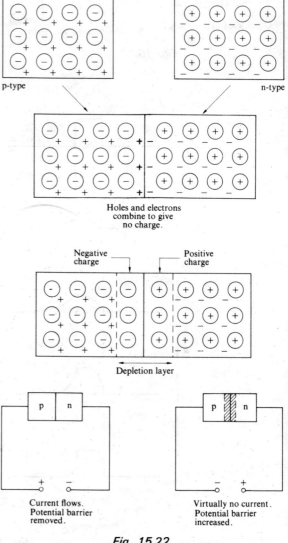

Fig. 15.22

side of the boundary becomes depleted of charge carriers. This narrow layer at the junction is called the depletion layer. Because both the n-type and p-type materials were initially neutral there is a negative charge on the p-type material side of the junction and a positive charge on the n-type material side. The movement of holes and electrons continues across the junction until the n side is sufficiently positive to stop further movements of holes and the p side sufficiently negative to stop the electrons. The potential difference that now exists between the two sides acts as a potential barrier to further charge movement.

If a battery is connected across the junction a significant current is only found to flow when the applied p.d. is sufficient to overcome the effect of the potential barrier. Thus when the p side of the junction is made sufficiently positive, this being called forward bias, a current will flow, limited only by the resistance of the material and that of the external circuit; when the p side is made negative, reverse bias, virtually no current flows. The junction is a rectifier, giving only a current in one direction.

Figure 15.23 shows the current–voltage graph (called the characteristic) for a p-n junction. With forward bias a current of the order of a few milliamps can flow. With reverse bias there is a very small current, of the order of a microamp. This is called the leakage current and occurs because though the majority charge carriers in p-type material are holes there are also some electrons, minority carriers. Similarly in n-type material, the majority charge carriers are electrons with holes as minority carriers. The minority charge carriers are responsible for the leakage current.

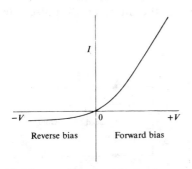

Fig. 15.23   p-n junction diode characteristic

Rectification

If a p–n junction diode (or a diode valve) is put in an a.c. circuit, Fig. 15.24a, then rectification occurs. The direction of the arrow head in the diode symbol is the forward bias direction for current. The rectification is said to be half wave because only when the applied voltage is positive is there any current in the circuit and so only half the input wave gives a current (Fig. 15.24b).

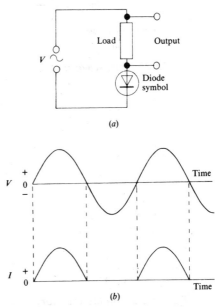

Fig. 15.24   Half-wave rectifier

Figure 15.25 shows a full-wave rectifier, a rectified current being produced in both halves of the alternating voltage input. When the potential at A is greater than that at B current passes through diode 1, when the potential at C is greater than that at B the current flows through diode 2. The result is that alternate current pulses are given by one diode, the other giving the intervening pulses.

An alternative to the circuit shown in Fig. 15.25 is the bridge rectifier (Fig. 15.26), this also giving full-wave rectification. When A is positive then the current flow through the bridge is in the directions indicated by the solid arrows, when A is negative the current flow is that indicated by the dotted arrows.

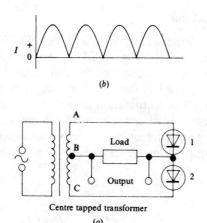

(b)

Centre tapped transformer

(a)

Fig. 15.25 Full-wave rectifier

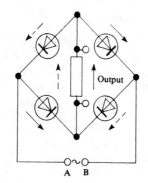

Fig. 15.26 Bridge rectifier

The output from both a half-wave and a full-wave rectifier is not smooth d.c. The output can be made smoother by connecting a capacitor in parallel with the load, Fig. 15.27. During AB the potential difference across the load, and hence the capacitor, is increasing and so the capacitor becomes charged. During BC the capacitor is dis-

charging through the load and so smoothing out the drop to zero potential difference that would otherwise occur. The remaining fluctuation in the output potential difference is termed the ripple.

Electronic systems

Electronic circuits look complex. If we look in, say, a transistor radio set there are lots of wires and components. If we look at a circuit diagram of the set, it looks neater but still complex. If we look at the inside of a computer and its circuit diagram there seems to be even more complexity. There are, however, in all circuits certain building blocks with simple functions. We can by looking for these building blocks discern the method by which a circuit performs its function. We can also do the reverse job and by putting together appropriate building blocks assemble a system to do a job.

Figure 15.28 shows the breakdown into building blocks of a simple radio set. Each block in some way modifies the input signal to give the required output. The tuner has as input a large number of radio frequencies, modulated by the audio signals (see Chapter 9), and gives as output just one narrow radio frequency band, modulated by the audio signal. We are thus able to select the radio station we wish to listen to.

Figure 15.29 shows the breakdown of a nuclear ratemeter. From an input to the Geiger tube of random radiation packets, random electrical pulses of various sizes are produced. The next block chops all the pulses down to the same size. After amplification the pulses reach the integrator unit. Here the pulses are summed over some definite time interval and the output current, proportional to the number of pulses, fed to a meter.

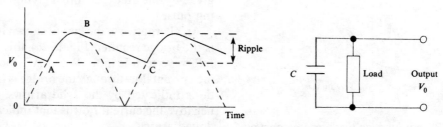

Fig. 15.27 Smoothing with a capacitor

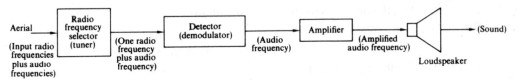

Fig. 15.28

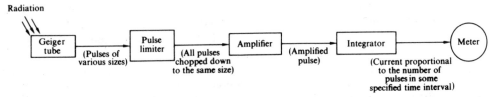

Fig. 15.29

Amplifiers

We can describe the performance of all amplifiers as systems which take an input signal and produce a larger replica of that signal as the output (Fig. 15.30). The term gain is used to relate the output and input

$$\text{Gain} = \frac{\text{output signal}}{\text{input signal}}$$

We can talk of voltage or current gain, depending on what attribute of a signal we are considering.

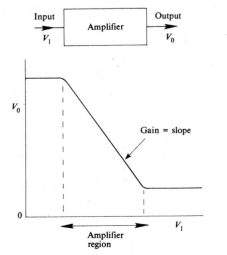

Fig. 15.30   An amplifier characteristic

Some amplifiers produce output signals which are 180° out of phase with the input signal, i.e., the same form as the input signal but inverted.

Feedback

A rise in the general cost of goods causes a demand for an increase in wages, which if met causes an increase in manufacturing costs, which in turn results in an increase in the cost of goods. The cost of the goods thus spirals upwards—there is inflation. Power stations in a city produce air pollution, which means that more people buy air conditioners, which need more power, which means more power stations, which means more air conditioners, and so on.

These are examples of feedback. We have a stimulus which produces a response which feeds back a signal to modify the stimulus. In some cases the return signal reinforces the stimulus, as in the above examples, and is known as positive feedback. Such feedback is characterized by a tendency for situations to rapidly go out of control and become unstable. With negative feedback the return signal produces a decrease in the stimulus.

Amplifier with negative feedback

Consider an amplifier where we take part of the output and feed it back as a signal to the input

(Fig. 15.31). If a fraction β of the output is fed back to the amplifier input as negative feedback, then

$$\text{modified input} = \text{input} - \beta \times \text{output}$$

But the output must be related to the modified input by the gain A.

$$A = \frac{\text{output}}{\text{modified input}}$$

Hence

$$\text{output} = A(\text{input} - \beta \times \text{output})$$

The gain with feedback A_f is thus

$$A_f = \frac{\text{output}}{\text{input}} = \frac{A}{1 + \beta A}$$

Thus if an amplifier has a gain of 100 before negative feedback and 5 per cent of the output is fed back then

$$A_f = \frac{100}{1 + 0.05 \times 100} = 16.7$$

The gain has been reduced. But there is a great benefit over the amplifier without negative feedback—greater stability.

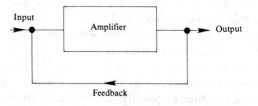

Fig. 15.31 A feedback amplifier

Suppose temperature fluctuations affect amplifier components so that the gain without feedback drops by 10 per cent, i.e., to 90. With negative feedback the gain is

$$A_f = \frac{90}{1 + 0.05 \times 90} = 16.4$$

This is only a percentage change of less than 2 per cent. The amplifier is more stable.

Oscillators

The gain of an amplifier with positive feedback can be derived in the same way as was done for negative feedback.

$$A_f = \frac{A}{1 - \beta A}$$

The effect of positive feedback is to increase the gain. Thus if we have β as 2 per cent and A as 30, then A_f is 75. If A was 40 then A_f becomes 200. If we make the value of βA to be 1, e.g., $\beta = 2$ per cent or 1/50 and $A = 50$, then A_f is infinity. This implies that however small the input signal, an output signal will be generated. A stray signal might thus lead to an output so that we do not have to supply an input to obtain an output. This is the basis of the oscillator—an amplifier under these conditions with positive feedback.

If we want oscillations at just one frequency then we have to arrange that the above conditions only occur for one frequency. One way of doing this is to use an amplifier which inverts the input to give an output which is out of phase with the input. A direct feedback in such a situation would give negative feedback. However, if we put in the feedback loop components which will change the phase such that for just one frequency the feedback is positive, then we can produce oscillation at just this frequency. This can be done using combinations of resistors and capacitors, the Wien network referred to later is one example of this.

Another method involves the use of a tuned circuit, a capacitor in parallel with an inductor (Fig. 15.32). A coupling coil is used to take a fraction of

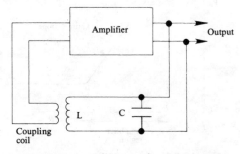

Fig. 15.32 A tuned circuit oscillator

the oscillating signal from the inductor and feed it, at the appropriate phase, to the input. Since the tuned circuit only oscillates at one frequency, feedback only occurs at a single frequency.

Operational amplifiers

The term operational amplifier was originally introduced for an amplifier that was designed to carry out mathematical operations such as adding, multiplication, etc. Nowadays it is more widely used. Such amplifiers have very high gains, i.e., high values of output/input.

Figure 15.33 shows the op-amp symbol. There are two inputs for signals, a non-inverting input identified by a + sign and an inverting input identified by a − sign. In addition to the output, there are obviously connections for a power supply to the amplifier though these are not generally shown on circuit diagrams. With the non-inverting input the output is in phase with the input, with the inverting input the output is 180° out of phase with the input, i.e., it is inverted.

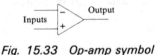

Fig. 15.33 Op-amp symbol

Figure 15.34 shows how the op-amp can be connected as an amplifier. With the inverting amplifier shown in (a) the input potential difference V_i tends to drive the potential at point X positive. The output at Y, however, becomes negative because the amplifier inverts. A current will thus flow between points X and Y since there is a potential difference. Because the amplifier has a high gain the feedback signal from Y will be large enough to just about cancel out the potential at X and keep it therefore at a very low level. Because of this we can take X to be at earth potential—the term virtual earth is used.

Since the op-amp has a very high impedance and draws very little current from the input, we can consider I_f to equal I_i. Then since we can take X to be at earth potential, V_i is across R_1 and so $I_i = V_i/R_1$. Similarly we take V_o to be across R_2 and

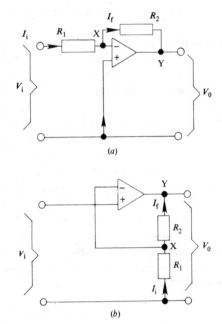

Fig. 15.34 (a) An inverting amplifier. (b) A non-inverting amplifier

so $I_f = -V_o/R_2$. The negative sign is because V_o is an inverted form of V_i. Thus since $I_i = I_f$, we have

$$\frac{V_i}{R_1} = -\frac{V_o}{R_2}$$

Hence the gain of the amplifier is

$$\text{gain} = \frac{V_o}{V_i} = -\frac{R_2}{R_1}$$

The gain thus depends only on the resistances.

A similar analysis for the non-inverting amplifier gives

$$\text{gain} = 1 + \frac{R_2}{R_1}$$

Both the above circuits use negative feedback in that the signal feedback is out of phase with the input signal to which it is added. This has the effect of reducing the change responsible for producing it. Negative feedback improves the stability of the amplifier in that changes in the op-amp gain

303

have very little effect on the overall gain of the system.

One use of the op-amp when positive feedback is used is as an oscillator. As has been described earlier in this chapter, a tuned LC circuit can be used to determine the frequency of oscillation and inductive coupling to the inductance used to take part of the signal and feed it back through the amplifier. An alternative method uses just an RC network to determine the frequency and feedback a signal to the amplifier. One form of this is the Wien bridge oscillator shown in Fig. 15.35. The Wien network determines the frequency at which the fed-back signal is in phase with the input to the non-inverting amplifier. Only when the frequency is $1/(2\pi CR)$ and $R_2 = 2R_1$ does this condition occur, and hence oscillations of just one frequency occur.

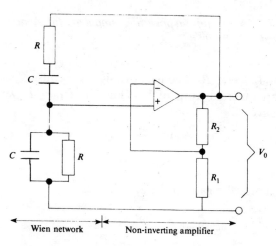

Fig. 15.35   An oscillator

Switching

A switching system has the characteristic that when the input changes in value the output switches from, say, a high to a low value. The output can effectively exist in only two forms, a high or a low value. Figure 15.36 shows the characteristic of such a system; an input change from V_1 to V_2 causes the output to switch from a high to a low value.

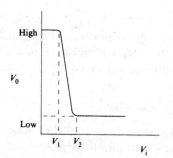

Fig. 15.36   A switch system characteristic

Digital systems

Systems can be considered to be analogue or digital, just like wrist watches. An analogue wrist watch has hands which rotate, the angle rotated being the analogue of time. A digital watch has a purely numerical display, a display of digits. Much of modern electronics is concerned with digital inputs and outputs, not analogue. Thus the electronic systems have to respond to digital signals, not continuously variable signals. The digital signals generally used are 'two state' signals, on or off, open or closed, signal present or not, etc. Such signals can be represented by the digits 0 and 1, these being referred to as *bi*nary digi*t*s or bits.

To illustrate this, consider the light in a refrigerator. This comes on when the door opens, going off when the door is closed. Thus we have the following input conditions:

Condition	Input signal
Door open	0
Door closed	1

The output conditions are:

Condition	Output	Output signal
The input is 0	Light off	0
The input is 1	Light on	1

We can group the inputs and outputs in a table. Such a tabulation of inputs and outputs is called a truth table.

Input	Output
0	0
1	1

Gates

The term gate is used for a device, a circuit, which provides the required relationships between digital inputs and outputs.

For the refrigerator example referred to earlier, a non-inverting gate is required, Fig. 15.37a, showing the circuit symbol. A non-inverting gate fits the truth table:

Input	Output
0	0
1	1

An inverter, or NOT, gate has a behaviour described by the following truth table, its symbol being shown in Fig. 15.37b (notice the slight difference between its symbol and the non-inverting symbol).

Input	Output
0	1
1	0

Thus if the input is 1 the output is *not* the same but 0.

The above gates had just one input, the following gates all have more than one input. The OR gate (Fig. 15.37c) has a behaviour described by the truth table:

Inputs		Output
A	B	
0	0	0
0	1	1
1	0	1
1	1	1

If either A *or* B input is 1 then the output is 1.

A NOR gate (Fig. 15.37d) gives a 1 output when neither input A *nor* input B is 1, the following being the truth table.

Inputs		Output
A	B	
0	0	1
0	1	0
1	0	0
1	1	0

The AND gate (Fig. 15.37e) gives a 1 output when input A *and* input B are both 1, the following being the truth table.

Inputs		Output
A	B	
0	0	0
0	1	0
1	0	0
1	1	1

The NAND gate (Fig. 15.37f) is a NOT AND gate, the output is *not* 1 when input A *and* input B is 1, the following being the truth table.

Inputs		Output
A	B	
0	0	1
0	1	1
1	0	1
1	1	0

The EXCLUSIVE OR (XOR) gate (Fig. 15.37g) gives a 1 output if input A *or* B is 1 but *not both*, the

BS 3939: 1985 (IEC 617–12: 1983) symbols

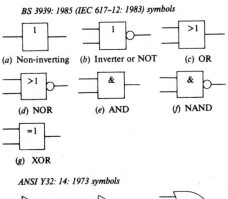

(a) Non-inverting   (b) Inverter or NOT   (c) OR

(d) NOR   (e) AND   (f) NAND

(g) XOR

ANSI Y32: 14: 1973 symbols

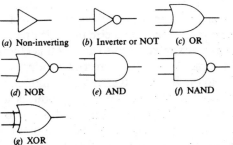

(a) Non-inverting   (b) Inverter or NOT   (c) OR

(d) NOR   (e) AND   (f) NAND

(g) XOR

Fig. 15.37   Gates

following being the truth table.

Inputs		Output
A	B	
0	0	0
0	1	1
1	0	1
1	1	0

The following illustrates the use that could be made of one such gate. Thus if we want an electronic system by which a cassette recorder will record if both the record and forward play buttons are depressed then we need an AND gate, as the following table indicates.

Inputs		Output
A	B	
Record button	Forward play button	
Up (0)	Up (0)	No record (0)
Up (0)	Down (1)	No record (0)
Down (1)	Up (0)	No record (0)
Down (1)	Down (1)	Record (1)

Binary arithmetic

Binary digits can be used to represent numbers. In such situations we need to be able to add them together. Such an operation is an important feature of any digital computer.

The denary system uses ten symbols, 0, 1, 2, 3, ... 9, arranged side by side to represent numbers, the significance of any symbol depending on its position. Thus 125 is $1 \times 10^2 + 2 \times 10^1 + 5 \times 10^0$. The binary system uses just two symbols 0 and 1, arranged also side by side to represent numbers, with again the significance of any symbol depending on its position. Thus 101 is $1 \times 2^2 + 0 \times 2^1 + 1 \times 2^0$ (in denary form 5).

In adding, on denary notation, 15 and 26 we first add the 5 and 6 to give 1 with 1 carried. This carried 1 we then add to the 'tens' column to give 4, a final answer of 41. Similarly we use the carry operation in adding binary numbers. The rules by which such numbers are added are:

0 plus 0 equals 0
0 plus 1 equals 1
1 plus 0 equals 1
1 plus 1 equals 0, carry 1.

Thus if we add 011 to 001 we have:

for the 2^0 column   0, carry 1;
for the 2^1 column   0, carry 1;
for the 2^2 column   1.
Hence a final answer of 100.

The gates system required to add binary numbers is going to need to have multiple outputs, an output for each digit in the final sum. It must also have the facility to 'carry' digits. A system which will add bits and carry 1 to the next column is called a half-adder. Such a system can be made from an XOR gate and an AND gate (Fig. 15.38). A number of half-adders can be combined to give a full-adder which will add up each of a number of columns in the sum and carry bits as appropriate. Figure 15.39 shows a full-adder for adding two two-bit numbers.

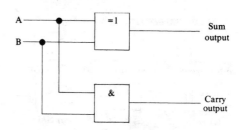

Fig. 15.38   A half-adder

Bistable and astable circuits

Feedback has many applications in electronics. For example, consider a circuit made up of two of the inverters referred to earlier in this chapter. A high input to the first inverter produces a low input to the second inverter and a high output. A low input to the first inverter produces a high input to the second inverter and a low output. What happens if we take the output from the second inverter and use it as the input to the first inverter (Fig. 15.40)? A high input to the

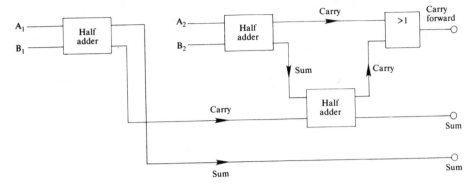

Fig. 15.39 A full-adder

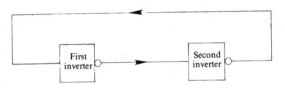

Fig. 15.40 A bistable circuit

first inverter produces a low input to the second inverter which produces a high input to the first inverter which produces a low input to the second inverter, and so on. Once the first input has been made high the feedback will maintain the high state. This is positive feedback. This arrangement is known as a bistable circuit: it 'remembers' what was last done to it. If the input to the first inverter was last made high it remains high, if it was last made low it remains low. The circuit has two stable states, the output from inverter one low and from inverter two high or that from one high and two low. This is one form of a memory unit used in computers.

If instead of just using two inverters we use modified inverters which give pulses when the input to a capacitor drops from high to low, we can produce a continuous train of pulses (Fig. 15.41). Once the first pulse has been produced the process continues, a series of equally spaced pulses being produced. The duration of the pulses depends on the values of capacitance and resistance used. This circuit is known as an astable multivibrator. Astable means there is no stable state.

The cathode ray oscilloscope

The cathode ray oscilloscope has three basic components (Fig. 15.42).

1. An electron gun to produce a focused beam of electrons on a fluorescent screen. The gun consists of an indirectly heated cathode to emit electrons, a grid whose potential relative to the cathode controls the number of electrons passing through per second and hence the brightness of the impact 'spot' on the screen, and an electron lens to both cause the electrons to travel down the tube to the screen and also to focus them.

2. A deflection system consisting of two pairs of parallel plates so arranged that, when potential differences are applied across them, one deflects the electron beam in the X-direction and the other in the Y-direction.

3. A screen which fluoresces when the electron beam strikes it.

A time base signal can be applied to the X-plates. Such a signal (Fig. 15.43) causes the electron beam to traverse the screen from left to right at a steady speed, so that the position of the beam across the screen is proportional to time elapsed, and then when it reaches the right-hand side of the screen to fly back to the start point. The rate at which the beam sweeps across the screen, and hence the time taken to cover 1 cm, can be changed. A 'trig level' control can be used to start the sweep at the same point on a particular waveform input to the oscilloscope Y-plates, so

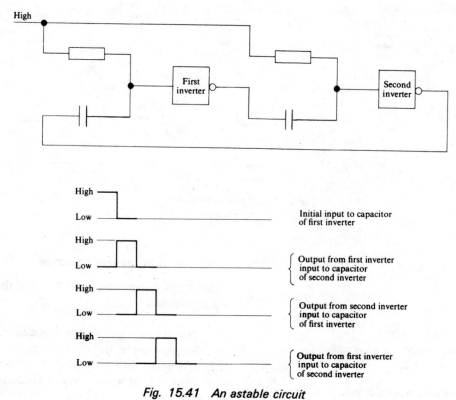

Fig. 15.41 An astable circuit

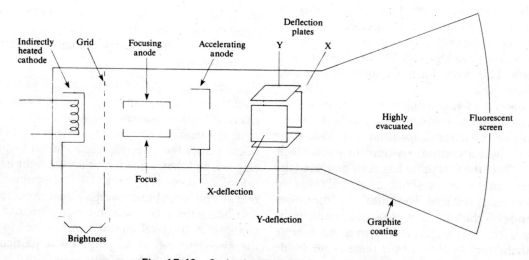

Fig. 15.42 Cathode ray oscilloscope elements

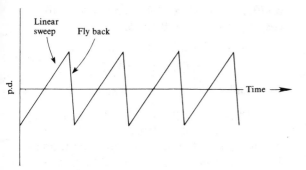

Fig. 15.43   Time base signal

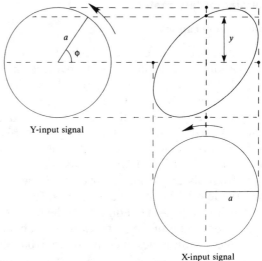

Y-input signal

X-input signal

Fig. 15.44   The summation of two simple harmonic motions, with a phase difference φ, where y/a = sin θ. For φ = 90°, a circular trace is produced

enabling the waveform to be 'frozen' on the screen.

The following are some of the uses to which the CRO can be put.

(a) *As a d.c. voltmeter*. The potential difference can be connected across the Y-plates with the time base off. The vertical deflection of the 'spot' on the screen is then proportional to the potential difference. Either the calibrated Y-deflection controls can be used or the spot deflection calibrated using known potential differences. The CRO has a very high impedance.

(b) *As an a.c. voltmeter*. The CRO is used as with d.c. voltages but the result is a vertical line on the screen, the length of which is twice the maximum voltage of the a.c.

(c) *Displaying waveforms*. The signal is fed to the Y-plates with the time base switched on, the result being essentially a voltage–time graph of the signal.

(d) *Measurment of time intervals*. With the time base switched on the signals are fed into the Y-plates, as in Fig. 8.13 for the measurement of sound.

(e) *Measurement of phase relationships*. If two sinusoidal potential differences of the same frequency and amplitude are fed into the X and Y plates, the electron beam is subject to two mutually perpendicular simple harmonic motions. The trace displayed on the screen depends on the phase difference between the two inputs, Fig. 15.44, and thus the phase difference can be ascertained.

(f) *Comparison of frequencies*. The two potential differences of different frequencies are applied to the X and Y plates. The pattern produced on the screen depends on the ratio of the two frequencies, the pattern being called a Lissajous figure (Fig. 15.45).

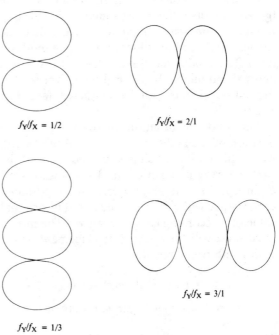

$f_Y/f_X = 1/2$

$f_Y/f_X = 2/1$

$f_Y/f_X = 1/3$

$f_Y/f_X = 3/1$

Fig. 15.45   Lissajous figures

309

Supplementary material

Telecommunications

Telecommunication can be defined as communication at a distance and involves such methods as signals along telephone cables, microwave transmission, radio waves and light signals along optical fibres. In the case of telephone cables the signals that are sent along the cables have to correspond to the frequencies of the sound used in normal human speech. These range from about 200 Hz to 4000 Hz. However, since the loss of the lowest and highest frequencies has little effect on the quality of the detected speech, the range of frequencies for which the telephone system is designed is 300 to 3400 Hz, i.e., a frequency range of 3100 Hz. This range is called the bandwidth.

Music can, however, have frequencies ranging from 50 to 15 000 Hz and thus transmission of music through a telephone system designed for speech would lead to very poor quality sound being received. VHF (Very High Frequency) radio is designed for a bandwidth of 12 kHz, hence much better quality sound can be heard via radio.

The transmission of information such as music by radio involves the music signals being used to modulate some radio frequency wave, called the carrier wave (see Fig. 9.40 for amplitude modulation). The modulated wave is then transmitted, being demodulated by the radio receiver so that the music signals can be extracted (see Fig. 15.28).

Amplitude modulation involves the superposition of the audio wave on top of the carrier wave which has a much greater frequency. If the carrier waves is $A \sin \omega_c t$ and the audio wave $B \sin \omega_a t$, then the amplitude of the modulated carrier wave will vary with time about its original value of A according to $(A + B \sin \omega_a t)$. The modulated wave will thus have a displacement which varies with time according to

$$y = (A + B \sin \omega_a t) \sin \omega_c t$$

$$= A \sin \omega_c t + B \sin \omega_a t \times \sin \omega_c t$$

This can be simplified using the relationship

$\cos(\theta \pm \phi) = \cos\theta\cos\phi \mp \sin\phi$, hence $\cos(\theta - \phi) - \cos(\theta + \phi) = 2\sin\theta\sin\phi$.

$$y = A \sin \omega_c t + \tfrac{1}{2}B \cos(\omega_c - \omega_a)t - \tfrac{1}{2}B \cos(\omega_c + \omega_a)t$$

The displacement thus consists of three terms:

1. $A \sin \omega_c t$ corresponding to the carrier wave.
2. $\tfrac{1}{2}B \cos(\omega_c - \omega_a)t$ corresponding to a wave of frequency $f_c - f_a$ and maximum amplitude $\tfrac{1}{2}B$.
3. $\tfrac{1}{2}B \cos(\omega_c + \omega_a)t$ corresponding to a wave of frequency $f_c + f_a$ and maximum amplitude $\tfrac{1}{2}B$.

We can thus consider the modulated wave to be composed of three waves. The analysis has only considered there to be a single audio frequency; where there is a band of audio frequencies we still end up with the carrier wave and on either side of it bands of frequencies each occupying the same bandwidth as that of the audio frequencies (Fig. 15.46). These are termed the upper and lower sidebands. The bandwidth occupied by the modulated wave thus ends up as $(f_c + \Delta f_a) - (f_c - \Delta f_a) = 2\Delta f_a$, i.e., twice the bandwidth of the audio waves alone.

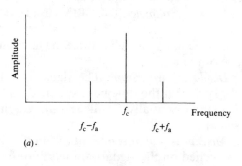

(a)

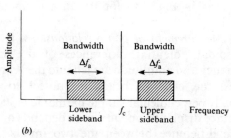

(b)

Fig. 15.46 (a) Frequency spectrum with a single audio frequency. (b) Frequency spectrum with a band of audio frequencies

Thus to transmit the modulated wave for an audio wave with bandwidth 10 kHz would require a bandwidth of 20 kHz.

The greater the bandwidth of a signal the greater the spacing has to be between carrier frequencies if the signals are to be kept separate. Thus the number of channels of communication along, say, a coaxial cable will be determined by the bandwidths of the signals. Coaxial cables used for the UK telephone system might carry a group of 12 channels, operating in the frequency range 12 to 60 kHz. Some modern cables operate at 60 MHz and can carry some 5000 channels.

The future, however, seems to lie with digital transmission rather than amplitude modulated signal transmission. The later section on optical fibres discusses the method by which a number of digital transmissions can be interleaved and sent along the same cable.

Transatlantic telephone cables

The first transatlantic cable was laid in 1857–8; only some 700 messages were, however, transmitted before it broke. 1866 saw the next completed cable across the Atlantic. These early cables were for the transmission of pulse signals, not speech. The first telephone cable was not laid across the Atlantic until 1956. Since that time more long-distance cables have been laid. Telephones were first used, for speech transmission over a very short distance, in 1876—why the delay before speech could be transmitted over a transatlantic cable? What were the difficulties?

The first transatlantic cable was made of seven copper wires, about 1 mm in diameter, covered in a mixture of hemp, tar, and wax and enclosed in an armouring of eighteen-strand iron wires. The distance the cable covered was about three thousand kilometres. The copper wire in such a length would have a resistance of about $9 \times 10^3 \ \Omega$. The capacitance of such an arrangement would be of the order of 20 μF. This gives a time constant CR of about 0.2 s. (The inductance would be about 1 H and L/R about 5×10^{-6} s and thus insignificant by comparison with 0.2 s.)

The cable behaves like a capacitor which needs about 0.2 s for a pulse to grow, or decay, by about one-third. For a pulse passing along such a cable there would have to be a growth time at the beginning of the pulse of the order of 5 CR and a similar time at the end of the pulse for it to decay. The minimum length of a pulse would thus have to be about 2 s. Thus only a small number of pulses could be transmitted in any one minute. To pass a message, in the form of pulses of differing lengths, along the cable would take many minutes. The transmission of audio frequency signals or audio modulated signals was therefore not possible—the time interval between wave crests would be much less than CR.

The capacitance of the cable is proportional to the length L of the cable

$$C \propto L$$

The resistance of the cable is proportional to the length.

$$R \propto L$$

Thus the time constant CR is proportional to L^2.

$$CR \propto L^2$$

The improvement which enabled the 1956 telephone cable to operate successfully was the insertion in the cable of repeaters at regular intervals. Fifty-one repeaters were used in the transatlantic cable. The repeaters, as the word suggests, repeat the signal with some amplification. This effectively reduces the length of the cable and so the time constant decreases by a factor of about 5^2 to about 1.5×10^{-3} s. The 1956 cable was also of different construction; the copper had three times the diameter of the first cable and thus only 1/9 of the resistance. The cable is thus able to operate at a frequency of 144 kHz. The audio signals are used to modulate this high-frequency signal.

The future of telecommunications by cable may, however, lie with the use of pulse code modulation. This is the conversion of the audio signal to a sequence of pulses for transmission over the cable, converting back to the audio signal at the receiver. The first lines using this were introduced in 1960.

311

Satellite communications

Intercontinental telephone calls take place either by submarine cable or satellite transmission (Fig. 15.47). Geostationary satellites are used, these being satellites which orbit the earth in such a way that they remain stationary relative to a particular fixed point on the earth's surface. This means that the time T taken to complete one orbit is just one day, i.e., 24 hours, since they rotate at the same rate as the earth rotates. Using $F = GMm/R^2 = mv^2/R$ with $v = 2\pi R/T$ enables us to derive the relationship $R^3 = GMT^2/4\pi^2$. The radius R of the satellite orbit can thus be computed, 35 500 km. Such a satellite is the INTELSAT V (its actual radius is 35 800 km).

The satellite is equipped with a number of aerial systems. Those to receive and transmit signals over the entire side of the earth visible to the satellite are conical horns, those concerned with large continental areas are parabolic 1.5 to 2.5 m diameter reflectors with microwave horns close to the focus. The aerials responsible for coverage of a very small area of the earth are 1 m diameter reflectors illuminating or feeding horns. To keep the highly directional aerials aligned with the earth receiving aerials, control systems have to be adopted to keep the satellite in the correct orientation.

The satellites receive signals from the earth at 6 and 14 GHz and transmit them back to the earth at 4 and 11 GHz, after amplification. The signal received by the satellite is likely to be of the order of $1/10^{20}$th of the signal strength that started out from the earth. The Madley station in the UK transmits signals at powers of up to 3 kW.

The INTELSAT satellite uses about 1.3 kW of power. This is provided by solar cells. A total solar panel area of 18.12 m^2 is used, consisting of 17 568 solar cells.

Aerials

The basic dipole aerial consists of two conducting rods, each having a length of one-quarter of the wavelength to be transmitted or received (Fig. 15.48). The conventional television aerial is generally, however, more complicated (Fig. 15.49). A conducting rod called a reflector is placed ¼λ behind the dipole. This is so that the waves it reflects back to the dipole arrive in phase with the main wave at the dipole. The extra path length of this reflected wave is 2 × ¼λ and there is a phase change of ½λ on reflection, hence the reflected wave is 2 × ¼λ + ½λ = 1λ displaced from the main wave and so in phase. In front of the dipole are director conducting rods. These have the function of giving a directional property to the aerial.

Parabolic dish aerials are widely used in telecommunications involving microwaves. Figure 15.50 shows the type of arrangement that might be used. The radio waves could after reflection from the parabolic dish be focused directly onto a microwave feed horn placed at the focus; it is, however, more usual to use a sub-reflector to direct the waves to the feed. The sub-reflector may be a plane reflector or a hyperboloid shape. The reverse sequence of events occurs when the dish is used to transmit.

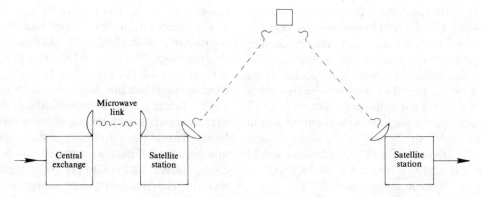

Fig. 15.47 Sending a telephone message by satellite

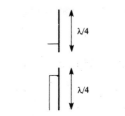

Fig. 15.48 A simple dipole

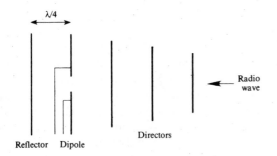

Fig. 15.49 A typical television aerial

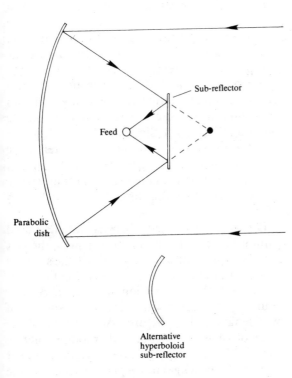

Fig. 15.50 A parabolic dish aerial

Aerials are directional, whether they be dipoles or dishes. We can think of the waves as emerging from holes, in the case of a dipole a thin rectangular slit and in the case of a dish a circular hole. Because the sizes of these holes are comparable with the wavelength, there will be pronounced diffraction patterns (see Fig. 9.10a) with a strong central maximum and a number of maxima at other angles. This is usually shown in the form of a polar diagram (Fig. 15.51). The strength of the signal in the various radial directions is plotted. For a slit the angular width of the central maximum is (see Chapter 9) given by $\sin \theta = \lambda/b$, where b is the width of the slit. For a circular hole the width is given by $\sin \theta = 1.22 \lambda/b$. This means a parabolic reflector of diameter 2.0 m used with microwaves of wavelength 2 cm will have a central maximum of angular width $\theta = 0.7°$.

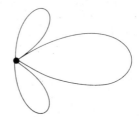

Fig. 15.51 A polar diagram

Optical fibres

Optical fibres consist of a central core of material which has a higher refractive index than its surrounding cladding. Light is transmitted along such a fibre by total internal reflection at the core–cladding interface (Fig. 15.52). The minimum angle for this to occur is the critical angle C, where

$$n_1 \sin C = n_2$$

If n_1 is 1 per cent greater than n_2, then $\sin C = 100/101$ and $C = 82°$. Rays passing through the core which reflect from the core–cladding interface at angles less than the critical angle will also give a refracted ray into the cladding and so lose some energy at each reflection. The result of this is that such rays cannot be transmitted for any significant distance. Only rays with angles equal to or

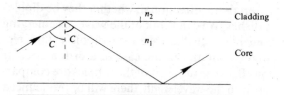

Fig. 15.52   An optical fibre

greater than the critical angle can be transmitted. However, because there is a range of angles there will be a range of paths that can be followed by rays (Fig. 15.53). The distance between reflections will differ and hence so will the total distance travelled by a ray in passing through a length of fibre. The result of this is that the different rays arrive at the end of the fibre at different times, thus a sharp pulse becomes spread out during transmission (this is called dispersion). Transmission which can involve a number of paths is called multimode transmission.

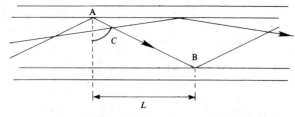

Fig. 15.53   Multimode transmission

For a ray reflected at the critical angle C the distance travelled by the ray AB is greater than the distance travelled L along the length of the fibre, being

$$\frac{L}{\sin C} - L = L\left(\frac{n_1}{n_2} - 1\right)$$

If c_f is the speed of light in the fibre this means a time difference between a ray at grazing incidence and one at the critical angle, i.e., the maximum angular variation, of

$$\Delta t = \frac{L}{c_f}\left(\frac{n_1}{n_2} - 1\right)$$

The speed of light in a vacuum c is related to that in the fibre by $c/c_f = n_1$. Hence

$$\Delta t = \frac{Ln_1}{c}\left(\frac{n_1 - n_2}{n_2}\right)$$

Since n_1 is very close to the value of n_2, perhaps a 1 per cent difference, then the expression approximates to

$$\Delta t = \frac{L}{c}(n_1 - n_2)$$

If n_1 is about 1.5 and there is a 1 per cent difference in refractive indices, then over 1 km the time difference will amount to 50 ns.

The number of possible paths, i.e., modes, can be reduced if the core diameter is reduced. A multimode fibre might have a core of diameter 50 μm, however if the core is only 5 μm only one mode, that of straight through, becomes possible. Such a fibre is called a single mode fibre. This effect occurs because the diameter of the core is close to the wavelength of the light used, generally about 1.3 μm.

Another way of reducing multipath dispersion is to use a graded index fibre. Instead of the abrupt step in refractive index that occurs between the core and the cladding, the refractive index is gradually varied between a high value in the centre of the core to the lower value in the cladding (Fig. 15.54). Since the speed of light in the fibre is inversely proportional to the refractive index, the light travelling the greatest distance in such a fibre does so at the highest average speed. The dispersion can be limited to about 1 ns in 1 km.

Dispersion also occurs because the light used cannot be of precisely one wavelength, there is always a spread of wavelength. Since the speed of light in a fibre depends on its wavelength ($c/c_f = \lambda/\lambda_f = n_1$), then dispersion will occur. A laser source gives light with very little spread of wavelength and so the dispersion can be of the order of 0.4 ns per km, while other sources such as the LED (light-emitting diode) in giving a greater spread of wavelength might give dispersion of the order of 1 ns per km.

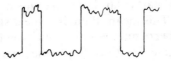

Fig. 15.55   Noise superimposed on a digital signal

original form of the signal can be readily restored since the beginning and end of the pulse can still be detected and so used to regenerate the digital signal without noise.

The converting of an analogue signal, perhaps the result of someone speaking into a microphone, into a digital signal is called pulse coded modulation (PCM). Three operations are involved. First the signal is pulse amplitude modulated (PAM). This involves sampling the signal at regular time intervals (Fig. 15.56). The frequency of the sampling depends on the frequencies present in the input signal; the higher the frequency the more often the sampling has to occur.

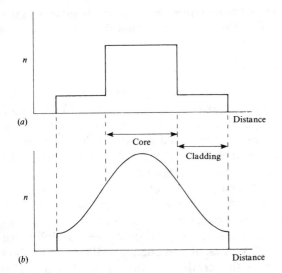

(a)

Core

Cladding

(b)

Fig. 15.54 The refractive index profile across (a) a step index, (b) a graded index fibre

The optical power output P_o from a fibre is invariably less than the power input P since some absorption occurs in the glass. The absorption occurs because of impurities in the glass, scattering by natural bunching of atoms in the glass and at joints between lengths of fibre. The relationship between P and P_o is

$$P = P_o e^{-\alpha x}$$

where x is the length of fibre and α a constant called the attenuation coefficient. x is usually in km and so α has the unit km^{-1}. Attenuation depends on the frequency of the light used. Because of attenuation, repeater stations are required at regular intervals along a line.

Signals can be carried along optical fibres in either analogue or digital form. In analogue form this could be done by amplitude modulation of the light beam (see Fig. 9.40). There are, however, problems. Noise, i.e. unwanted signals, invariably occurs and becomes superimposed on the input signal. When the signal is amplified not only is the required signal amplified but so is the noise. The quality of the transmitted signal can thus become fairly low. Digital transmission overcomes this noise problem. The noise still becomes superimposed on the input digital signal (Fig. 15.55) but when the output signal is extracted the

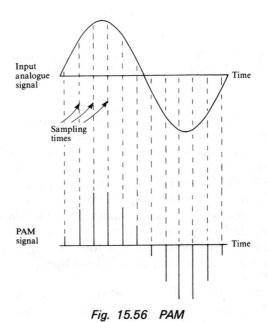

Fig. 15.56   PAM

Typically, sampling takes place every 125 µs. Each of the samples is then quantized (Fig. 15.57). This means the size of the signal is compared against a scale and given a binary number. The scale consists of a number of levels and all signals

315

within a particular level are given the same number. This means there is some distortion but the number of numbers required is kept down to a manageable size. Encoding is the final operation and involves the allocation of a binary number; one of the digits is used to indicate whether the level is positive or negative. After transmission through the fibre this sequence of events is reversed.

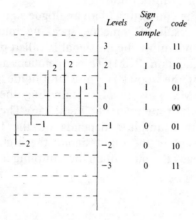

Levels	Sign of sample	code
3	1	11
2	1	10
1	1	01
0	1	00
−1	0	01
−2	0	10
−3	0	11

Fig. 15.57 Quantizing and encoding only a few bits of what is probably an 8-bit code being shown.

With sampling only taking place every 125 μs and each sampling lasting for only 2 or 3 μs, if only one signal was transmitted at once there would be a lot of 'waste' time when no transmission was occurring. Therefore more than one signal is sent down the fibre; we talk of their being a number of channels. 32 channels are used in a British Telecom system, with two of them being reserved for control information. This type of operation is known as time division multiplexing (TDM).

A sample every 125 μs is 8000 per second. With 32 channels this is 32 × 8000 samples transmitted per second. Each sample has an 8-bit code. Thus the number of bits of information transmitted per second is 8 × 32 × 8000 = 2 048 000, i.e., a 2 Mbit system. This is comparatively slow and a 565 Mbit system is planned for 1986, with talk of a 2.4 Gbit. The best that can be transmitted along a coaxial cable is 140 Mbit, and by a microwave link 70 Mbit. Optical fibres have great advantages in the amount of information that they can carry.

Problems

1. A lamp, which may be regarded as a non-inductive resistor, is rated at 2 A, 220 W. In order to operate the lamp from the 240-V, 50-Hz mains, an inductor is placed in series with it. If the resistance of the inductor is 5.0 Ω what should the value of its inductance be?
(University of London, Q6, Paper 2, June 1982)

2. A sealed box with two external terminals is known to contain a resistor and a capacitor connected in some way. When a potential difference of 32 V r.m.s. at a frequency of 100 Hz is applied across the terminals of the box as shown in Fig. 15.58 a current of 1.0 mA r.m.s. flows in it. If the frequency of the applied potential difference is gradually increased, the current at first rises and then reaches a steady value of 2.0 mA r.m.s. no matter how high the frequency. There is no current when a d.c. power supply is used instead.

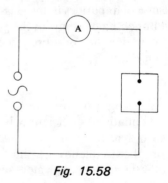

Fig. 15.58

What is the most likely arrangement of the two components inside the box? Explain.
Calculate the resistance of the resistor.
(University of London, Q7, Paper 2, January 1979)

3. An inductive coil is connected across a variable frequency supply and the following readings are noted:

Test	Supply	Current through coil
1	10 V, 50 Hz	42 mA
2	20 V, 100 Hz	62 mA

Determine the resistance and the inductance of the coil.

(University of London, Engineering Science, Q10, Paper 1, June 1982)

4. A heater is rated 1.00 kW 200 V. It is required to use it on a 250 V 50 Hz supply. This may be done by placing either (a) a resistor or (b) an inductor in series with the heater. Calculate

(i) the resistance of the resistor,

(ii) the inductance of the inductor if its resistance is 5.0 Ω.

State an advantage of using an inductor rather than a resistor.

(AEB, QA8, Paper 3, June 1982)

5. A constant voltage a.c. generator, of 20 V r.m.s. and variable frequency, is connected in series with a resistor of resistance 2.0 Ω, a coil of inductance 5.0 H and a capacitor of capacitance 2.0 μF. The frequency is adjusted until the current in the circuit has a maximum value of 2.0 A r.m.s. Calculate the resistance of the wire of the inductor and the value of this frequency.

(University of London, Q8, Paper 2, January 1978)

6. (a) What is meant by the root mean square value of an alternating current? Why is this particular value used when measuring an alternating current?

(b) Explain why no power is dissipated when an alternating current flows through a pure capacitor or a pure inductor.

(c) In a circuit containing a capacitor, an inductor, a resistor and a source of alternating potential difference in series, it is found that the current varies with the frequency of the source. Explain why this occurs. On what does the maximum current depend? Explain whether or not the power dissipated depends on the frequency of the source.

(d) A resistor of resistance 50 Ω and a coil of inductance 0.20 H are connected in series with an alternating voltage supply of frequency 50 Hz. If the r.m.s. voltages across the resistor and the coil are 120 V and 180 V respectively, calculate

(i) the impedance of the coil, and

(ii) the resistance of the coil.

(AEB, QB14, Paper 3, November 1982)

7. (a) Explain what is meant by the root-mean-square (r.m.s.) value of an alternating current. Why is this a useful way of describing its magnitude?

(b) A 100 Ω resistor, 2 μF capacitor, and a 0.1 H inductor are connected in series with a supply of sinusoidal alternating e.m.f. 10 V (r.m.s.) whose frequency f can be varied (see Fig. 15.59). What will be the approximate r.m.s. current, if any, in the circuit

(i) when f is zero, that is, the supply is 10 V d.c;

(ii) when f is set very high, at 1 MHz?

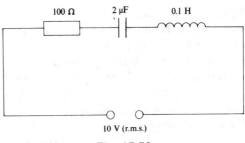

Fig. 15.59

It is found that the current in the circuit reaches a maximum value at a certain frequency of the supply. Explain this, and calculate

(iii) the frequency at which the current is a maximum;

(iv) the value of the maximum r.m.s. current;

(v) the r.m.s. voltage across each of the components at this frequency.

Explain why these three voltages do not add up to the e.m.f. of the supply.

(Oxford Local Examinations, Q12, Paper I, June 1981

8. The circuit elements shown in Fig. 15.60 are in resonance when supplied with a signal of voltage 250 V r.m.s. at a frequency 600 Hz. Determine

(a) the reactance of the inductor at resonance,

(b) the reactance of the capacitor at resonance,

(c) the capacitance of the capacitor,

(d) the current in the circuit at resonance.

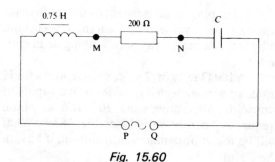

Fig. 15.60

What are the phase relationships between the potential differences across each of the three components in the above circuit and the supply voltage?

What is the value of the voltage existing between points P and N? Describe the phase of this voltage relative to the current.

Explain why in a practical tuned circuit, the series resistance is made as small as possible.

If the resistance of the circuit above were reduced to 20 Ω, what would be the percentage increase in the voltage between points P and N?

(University of London, Q14, Paper 2, June 1981)

9. How would you make the following changes occur for voltage pulses?

(a) A sinusoidal voltage signal to a square wave signal.

(b) A square wave signal to a series of sharp blips.

(c) A sinusoidal signal to a series of sharp blips.

10. (a)

(i) Explain the origin of holes in intrinsic semiconducting materials. What is the process by which holes participate in current flow?

(ii) Explain how the presence of the donor impurities in an n-type semiconducting material raises the number of free electrons per unit volume without increasing the number of mobile holes per unit volume.

(b) Figure 15.61 shows two kinds of semiconducting material, p-type and n-type, in contact. What is the important characteristic which distinguishes the depletion layer from the rest of the assembly?

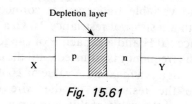

Fig. 15.61

Explain the effect on the depletion layer of applying a small potential difference (about 0.1 V) across XY

(i) if X becomes negative with respect to Y,
(ii) if X becomes positive with respect to Y.

Hence explain the rectifying action of a p–n junction.

(c) Figure 15.62 shows a half-wave rectifying circuit connected to a resistor R through a switch

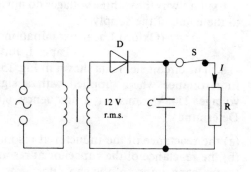

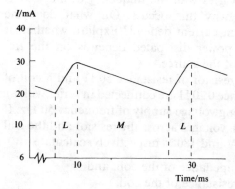

Fig. 15.62

S. The graph shows how the current I in resistor R varies with time.

Write down the source of the current in R

(i) during the period L,
(ii) during the period M.

Calculate the maximum reverse bias potential difference the diode, D, must be capable of withstanding when the switch, S, is open.

(University of London, Q15,
Paper 2, June 1984)

11. (a) By considering energy levels in a solid explain the difference between conductors, semiconductors and insulators.

(b) Explain the difference between the effects of a temperature rise on a semiconductor compared with that on a conductor such as copper.

(c) Explain the meaning of

(i) intrinsic conduction and
(ii) extrinsic conduction. What do you understand by
(iii) donor impurities and
(iv) acceptor impurities?

(d) What are meant by p-type and n-type materials? Describe the action of a p–n junction.

(AEB, QB16, Paper 3, November 1982)

12. (a) Explain, with the aid of suitable diagrams, how a potential barrier comes to exist across a semiconductor p–n junction.

By means of appropriate circuit diagrams, show how a p–n junction can be

(i) forward biased, and
(ii) reverse biased.

State in which of these situations the diode will conduct.

(b) The graph in Fig. 15.63b (page 320) shows how the output potential difference from the amplifier varies as the input potential difference is altered.

(i) Describe an arrangement (giving a circuit diagram) for producing a continuously variable 0–6 V d.c. potential difference to use as the input to the amplifier.
(ii) Over what range of input potential difference does the graph indicate that

(1) a 6-V output is produced, and

(2) a constant low output is produced?

(iii) Figure 15.63c shows a sinusoidally varying potential difference which is applied to the input of the amplifier. Use the graph of Fig. 15.63b to construct the waveform of the output potential difference. Also draw the output potential difference that would result if 3.0 V were added at every point to the input potential difference shown in Fig. 15.63c.
(iv) Over what range of input potential difference could this amplifier be used to produce distortionless amplification? If an input signal voltage varying between −0.25 V and +0.25 V is to be accurately amplified, what d.c. voltage would it be necessary to add to the input?

(University of London, Q13,
Paper 2, January 1982)

13. Figure 15.64 (page 321) is of a very simple radio receiver which can be used for broadcasts from one station only.

(a) The tuning circuit selects one station (one frequency). Is the output of energy of the selected signal coming from the tuning circuit greater than the energy of the signal collected by the aerial? Explain your answer briefly.

(b) For which of the other three boxes is the energy of the output signal larger than the energy of the input signal to the box? Give the name of the box or boxes for which there is an energy increase.

(c) How could the tuning circuit be altered so that it could select other stations?

(d) Which box or boxes is/are designed to transform energy from one form to another?

(e) The frequency of the signal received at the aerial is about 10^6 Hz, and the frequency of the speaker output is about 10^3 Hz. Would it matter if the amplifier could only amplify signals of 10^6 Hz? Explain your answer.

(Oxford and Cambridge Board, Nuffield,
Short answer paper, 1970)

14. (a) Draw a clear labelled diagram showing the essential features of a single beam cathode ray oscilloscope tube.

Explain, without giving circuit details, how the brightness and focusing of the electron beam are controlled.

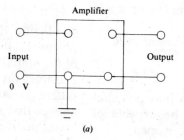

Amplifier

Input

0 V

Output

(a)

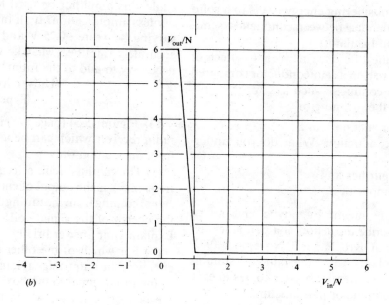

(b)

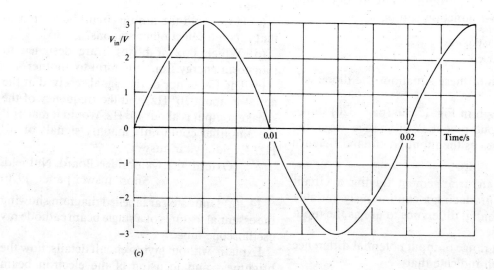

(c)

Fig. 15.63

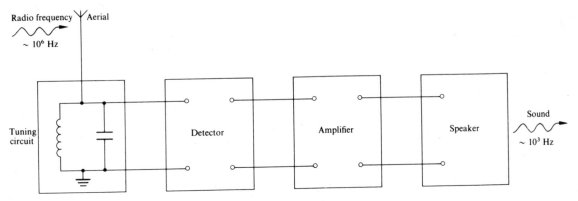

Fig. 15.64

(b) What is the time base in an oscilloscope? Sketch a graph showing the variation of time base voltage with time.

(c) How would you use an oscilloscope, the time base of which is not calibrated, to measure the frequency of a sinusoidal potential difference which is of the order of 80 Hz?

(d) With the time base disconnected, two alternating potential differences of the same frequency are applied to the X and Y plates respectively, the gains being equal. Figure 15.65 shows the appearance of the trace on the screen. The potentials may be represented by $x = a \sin \omega t$ and $y = a \sin (\omega t + \phi)$. What is the value of ϕ, the

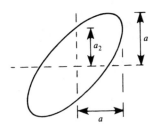

Fig. 15.65

phase angle between the potentials? Explain your reasoning.

(University of London, Q14, Paper 2, January 1980)

Part 4
Matter

Part 4
Matter

16 Solids, liquids and gases

The structure of crystals

Crystals have smooth flat faces and all the crystals of a particular substance have the same basic form, whether they be large or small. This led Wollaston in 1813 to the idea of crystals being made up of 'basic building blocks' (atoms) stacked together in an orderly manner.

Suppose we examine the forms of piles of stacked spheres. Figures 16.1a and b show two possible sequences. In (i) we start off with the spheres packed, on one plane, as close together as possible. In (ii) we place on top of the first layer, called layer A, another layer of spheres. These are placed so that their centres rest over the voids in the lower layer. This gives a stable arrangement. This second layer we call layer B. In (iii) we have two different ways of stacking the next layer. In part a of the diagram we have placed another layer identical in placing to the first layer, layer A. This thus gives a layer sequence of ABA. In part b of the diagram the spheres have been placed in a different stable arrangement. This gives a layer called C. The arrangement is thus ABC. These two arrangements can be repeated to give large structures,

ABABABABABABABABABA . . .

and ABCABCABCABCABC . . .

The first gives a structure known as hexagonal close-packing (Fig. 16.2) and the second a face-centred cubic structure (Fig. 16.3).

How can we check whether these arrangements exist in solids? X-ray, or electron, diffraction methods enable us first of all to determine that there is an orderly structure in a particular solid and then to measure the various interatomic spacing distances.

X-ray diffraction

X-rays have wavelengths comparable with the interatomic spacings in crystals and reflect from layers of atoms like light reflecting from a mirror. However, X-rays reflect from each layer of atoms in a crystal and so there are many reflected beams. These reflected beams interfere with each other and only at certain angles do the reflected beams constructively interfere and give a reflected beam, for a particular wavelength. At other angles destructive interference occurs and there is no reflection.

The planes of atoms act like mirrors behave with light. Thus for each plane we have an image of the X-ray source. Interference occurs between the waves which apparently originate at these images. The path difference between the waves from successive images is $2d \sin \theta$ (see Fig. 16.4). Thus the condition for constructive interference is

$$2d \sin \theta = m\lambda \quad \text{(Bragg equation)}$$

where d is the spacing between the planes of atoms, θ the angle between the atomic plane and

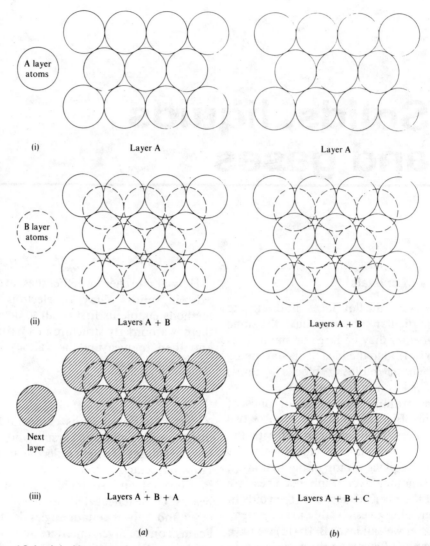

(i)   Layer A   Layer A

A layer atoms

B layer atoms

(ii)   Layers A + B   Layers A + B

Next layer

(iii)   Layers A + B + A   Layers A + B + C

(a)   (b)

Fig. 16.1 (a) Hexagonal close-packed structure. (b) Face-centred cubic structure

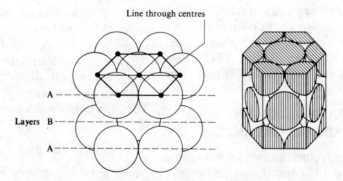

Line through centres

A

Layers   B

A

Fig. 16.2 Hexagonal close-packed structure

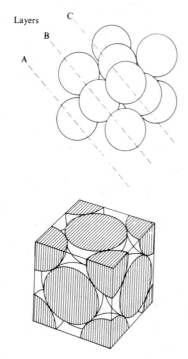

Fig. 16.3   Face-centred cubic structure

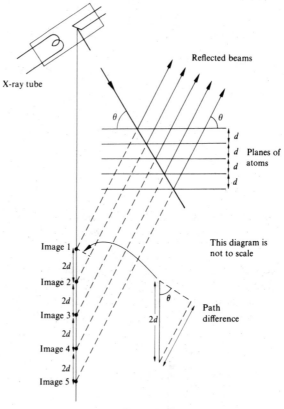

Fig. 16.4

the incident (or reflected) X-rays, λ the wavelength of the X-rays and *m* an integer, i.e., 0, 1, 2, 3, etc.

Measurements of the angles at which reflections occur, θ, and use of the Bragg equation enable values for the spacings between the layers of atoms in a solid to be determined. All the ways of packing atoms give rise to many planes of atoms. Figure 16.5a shows some of the possible planes for the hexagonal close-packed structure. We can calculate the various spacings between the planes in terms of the distance between atom centres. For a hexagonal close-packed structure we have planes with spacings of

$$a, \frac{a}{\sqrt{4/3}}, \frac{a}{2}, \frac{a}{\sqrt{8}}, \frac{a}{\sqrt{28/3}}, \text{etc}$$

For a simple cubic array (Fig. 16.5b) the spacings are

$$a, \frac{a}{\sqrt{2}}, \frac{a}{\sqrt{3}}, \frac{a}{\sqrt{4}}, \frac{a}{\sqrt{5}}, \text{etc}$$

For a face-centred cubic array we have

$$a, \frac{a}{\sqrt{3}}, \frac{a}{\sqrt{4}}, \frac{a}{\sqrt{8}}, \frac{a}{\sqrt{11}}, \frac{a}{\sqrt{12}}, \text{etc.}$$

By examining the spacing results from the X-ray diffraction picture we can establish the nature of the atomic packing.

For example, sodium chloride is a face-centred cubic; as also are copper, gold, and lead. Solid helium is hexagonal close-packed; as also are magnesium, zinc, and calcite.

X-ray diffraction patterns

Figure 16.6 shows the results that are obtained when a beam of X-rays, not monochromatic, is directed at different materials. A single sodium chloride crystal gives rise to a number of discrete

327

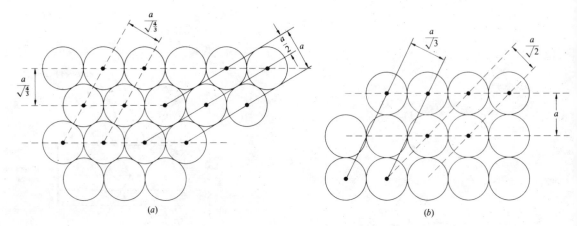

Fig. 16.5 *(a) Some of the possible planes of atoms in a hexagonal close-packed structure. (b) Some of the possible planes of atoms in a simple cubic array*

reflections (Fig. 16.6b). Each reflection corresponds to X-rays hitting layers of atoms in the crystal at the right angle to give a Bragg reflection for the wavelength concerned. Pyrex glass, Fig. 16.6c, does not, however, give rise to any regular reflections. The conclusion we are led to is that the atoms in the glass are not packed together in an orderly manner. Only orderly packing can give

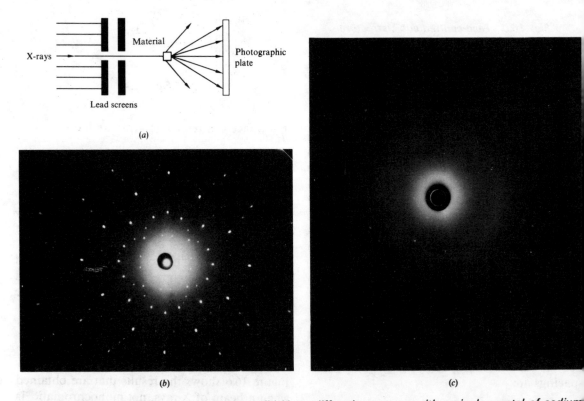

Fig. 16.6 *(a) X-ray diffraction arrangement. (b) X-ray diffraction pattern with a single crystal of sodium chloride (Miss P. Mondal, Department of Crystallography, Birkbeck College, University of London). (c) X-ray diffraction pattern with 'Pyrex' glass (Pilkington Brothers Ltd, Research and Development Laboratory)*

328

rise to planes of constant separation which will give Bragg reflections.

Many materials are polycrystalline, i.e., they consist of a 'jumble' of small crystals rather than a single large crystal. Metals are polycrystalline. When X-rays are incident on polycrystalline materials, Bragg reflections occur for those crystal planes of atoms that are at the right angle for the wavelength and thus, as Fig. 16.7 illustrates, rings of reflected rays occur. The larger the crystals the more broken the rings, the smaller the crystals the more continuous. Figure 16.8

Fig. 16.8 Electron diffraction patterns for white tin crystals deposited on a film of silicon monoxide. The wavelength was 0.04×10^{-10} m (100 keV electrons). (a) Average crystal size 600×10^{-10} m. (b) Average crystal size 200×10^{-10} m. (Berkeley Physics Course Vol. 4, Quantum Physics, E. H. Wichman, McGraw-Hill Book Company. Copyright Educational Development Centre)

shows electron diffraction patterns (the wavelengths are similar to X-rays) for polycrystalline tin.

Types of solids

Solids can be divided into two groups: crystalline and amorphous. In the crystalline solids the atoms are arranged in a regular way, in an amorphous solid there is little regularity—certainly not the long-range regularity that occurs in crystalline solids.

Metals are crystalline, generally consisting of a large number of crystals, polycrystalline. A particularly easy surface in which to see crystals is that of galvanized buckets or pipes.

Glasses, polymers, and rubbers are all generally amorphous. They are made up of long molecules which during solidification become tangled. X-ray diffraction photographs do not show the many sharp rings or dots which are characteristic of crystals and long-range order but show only a few diffuse rings or spots, indicating only short-range order.

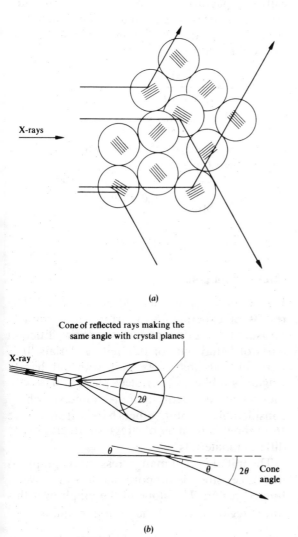

Fig. 16.7 X-ray diffraction. (a) Two-dimensional view. (b) Three-dimensional view

Stretching and compressing materials

When a spring fixed to a rigid support at one end has a force F applied to the other end it extends. If the extension is proportional to the force F the spring is said to obey Hooke's law. Figure 16.9 shows the type of graph that might be produced.

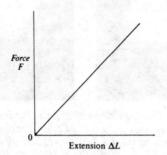

Fig. 16.9   A material obeying Hooke's law

A similar experiment can be done on the stretching of wires and a similar relationship and graph obtained. We can represent this relationship by the equation

$$F = k \, \Delta L$$

where F is the applied force, ΔL the change in length and k a constant, called the force constant. The value of k depends on the material used, its length and its cross-sectional area.

Stress and strain

When you pull a length of rubber it gets longer. On what factors does the change in length depend? A simple experiment for investigating the possible variables involves a length of rubber of uniform cross-sectional area held vertical with the upper end in a clamp and the lower end attached to weights. With a constant weight, doubling the length of the rubber doubles the extension; the extension seems to be proportional to the length of the sample. A constant force, load, produces a constant value of extension/original length. This is called the strain.

$$\text{Strain} = \frac{\text{extension}}{\text{length}}$$

Doubling the cross-sectional area of the rubber,

with both the length and weight constant, halves the extension. The extension is inversely proportional to the area. With double the area, $2A$, we can obtain the same extension as for area A if we double the weight. A constant extension is produced by a constant value of force/area. This is called stress.

$$\text{Stress} = \frac{\text{force}}{\text{area}}$$

We can repeat the experiment with other materials and find the same relationships.

Stress has the unit of N m^{-2}, such a unit being called the pascal (Pa). Strain, since it is a ratio, has no units. Thus if we stretch a copper wire with a cross-sectional area of 1.00 mm^2 with a force of 100 N, the stress is

$$\text{Stress} = \frac{100}{1.0 \times 10^{-6}}$$

$$= 1.0 \times 10^8 \text{ N m}^{-2} = 1.0 \times 10^8 \text{ Pa}$$

If a 1.2 metre length of copper wire extends by 2.0 mm then the strain is

$$\text{Strain} = \frac{2.0 \times 10^{-3}}{1.2}$$

$$= 1.7 \times 10^{-3}$$

Stress–strain graphs

How does the strain depend on the stress? The results of experiments in which the strain is measured for different stresses show different types of behaviour for different materials. It is fairly obvious that if we pull, with our hands, lengths of rubber, copper, steel, plastics, glass, etc., they stretch different amounts. Some stretch by considerable amounts, others barely at all. Figure 16.10 shows a number of stress–strain graphs for different materials.

The initial part of many stress–strain graphs is linear, i.e., stress is proportional to strain over a limited region. The slope of the graph over this linear region is called the Young modulus.

$$\text{Young modulus } E = \frac{\text{stress}}{\text{strain}}$$

The Young modulus has the unit of Pa. Typical values of this modulus are:

Young Modulus/10^{10} Pa

Steel (mild)	21	
Steel (stainless)	22	
Iron (cast)	15	
Lead	2	
Glass (crown)	7	
Wood (spruce)	1.2	along the grain
	0.06	at right angles to grain
Nylon	0.2	
Rubber	0.0007	

A low value for the Young modulus means a material which extends a lot for small stresses. If we pull or flex a strip of rubber and then a strip of steel between our hands we can easily tell the difference between the low modulus rubber and the high modulus steel. The modulus can be taken as a measure of the stiffness of a material.

A vertically suspended brass wire of length 1.2 m and cross-sectional area 0.10 mm² stretches by 0.30 mm when a load of 0.28 kg is attached to its lower end. If Hooke's law is obeyed, what is the value of the Young modulus?

$$E = \frac{\text{stress}}{\text{strain}} = \frac{(F/A)}{(\Delta L/L)} = \frac{FL}{A\Delta L}$$

$$= \frac{0.28 \times 9.8 \times 1.2}{0.10 \times 10^{-6} \times 0.30 \times 10^{-3}}$$

$$= 1.1 \times 10^{11} \text{ Pa}$$

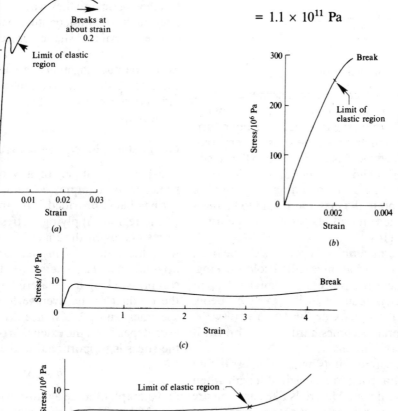

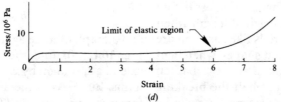

Fig 16.10 *Stress–strain graphs (the axes not the same for each graph). (a) Steel; (b) cast iron; (c) polythene; (d) rubber*

Consider a steel wire 0.80 m long and a copper wire 1.4 m long, each of cross-sectional area 0.10 mm^2, joined end to end and stretched with a tension of 400 N. If Young's modulus is 2.1×10^{11} Pa for steel and 1.3×10^{11} Pa for copper, what will be the elongation of each wire?

Each wire can be considered to be separately under a tension of 400 N, hence since

$$E = \frac{(F/A)}{(\Delta L/L)} = \frac{FL}{A\Delta L}$$

for steel, $\Delta L = \dfrac{400 \times 0.80}{0.10 \times 10^{-6} \times 2.1 \times 10^{11}}$

$= 0.015 \text{ m} = 15 \text{ mm}$

for copper, $\Delta L = \dfrac{400 \times 1.4}{0.10 \times 10^{-6} \times 1.3 \times 10^{11}}$

$0.043 \text{ m} = 43 \text{ mm}$

Ductile and brittle behaviour

There is another factor which determines how a material behaves when stressed—the value of the stress beyond which the material does not return to its original length when the stress is removed, this being called the elastic limit. Up to the elastic limit a material shows no permanent deformation after loading and unloading (Fig. 16.11a). Beyond that point the material is said to be plastically deformed and suffers permanent deformation (Fig. 16.11b).

Stretching a material to beyond its elastic limit to produce a deformation is called cold working. In a manufacturing process this might happen when a sheet is reduced in thickness by being passed through a roller. One effect of this process is that the material becomes harder, more brittle. It is said to work harden.

Cast iron is almost at its breaking stress before it stops coming back to its original length when the stress is removed. Materials like cast iron are difficult to form into different shapes, when bent they do not retain the bent shape. Steel when stretched to more than about half the breaking strain becomes permanently deformed. A material like 'Plasticine' is permanently deformed at vir-

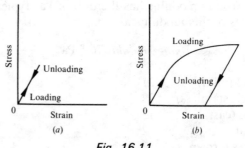

Fig. 16.11

tually all strains. 'Plasticine' can thus be easily shaped.

Cast iron is a brittle material. Such materials do not distort, or not significantly, before failure. A ductile material, like 'Plasticine', suffers considerable distortion before failure. A brittle material when broken can have the pieces all stuck back together again and they will fit. A ductile material after fracture cannot be stuck back together again to give the original shaped object. A china teacup is made of a brittle material; a car after a crash cannot be stuck together again to give the original car, steel is ductile. You can, however, hammer the material of the car back into shape, unlike the teacup.

Energy stored in strained material

If a piece of rubber, or any other material, is stretched or compressed and then released it springs back, provided it is stretched within its elastic region. Applying a stress to the material stores energy in the material, which is released when the material is allowed to spring back to its original size. The energy needed to stretch, or compress, a length of material by a distance Δx is the product of the average force acting on the specimen and the distance Δx. The force, however, depends on the extension of the specimen. If the stress is proportional to the strain we have

$$F \propto \Delta x$$

and a graph of force against extension looks like Fig. 16.12. To find the total energy needed to extend a specimen by x we must sum all the $F \Delta x$ terms. But $F \Delta x$ is the area of a strip below the force–extension graph. Therefore the total energy will be the total area under the graph between

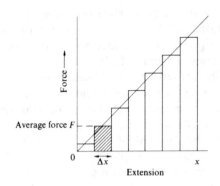

Fig. 16.12

extension being equal to zero and equal to x.

$$\text{Energy} = \tfrac{1}{2}Fx$$

If the cross-sectional area of the specimen is A and its length L then we can write the equation as

$$\frac{\text{Energy}}{AL} = \frac{1}{2}\frac{F}{A}\frac{x}{L}$$

or

Energy per unit volume = ½(stress)(strain)

This is the energy needed to extend or compress the specimen and if we assume that all this energy is stored in the sample, then the energy stored in unit volume of the specimen is half the product of the stress and the strain. As stress/strain equals the Young modulus, E, the energy stored per unit volume can be expressed as

$$\text{Energy/volume} = \tfrac{1}{2}(\text{stress})^2/E$$

Interatomic forces in a crystalline solid

The atoms in a solid are held together by interatomic forces. We can picture them as small springs linking the atoms. If we stretch a spring we find a linear relationship between the force and the extension, provided the spring does not become overstretched and deformed. We can write

$$F = k\,\Delta x$$

where F is the force, Δx the extension and k a constant we can call the stiffness or force

constant. Suppose we assume that we can apply the same relationship to atoms in a solid: if we displace an atom by a distance Δx from another atom then a force F is needed and F is directly proportional to Δx.

For simplicity we will consider a solid in which the atoms are in a simple cubic array, Fig. 6.13. Stretching increases the separation between two atoms by Δx, thus the force necessary to cause the stretching (also the force trying to restore the atoms to their original sites) is $k\,\Delta x$.

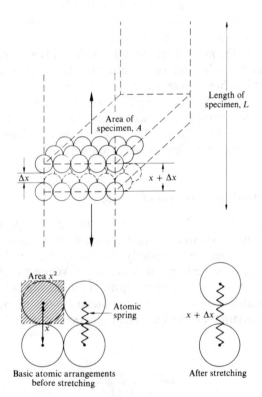

Basic atomic arrangements before stretching

After stretching

Fig. 16.13

If the cross-sectional area of the sample is A, there will be A/x^2 atoms with springs being stretched. Thus the total force involved is

$$\frac{A}{x^2}k\,\Delta x$$

The stress is therefore

$$\frac{k}{x^2}\Delta x$$

333

The strain is $\Delta x/x$. This is the strain for the entire specimen: we are assuming that every pair of planes has been separated by the same distance Δx. Thus

$$\text{Young modulus } E = \frac{\text{stress}}{\text{strain}}$$

$$E = \frac{k}{x}$$

If we assume that iron atoms are arranged in the cubic array then, as $E = 15 \times 10^{10}$ N m^{-2} and the spacing of the atoms is about 3×10^{10} m, the value of k is about 45 N m^{-1}.

In the above argument the material is assumed to be behaving in a perfectly elastic manner. What, however, happens if we have plastic deformation? We can explain this by considering entire planes of atoms to slip over one another (Fig. 16.14). The material is permanently deformed because the slippage is permanent.

Plastic deformation of metals

Metals are polycrystalline, i.e., they are composed of many small crystals. A crystal within a metal is just a region of orderly packed atoms, such a region being referred to as a grain. When a metal is stretched beyond its elastic limit, plastic deformation can occur with the metal becoming permanently deformed. When this occurs planes of atoms within a grain slide over other planes, as illustrated in Fig. 16.14. The planes along which such slip occurs are called slip planes. Because the planes of atoms within one grain do not line up with the planes in neighbouring grains the slip does not cross over from one grain to another. The size of the grains thus determines the amount of slip that can occur, the bigger the grains the greater the amount of slippage and hence the greater the amount of plastic deformation. A large grain arrangement within a metal thus makes it more ductile, a brittle material being one where the slip is confined to a very short run and not allowed to spread through the material.

When a material is cold worked, i.e., plastically deformed in the cold state, the grains become deformed owing to slippage within them. The ability to slip becomes reduced and the material becomes more brittle, the term used is work hardened.

If a metal is heated to a sufficiently high temperature (0.3–0.5 of the melting point temperature on the kelvin scale) recrystallization occurs with the atoms beginning to re-order themselves into new grains. The grains can grow bigger. The result is that the material becomes more ductile. The process is called annealing.

Dislocations

About 1920 A. A. Griffith investigated glass, in order to try and find an answer to the problem of why materials were much weaker than the theoretical reasoning indicated. He estimated that glass should have a breaking stress of about 10^{10} N m^{-2}. The glass he was using had a breaking stress of only about 10^8 N m^{-2}. However, he found that when he made very thin fibres he obtained much higher breaking stresses; fibres about 10^{-3} mm diameter having breaking stresses of about 3×10^9 N m^{-2}. Thin fibres were much nearer the theoretical value than bulk glass. The reason for this strange behaviour was cracks— very fine, almost invisible cracks. Thin fibres were less prone to damage and so had fewer cracks. It is now possible to produce very thin fibres of many materials and obtain very high breaking stresses. Herring and Galt in 1952

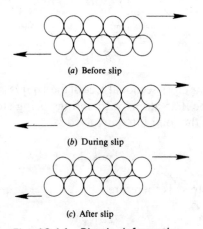

(a) Before slip

(b) During slip

(c) After slip

Fig. 16.14 Plastic deformation

produced the first high-strength metal fibres—they were called whiskers and were found growing from the surface of tin.

The low strength of metals is now ascribed to the presence of dislocations inside the metal. Figure 16.15 shows a diagram of a dislocation in a simple cubic crystal. G. I. Taylor in 1934 first thought of the idea but it was not until the 'fifties that convincing evidence for their existence was found. Dislocations are imperfections in the way the atoms are packed together in the solid.

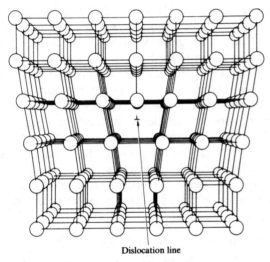

Dislocation line

Fig. 16.15 A dislocation

The structure of rubber

The diffraction photograph for rubber changes quite significantly when the rubber is stretched. Stretched rubber shows a significant amount of crystallinity; unstretched rubber shows very little, giving a pattern more like that of glass. The atomic arrangement in rubber is thought to change from a liquid-like state to a crystal state, i.e., a disordered state to an ordered state. The stress–strain graph for rubber (Fig. 16.10d) is much steeper at high strains than at low strains and corresponds more to the stiffness of a crystalline solid.

Rubber molecules are long chain molecules, in natural rubber basic units of C_5H_8 linked together in very long chains. In the unstretched state these

molecules are considered to be randomly orientated. When rubber is stretched these long molecules uncoil and so straighten. This is completely different from metals and other crystalline substances where stretching involves lengthening atomic bonds. It is because of this difference that we have the characteristic rubber-like elasticity—easily stretched, can be stretched to large strains, elastic behaviour. When the rubber molecule chains have been straightened then the stretching force has to extend interatomic bonds. The rubber is then like a crystal.

The structure of polymers

Polymers are materials composed of long-chain molecules. These long chains may be linear chains of molecules, chains with branches or a cross-linked array (Fig. 16.16). The chains may be completely tangled up with no order, such materials being called amorphous, or arranged in an orderly manner and called crystalline. Because long chains can easily become tangled up, polymers are often only partly crystalline.

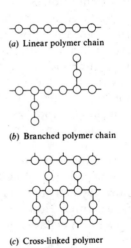

(a) Linear polymer chain

(b) Branched polymer chain

(c) Cross-linked polymer

Fig. 16.16 Idealized picture of polymer chains

The greater the degree of crystallinity in a polymer the stiffer the material, i.e., the higher the Young modulus. This is because an orderly packing of chains allows closer packing and forces of attraction between molecules in neighbouring chains become larger. Polythene, which has linear molecular chains, can show quite high crystallinity (linear chains are easier to pack together than chains with branches). Polythene with 95 per cent crystallinity has a Young modulus of about 21–38 kPa, whereas with 60 per cent crystallinity the modulus is only about 7–16 kPa.

When an amorphous polymer is heated it shows no definite melting point but progressively becomes less rigid. This is because there is no sharp transition between the disorderly arrangement in the solid and liquid, both are disorderly. With a crystalline polymer there is a transition between orderly and disorderly arrangement in melting and so there is a definite melting point.

Another important temperature which helps to define the useful temperature range of a polymer is the glass transition temperature. This is the temperature at which a polymer changes from a glass-like material, i.e., rigid, stiff, with a high Young modulus, to a rubber-like material, i.e., flexible, easily bent, with a low Young modulus. Above the glass transition temperature the polymer chains are reasonably free to move and the application of stretching forces causes the molecular chains to slide over one another and uncoil. Large extensions are thus possible with small forces. However, at temperatures below the glass transition temperature the density has increased to such an extent that the movement of the polymer chains is hindered and so the application of stretching forces produces little extension. Polythene has a glass transition temperature of $-120°C$.

A plastic teaspoon at room temperature is fairly rigid, being a polymer below its glass transition temperature. If you try to bend it it is likely to break in a brittle manner. However, if the spoon is put in boiling water it behaves quite differently, very little stress being required to bend it as it becomes very flexible. At this temperature the plastic is above its glass transition temperature.

Polythene is an example of what is termed a thermoplastic. Such polymers soften if heated and can be shaped, the shape being retained when the polymer cools. The process can be repeated any number of times. Polythene has linear chains. Thermosetting polymers, such as melamine and 'Bakelite', are, however, cross-

linked polymers. They are stronger and stiffer than thermoplastics and as they do not soften when heated cannot be shaped when hot. The cross-linking prevents movements of chains past each other and so makes for a very rigid structure.

The structure of glass

As the diffraction photograph for 'Pyrex' glass, Fig. 16.6c, indicates there is little order in the arrangement of atoms within glass. Glass has a relatively high Young modulus and is a rather brittle substance. This would indicate rather strong bonds between atoms and a considerable amount of linkage between the atoms in the solid. Glasses are produced when very viscous liquids solidify. The simplest glass is formed from silicon dioxide and the viscous nature of the liquid glass near solidification would seem to indicate that strong bonds are being formed between the silicon dioxide molecules even before the solid is formed. These bonds prevent the atoms in the liquid arranging themselves into the orderly crystal arrangement. Thus glass can be considered a network of linked silicon dioxide molecules.

Concrete and its reinforcement

Concrete has a very low tensile fracture stress, but a high compressive fracture stress, and thus has to be used in situations where the only stresses the concrete will experience are compressive. Reinforcement of concrete by steel rods does enable the concrete composite to carry greater tensile loads than would otherwise be possible with just the concrete alone. If, however, the reinforcement bars are put in tension in the concrete, they put the concrete into a permanent state of compression. When tensile stresses are applied to the pre-stressed concrete the concrete is not put into tension until the tensile stresses exceed the value of the compressive stresses built into the system. Such pre-stressed concrete gives a very useful building material.

To produce reinforced concrete steel bars have the wet concrete poured round them. When the concrete sets it shrinks and grips the bars firmly. When the beam is loaded there is thus no slip between the bars and the concrete. In a simple beam which is to be subject to bending loads the steel bars are placed in that part of the beam which would be subject to tensile forces (Fig. 16.17). The steel thus takes the tensile stresses and the concrete the compressive stresses.

Pre-stressed concrete is produced by running wires through the wet concrete. The wires are held under tension while the concrete sets. The tension is released after the concrete has set and the wire in endeavouring to revert to its original length puts the concrete in compression. Another way of achieving the same result is to place the wires in ducts in the concrete and apply the tension only when the concrete is set. In this last method the tension has to be maintained during the life of the beam and thus careful anchoring of the ends of the tensioned wire is necessary.

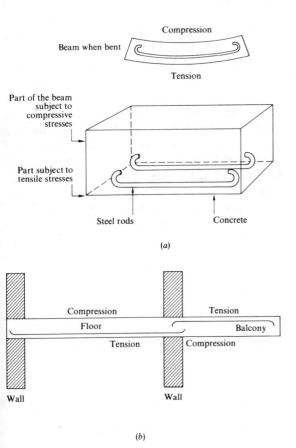

Fig. 16.17 (a) Reinforced concrete beam. (b) Reinforced concrete floor with cantilevered balcony

Composites

The term composite is used for a material composed of two different materials bonded together with one serving as a matrix surrounding fibres or particles of the other. Reinforced concrete is an obvious example, a matrix of concrete surrounding steel rods. Concrete itself, without the reinforcement is a composite, consisting of gravel (aggregate) in a matrix of cement. Wood is a natural composite with tubes of cellulose bonded in a matrix of a natural polymer called lignin. Reinforced plastics often consist of glass fibres in a polymer matrix.

The effect of fibres or particles in another material is to increase the tensile strength and also the Young modulus.

Laminates

Laminated materials are products obtained by bonding two or more sheets of material together. Plywood and corrugated cardboard are examples. Plywood consists of two thin sheets of wood with their grain directions at right angles to each other. Whereas the unbonded sheet had properties which were highly directional the laminate has non-directional properties—think of bending such sheets.

The structure of liquids

X-ray diffraction photographs for liquids (Fig. 16.18) show some diffuse maxima indicative of some degree of order among the molecules in a liquid. Suppose instead of packing spheres together in a careful well-ordered array, as with solids, we toss the spheres into a container and let them take up their positions completely by chance; does this give sufficient order to conform with the X-ray diffraction evidence? In a hexagonal close-packed solid each sphere is in contact with twelve other spheres. In the random array each sphere is in contact with between four and eleven spheres, the number is not constant as is the case for the hexagonal packing. If we take a number of spheres and measure the different distances neighbouring spheres make from each of the spheres, we can obtain a graph of the radial distribution of spheres round a sphere. Figure 16.19

337

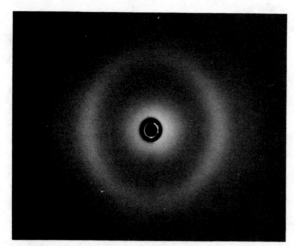

Fig. 16.18 X-ray diffraction photograph for water. (Pilkington Brothers Ltd, Research and Development Laboratory)

shows results of such measurements made by Bernal and Scott. The results are compared with the distribution forecast by the result of neutron diffraction; remarkably good agreement is obtained. The density of liquid argon is about 12 per cent less than that of solid argon; the random packing of the spheres gives a volume about 10 per cent greater than that obtained with close packing—again reasonable agreement.

In the solid we consider the atoms to remain in their positions, oscillating but not moving to new positions. In the liquid we must, however, consider our random arrangement to be just a snapshot of the arrangement at some instant, the molecules constantly shifting around but retaining the same radial distribution.

Surfaces

In a liquid we consider the molecules to be moving around, constantly interchanging positions. Why do those molecules moving near the edges of the liquid not all leave? Some leave (evaporation) but not generally all. The obvious answer would be to postulate a force of attraction between the molecules in the liquid. A drop of mercury on a clean glass surface, drops of water falling from a tap, all show a tendency to assume a spherical shape. A sphere has the minimum surface area—this would be consistent with an attractive force between molecules. The molecules in the surface are acted on by a force directed towards the molecules in the bulk of the liquid; the molecules in the bulk of the liquid are, on average, uniformly surrounded by other molecules and thus experience no net force. Thus the surface assumes the minimum area. A force acting on a molecule in the surface would tend therefore to pull the molecule into the bulk of the liquid—liquids, however, do not shrink to a vanishingly small point, there must therefore be another force which stop the molecules moving too close to one another. Liquids are not easily compressed, there are therefore strong repulsive forces resisting the movement of molecules closer together. The variation of force with distance between the centres of two molecules is thus likely to be of the form described by Fig. 16.20.

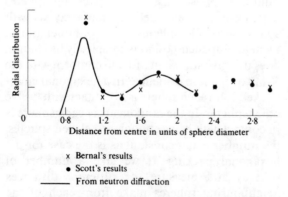

x   Bernal's results
•   Scott's results
———   From neutron diffraction

Fig. 16.19 Radial distribution for liquid argon. (D. Tabor (1969), Gases, Liquids and Solids, Penguin).

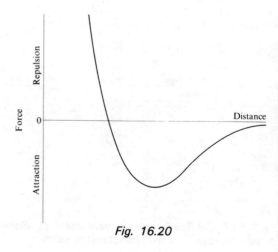

Fig. 16.20

Free surface energy and surface tension

Suppose we want to increase the surface of a liquid—we must push more molecules into the surface against the attractive forces between molecules. Energy is necessary to do this. A simple measurement of this energy is possible with liquids, like soap solutions, which form thin films. Figure 16.21 shows a simple wire frame containing a soap film. To increase the area a force must be applied. The energy needed, with no change in temperature, to produce unit area of a surface is called the free surface energy, σ.

$$\sigma = \frac{\text{energy to form a surface}}{\text{area of the surface formed}}$$

With the soap film the area produced is $2WL$, there are two surfaces to the film. The energy needed is FL. Thus

$$\sigma = \frac{FL}{2WL} = \frac{F}{2W}$$

F is the force parallel to the film surface which is necessary to keep the film extended at the increased area. We can think of this force being balanced by an opposite and equal force, a tension, within the liquid and parallel to its surface. The value of this force per unit length is called the surface tension, γ.

$$\gamma = \frac{F}{2W}$$

γ is thus equivalent to σ. This is provided there is no temperature change.

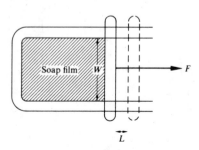

Fig. 16.21

Breaking intermolecular bonds

We can obtain a rough estimate of the energy needed to break an intermolecular bond from the surface energy value. When a new surface is created the molecules moved into that surface have had their number of near molecular neighbours reduced by a factor of two. Typically, the number of near neighbours may be reduced from ten to five. If n is the number of molecules per unit area of surface then $5n$ bonds are broken for each two unit areas of surface produced. If ε is the energy needed to break one bond then $5n\varepsilon/2$ is the energy needed to produce unit area of surface. Thus

$$\sigma = \frac{5n\varepsilon}{2}$$

If the effective radius of a molecule is r then

$$n = \frac{1}{\pi r^2}$$

Thus

$$\sigma = \frac{5\varepsilon}{2\pi r^2}$$

Thus for benzene: $\sigma = 0.029$ J m^{-2}, $r = 2.6 \times 10^{-10}$ m and we obtain for ε a value of 3.1×10^{-21} J or about 2×10^{-2} eV.

Bubbles

Blowing bubbles is a way of determining surface energies. When we blow a bubble under the surface of a liquid we are increasing the surface area between the liquid and air (plus the liquid's own vapour). Suppose the radius of the bubble increases by ΔR, the surface area will have increased from $4\pi R^2$ to $4\pi(R + \Delta R)^2$, the initial radius of the bubble being R.

Change in area = $4\pi(R^2 + 2R\,\Delta R + \Delta R^2) - 4\pi R^2$. If we neglect ΔR^2

$$\text{Change in area} = 8\pi R\,\Delta R$$

The energy needed to produce this increase in area will be

$$\text{Energy needed} = 8\pi R\sigma\,\Delta R$$

This energy must be supplied by pressure inside the bubble. If the pressure necessary for the bubble to exist at this radius is p, then as pressure is force per unit area, the force will be

$$\text{Force} = 4\pi R^2 p$$

This force pushes out the surface of the bubble by a distance ΔR, therefore the energy supplied is

$$\text{Energy supplied} = 4\pi R^2 p\,\Delta R$$

Thus if we neglect temperature changes produced by the change in area

$$4\pi R^2 p\,\Delta R = 8\pi R\,\Delta R\sigma$$

$$p = \frac{2\sigma}{R}$$

If we blow soap bubbles in air we produce two surfaces and thus for such bubbles

$$p = \frac{4\sigma}{R}$$

p is the amount by which the pressure inside the bubble is greater than the pressure in the surrounding liquid, or air in the case of soap bubbles.

Figure 16.22 shows the stages in the blowing of a bubble within a liquid. At the beginning the radius of the bubble is very large (a). Increasing the pressure decreases the radius of the surface (b). In c the bubble has become a hemisphere, its radius is a minimum at this point and thus the pressure a maximum. Any increase in pressure beyond this point causes the bubble to increase its radius; the pressure needed to maintain this larger radius is, however, less than the value for the hemispherical bubble. The condition is thus unstable and the bubble expands further, becomes more unstable, and either bursts or breaks away.

Capillary action

The pressure difference across a curved liquid surface has many consequences. If a narrow bore tube is dipped into water, the water rises up the tube (Fig. 16.23). The water surface inside the tube is almost a hemisphere, concave to the air. Thus the situation is like the bubble in the liquid—a curved surface means a pressure difference, the pressure being greater on the air side of this surface. The pressure at X is thus greater than that at Y by $2\sigma/R$, where R is the radius of curvature of the liquid surface and the tube radius. But the pressure at X must be the same as that at Z, i.e., the atmospheric pressure. Therefore the pressure at Y must be below atmospheric pressure. Y cannot remain on the same level as Z, Fig. 16.23a, because the pressure difference between Z and Y will force the liquid up the tube. The liquid will go up the tube until the pressure at W is the same as that at Z (Fig. 16.23b).

Pressure at W due to the liquid column $= h\rho g$

This must be equal to the pressure difference produced by the curvature of the liquid surface.

$$h\rho g = \frac{2\sigma}{R}$$

Hence

$$h = \frac{2\sigma}{R\rho g}$$

The above derivation assumes that the angle of contact between the liquid and the tube is zero, as is the case with clean water and clean glass. The

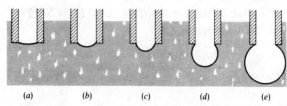

(a)   (b)   (c)   (d)   (e)

Fig. 16.22   Stages in the blowing of a bubble

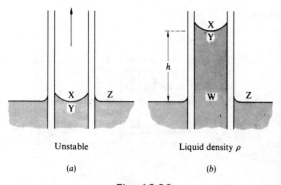

Unstable   Liquid density ρ

(a)   (b)

Fig. 16.23

angle of contact θ is the angle between the tangent planes to the two surfaces, measured through the liquid (Fig. 16.24). If θ is not zero

$$H = \frac{2\sigma\cos\theta}{R\rho g}$$

When $\theta < 90°$, h is positive; $\theta = 90°$, h is zero; $\theta > 90°$, h is negative.

Fig. 16.24   Angle of contact

Liquids spreading over surfaces

Consider a drop of liquid resting on a horizontal surface (Fig. 16.25). If the drop spreads a little farther over the solid surface the area of liquid–solid interface has been increased. Suppose the increase in area to be ΔA. Solids have surface energies and thus as we have reduced the area of exposed solid surface by ΔA we have decreased (released) the energy associated with the solid surface by $\sigma_{SV}\,\Delta A$. The symbol σ_{SV} is used for the surface energy of the solid when in contact with its own vapour. The spreading liquid has increased the solid–liquid interface area by ΔA and thus if we consider σ_{SL} to be the energy needed to form unit area of such an interface, the energy increase

needed is $\sigma_{SL}\,\Delta A$. The spreading drop will also have increased the surface area of the liquid–vapour surface. The increase in area is $\Delta A \cos\theta$, where θ is the contact angle. Thus the energy increase needed is $\sigma_{LV}\Delta A \cos\theta$. The net change in energy is thus

$$\sigma_{SL}\,\Delta A + \sigma_{LV}\,\Delta A \cos\theta - \sigma_{SV}\,\Delta A$$

If spreading the liquid farther over the surface produces a net energy release, then spreading will occur. The spreading will continue until no change in energy occurs, i.e., when

$$\sigma_{SL} + \sigma_{LV}\cos\theta = \sigma_{SV}$$

The equation for the spreading of liquids over solid surfaces has many implications. An adhesive if it is to be of any use must spread over the surfaces to be glued together. For spreading to occur we must have

$$\sigma_{SV} > \sigma_{SL} + \sigma_{LV}\cos\theta$$

Solids with low surface energies are difficult to stick together. For example, 'Teflon', with a surface energy of about 0.018 J m^{-2} presents considerable difficulties. Most metals have surface energies of the order of 1 J m^{-2}, about 60 times larger than that of 'Teflon'.

Water runs off a duck's back. Here we have a case where it would be disastrous if the liquid, water, spread over the surface, feathers. Similarly for a water beetle skimming over the surface of a pond, the water must not spread over the surface of the beetle. To remove grease from clothes or dishes we add a detergent to the washing water. The effect of the detergent is to increase the angle of contact between the grease and the material so that it no longer spreads over it but rolls up into globules.

Measurement of surface tension

There are three main methods used for the measurement of the surface tension (free surface energy) of liquids.

1. The chemical balance method

A wire ring is dipped into the liquid and the force required to pull it free from the liquid measured

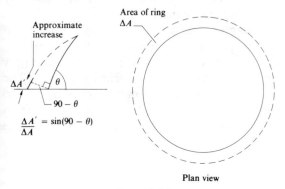

Fig. 16.25

by some form of balance. The length of the liquid–solid boundary is $2(2\pi r)$, where r is the mean radius of the ring (Fig. 16.26). Hence the force measured equals $2(2\pi r)\gamma$.

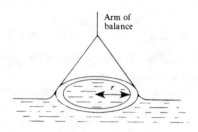

Fig. 16.26 Ring method

2. Capillary rise method

The height to which a liquid rises up a capillary tube is measured. If the angle of contact between the liquid and tube is $0°$, as for clean water with a clean glass surface, then $\gamma = hR\ \rho g/2$. R is the radius of the tube at the meniscus level and can be measured by using a vernier microscope to determine the internal diameter at this point when the tube is broken.

3. Jaeger's method

Figure 16.27 shows the form of the apparatus. As the water drips into the large vessel, air is forced out and bubbles formed in the liquid under test.

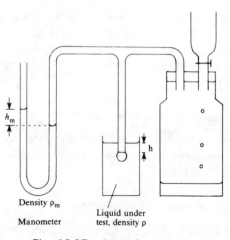

Density ρ_m
Manometer
Liquid under test, density ρ

Fig. 16.27 Jaeger's method

Figure 16.22 shows the stages in the blowing of a bubble. The bubble radius initially is very large, and so the pressure indicated by the manometer is low. As the bubble grows its radius decreases, the pressure then growing. When the bubble is hemispherical, i.e., having a radius equal to that of the internal radius R of the tube from which it is blown, the radius is a minimum and so the pressure a maximum. As the bubble grows larger its radius increases and so the pressure drops. The maximum reading of the manometer h_m is determined. The maximum pressure is then $(h_m\rho_m - h\rho)g$. Hence since this equals $2\gamma/R$ the surface tension can be determined. This method can be used to determine the variation of surface tension with temperature.

Viscosity

Knock over a cup of water and the water soon flows out of the overturned cup. Knock over a cup of treacle and quite an appreciable time elapses before the treacle all flows out. We say that treacle is more viscous than water. We can regard the pouring as a sliding of layers of liquid molecules over one another—it seems easier to slide water molecules over one another than treacle molecules over one another.

Figure 16.28 shows the type of results obtained when a liquid flows near a wall. The layer of liquid at the surface of the wall does not move. The layers of liquid well away from the wall move with constant speed. A velocity gradient is created by the presence of the wall; this gradient exists in what is called the boundary layer. The velocity gradient is almost constant within the boundary layer. The bigger the velocity gradient the bigger the drag experienced by the wall. The liquid flowing past the wall tries to pull the wall with it. The force necessary to keep the wall stationary depends on the size of the velocity gradient. The drag force also depends on the area of the wall in contact with the liquid. The drag will differ from liquid to liquid. Newton defined a coefficient of viscosity η in terms of the velocity gradient.

$$F = \eta A\ \frac{dv}{dx}$$

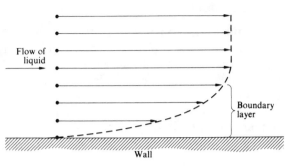

Fig. 16.28 *Distances covered by particles of fluid in the same time*

where F is the drag force, A, the surface area and dv/dx the velocity gradient. Fluids which obey this are known as Newtonian fluids. Many liquids encountered in daily life do not obey this relationship, the viscosity depending on the applied stress, e.g., a paint which can be brushed on easily but does not drip.

Stokes' law

An air bubble rising through water, dust particles falling through air, objects falling through fluids, are all experiencing viscous drag forces. If there is a relative velocity between an object and a fluid then there will be viscous drag. In 1846 Sir George Stokes derived a relationship for the drag on an object in a fluid:

Drag force $\propto$ (velocity) $\times$ (viscosity) $\times$ (size)

In the case of a sphere this becomes

Drag force $= 6\pi\eta rv$

where r is the sphere radius, v the velocity of the sphere and η the coefficient of viscosity of the medium in which the sphere is moving.

A ball falling freely in a vacuum accelerates, with a constant acceleration, over its entire path. The force causing such a ball to accelerate is mg, where m is the mass and g the acceleration due to gravity. In a fluid another force will act on the object—viscous drag. As the viscous drag is proportional to the velocity its value will increase as the object accelerates from rest. At some value

the force on the object will balance and there will be no net force to cause any further acceleration. The object will then continue its motion with a constant velocity. This is called the terminal velocity. For the ball this will occur when

$$m'g = 6\pi\eta rv$$

where m' is the mass of the sphere in the fluid. This will be less than its value in a vacuum, giving to the upthrust exerted on the sphere due to its immersion in a fluid.

$$m'g = mg - V\rho g$$

where V is the volume of the object and ρ the density of the fluid.

Raindrops falling in air or air bubbles rising in liquid columns might be expected to obey Stokes' law. Because the raindrops and air bubbles are deformed by their motion through the fluid, the law is only valid for very small diameter drops or bubbles, where the deformation is very small.

Further reading

A. H. Shapiro. *Shape and Flow*, Heinemann Science Study Series, No. 20.

Ideal gases

Experiments with fixed amounts of many common gases such as oxygen and nitrogen (or air) show that their behaviour can be described by a number of laws.

1. Boyle's law

If the temperature of the gas is constant then the pressure p is inversely proportional to the volume V, i.e.

$$pV = \text{a constant}$$

2. Charles' law

The volume of a given mass of gas, at constant pressure, increases by $1/273$ of its value at $0°C$, for every degree rise in temperature, i.e.

$$V - V_0 = (1/273)V_0\theta$$

343

MATTER

where V_0 is the volume at 0°C and V at temperature θ. This can be rearranged to give

$$V = V_0 (1 + (1/273)\theta)$$

The (1/273) per °C is the cubic expansivity of the gas at constant pressure. An alternative way of expressing this equation, and hence Charles' law, involves changing the temperature scale to one where 273 is added to θ (the Kelvin scale).

$$V = \frac{V_0(273 + \theta)}{273}$$

$$\frac{V}{273 + \theta} = \frac{V_0}{273}$$

$$\frac{V}{T} = \text{a constant}$$

If the pressure is constant for a fixed mass of gas, the volume is directly proportional to the temperature T on the Kelvin scale.

3. Pressure law

The pressure of a given mass of gas, at constant volume, increases by 1/273 of its value at 0°C, for every degree rise in temperature. Thus, as for Charles' law:

$$p = p_0(1 + (1/273)\theta)$$

or

$$\frac{p}{T} = \text{a constant}$$

In the above discussions the question of defining a temperature scale has not been addressed. At one time the temperature scale, the ideal gas scale, was defined by the above gas laws. If this definition is accepted then the Charles' and Pressure laws are consequences of the definition and not experimental facts. Chapter 17 discusses temperature scales in more detail.

We can combine the above three laws in a single equation:

$$\frac{pV}{T} = \text{a constant}$$

Gases which obey this equation are called ideal gases.

Ideal gas constant

The value of the constant in pV/T = a constant depends on the mass of gas considered and which gas. The constant has, however, the same value for all 'ideal' gases if we consider one mole of a gas. One mole is the amount of substance which contains the same number of elementary entities as there are atoms in 12 grammes of the carbon-12 isotope. For hydrogen this is 2 g, for oxygen 32 g.

For one mole

$$\frac{pV}{T} = R_0 \text{ or } pV = R_0T$$

where R_0 is the universal gas constant, 8.31 J mol^{-1} K^{-1}. The equation is known as an equation of state.

If we have μ moles of the gas the equation becomes

$$pV = \mu R_0 T$$

In other words, for 2 moles the constant is doubled, for 3 moles trebled, etc.

If we have a mass m, in grammes, of a gas of relative molecular mass M then, since the relative molecular mass is the mass, in grammes, of one mole of the substance, we have m/M moles and so

$$pV = \frac{m}{M} R_0 T$$

The quantity R_0/M is sometimes referred to as the specific gas constant R, hence $pV = mRT$.

To illustrate a possible use of such equations, consider a gas cylinder containing 1.2×10^{-2} m^3 of oxygen at 300 K and a pressure of 2.5×10^5 Pa. If after use the pressure drops to 1.5×10^5 Pa, what was the mass of gas used?

The relative molecular mass of oxygen is 32 g, hence we have, given R_0 = 8.31 J mol^{-1} K^{-1}

$$pV = \frac{m}{M} R_0 T$$

Initially $m = \dfrac{2.5 \times 10^5 \times 1.2 \times 10^{-2} \times 32}{8.31 \times 300}$

Finally $m' = \dfrac{1.5 \times 10^5 \times 1.2 \times 10^{-2} \times 32}{8.31 \times 300}$

Thus mass used $= m - m'$

$$= 15.4 \text{ g}$$

Note that the answer is in grammes since the relative molecular mass is in grammes.

Simple kinetic theory

Simple kinetic theory is an attempt to apply the laws of mechanics to gas molecules in order to explain their macroscopic properties, e.g., the ideal gas laws. A simple model of a gas is postulated:

1. A gas consists of small particles called molecules.
2. There are large numbers of these molecules in any gas sample we consider.
3. The molecules are in constant, random motion. Because of this and because we are dealing with such large numbers, there are as many molecules travelling in one direction as in any other.
4. The volume of the gas molecules is negligible compared with the volume occupied by the gas, i.e., most of a gas is empty space.
5. Intermolecular forces are negligible, except during collisions.
6. The duration of a collision is negligible compared with the time spent by a molecule in free motion.
7. A molecule moves with uniform velocity between collisions.
8. Collisions between molecules and between molecules and the walls of a container are considered to be perfectly elastic.
9. We can apply Newtonian mechanics to collisions involving molecules, i.e., they can be considered to behave like billiard balls or table tennis balls colliding.

Consider just a single molecule that happens to be moving backwards and forwards along the length of a box (Fig. 16.29). When it hits the walls at the ends it bounces back. If the speed of the molecule is v and the length of the box L then the number of collisions it will make with one end wall in time t will be $vt/2L$, i.e., the total distance the molecule travels in time t divided by the distance between collisions with the particular

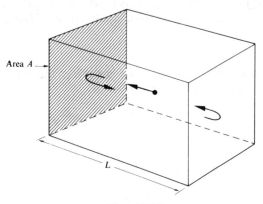

Fig. 16.29

end wall. Each time the molecule collides with the wall we are assuming that it bounces back with its speed undiminished. The change of momentum of the particle when it hits the wall is $mv - m(-v)$ $= 2mv$. Thus in time t the total change of momentum will be $2mv \times vt/2L$. The force on the wall, averaged over this time, will be equal to the rate of change of momentum.

$$\text{Force} = \frac{vt}{2L} \times 2mv \times \frac{1}{t} = \frac{mv^2}{L}$$

The pressure is force per unit area, thus if the area of the end wall is A

$$\text{Pressure } p = \frac{mv^2}{AL}$$

But AL is the volume v of the box. Thus

$$pV = mv^2$$

This was for just one molecule. Suppose we have n molecules in the box. Not all the molecules will hit the end face, some will be moving towards faces of the box which are perpendicular to the end face. The velocities of all the molecules can be resolved into three mutually perpendicular directions and thus we can consider that $n/3$ molecules will move towards the particular end face. Hence

$$pV = \tfrac{1}{3}nmv^2$$

Not all the molecules will have the same speeds, thus we have to consider in the above equation the mean value of v^2; this is represented by $\overline{c^2}$ with $\sqrt{\overline{c^2}}$ being the root mean square speed. Hence

$$pV = \tfrac{1}{3}\,nm\overline{c^2}$$

Since the total mass of the gas is nm, the density $\rho = nm/V$ and so we can write

$$p = \tfrac{1}{3}\rho\overline{c^2}$$

The speeds of molecules

Since the density of hydrogen at $0°C$ and a pressure of 1.013×10^5 Pa (i.e., normal atmospheric pressure) is 0.0899 kg m^{-3} then

$$\overline{c^2} = \frac{3 \times 1.013 \times 10^5}{0.0899}$$

$$\sqrt{\overline{c^2}} = 1840 \text{ m s}^{-1}$$

This is the root mean square speed. Individual molecules will have a range of speeds. The distribution of speeds among the molecules follows what is called a Maxwell distribution (Fig. 16.30), J. C. Maxwell having first deduced the relationship in the mid 19th century. The higher the temperature of a gas the higher the most probable speed (this is not the same as the root mean square speed, being about $0.8\,c$ and also there will be more high-speed molecules).

Deducing the ideal gas laws

If we have a fixed mass of gas and a constant value for the root mean square speed then simple kinetic theory gives $pV = $ a constant, i.e., Boyle's law. The obvious deduction is that $\overline{c^2}$ is related to temperature, on the Kelvin scale.

$$pV = \tfrac{1}{3}mn\overline{c^2} = \tfrac{2}{3}n\,(\tfrac{1}{2}m\overline{c^2})$$

$\tfrac{1}{2}m\overline{c^2}$ is the mean kinetic energy of a molecule. Thus we can take temperature, on the kelvin scale, to be directly proportional to the mean kinetic energy of its molecules. When we do this we have $pV/T = $ a constant.

Boltzmann constant

For one mole of an ideal gas $pV = R_0T$. The number of molecules in one mole of gas is the Avogadro constant L. Hence

$$pV = R_0T = \tfrac{2}{3}L(\tfrac{1}{2}m\overline{c^2})$$

Hence

$$\tfrac{1}{2}m\overline{c^2} = (R_0/L)T$$

The ratio R_0/L must be a universal constant, since both R_0 and L are. This ratio is called Boltzmann's constant k.

$$k = R_0/L$$

Hence

$$\tfrac{1}{2}m\overline{c^2} = 3/2\,kT$$

The mean kinetic energy of a molecule thus only depends on the temperature of the gas.

Suppose a gas was composed of two different mass molecules, m and m'. Because the gas was all at the same temperature we must have the mean kinetic energy the same for both sets of molecules. The energy is shared out so that the average kinetic energy of one set of molecules is equal to the average kinetic energy of the other set.

We can think of all the molecules in a gas as being divided into groups moving in three independent directions at right angles to each other, the x, y, and z directions. As there is no reason to believe that the molecules moving in

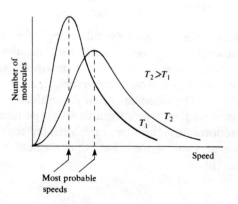

Fig. 16.30 Maxwell distribution of molecular speeds

any one direction have more average kinetic energy than those in another direction, the mean kinetic energy in the x direction will be equal to the mean kinetic energy in the y direction, will be equal to the mean kinetic energy in the z direction. The total mean kinetic energy is thus divided into three shares. Hence the mean kinetic energy in any one of these directions will be $\frac{1}{2}kT$. These directions are called degrees of freedom.

We can generalize this result to: the mean kinetic energy per degree of freedom is $\frac{1}{2}kT$.

Deducing Graham's law of diffusion

The term diffusion is used for a gas passing through a porous membrane when the process is not the motion of the gas in bulk but the result of the motion of individual molecules. Graham's law is that the rate of diffusion of a gas is inversely proportional to the square root of the gas density.

Since $p = \frac{1}{3}\rho \overline{c^2}$, then the speed c is $\sqrt{(3p/\rho)}$. The speed is inversely proportional to the square root of the density. Hence since the rate of diffusion will be proportional to the speed. Graham's law has been deduced.

Deducing Dalton's law of partial pressures

Dalton's law is that when two or more gases, which do not react chemically, are present in the same container the total pressure is the sum of the pressures which each gas would exert if alone in the container.

Consider two gases, each occupying a volume V at the same temperature. Then

$$p_1 V = \tfrac{1}{3}n_1 m_1 \overline{c_1^2} \quad \text{and} \quad p_2 V = \tfrac{1}{3}n_2 m_2 \overline{c_2^2}$$

But since they are at the same temperature

$$\tfrac{1}{2}m_1 \overline{c_1^2} = \tfrac{1}{2}m_2 \overline{c_2^2}$$

If we call this common value $\frac{1}{2}m\overline{c^2}$, then

$$(p_1 + p_2)V = \tfrac{1}{3}(n_1 + n_2)m\overline{c^2}$$

A mixture of the two gases is thus giving a total pressure equal to the sum of the pressures which each would have exerted if alone in the container, i.e., Dalton's law is deduced.

Deducing Avogadro's law

Avogadro's law is that equal volumes of all ideal gases under the same conditions of temperature and pressure contain the same number of molecules. Thus if we consider two ideal gases we have:

$$p_1 V = \tfrac{1}{3}n_1 m_1 \overline{c_1^2} \quad \text{and} \quad p_2 V = \tfrac{1}{3}n_2 m_2 \overline{c_2^2}$$

Since they have the same pressure $p_1 = p_2$, volume $V_1 = V_2$, temperature $\frac{1}{2}m_1 \overline{c_1^2} = \frac{1}{2}m_2 \overline{c_2^2}$, then we must have $n_1 = n_2$ and so Avogadro's law follows.

Evaporation

Evaporation is the escape of molecules from a liquid. If no energy is supplied to the liquid the evaporation causes a drop in temperature of the liquid. The mean energy of the molecules in the liquid must have fallen. This would suggest that the molecules escaping are the high-energy ones.

We can estimate the energy a molecule must have to escape from a liquid. If the latent heat is measured for one mole of liquid, then as there are 6×10^{23} molecules in a mole the energy needed for one molecule to escape is

$$\frac{\text{Molar latent heat}}{6 \times 10^{23}} = \frac{\Delta H_{vap}}{6 \times 10^{23}}$$

At 20°C the molar latent heat of vaporization for water is $34\,000$ J mol^{-1}. Hence the escape energy for a molecule is 5.7×10^{-20} J.

When a vapour condenses energy is released. When in a cloud water droplets grow, because of condensation there is a rise in temperature of the surroundings.

With a liquid, equilibrium conditions will occur when the rate of evaporation equals the rate of condensation, i.e., the rate at which molecules leave the surface is equal to the rate at which the molecules enter the surface. At this condition the pressure due to the molecules of the liquid in the vapour state is called the saturation vapour pressure. A simple method that has been used to measure this vapour pressure is to inject the liquid into the vacuum space above the mercury in a simple barometer (Fig. 16.31). The evaporating liquid gives a vapour which produces a pressure which depresses the mercury level. At saturation no further drop in mercury level occurs. The total drop in mercury level is the saturation vapour pressure.

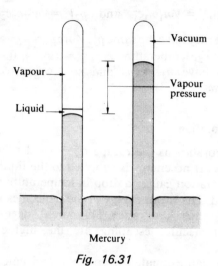

Fig. 16.31

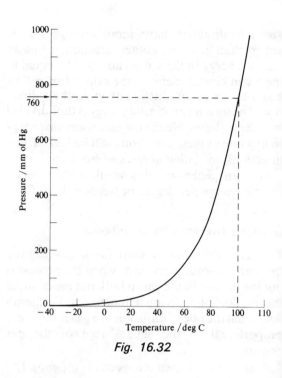

Fig. 16.32

The saturation vapour pressure depends on the temperature. Figure 16.32 shows how the saturation vapour pressure of water changes with temperature.

At boiling evaporation takes place not only from the liquid surface but also internally with the formation of bubbles of vapour. The vapour in these bubbles will be at the saturation vapour pressure, or higher, if the bubbles are to exist, or grow. The bubbles can only exist if the saturation vapour pressure is equal to or greater than the external pressure. Boiling occurs, therefore, when the saturation vapour pressure is equal to the atmospheric pressure, assuming the liquid is exposed to the atmosphere and that it is shallow so that the depth of the liquid does not introduce significant extra pressure. If the atmospheric pressure is 760 mm of mercury then the boiling point of water must be 100°C, as this is the temperature at which the saturation vapour pressure is equal to 760 mm. Increasing the atmospheric pressure increases the temperature of boiling,

decreasing the atmospheric pressure decreases the boiling temperature.

Liquefying gases

In 1823 Faraday liquefied chlorine by applying pressure. By 1908 the last of the so-called 'permanent' gases had been liquefied (this was helium). How good are the gas laws in describing the pressure, volume, temperature relationships when a gas is near liquefaction?

The classic work on this was that by T. Andrews in 1863 on the liquefaction of carbon dioxide. He measured pressures and volumes for a sample of carbon dioxide at different temperatures. Figure 16.33 shows his results. Above about 50°C his results gave reasonable agreement with the gas laws. At temperatures below 31.4°C pressure was able to produce liquefaction, above that temperature liquefaction could not be produced, however great the pressure. This temperature is called the critical temperature. At, say a temperature of 13.1°C we have the following sequence of events as the volume of the gas is decreased: from A to B a large decrease in volume produces only a small change in pressure; at B liquefaction commences.

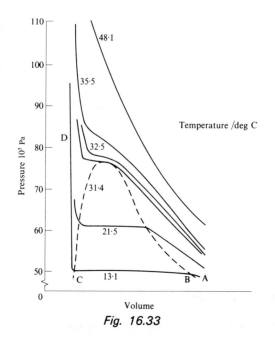

Fig. 16.33

from B to C liquefaction is occurring and the large change in volume produces no change in pressure; at C liquefaction is complete; from C to D the liquid is being compressed and only small changes in volume occur for large changes in pressure.

The following are the values for some materials of the critical temperatures and the pressures needed at those temperatures to produce liquefaction.

	Critical temp./ K	Critical pressure/ 10^5 Pa
Carbon dioxide	304.2	73.8
Oxygen	154.8	50.8
Nitrogen	126.2	33.9
Hydrogen	32.99	12.94
Helium	5.2	2.29

The reason for helium being one of the last gases to be liquefied becomes obvious from the fact of its very low critical temperature; it cannot be liquefied at temperatures greater than 5.2 K.

Van der Waals' equation

There have been many attempts to modify the gas equation to fit the behaviour of gases. A useful equation was put forward by van der Waals in 1873.

$$\left(P + \frac{a}{V^2}\right)(V - b) = RT$$

where a and b are constants. The volume term in the gas equation is reduced by b to account for the finite size of the molecules. This is because the volume of a container which is available for the molecules to move in is significantly reduced by the volumes of the molecules themselves. In our kinetic theory derivation we were assuming that a molecule could move to any other part of the container. The pressure term is modified to take into account intermolecular forces. These would become significant when the gas molecules become closely packed together. Because of these forces the molecules spend more time near each other than in the absence of such forces, and thus the number of impacts on the wall in a given time is reduced; also the attractive forces reduce the momentum with which a molecule hits the wall. Both these effects will depend on the number of molecules per unit volume, n/V, and thus we have a term proportional to $1/V^2$. The agreement is only approximate and there is considerable divergence in the liquefaction region. The equation is, however, a useful approximation.

Intermolecular forces and energies

The force between two molecules at some particular separation can be considered to be the sum of two forces—a force of attraction and a force of repulsion (Fig. 16.34). The net force is zero when the molecules are at their equilibrium separation in the solid and liquid states. At separations less than this equilibrium value there is a net repulsive force, at separations greater than the equilibrium value the net force is attractive. This force of attraction becomes very small at large molecular separations. In a gas where the separation is very large the attractive force is effectively zero.

Consider a solid with the atoms at their equilibrium positions. Compressing the solid moves the atoms closer together and so makes their separation less than the equilibrium value; the net force

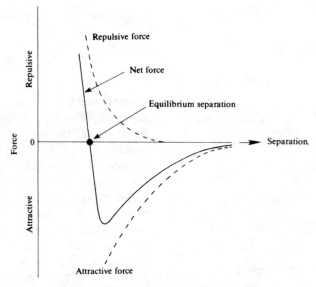

Fig. 16.34   Intermolecular forces

then becomes repulsive and there is thus resistance to the compression. Stretching a solid increases the separation to a value greater than the equilibrium value; the net force then becomes attractive and there is thus resistance to the extension. This is the reason why when a solid is picked up it keeps together, e.g., why when you pick up a ruler by one end the other end follows. Intermolecular forces come into play, opposing change from the equilibrium separation.

Hook's law describes the relationship between the forces applied to a solid and the resulting changes in length, the change in length being proportional to the force. This implies that the change in separation between molecules close to their equilibrium value should be proportional to the net force, i.e., the slope of the force-separation graph should be a straight line. This is the case for separations close to the equilibium value (see Fig. 16.34).

A graph of intermolecular energy against separation can be obtained from the force-separation graph. The potential energy of the molecules at a particular separation is the area under the graph between this separation and infinite separation.

$$\text{Potential energy at separation } r = \int_{r}^{\infty} F \, dr$$

Figure 16.35 shows the resulting graph.

At the equilibrium separation the energy is a minimum. If you think of a molecule as being like two spheres joined by a spring, then there is no net force stretching the spring at the equilibrium value and so the energy stored in the spring is a minimum. Increasing or decreasing the separation increases the energy stored in the spring.

Only at absolute zero can we conceive of a molecule being at rest. At higher temperatures the energy of the molecules is greater than the equilibrium value and thus a molecule oscillates between two separations r_1 and r_2 as illustrated by

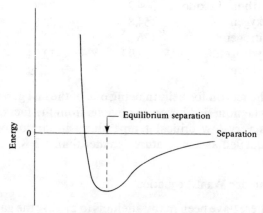

Fig. 16.35   Intermolecular energies

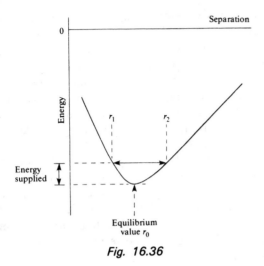

Fig. 16.36

Fig. 16.36. Because the graph is not symmetrical about the equilibrium separation r_0, $(r_2 - r_0)$ being greater than $(r_0 - r_1)$, expansion occurs.

Supplementary material

Tearing ions apart

To separate two oppositely charged objects requires energy. To separate them their force of attraction has to be overcome and the charged objects moved through a distance.

We can make a rough calculation of the energy needed to pull a pair of ions apart, e.g., the sodium and chlorine ions in a sodium chloride crystal. The force of attraction between the ions is

$$F = \frac{-q^2}{4\pi\varepsilon_0 r^2}$$

where q is the charge on the ions, 1.6×10^{-19} C, r the distance apart of the two ions, and ε_0 is a constant, 8.85×10^{-12} C^2 N^{-1} m^{-2}. The minus sign is because the charges are of opposite sign. We will take the distance apart of the ions to be the lattice spacing in the sodium chloride crystal, 2.8×10^{-10} m. The equation shows how the force varies with distance. We want to change the distance from 2.8×10^{-10} m to infinity, i.e., pull the ions completely apart. We could use the equation to plot a graph of force F against distance r and then obtain a value for the energy by measuring

the area under the graph (Fig. 16.37) between the lines $r = 2.8 \times 10^{-10}$ m and $r = \infty$, or use the integration

$$\int_{2.8 \times 10^{-10}}^{\infty} F \, dr = \text{Potential energy}$$

A rough estimate of the area under the graph suggests that the energy will be of the order of 8×10^{-19} J. Integration to obtain a more accurate result is as follows

$$\text{Potential energy} = \int_{2.8 \times 10^{-10}}^{\infty} F \, dr$$

$$= \int_{2.8 \times 10^{-10}}^{\infty} \frac{-q^2}{4\pi\varepsilon_0 r^2} \, dr$$

$$= \frac{-q^2}{4\pi\varepsilon_0} \left[-\frac{1}{r} \right]_{2.8 \times 10^{-10}}^{\infty}$$

$$= \frac{-q^2}{4\pi\varepsilon_0 \, 2.8 \times 10^{-10}}$$

$$= -8.2 \times 10^{-19} \text{ J}$$

If we wanted to find how the energy needed to tear apart ions depended on the separation of the ions, r, we could use the force–distance r graph and measure the area between different values of r and infinity, or use integration. The result in both

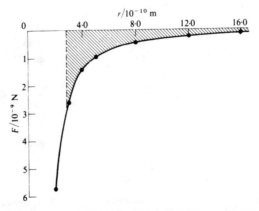

Fig. 16.37 The force of attraction between ions as a function of their distance apart

cases is shown in Fig. 16.38 and is described by the equation

$$\text{Potential energy} = \frac{-q^2}{4\pi\varepsilon_0 r}$$

Experimental results for the tear-apart energy for a pair of ions in a sodium chloride crystal give 12.7×10^{-19} J. The theoretical result 8.2×10^{-19} J is thus of the right order.

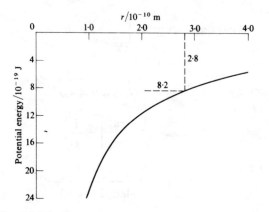

Fig. 16.38 *Energy to tear a pair of ions apart as a function of the distance apart of the ions*

What factors could explain the discrepancy between the theoretical and experimental results? We considered a pair of ions in isolation from the rest of the ions in the crystal—perhaps the other ions will affect the result? Around any one ion

there are six neighbours of opposite sign at distance 2.8×10^{-10} m, twelve neighbours of the same sign at distance $\sqrt{2} \times 2.8 \times 10^{-10}$ m, eight neighbours of opposite sign at distance $\sqrt{3} \times 2.8 \times 10^{-10}$ m, etc. (Fig. 16.39). We can find the energy to tear away this one ion by calculating the energy needed to take away each of these other groups of ions from our one ion. Thus the energy needed to take away the six near neighbours with opposite sign is $-8.2 \times 10^{-19} \times 6$ J, the energy needed for the twelve neighbours of the same sign is $+8.2 \times 10^{-19} \times 12/\sqrt{2}$ J, the energy needed to take away the eight neighbours of the opposite sign is $-8.2 \times 10^{-19} \times 8/\sqrt{3}$ J, and so on with all the other ions in the crystal. Summing the terms so far gives a result of 17.2×10^{-19} J. If all the terms are considered the result becomes -14.3×10^{-19} J.

This result is higher than the experimental result; what else have we forgotten? If there were only attractive forces between oppositely charged ions, as Coulomb's law predicts, the crystal would collapse. Repulsive forces must exist. Perhaps these account for the difference between the theoretical and experimental results. If we make this assumption then repulsive forces must account for an energy difference of 1.6×10^{-19} J. The existence of the repulsive forces meant that 1.6×10^{-19} J less of energy was needed to remove an ion. What was the repulsive force acting on the ion at 2.8×10^{-10} m which gave this amount of energy?

If an ion moved a small distance Δr, energy F Δr would be transformed. F is the force acting on

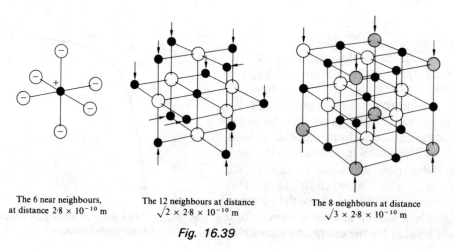

The 6 near neighbours, at distance 2.8×10^{-10} m

The 12 neighbours at distance $\sqrt{2} \times 2.8 \times 10^{-10}$ m

The 8 neighbours at distance $\sqrt{3} \times 2.8 \times 10^{-10}$ m

Fig. 16.39

the ion. Thus the change in energy Δ(energy) = $-F\,\Delta r$

$$F = -\frac{\Delta(\text{energy})}{\Delta r}$$

The force is therefore the slope of the graph of energy against distance (Fig. 16.40); in our case the slope at $r = 2.8 \times 10^{-10}$ m. But we do not know how the energy varies with distance for the repulsive force. We do, however, know how the energy varies with distance for the attractive force and at 2.8×10^{-10} m the attractive force must be equal to the repulsive force as the ions are in equilibrium at this distance. The slope of the graph gives a value of -5.1×10^{-9} N for the force. The force of repulsion at 2.8×10^{-10} m from an ion is thus $+5.1 \times 10^{-19}$ N.

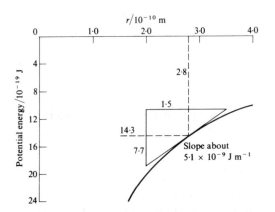

Fig. 16.40 *Energy to tear an ion from a crystal as a function of lattice spacing*

We could have obtained this result by differentiating the equation showing how the energy transformed varies with distance, modified to include the effects of other ions.

$$\text{Potential energy} = -\frac{1.747\,q^2}{4\pi\varepsilon_0 r}$$

$$F = -\frac{d(\text{energy})}{dr} = -\frac{1.747\,q^2}{4\pi\varepsilon_0 r^2}$$

At $r = 2.8 \times 10^{-10}$ m this gives $F = -5.1 \times 10^{-9}$ N. 1.747 is the factor the energy must be multiplied

by to convert the -8.2×10^{-19} J result, for a pair of ions, to that of -14.3×10^{-19} J, the result for an ion in the midst of a crystal. 1.747 is called the Madelung constant. Its value depends on the crystal structure.

Knowing the repulsion energy and the force at 2.8×10^{-10} m it is possible to arrive at equations showing how the repulsive energy and the force vary with distance.

For the attractive force

$$\text{Energy} \propto \frac{1}{r} \text{ and } F \propto \frac{1}{r^2}$$

Let us make a guess and suggest that for the repulsive force

$$\text{Energy} \propto \frac{1}{r^n}$$

and thus

$$\text{energy} = \frac{K}{r^n}$$

$$F = -\frac{d(\text{energy})}{dr} = \frac{nK}{r^{n+1}}$$

Thus

$$\frac{F}{(\text{energy})} = \frac{n}{r}$$

Check: for the attractive force $n = 1$. At 2.8×10^{-10} m, $F = 5.1 \times 10^{-9}$ N and energy = 14.3×10^{-19} J

$$\frac{F}{(\text{energy})} = \frac{5.1 \times 10^{-9}}{14.3 \times 10^{-19}} = \frac{1}{2.8 \times 10^{-10}}$$

Putting in the values for the repulsive force and energy we have

$$\frac{F}{(\text{energy})} = \frac{5.1 \times 10^{-9}}{1.6 \times 10^{-19}} = \frac{n}{2.8 \times 10^{-10}}$$

$$n = 8.9 \text{ or approximately } 9$$

Thus the repulsive energy and force relationships could be of the form

$$\text{energy} = \frac{K}{r^9} \qquad F = \frac{nK}{r^{10}}$$

Figure 16.41 shows how the repulsive force, the attractive force, and the net force on an ion vary with distance. The attractive force is calculated from

$$F = -\frac{1.747\,q^2}{4\pi\varepsilon_0 r^2}$$

and repulsive force from

$$F = \frac{9 \times 1.747\,q^2}{4\pi\varepsilon_0 r^{10}}$$

Figure 16.42 shows how the energy varies with distance for the attractive electrical forces, the repulsive forces, and the net result when the energies are summed. The net result could have been directly plotted from the equation

$$\text{Energy} = \frac{1.747\,q^2}{4\pi\varepsilon_0 r^9} - \frac{1.747\,q^2}{4\pi\varepsilon_0 r}$$

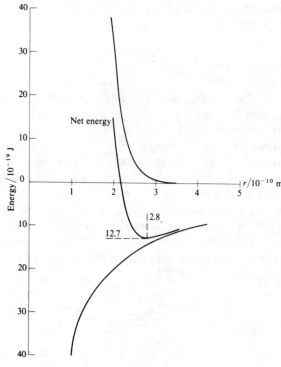

Fig. 16.42

At $r = 2.8 \times 10^{-10}$ m the net force on an ion is zero and the net potential energy is at a minimum.

Bridges

The materials available to man for constructional purposes have changed over the years. The early materials were the naturally occurring ones, timber and stone. The properties of these materials dictated the way in which they could be used in structures. Timber is weaker in compression than in tension, stone is strong in compression and weak in tension.

The simplest form of bridge is a horizontal beam resting on columns, Fig. 16.43. The columns are in compression and the beam when loaded has the lower surface in tension and the upper surface in compression. Stone is thus a suitable material for the columns but if used for the horizontal beam has to be quite thick to keep the tensile stresses low. Because of the weight of stone beams they were only able to be used, even in considerable thicknesses, to bridge small gaps; the

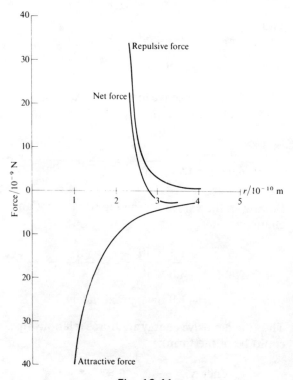

Fig. 16.41

Upper surface compressed

Beam being bent | Lower surface extended

The arrows denote the direction of the forces

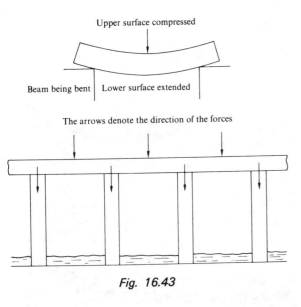

Fig. 16.43

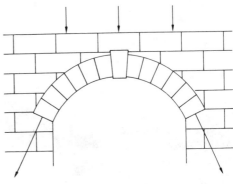

Fig. 16.44

weight of the stone itself caused bending. Use of wood for the beam enabled the thicknesses to be reduced.

One way of overcoming the weakness of stone in tension was to build arches (Fig. 16.44). The action of the forces on the arch is to endeavour to straighten it out, i.e., shorten both the upper and lower surfaces of the arch, and this puts the arch material in compression. The supporting columns must, however, be able to withstand the sideways push of the arch, also the foundations must be secure enough to stop the base of a column being displaced. Figure 16.45 shows the Roman bridge at Rimini in Italy, the maximum span of an arch being about 9 metres.

The end of the eighteenth century saw the introduction into building of a new material—iron. Cast iron was used to build the first iron bridge in 1779 (Fig. 16.46). Cast iron is strong in compression and weak in tension, like stone. Thus the iron bridge followed much the same arch design as a stone bridge.

Fig. 16.45 Roman bridge at Rimini, Italy, built by Augustus and Tiberius. (J. Allan Cash)

Fig. 16.46 *The world's first iron bridge 1779. At Ironbridge over the River Severn, built by Abraham Darby of cast iron. About 8 m wide and 100 m long (still standing). (J. Allan Cash)*

The beginning of the nineteenth century say the introduction of suspension bridges (Fig. 16.47). A suspension bridge is the inverse of an arch—the cable being in tension. The cable supports the bridge deck. The cables have to be anchored on the land sides of the towers so that the forces on the cables do not pull the cable supporting towers out of the vertical. Early suspension bridges used chains made of wrought iron.

Wrought iron differs from cast iron in being much purer iron; it is ductile and much stronger in tension than cast iron, having properties much closer to those of mild steel. Later suspension bridges used steel for the cables. A more recent suspension bridge is that over the river Severn, near Bristol. This bridge (Fig.16.48) was completed in 1966. The supporting cables consist of 440 parallel high-tensile steel wires about 5 mm in

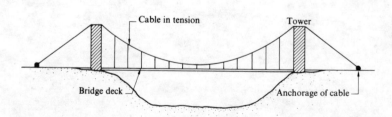

Fig. 16.47

356

Fig. 16.48   The Severn suspension bridge. (J. Allan Cash)

diameter. The fracture stress for the cable material is about 14×10^8 Pa. It was only with the development of materials that were strong in tension that suspension bridges became feasible.

Wrought iron began to displace cast iron as a bridge-building material about the middle of the nineteenth century. The end of the nineteenth century saw mild steel replacing wrought iron. The strength of these new materials in tension led to the use of what is almost the old 'beam resting on columns' bridge. Instead of using a continuous beam, a beam is built up of separate members jointed together. Figure 16.49 shows such an arrangement. In the same way as the loaded beam, the top of this structure is in compression and the lower part in tension. The diagonal struts are hinged, some of them carrying tensile and some compressive stresses. Many different forms of such trusses were used in bridge building. Figure 16.50 shows a truss bridge built in 1864 by Eiffel, the same man who was responsible for the

Eiffel tower in Paris (that is also based on the use of trusses).

Reinforced and pre-stressed concrete have become the materials for twentieth century bridge building. The Gladesville bridge in Sydney, Australia (Fig. 16.51) shows a modern pre-stressed concrete arch bridge, very similar in design to the old Roman bridges.

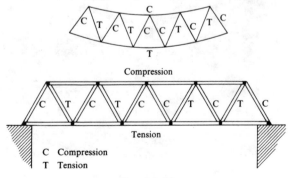

Fig. 16.49

Fig. 16.50   The viaduct by Eiffel at Busseau sur Creuse. The distance between the piers is about 60 m. (Prof. Arch. Italo Insolera)

Fig. 16.51   The Gladesville Bridge, span about 330 m. (Australian News and Information Bureau)

Problems

1. Distinguish between crystalline, glassy, amorphous and polymeric solids.

2. A monochromatic beam of X-rays of wavelength 1.4×10^{-10} m is found to give a first-order Bragg reflection from a sodium chloride crystal of 15°. What is the spacing of the atomic planes in the crystal responsible for this reflection?

3. (a) Derive the Bragg equation, $n\lambda = 2d \sin \theta$, for X-ray diffraction by crystals.

(b) A beam of X-rays of wavelength 0.154 nm is diffracted by a copper crystal. A first-order reflection is found at a Bragg angle of 20°. What is the spacing of the atomic planes responsible for this reflection?

4. Two copper wires A and B, of the same known areas of cross-section, are subjected to measured stretching forces and the corresponding extensions are measured. The results, on a force–extension graph, are shown in Fig. 16.52.

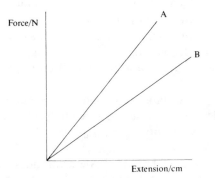

Fig. 16.52

Explain what deduction you could make about the difference between the two wires.

Define the quantities which you would plot to get the same graph for both wires. How would you use this second graph to evaluate an important physical constant of copper?

(University of London, Q5, Paper 2, January 1978)

5. A copper wire LM is fused at one end, M, to an iron wire (Fig. 16.53). The copper wire has length 0.900 m and cross-section 0.90×10^{-6} m².

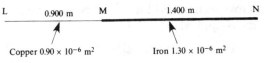

Fig. 16.53

The iron wire has length 1.400 m and cross-section 1.30×10^{-6} m². The compound wire is stretched; its total length increases by 0.0100 m. Calculate

(a) the ratio of the extensions of the two wires,
(b) the extension of each wire,
(c) the tension applied to the compound wire.

(The Young modulus of copper = 1.30×10^{11} N m⁻². The Young modulus of iron = 2.10×10^{11} N m⁻²)

(University of London, Q5, Paper 2, January 1985)

6. (a) A heavy rigid bar is supported horizontally from a fixed support by two vertical wires, A and B, of the same initial length and which experience the same extension. If the ratio of the diameter of A to that of B is 2 and the ratio of the Young modulus of A to that of B is 2, calculate the ratio of the tension in A to that in B.

(b) If the distance between the wires is D, calculate the distance of wire A from the centre of gravity of the bar.

(JMB, Q2, Paper II, June 1978)

7. (a) Figure 16.54 is a graph showing how the extension of a steel wire of length 1.2 m and area

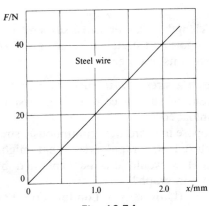

Fig. 16.54

of cross-section 0.012 mm² alters as a stretching force is applied.

(i) Use the graph to calculate the Young modulus for steel.

(ii) Draw a labelled diagram of an experimental arrangement suitable for obtaining such a set of results.

(b) Figure 16.55 shows the results of a similar experiment with a copper wire. In this case the wire has been stretched until it breaks.

(i) The graph drawn in this instance is a stress–strain curve. Explain one advantage of representing the results in this way.

(ii) Account in molecular terms for the behaviour of the wire as it is stretched from A to B.

(iii) The copper wire used was 2.0 m long and 0.25 mm² in cross-section. Calculate the tension in the wire at A and an approximate value for the work done in producing a strain of 0.1.

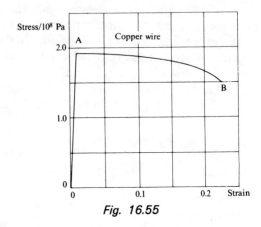

Fig. 16.55

(c) A length of rubber cord is suspended from a rigid support and stretched by means of weights attached to its lower end.

(i) Sketch a stress–strain curve to represent the behaviour of such a cord as it is first loaded then unloaded.

(ii) Suppose the cord were continuously stretched and relaxed at a rapid rate. What might you notice? How would this be explained by the stress–strain graph?

(University of London, Q13, Paper 2, June 1985)

8. (a) Explain what is meant by saying that a material obeys Hooke's law. Describe an experiment which would enable you to investigate the extent to which a given specimen of steel wire obeys this law.

(b) Explain why, in an experiment to measure the Young modulus for a material in the form of a wire (i) the wire chosen is usually long and thin, and (ii) a second wire is suspended alongside the first. Sketch a graph to show the results you would expect to obtain if the extension of the wire were measured for various loads below the elastic limit. What other measurements would have to be taken and how would you use your graph to obtain a value for the Young modulus of the material of the wire?

(c) A force is required to compress a body or to extend it. What does this imply about the intermolecular forces?

(d) A load of 35.0 N applied to a wire of cross-sectional area 1.50×10^{-7} m² and length 2.00 m causes an extension of 1.00 mm. What is the energy stored in the wire per unit volume?

(AEB, Q10, Paper 3, November 1981)

9. Figure 16.56 shows how the extension ΔL of a wire changed as the tension T in it was increased and then decreased. The original length L_0 of the wire was 2.07 m, and its area of cross-section A was 0.74 mm².

(a) Draw a labelled sketch of an apparatus that could be used to obtain the readings of T and ΔL, and explain how ΔL, L_0 and A would be measured.

(b) Over what range of extensions does Hooke's law apply? Find the original Young modulus of the wire.

(c) Use the graph to find the work done in extending the wire by 4.0 mm.

(d) Why does the graph follow different paths during loading and unloading? Discuss the significance of the shaded area.

(University of Cambridge, Q18, Paper 1, November 1979)

10. Suppose that the graph (Fig. 16.57) is the load–extension curve for rubber webbing used as the base of a chair:

(a) The following are predictions about what will happen when a person sits on the chair.

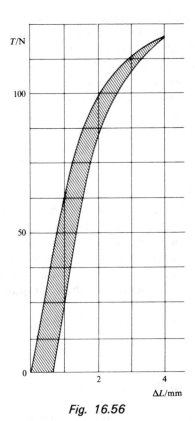

Fig. 16.56

(i) He will sink only a little, unless he is very heavy, when he will suddenly sink a lot.
(ii) He will sink a moderate distance and then be supported at about the same level whether he is heavy or light.

Explain which is the correct prediction.

(b) Suppose that in a test on the chair a weight of 250 newtons is set oscillating freely on the seat. Explain under what circumstances simple harmonic motion will be performed.

(Oxford and Cambridge Schools Examination Board, Nuffield advanced physics, Short answer paper Q2, 1971)

11. Explain briefly, with the aid of a diagram, what you would expect to happen to a nearly spherical water droplet resting on a clean horizontal surface if a tiny amount of detergent were added to it.

How do you account for the change that might occur?

(University of London, Q5, Paper 2, January 1979)

12. The pressure difference p across a spherical surface of radius r between air and a liquid, where γ is the surface tension of the liquid, is given by

$$p = \frac{2\gamma}{r}$$

(a) Show that this expression is consistent with γ being measured in N m^{-1}. It can be shown that γ is also equal to the energy stored per unit area in the surface. Show that this is also consistent with γ being measured in N m^{-1}.

(b) Describe a method for measuring γ which is based on measuring the excess pressure in a bubble.

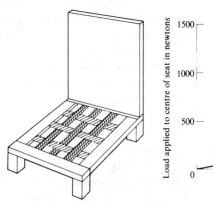

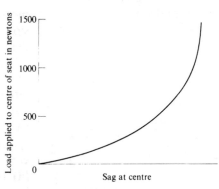

Fig. 16.57

(c) Using the energy definition of γ given above, calculate the energy stored in the surface of a soap bubble 2.0 cm in radius if its surface tension is 4.5×10^{-2} N m^{-1}. If the thickness of the surface is 6.0×10^{-7} m and the density of the soap solution is 1000 kg m^{-3}, calculate the speed with which the liquid fragments will fly apart when the bubble is burst. What assumptions have you made in your calculation?

(University of London, Q12, Paper 2, January 1984)

13. (a) Draw and label a diagram of apparatus suitable for measuring the surface tension of water by Jaeger's method.

Assume that the pressure p within the apparatus when it is assembled equals the pressure p_0 of the atmosphere outside. Sketch a graph which shows how the pressure difference $p - p_0$ changes with time from the instant p begins to increase until the moment a bubble is about to break away from the bottom of the capillary for the third time.

How are the pressure differences shown in the graph related to (i) the position of the liquid meniscus in the capillary and (ii) the radius of the bubble formed at the bottom of the capillary?

State which quantities you would measure if you were using this apparatus to determine the surface tension of water and describe how you would measure them.

(b) Figure 16.58, which is not to scale, shows two capillary tubes of uniform bore fitting tightly into a short length of rubber tubing. AB and CD are two threads of water. The capillary tube containing CD is kept horizontal while that containing AB is raised through an angle θ until the water surface at D is both flat and vertical.

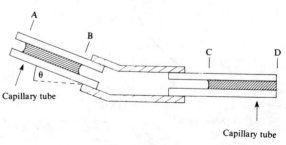

Fig. 16.58

(i) Calculate the surface tension of water given that θ is 10.5°, AB is 11.4 cm, the radius of the capillary tube at C is 0.72 mm and the density of water is 1.00×10^{-3} kg m^{-3}. The angle of contact between water and glass is zero.
(You may assume the relation $\Delta p = 2\gamma/r$)
(ii) Suggest an experimental procedure to determine when the water surface at D is flat.

(University of London, Q12, Paper 2, January 1985)

14. A small sphere of radius 2.0 mm and density 8.0×10^3 kg m^3 is released from rest at the surface of a long column of a viscous liquid of density 1.3×10^3 kg m^{-3}. The viscous force, F, in newtons, opposing the motion is proportional to the velocity, v, in m s^{-1}, of the sphere and is given by the formula $F = 0.057\, v$. Calculate the terminal velocity of the sphere. Sketch two graphs indicating how (a) the velocity, and (b) the acceleration of the sphere vary with the distance travelled. ($g = 9.8$ m s^{-2})

(AEB, Q1, Paper 3, June 1981)

15. The kinetic theory of gases rests on the assumption that a gas consists of molecules in constant random motion.

(a) Using this theoretical model state the molecular properties on which the density of a gas depends.

(b) Explain how the temperature of a gas is interpreted in terms of this theoretical model and state the molecular factors on which it depends.

(University of London, Q1, Paper 2, January 1984)

16. (a) The kinetic theory of gas predicts that the root mean square (r.m.s) speed of the molecules of an ideal gas is given by the expression $(3p/\rho)^{\frac{1}{2}}$, where p is the pressure and ρ is the density of the gas.

The graphs, Fig. 16.59, show how the pressure of oxygen gas depends upon its density at two different constant temperatures, T and 300 K.

(i) Use the graph to calculate a value for the r.m.s. speed of the oxygen molecules at 300 K. Explain your working.
(ii) Is the temperature T higher or lower than 300 K? Explain your reasoning.
(iii) The graphs are based upon experimental

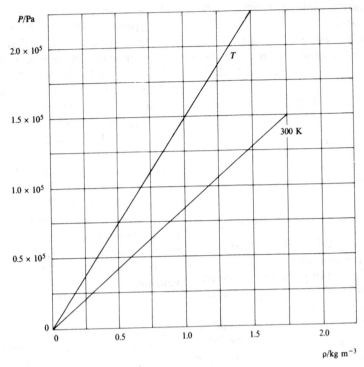

Fig. 16.59

results. What conclusion can you draw from the behaviour of oxygen?

(iv) Outline a simple experimental procedure for investigating how the pressure of a known mass of air varies as its density changes at room temperature. Include a labelled diagram of the apparatus used.

(b) The graphs, Fig. 16.60, show how the speeds of the molecules in an ideal gas are distributed at two temperatures. Use them to help you answer the following questions.

(i) In what two main ways does the temperature appear to affect the distribution of speeds?

(ii) What is the value of v for which the fraction of molecules with speeds in the range $v \pm 0.5$ m s^{-1} is a maximum at a temperature of 300 K? How does this value compare with the r.m.s. speed calculated in (a)(i) above?

(University of London, Q9, Paper 2, June 1984)

17. (a) Explain what is meant by an ideal gas.

What properties are assumed for the model of an ideal gas molecule in deriving the expression

$$p = \tfrac{1}{3}\rho c^2 \qquad \text{Equation (1)}$$

where the symbols have their usual meanings?

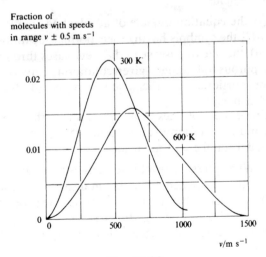

Fig. 16.60

(b) How is pressure explained in terms of the kinetic theory of gases?

Describe carefully, using diagrams where necessary, but without detailed mathematical analysis, the steps in the argument used to derive equation (1).

(c) Show that for a fixed mass of ideal gas at constant temperature, equation (1) can be written

$$pV = A$$

where A is a constant.

For some real gases, the pressure can be described in terms of the equation

$$p(V + B) = A \qquad \text{Equation (2)}$$

where B is also a constant for a fixed mass of the gas at a particular temperature.

Show that equation (2) implies a pressure less than the value predicted for an ideal gas. Suggest a reason for this in molecular terms.

(University of London, Q11, Paper 2, June 1983)

18. The kinetic theory of gases is based on the belief that the molecules of a gas are in a state of random motion. Describe some direct evidence for this belief.

According to the simple kinetic theory the pressure, p, of an ideal gas is given by the expression $p = \frac{1}{3}\rho c^2$ where ρ is the density of gas and c^2 the mean square speed of the molecules. Show that this expression conforms with the following statements:

(i) the equation of state of an ideal gas is $pV = nRT$, the symbols having their normal meanings,
(ii) the rate of passage of different gases through a porous wall under a given condition is inversely proportional to the square roots of their densities,
(iii) equal volumes of all gases under the same conditions of temperature and pressure contain equal numbers of molecules.

What pressure would be exerted by hydrogen gas if it contained 5.3×10^{15} molecules per cm^3, the molecules having a root mean square speed of 2.1×10^3 m s^{-1}? (Avogadro constant = 6.0×10^{23} mol^{-1}, relative molecular mass of hydrogen = 2.0)

(AEB, Q3, Paper S, June 1982)

19. A cylinder containing 19 kg of compressed air at a pressure 9.5 times that of the atmosphere is kept in a store at 7°C. When it is moved to a workshop where the temperature is 27°C a safety valve on the cylinder operates, releasing some of the air. If the valve allows air to escape when its pressure exceeds 10 times that of the atmosphere, calculate the mass of air that escapes.

(University of London, Q2, Paper 2, June 1980)

20. A container holds 120 cm^3 of air which is just saturated with water vapour. The pressure in the container is 100 kPa, the pressure exerted by the saturated water vapour at this temperature being 20 kPa. The air in the container is now compressed at constant temperature until the pressure in the container is 150 kPa. What is the new volume?

(University of London, Q2, Paper 2, June 1982)

21. A quantity of air is trapped by a small length of water in a horizontal tube of uniform bore, sealed at one end. The length of the air column is 11.3 cm and its temperature is 10°C. The temperature is now raised to 25°C. Given that the saturated vapour pressures of water at 10°C and 25°C are 1×10^3 Pa and 3×10^3 Pa respectively, calculate the new length of the air column. (Atmospheric pressure = 1.01×10^5 Pa)

(AEB, QA4, Paper 3, November 1982)

22. Draw a sketch graph showing a series of isothermals relating the pressure and volume of a given mass of carbon dioxide for a wide range of these variables. On your graph indicate the state of the carbon dioxide represented by the various regions. Mark the approximate temperatures corresponding to your isothermals. What is the relevance of your curves to the general problem of liquefaction of gases?

(AEB, QA4, Paper 3, June 1982)

23. An ideal gas cannot be liquefied; a real gas can, subject to certain conditions.

(a) How do the properties assigned to molecules of an ideal gas lead to the conclusion that an ideal gas cannot be liquefied?

(b)(i) Sketch graphs of pressure against volume for a fixed mass of a real gas at a number of temperatures both above and below the critical temperature. Label the critical isotherm.

(ii) Draw two straight lines on your set of graphs, one (WX) to show a possible transition from vapour to liquid by a reduction in volume, and the other (YZ) to show a possible transition from liquid in equilibrium with its vapour to gas at constant volume. In both cases, label appropriate portions of the lines with the relevant states of the substance.

(iii) Shade the area on your graph for which the liquid phase of the substance is present in the system.

When nitrogen, contained at room temperature in a cylinder under pressure, is released through a valve, the pressure falls continuously. On the other hand, the pressure in a cylinder of butane fuel remains nearly constant until the cylinder is almost empty. Account for this difference with reference to processes at a molecular level.

(Critical temperature: nitrogen, 126 K; butane, 425 K)

(University of Cambridge, Q17, Paper 1, June 1980)

24. A certain molecule consists of two identical atoms, each of mass 1.7×10^{-27} kg. The equilibrium separation of the atoms in the molecule is x_0. Figure 16.61 shows the way in which the force F of repulsion between the atoms varies with their separation x.

(a) Account for the general shape of the graph and use it to find x_0.

(b) Sketch a graph of the potential energy V of the molecule as a function of x, marking the position of x_0 on the x-axis. How is V related to F?

For very small displacements from x_0, the force F is given by the approximate relation $F = -k(x - x_0)$.

(c) Find the value of k in this equation.

(d) Describe the motion of atoms in the molecule when moving freely under the action of this force. By deriving the equation of motion of one of the atoms, or otherwise, find the frequency of the motion.

(University of Cambridge, Q18, Paper 1, June 1979)

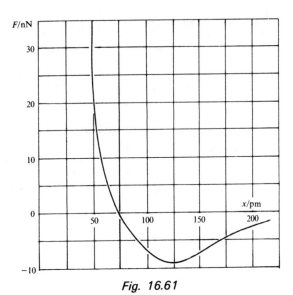

Fig. 16.61

25. The graph, Fig. 16.62 overleaf, shows how the resultant force, F, between a pair of molecules might vary as the separation, r, between them increases. Positive values of the force indicate that it is an attraction, negative values that it is repulsion.

(a) Use the graph to determine

(i) the equilibrium separation and the separation at which the attraction force is a maximum,

(ii) the energy required to decrease the separation of the molecules from 3.03×10^{-10} m to 2.88×10^{-10} m, and

(iii) the potential energy of the molecules at a separation of 2.88×10^{10} m measured with respect to the minimum value of the potential energy of the system.

(b) The model as represented by the graph can be used to help explain the elastic behaviour of solids. Use it to explain

(i) why solids resist being stretched or compressed,

(ii) why Hooke's law is obeyed for small changes in the length of a solid rod,

(iii) why, above a certain value of the tensile stress, a solid will break.

(c) It can be shown that the Young modulus for a solid is approximately given by

$$E = \frac{k}{x}$$

365

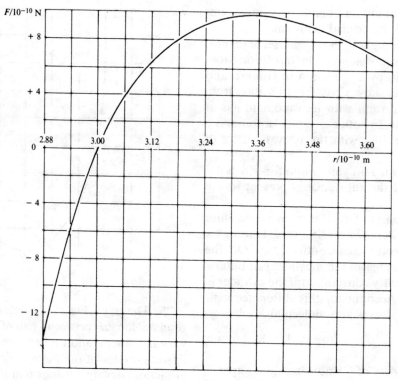

Fig. 16.62

for small displacements, where x is the equilibrium spacing between the molecules and k is the force per unit displacement between the molecules. To what quantity does k relate on the graph? Use the graph to make an estimate of the value of k, explaining how you obtained your result. Calculate a value for the Young modulus, for the solid represented by the graph.

(University of London, Q9, Paper 2, June 1982)

17 Temperature and heat

Temperature

Temperature is a quantitative measure of the 'degree of hotness' of an object; later in this chapter we will consider a better definition. Temperature is what we measure with thermometers. Thus, regardless of any consideration of temperature scales or calibration of thermometers, if we put a thermometer in contact with two separate objects and obtain the same reading, we say they are at the same temperature. This is a fundamental law, so fundamental it is called the zeroth law despite being formulated, in 1931 by R. H. Fowler, long after the first and second laws of thermodynamics. The zeroth law of thermodynamics is more formally stated as:

Two objects that are in thermal equilibrium with a third object will be in thermal equilibrium with each other.

Defining temperature scales

In order to give a value to a given degree of hotness so that it has the same meaning when communicated to others, we need to define a temperature scale. We do this by:

1. Stipulating some substance.
2. Selecting a thermometric property of that substance, i.e., some property whose value varies continuously with the degree of hotness.
3. Selecting two fixed points, giving values to them, and measuring the value of the thermometric property at those points.

4. Specifying a linear relationship between the thermometric property and temperature between those fixed points.

Thus if we now determine the value of the thermometric property at some temperature between the fixed points then, because a graph of property against temperature is a straight line by definition (Fig. 17.1), we have

$$\text{gradient of graph} = \frac{X_1 - X_0}{N} = \frac{X - X_0}{\theta - \theta_0}$$

Hence

$$\theta = \left(\frac{X - X_0}{X_1 - X_0}\right) N + \theta_0$$

The number of divisions N specified between the fixed points is called the fundamental interval.

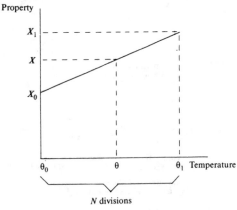

Fig. 17.1 Defining a temperature scale

Thermometric properties

Properties of substances that can be used as the basis of thermometers must give measurable changes when the temperature changes, and such changes must be reproducible no matter how many times the property is used for temperature measurement. The following are some thermometric properties that have been used:

1. The length of a liquid column in a glass capillary tube, e.g., the mercury-in-glass thermometer.
2. The pressure of a gas in a constant volume container, the so-called gas thermometer (Fig. 17.2a).

3. The resistance of a platinum wire coil, the so-called resistance thermometer (Fig. 17.2b).
4. The e.m.f. of a thermocouple (Fig. 17.2c).
5. The 'colour' of the light emitted by a hot object, e.g, the disappearing filament pyrometer (Fig. 17.2d).

Temperature scales

The ideal gas scale involves the measurement of the pressure of a fixed mass, fixed volume, of an ideal gas. The two fixed points used to specify the scale are absolute zero, to which a value of 0 K is assigned, and the triple point of pure air-free

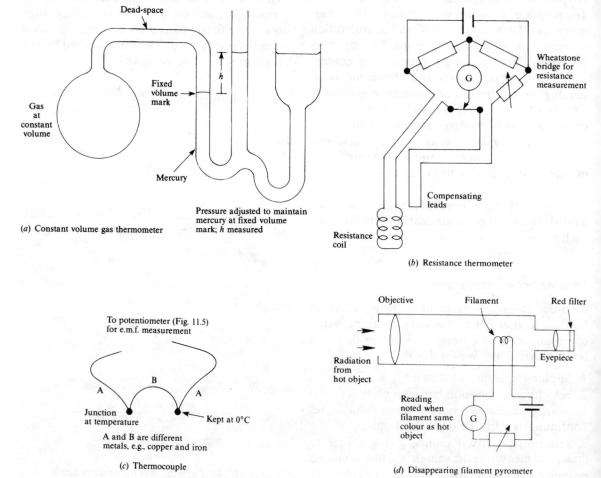

(a) Constant volume gas thermometer

(b) Resistance thermometer

(c) Thermocouple

(d) Disappearing filament pyrometer

Fig. 17.2 The basic principles of some thermometers

water, to which a value of 273.16 K is assigned. At absolute zero the thermometric property, pressure, has a zero value, hence the temperature scale equation becomes:

$$\theta = \frac{(p - 0)}{(p_{tr} - 0)} \, 273.16 + 0$$

$$\theta = \frac{p \times 273.16}{p_{tr}}$$

where p is the pressure at temperature θ, p_{tr} at the triple point.

The scale is based on the use of the constant volume gas thermometer (Fig. 17.2a). Such thermometers are cumbersome and allowances have to be made for such things as—the containing bulb for the gas changing its volume with temperature, the gas in the dead-space not being at the same temperature as the gas in the bulb, and the vapour pressure of the manometer liquid. In addition there is the major problem that the gas used is invariably not ideal. Different gases can give different scales. Also different scales can be produced with different masses of gas in the thermometer bulb. However, if small masses of gas are used, i.e., the pressures are very low, all the gases tend to more closely conform to the ideal gas behaviour. When the gas pressure is low the gas molecules are well separated, and so intermolecular forces become negligible and also the volume occupied by the molecules becomes insignificant in comparison with the total gas volume. If we extrapolate our pressure results to zero pressure (Fig. 17.3) the gases behave as ideal gases. Thus

$$\theta = \lim_{p \to 0} \left(\frac{p}{p_{tr}} \right) \times 273.16$$

The gas thermometer is not in practice a very convenient device, being bulky, intricate and tedious to use. For more general use there is an internationally agreed scale based upon the use of a number of standard thermometers and fixed points. The scale is called the International Practical Scale. The standard thermometers are:

From 13.8 K to 903.89 K—platinum resistance thermometer

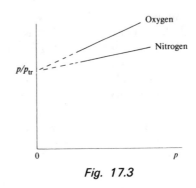

Fig. 17.3

From 903.89 K to 1337.58 K—the platinum–platinum/rhodium thermocouple

The International Practical Scale is the practical realization of the absolute thermodynamic scale, proposed by Kelvin. This, however, is a theoretical scale and will be discussed later in this chapter.

Celsius temperatures are related to thermodynamic scale temperatures by the relation

$$\theta_C = \theta_K - 273.15$$

where θ_C is the temperature in °C and θ_K the temperature in K. This means that the ice point of 273.15 K has the value of 0°C.

Fixed points

The fixed points used for defining temperature scales need to be points that can be easily and accurately reproduced. For this reason, change of state points are used. When a change of state occurs there is no change in temperature during the transition (Fig. 17.4). The boiling point of water at normal atmospheric pressure is an

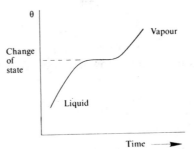

Fig. 17.4 Example of a change of state

369

example of such a change of state, giving the fixed point of 373.15 K (100°C). Another fixed point that used to be used was the freezing point of water. This has, however, been replaced by the triple point of water. The ice point, defined as the temperature of a mixture of ice and water saturated with air at normal atmospheric pressure, proved difficult to reproduce accurately. This was because the result depended on how much air was dissolved in the water and this was not easy to control. The triple point is the temperature at which ice, liquid water and water vapour coexist.

Expansion of solids and liquids

The linear expansivity α of a substance is defined as

$$\alpha = \frac{L_\theta - L_0}{L_0\theta}$$

where L_θ is the length after a temperature change of θ, L_0 being the original length. This equation is often written as

$$L_\theta = L_0(1 + \alpha\theta)$$

α is usually defined with reference to L_0 being the length at 0°C.

The superficial or area expansivity β is given by

$$\beta = \frac{A_\theta - A_0}{A_0\theta}$$

where A represents area. Likewise the cubic or volume expansivity γ is given by

$$\gamma = \frac{V_\theta - V_0}{V_0\theta}$$

where V represents volume. By considering the fact that, for an area $A = L^2$ and for a volume $V = L^3$, it is possible to show that β is approximately 2α and γ is 3α.

Heat capacity

If heat ΔQ is given to a body and its temperature

rises by $\Delta\theta$ then the heat capacity of the body C is

$$C = \frac{\Delta Q}{\Delta\theta}$$

C has the unit of J K^{-1}. Thus, for example, if a block of copper changes in temperature by 3 K when receiving 2340 J, then

$$C = \frac{2340}{3} = 780 \text{ J K}^{-1}$$

The specific heat capacity c is the heat capacity per unit mass (per kg), hence the unit of J kg^{-1} K^{-1}.

$$c = \frac{\Delta Q}{m\Delta\theta}$$

Thus if, in the above example, the block of copper had a mass of 2 kg, then the specific heat capacity would be 390 J kg^{-1} K^{-1}.

The molar heat capacity C_m is the heat capacity per mole, hence the unit J mol^{-1} K^{-1}.

$$C_m = \frac{\Delta Q}{M\Delta\theta}$$

where M is the mass of 1 mole of the substance (in its usual unit of grammes).

The measurement of specific heat capacity

The basis of many methods used for the measurement of specific heats of solids and liquids is to insert in a sample of the material an electric heating coil. The electrical energy converted into thermal energy per second when a current I is passed through the coil, with V being the potential difference across it, is IV. Hence if the current is passed for a time of t then IVt is the thermal energy supplied to the substance. Hence if the temperature rise is measured for a sample of known mass, the specific heat capacity can be calculated. This, however, assumes that all the thermal energy supplied by the heater is used to produce the temperature change of the sample and no heat losses occur.

Heat losses can be minimized in a number of ways. An obvious one is to lag the sample or, in the case of liquids, put the liquid in a vacuum flask. Another method is to arrange for the initial temperature of the sample to be as much below room temperature as the final temperature will be above. Then the heat gained when it is below balances the heat lost when it is above room temperature.

For many situations the rate of loss of heat is approximately proportional to the excess temperature the sample is over the surroundings. Thus if during an experiment the sample starts at the temperature of the surroundings and rises by θ in a time t, the excess temperature is θ. When the heating is switched off at this temperature the rate of cooling $d\theta/dt$ is measured. The average rate of cooling during the temperature rise is then taken to be $\frac{1}{2}(d\theta/dt)$. Then the correction to be applied to θ to allow for the heat loss is $\frac{1}{2}(d\theta/dt)t$, so the corrected temperature is $\theta + \frac{1}{2}(d\theta/dt)t$.

An important method used for the measurement of the specific heat capacity of a liquid is the continuous flow method (Fig. 17.5), sometimes referred to as the Callendar and Barnes method. The liquid is continuously passed, at a constant rate, over a heating coil. The temperatures of the liquid at the beginning and end of the heating coil are measured. When steady temperatures occur the values are noted. Then if I_1 is the heating current and V_1 the potential difference across it,

the thermal energy input per second is I_1V_1. If m_1 is the mass of liquid flowing through the apparatus per second then

$$I_1V_1 = m_1c(\theta_2 - \theta_1) + h$$

where h is the heat loss per second. The experiment is then repeated with different values of current I_2, potential difference V_2 and mass per second m_2, but with the same values of θ_2 and θ_1. Because the temperatures are the same the heat loss per second at equilibrium will be the same. Hence

$$I_2V_2 = m_2c(\theta_2 - \theta_1) + h$$

Subtracting the two equations gives

$$I_1V_1 - I_2V_2 = (m_1 - m_2)c(\theta_2 - \theta_1)$$

and so c can be determined.

The advantages of this method are that no allowance has to be made for the energy used to heat the containing vessel, it does not change temperature when equilibrium obtains, heat losses can be eliminated by the repeating of the experiment, static temperatures are being determined and so accuracy is feasible.

First law of thermodynamics

In discussing the first law of thermodynamics, care has to be taken with the meanings of the

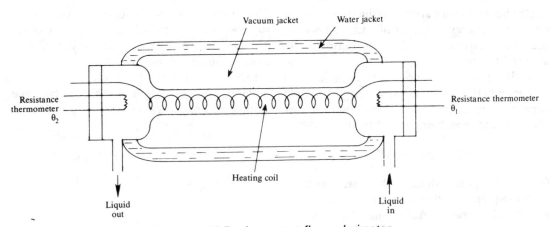

Fig. 17.5 A constant-flow calorimeter

terms heat and work. Both heat and work are energy transfer processes. Both are transient quantities, only describing the process of transfer. The two systems/objects involved in the transfer will not 'contain' work nor 'contain' heat. The result of the transfer will, however, be a change in the internal energy of the two systems.

Heat is the energy which moves from one point to another because there is a temperature difference between them.

Work is any transfer of energy process that is not heat. Work is energy that is transmitted from one system to another when each exerts on the other macroscopic forces whose points of application are moved through finite distances.

The term *system* is used to describe something within an identifiable boundary. The term is used in thermodynamics rather than talk of an object because we may be considering an assembly of objects, e.g., an engine, and be concerned with the energy transfer between assemblies. The term *internal energy* is used for the sum total of the kinetic and mutual potential energies of the particles that go to make up the system.

To illustrate the above, consider the following energy transfers. A piston is pushed down in a cylinder containing a gas, compressing it and resulting in the gas temperature increasing. Energy is transferred into the piston–gas system by work, resulting in a change in the internal energy of the gas (the gas molecules move around faster, having higher mean kinetic energies). Consider the case of a beaker of hot water slowly cooling down in a room. Energy is transferred from the beaker–water system to the room system by heat. The energy transfer only occurs because there is a temperature difference between the water and the room.

The first law of thermodynamics is just the application of the conservation of energy principle to energy transfer processes involving either or both work and heat, being stated by the equation

$$\Delta Q = \Delta U + \Delta W$$

ΔQ is the energy transfer into the system as heat. The consequence of this transfer is a change in the internal energy of ΔU of the system and a transfer out of the system of energy as work ΔW.

In other words, the equation is stating:

Energy transferred in =
energy staying in the system
+ energy transferred out

Molar heat capacities of gases

A gas has an infinite number of molar heat capacities since heat supplied to a gas can be made to do a variable amount of work and so the change in internal energy is variable. However, we normally define two principal molar heat capacities, one at constant volume and one at constant pressure. The principal molar heat capacity at constant volume is the heat required to raise the temperature of one mole of the gas by 1 K at constant volume. The principal molar heat capacity at constant pressure is the heat required to raise the temperature of one mole of the gas by 1 K at constant pressure. These heat capacities must differ because in the case of the one at constant volume no external work is done and all the heat goes into changing internal energy, while at constant pressure there will be a change in volume and so work is done and the heat energy is thus split between work and internal energy.

Suppose we supply heat to 1 mole of an ideal gas at constant volume. Then applying the first law of thermodynamics we have, since $\Delta W = 0$

$$\Delta Q = 1 \times C_V \Delta T = \Delta U + 0$$

The change in internal energy is thus $C_V \Delta T$. Now suppose we supply heat to the gas at constant pressure to produce the same internal energy change. Since the internal energy of an ideal gas is proportional to the temperature in kelvin (see previous chapter) then the same internal energy change means the same temperature change.

$$\Delta Q' = 1 \times C_P \Delta T = \Delta U + \Delta W$$

$$C_P \Delta T = C_V \Delta T + \Delta W$$

But $\Delta W = p \Delta V$ (see Chapter 4), hence

$$C_P = C_V + \frac{p \Delta V}{\Delta T}$$

For the ideal gas we have initially $pV/T = R_0$ and after the change of ΔT in the temperature

$$\frac{p(V + \Delta V)}{T + \Delta T} = R_0$$

Hence $\quad pV + p\Delta V = R_0 T + R_0 \Delta T$

$$p\Delta V = R_0 \Delta T$$

Thus $\quad C_P = C_V + R_0$

Degrees of freedom

With simple kinetic theory the mean kinetic energy of a gas molecule is $\frac{3}{2} kT$, where k is Boltzmann's constant and equals R_0/L with L being the number of molecules in a mole, i.e., Avogadro's number. Thus if we consider one mole of an ideal gas at a temperature T, then the total internal energy will be $L \times \frac{3}{2} kT = \frac{3}{2} R_0 T$. If the gas is at constant volume then the heat input needed to produce this change would be $1 \times C_V T$, i.e., we are considering the heat input to raise the temperature from 0 K to T. Thus $C_V T = \frac{3}{2} R_0 T$ and so

$$C_V = \frac{3}{2} R_0$$

Since R_0 has the value 8.31 J mol^{-1} K^{-1}, this means $C_V = 12.5$ J mol^{-1} K^{-1}. This is in quite good agreement with the values for monatomic gases such as helium and argon. However, diatomic gases such as hydrogen and oxygen have, at room temperature, molar heat capacities at constant volume of about 21 J mol^{-1} K^{-1}. We can explain this if we take into account the various ways the molecules can absorb energy.

A monatomic gas molecule can absorb energy in three ways, by translational motion in the x, the y or the z direction. If we consider the energy to be equally divided between these three ways, we can take $\frac{1}{2}kT$ for each to give our total of $\frac{3}{2} kT$. Each way is referred to as a degree of freedom. Thus a monatomic molecule has three degrees of freedom. A diatomic molecule can absorb energy by translational motion in the x, the y and the z directions, by rotating or vibrating (Fig. 17.6). However, since molar heat capacities vary with temperature, we consider that vibrational degrees of freedom are only involved at high temperatures. Thus the diatomic molecule at about room temperature has three translational degrees of freedom and two rotational. Hence the mean energy of a molecule is $5 \times \frac{1}{2}kT$ and $C_V = \frac{5}{2} R_0 T = 20.8$ J mol^{-1} K^{-1}; close agreement with practice.

We can determine the molar heat capacities at constant pressure by using the relation $C_P = C_V + R_0$. Hence for a monatomic gas $C_P = \frac{3}{2} R_0 + R_0 = \frac{5}{2} R_0$. For a diatomic gas we have $C_P = \frac{7}{2} R_0$.

For monatomic gases the ratio of the molar heat capacity at constant pressure and that at constant volume $\gamma = C_P/C_V$ is 5/3, for diatomic gases 7/5.

Dulong and Petit's law

We can try to apply these ideas to solids. The atoms in a solid can only vibrate and if we consider there to be three different modes of vibration (along the x-axis, the y-axis, and the z-axis) there will be six degrees of freedom and thus

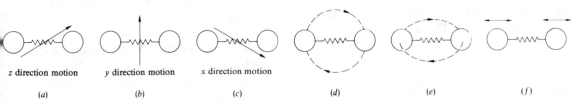

z direction motion   y direction motion   x direction motion

(a)   (b)   (c)   (d)   (e)   (f)

Fig. 17.6   (a), (b), (c) Translational degrees of freedom. (d), (e) Rotational degrees of freedom. (f) Vibrational degree of freedom

the specific heat capacity will be $3R_0$ or 25 $J K^{-1} mol^{-1}$.

Solid	Specific heat capacity, at constant volume, $/J K^{-1} mol^{-1}$
Copper	23.8
Bismuth	25.3
Aluminium	23.4
Tin	25.4
Platinum	25.4
Sodium	25.6
Lead	24.8

For many solids the predicted result appears to be very close to the experimental result. That solids should have this value of specific heat capacity was arrived at empirically by Dulong and Petit in 1819 and is known as the Dulong and Petit law. The law, however, only holds above a certain temperature. Figure 17.7 shows how the specific heat capacity of lead varies with temperature. For lead the law holds above 200 K.

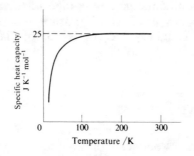

Fig. 17.7   Specific heat capacity of lead

Isothermal and adiabatic processes

An isothermal process is one that takes place at constant temperature. This means that there is no change in the internal energy for an ideal gas. For such a change pV = a constant. To obtain a constant temperature during a volume change we must make the change very slowly. Thus if a gas is compressed, normally its temperature would rise since the molecules would be rebounding from the moving piston; we are assuming the gas is being compressed in a cylinder by a piston, with a velocity greater than their incident velocity. Thus the average kinetic energy of the molecules would rise. To avoid this and maintain a constant temperature, a constant average kinetic energy for the molecules, the change has to be made so slowly that heat can escape from, or in the case of an expansion into, the gas.

An adiabatic process is one that takes place under conditions when no heat enters or leaves the gas. Thus, the first law of thermodynamics indicates

$$\Delta Q = 0 = \Delta U + \Delta W$$

Hence $\qquad \Delta W = -\Delta U$

Thus if the gas does work then it is entirely at the expense of the internal energy. The internal energy decreases and this means a drop in temperature. For such a change the relationship pV^γ = a constant holds, where γ is the ratio of the molar heat capacities, i.e., C_P/C_V. Since the equation pV/T = a constant also holds we can derive a number of relationships

$$\left(\frac{pV}{T}\right)^\gamma = \text{a constant}$$

$$(pV^\gamma)\left(\frac{p^{\gamma-1}}{T^\gamma}\right) = \text{a constant}$$

Hence

$$\frac{p^{\gamma-1}}{T^\gamma} = \text{a constant} \qquad T^\gamma p^{1-\gamma} = \text{a constant}$$

Likewise we can derive $TV^{\gamma-1}$ = a constant.

To illustrate how such equations can be used in calculations, consider a gas enclosed in a cylinder by a piston. If the initial pressure of the gas is 140 kPa at a temperature of 300 K, what will be the change in temperature when the piston is suddenly moved and the pressure drops to 110 kPa? The word 'sudden' is often used in problems to indicate that the change is so fast that there is no time for heat to either enter or leave the gas and so it can be assumed to be an adiabatic process.

Thus if γ has the value 1.40 for the gas

$$T_1^\gamma p_1^{1-\gamma} = T_2^\gamma p_2^{1-\gamma}$$

$$T_2 = 300 \times \left(\frac{100}{140}\right)^{0.4/1.4}$$

$$= 280 \text{ K}$$

There is a temperature drop of 20 K.

Graphs of pressure against volume for an adiabatic change have steeper gradients at any point when compared with isothermal changes. For an isothermal change, gradient = dp/dV = p/V, whereas for an adiabatic change, gradient = $dp/dV = -\gamma p/V$. Figure 17.8 shows such graphs.

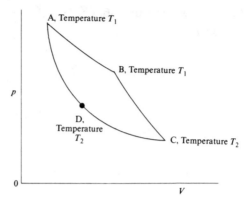

Fig. 17.9 A cycle for a heat engine

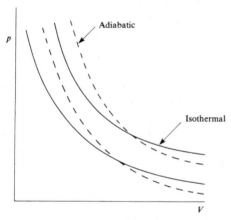

Fig. 17.8 Isothermals and adiabatics

Heat engines

The essential elements of a heat engine are a reservoir from which heat may transfer, a working fluid to process the heat, a means of extracting work from this fluid and a reservoir into which heat may transfer. Such an engine is known as a Carnot engine. Suppose we take as a heat engine an ideal gas enclosed in a cylinder by a piston. We will assume no gas leakage and no friction between the piston and the cylinder. In this way all events can be made perfectly reversible. We then follow the following cycle of events:

1. Starting at point A on Fig. 17.9, the piston is moved outwards as a result of a heat input Q_1,

so expanding the gas. This change is made isothermally so that the gas expands to point B on the graph.

2. The gas is then allowed to further expand but this time adiabatically. Since adiabatics are steeper than isothermals the result is that point C is reached.

3. The gas is then compressed isothermally to point D, giving out heat Q_2.

4. Finally the gas is restored to its original pressure and volume by an adiabatic compression.

During the expansion the volume increases so that in going from A to B to C work is taken from the gas. Since work is the sum of all pdV elements, it is the area between the ABC graph line and the zero axis. During the compression work is done on the gas since the volume is decreased. Thus in going from C to D to A the work done is the area between this line and the zero axis. The work taken from the gas is greater than the work done on the gas, this difference being the area enclosed in the ABCD shape. Useful work W can thus be extracted.

Since we ended up after the cycle at the same temperature as we started, there is no net change in internal energy. Thus according to the first law of thermodynamics we must have

$$Q_1 - Q_2 = W$$

The thermal efficiency of a heat engine is defined

as the ratio of the work obtained to the energy supplied (Q_1). Hence

$$\text{thermal efficiency} = \frac{W}{Q_1} = \frac{Q_1 - Q_2}{Q_1}$$

For an ideal gas it can be shown that this equation can be written in the form

$$\text{thermal efficiency} = \frac{T_1 - T_2}{T_1}$$

A consequence of this is that all heat engines operating between reservoirs at the same temperatures will have the same efficiency. Heat is transferred from the high temperature reservoir to the engine, work is done and heat transferred out from the engine to a lower temperature reservoir. The thermal efficiency is defined by the temperature of the reservoirs between which it operates. Our equation gives the efficiency for the perfectly reversible engine, no energy being lost as a result of friction, etc. Real engines can never be perfectly reversible. Thus the efficiency given by the equation is the maximum efficiency possible.

The early steam engines operated between temperatures of about 10°C and 100°C. The maximum efficiency possible was thus (373 − 283)/373 or about 24 per cent. As indicated in the supplementary topic to Chapter 4, this was far greater than the efficiencies realized.

Latent heat

During the melting of a solid or the vaporization of a liquid, though energy is supplied there is no change in temperature. The energy is needed to effect the change of state. Because the energy produces no temperature change it is called latent heat, the term sensible heat being used for that which does cause a temperature change.

The molar latent heat of transformation is the heat required to change the state of one mole of that substance. The specific latent heat of transformation is the heat required to change the state of 1 kg of that substance. For the change from solid to liquid the term latent heat of fusion is used, for the change from liquid to vapour the latent heat of vaporization. The values of the latent heats depend on the pressure acting on the substance, being usually quoted for standard pressure, i.e., normal atmospheric pressure.

Water has a specific latent heat of fusion of 3.3×10^5 J kg^{-1} and of vaporization of 23×10^5 J kg^{-1}, at standard pressure. This means that to change 5 kg of ice at 0°C to liquid at 0°C requires $5 \times 3.3 \times 10^5 = 1.65 \times 10^6$ J.

Figure 17.10 shows the basic principle of the Henning's method for the measurement of specific latent heat of vaporization. When the liquid is boiling the vapour is conducted down the outside of the containing vessel in a jacket so that the vapour is at the same temperature as the boiling liquid. This reduces heat losses and helps to maintain a steady state. At the steady-state condition

$$IVt = mL + Q$$

where Q are the heat losses and t the time for which the mass m of condensed vapour was collected. If the experiment is repeated for the same time but different values of I, V and hence m, then the heat loss will be the same and can be eliminated.

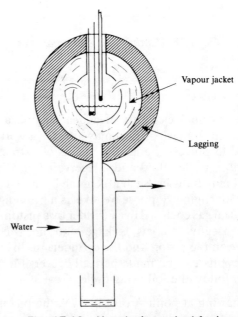

Fig. 17.10 Henning's method for L

Latent heat and bond breaking

For a solid in a close-packed arrangement an atom has twelve near neighbours; if in the liquid form we assume that the same substance has only ten near neighbours to each atom, then bonds must have been broken when the solid turned into a liquid. When the liquid turns to vapour the atoms lose these ten near neighbours. On this basis we would expect that the energy needed to form unit mass of a liquid from the solid would be roughly about 2/10 times that needed to convert the same mass from liquid to vapour, i.e., the ratio of the number of bonds broken. This is in fact the ratio of the molar latent heats of fusion compared with those of evaporation for some elements.

Element	Molar latent heat of fusion L_F/kJ mol^{-1}	Molar latent heat of vaporization L_V/kJ mol^{-1}	Ratio L_F/L_V
Argon	1.18	6.5	0.18
Neon	0.33	1.8	0.18
Krypton	1.64	9.0	0.18
Xenon	2.29	12.6	0.18
Chlorine	3.20	10.2	0.32
Bromine	5.29	15.0	0.35
Iodine	7.89	20.9	0.39
Sodium	2.60	89.0	0.029
Potassium	2.30	77.5	0.030
Rubidium	2.36	69.2	0.029

The ratio of the molar latent heat of fusion to that of vaporization for the inert gases would seem to be about the ratio 2/10, i.e., 0.2. The group of chlorine, bromine, and iodine would seem to fit a ratio of 3/9 while the alkali elements form another group with what would appear to be atoms in the liquid having almost the same number of neighbours as those in the solid.

In one mole we have 6×10^{23} atoms and thus if we take each atom in the liquid to have 10 near neighbours we have to break

$$\frac{10}{2} \times 6 \times 10^{23}$$

bonds to evaporate the liquid. The 2 occurs in the expression because each bond is between two atoms, and must be only counted once. Argon has a latent heat of vaporization of 6.5 kJ mol^{-1}, this must be equal to

$$\frac{10}{2} \times 6 \times 10^{23} \times \text{(energy to break one bond)}$$

Thus the energy necessary to break a bond in liquid argon is about 2.2×10^{-21} J, about 0.014 eV. (Most molecules need energies of this order to break their bonds.)

We can write this as

$$\text{Molar latent heat} = 5L\varepsilon$$

where L is Avogadro's number and ε the energy to break a bond.

The model of matter we have been using has assumed that when a change of state occurs all the energy is used to separate molecules. However, there may be a change in volume when a change of state occurs. This would mean that latent heat is composed of two aspects: energy to separate molecules and also work done in an expansion. For a solid changing to a liquid the change in volume is generally fairly small and thus most of the latent heat is energy involved in separating molecules. However, when a liquid changes to a gas there is a considerable change in volume and so a very significant part of the latent heat is due to this.

At normal atmospheric pressure of 1.01×10^5 Pa, 1.00 kg of water having a volume of 1.00×10^{-3} m^3 becomes 1.671 m^3 of steam when boiled. The work done in this expansion is $p(V_2 - V_1) = 1.01 \times 10^5 \times 1.670 = 1.695 \times 10^5$ J. Since the specific latent heat of vaporization is 22.5×10^5 J kg^{-1}, this means that 20.8×10^5 J must go into separating molecules.

Causal laws in science

Causal laws can be summarized as—to every effect there is a precise cause. If an object accelerates we say that there is a cause—a force. We do not say—there might be a force. When an apple fell off a tree Newton considered there must be a force acting on the apple—the force of gravity. The ancient Greeks did not consider a force but considered the apple to fall because it

377

was the natural thing for apples to fall—no cause was considered.

For example, consider two billiard balls colliding. From a knowledge of their velocities before the collision we can plot their paths and determine their positions at different times. Knowing their masses we can compute their velocities after the collision and hence their positions at different times. To determine the positions of the balls at all times we needed only their velocities, masses, their initial positions, and the laws of conservation of momentum and kinetic energy.

Can we on the basis of causal laws explain the whole of science? The two billiard balls colliding would seem to offer a simpler version of the collisions between molecules of a gas in a container. If we know the initial conditions, can we calculate the positions of all the molecules at every future instant of time? The first difficulty is how to determine the initial conditions with sufficient accuracy to permit accurate calculations of the future positions. Only very small errors in the knowledge of the initial positions would considerably affect the behaviour of a single molecule. If our knowledge of the position of a single molecule was incorrect by, say, 10^{-10} m we could not calculate its position after just one collision with another molecule. Molecules have a size of about 10^{-10} m and an error in position of this amount might mean that a collision did not take place because the two molecules miss each other. Knowledge of positions to a greater accuracy than this may not be sufficient to determine the angle at which the two molecules collide for their directions after a collision to be accurately calculated. When we think of the large number of molecules in a container then the calculation seems impossible.

Causal laws have their uses in the macroscopic sphere, i.e., large-scale effects, but are severely limited in the microscopic sphere, i.e., on an atomic level. If we have just two atoms then we cannot calculate what will happen—they might collide if we somehow aim them at each other but because of the limitations of the accuracy of our aim we cannot forecast their paths. If, however, we fired a large number of atoms at each other then perhaps we could expect some of them to make collisions and perhaps we could expect

some of them to make collisions at certain angles. In such a case perhaps we can calculate how such atoms would move after a collision. Large numbers enable us to argue events on the basis of chance—chance that some of the atoms will follow particular paths.

In a rainfall we would expect that the amount of rain falling on each square metre would be the same—we would certainly not expect that only every alternate square metre would have rain, the others remaining dry. We would not, however, feel able to predict the path of a single raindrop.

On an atomic scale we need the idea of chance—is this because of our limitation on the accuracy of our measurements or is it because the events are dictated by chance? The majority opinion is that the events are chance events.

Chance

If we throw a six-sided die there are just six ways it can land. We have a 1 in 6 chance of finding one particular die face uppermost, say a five. If we throw 120 dice then we shall expect that we will obtain about 1/6 of them, i.e., 20, showing a five uppermost. We may only get 18 or perhaps 23, but 20 is the most likely result. If we throw the dice a large number of times then we will obtain 20 out of the 120 showing five more often than any other number.

Chance is the ratio of the number of ways an event, such as a five with a die, can be realized compared with the total number of possible outcomes (with the die—six). We are assuming, in this definition, that each way or outcome is equally likely (our die is not biased). An alternative way of expressing chance is as the ratio of the number of times an event occurs compared with the number of times it could occur.

What is the chance of a coin, when spun, landing heads uppermost? There are just two, equally likely, ways an unbiased coin can land, heads or tails. The total number of possible outcomes is thus two. The number of ways heads can be realized is one. The chance is thus 1/2. A coin spun 1000 times landed with heads uppermost 502 times—this gives the chance of heads as 502/1000 or near enough 1/2.

What is the chance of obtaining two heads

when two coins are spun? The possible outcomes are

HH, HT, TH, TT

There are four possible outcomes, one of which gives two heads. The chance is thus 1/4.

What is the chance of obtaining both a head and a tail when two coins are spun? Two ways out of the four give this outcome. The chance is thus 2/4 or 1/2.

If an event can be realized in many ways it is often likely to occur—many ways mean often.

Diffusion

Consider a hypothetical case of a single molecule in a box. What are the chances of finding the molecule in one particular half, say the left-hand half, of the box? The molecule has two alternative positions—in the left-hand half or the right-hand half of the box. There are thus two possible outcomes of which one gives the molecule in the left-hand half. The chance of finding the molecule in the left-hand half is thus 1/2. This assumes that each half is an equally likely place for the molecule to be found.

Now consider two molecules in the box. What are the chances of finding the two molecules in the left-hand half? The possible outcomes are shown in Fig. 17.11. There are four possible outcomes of which one gives all the molecules in the left-hand half. The chance of finding the molecules in the left-hand half is thus 1/4.

With the two molecules, what are the chances of finding one molecule in each half? There are two of the four possible outcomes giving this. The chance is thus 2/4. If our molecules freely wander

between the two halves then there is a greater chance of us finding them at any instant with one in each half than with them all in one particular half.

Suppose we have four molecules. Figure 17.12 shows the possible outcomes. There are 16 possible arrangements of the molecules, one of which has all the molecules in the left-hand half. The chance of all the molecules being in the left-hand half is thus 1/16. The chance of there being equal numbers of molecules in each half is 6/16—a much greater chance.

Why do the molecules in a room seem to be reasonably uniformly distributed over the room? The molecules are free to move about the room—why could they not by some fortuitous sequence of collisions all be in one half of the room? What are the chances of finding all the molecules in one particular half of a room? With one molecule in a box we had two possible arrangements (i.e., 2^1), with two molecules four possible arrangements (i.e., 2^2), with four molecules sixteen possible arrangements (i.e., 2^4). If there are two ways a molecule can be located in a box, or room, then with n molecules there are 2^n possible outcomes. In all the previous arrangements only one outcome was with all the molecules in one particular half. The chance of n molecules all being in one half of a room is thus $1/2^n$. How big is n? A room about 5 $\times$ 4 m floor area and 3 m high would under normal conditions contain about 1.5×10^{27} molecules. Thus the chance of finding them all in one half is about 1 in $2^{10^{27}}$ (or about 1 in $10^{3 \times 10^{26}}$; $2^n = 10^{n \log 2}$). If we took a photograph of the molecules, assuming them to be visible to our special camera, once a second for a year we would have 3.2×10^6 pictures. In one year the chance of

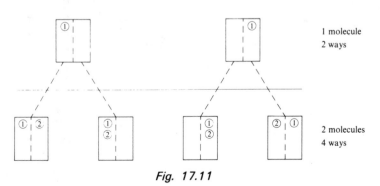

Fig. 17.11

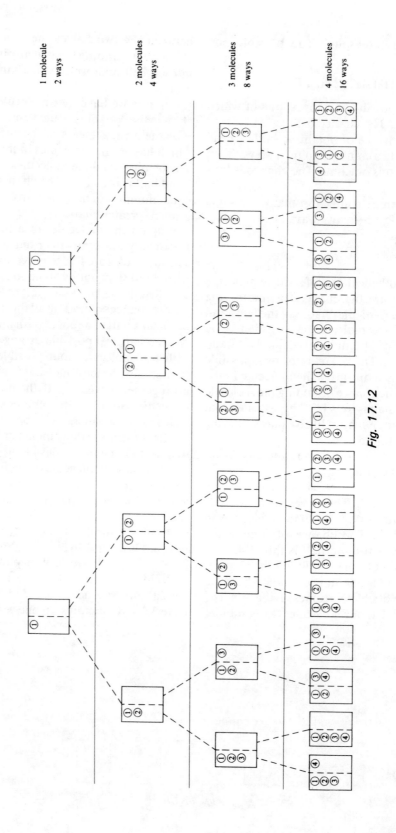

Fig. 17.12

seeing all the molecules in one half is rather remote. The universe is about 10^{10} years old. If we took photographs every second for the entire life of the universe, about 10^{16}, there is very little chance that we would see all the molecules in one half. We would need to wait about $10^{3 \times 10^{26}}$ seconds for there to be a chance of one such event occurring. This would seem to be as good as saying that the chance of all the molecules being in one half is extremely improbable.

'Not until after a time enormously long compared with $10^{10^{10}}$ years will there be any noticeable unmixing of the gases. One may recognize that this is practically equivalent to never, if one recalls that in this length of time, according to the laws of probability, there will have been many years in which every inhabitant of a large country committed suicide, purely by accident, on the same day, or every building burned down at the same time—yet the insurance companies get along quite well by ignoring the possibility of such events. If a much smaller probability than this is not practically equivalent to impossibility, then no one can be sure that today will be followed by a night and then a day.'
  L. Boltzmann (1964) *Lectures on Gas Theory*, Univ. California Press/Cambridge Univ. Press.

This argument involving chance suggests that the diffusion of a gas is a result of purely the chance movements of molecules. A gas placed in a container will diffuse throughout the container to give a reasonably uniform spread of the gas— purely by the chance movements of the molecules. The greatest chance is for an even distribution of gas within a container; there is, however, a finite chance that the distribution will be non-uniform— but the chance is considerably smaller. This is an essential feature of processes determined by chance—there will be fluctuations from the uniform or most probable state. If we find such fluctuations, for example the gas density varying slightly, then it is strong evidence for a chance-ruled state.

Fluctuations in the distribution of gas molecules in a container would be expected to lead to pressure fluctuations. The pressure of a gas is due to molecular bombardment of a surface. Small particles of, say, ash, in a gas show irregular motion, known as Brownian motion. This can be explained as being due to slight differences in the number of molecules bombarding the different sides of a particle—evidence for pressure fluctuations and thus fluctuations in the molecular distribution in space.

Reversible and irreversible events

'If, then, the motion of every particle of matter in the universe were precisely reversed at any instant, the course of nature would be simply reversed for ever after. The bursting bubble of foam at the foot of a waterfall would reunite and descend into the water; the thermal motions would reconcentrate their energy, and throw the mass up the fall in drops re-forming into a close column of ascending water. Heat which had been generated by the friction of solids and dissipated by conduction, and radiation with absorption, would come again to the place of contact, and throw the moving body back against the force to which it had previously yielded. Boulders would recover from the mud the materials required to rebuild them into their previous jagged forms, and would become reunited to the mountain peak from which they had formerly broken away....'
  W. Thomson (1874) *Proc. Roy. Soc. Edinburgh*, **8**, 325.

'A birch log, for example, cannot be burnt twice. One cannot take the hot flue gases of a wood fire and the warmth of the fire and from these reconstitute an unburnt log, fresh air, and room chilliness. Passage from the burnt state—the hot flue gases and a warm room—to the pre-burnt state—a birch log, fresh air, and a cold room—is impossible, or at most, highly improbable.

Similarly, the onrush of a passing car cannot be reversed in all aspects. Many cars, of course, can be driven backwards. But no car, in an exact reversal of its motion forward, can suck through its tailpipe exhaust fumes and from these produce in its cylinders an ignition spark, liquid gasoline, and fresh air.

Burning logs and onrushing cars are typical

examples of irreversible events. Viewed in their entirety, such events always produce unalterable changes in the universe. . . .

Seldom noticed . . . is the thermal energy produced as a bouncing ball comes to rest. Yet if energy is conserved during this event, and we believe energy is always conserved, the loss in potential energy of the system (the ball plus the earth) should appear somewhere in some form. Permanent distortion of the ball or the floor might account for part of the energy; even so, it would be difficult to escape production (through friction and sound waves) of some thermal energy. In time, this thermal energy would become distributed between the ball and its thermal surroundings (the floor, the air, the walls, the furniture of the room), to each according to its heat capacity.

Thus, merely bringing the ball back to its initial position above floor-level would not restore the universe (the ball plus its thermal surroundings) to its initial condition. That is impossible. How remarkable would be a complete restoration of the universe can be appreciated by looking at a movie of a bouncing ball coming to rest, run backwards. Objects obviously are not in the habit of springing spontaneously into the air at the expense of the thermal energy of their surroundings. The idea that they might is absurd. They never do. . . .'

H. A. Bent (1965) *The Second Law*, Oxford Univ. Press, New York.

There would appear to be no reason why events should not be reversible. Why should an object not spring up from the floor and the floor (and object and surroundings) become cooler? Provided energy is conserved, and there is no reason why it should not be, the event seems possible. There is nothing in the conservation of energy law which says which direction an event should occur. Why is burning, for example the birch log, a one-way process? Energy can be conserved whichever way the event occurs.

Consider a collision between two perfectly elastic balls, A and B. Initially A has a velocity of 4 m s^{-1}, its mass is 30 g. Initially B is at rest, its mass is 10 g. After the collision, the velocity of A becomes 2 m s^{-1}, in the same direction as before, and B is knocked in the same direction with a velocity of 6 m s^{-1}. We could have the exact reverse of this collision, i.e., B moving towards A and colliding with it so that B comes to rest. The velocities would only differ in their directions. B would move with a velocity of 6 m s^{-1} and A 2 m s^{-1} before the collision. After the collision B would be at rest and A would have a velocity of 4 m s^{-1} (Fig. 17.13). All these figures were calculated by the use of the conservation of momentum and the conservation of kinetic energy laws. This theoretical event appears to be perfectly reversible. The event is, however, only theoretical; in practice some kinetic energy would be lost at the collision and a small temperature change produced. If the event were perfectly reversible there should be an increase in temperature at one collision and a drop in temperature for the reverse collision. This does not occur. Our equations of motion are perfectly reversible—real processes are not.

This still does not tell us why the events are not reversible—the bullet moving through the air raises the temperature of the air and so slows down; why does the air temperature not fall and increase the speed of the bullet? The bullet moving from north to south slows down because of damping. Why cannot the bullet moving from

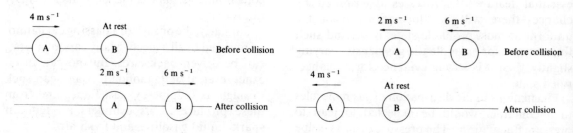

Fig. 17.13

south to north speed up, by just the right amount to give the same behaviour as the first bullet?

Why are events irreversible? What determines the direction an event will go?

In any frictional effect, e.g., the bullet being slowed down by the air, the organized motion is changed into disorganized motion of atoms. The orderly motion of the bullet is changed into the disorganized motion of air molecules. Whenever an event produces a temperature rise there is an increase in the disorganized motion of atoms. Perhaps the sequence is always order to disorder and this is the clue to the direction an event will go. Consider some of the examples already mentioned in this section: a bouncing ball, the orderly motion is changed into the disorganized motion of atoms (a temperature rise); a burning log, the orderly arrangement of atoms in the log is changed to the disorderly motion of atoms in the flue gas, the energy localized initially in the log is spread around among air molecules; boulders crumbling to mud, an orderly arrangement of atoms in the boulder changed to a disorderly arrangement of atoms in the mud.

Why should the sequence appear to be order to disorder for events?

Number of ways

Consider diffusion as a one-way process. A gas released at one end of a container spreads throughout the container until the gas is uniformly spread throughout the container. A gas spread throughout the container does not reconcentrate itself at one end. Diffusion would seem to be an irreversible process with the direction of events being from concentrated to spread out.

Earlier in this chapter we considered the chance of finding all the molecules in a box in one half of that box. With four molecules there are sixteen possible arrangements or ways of arranging the molecules between the two halves of the box. Only one of these ways has all the molecules in one particular half. Six of these ways have the molecules uniformly spread through the box, i.e., equal numbers in each half. The chance of seeing the molecules all in one particular half is thus only one-sixth of the chance of seeing them uniformly distributed. The greater the

chance the more often we expect to find the molecules in a particular arrangement. Thus freely left to itself there is a greater chance that the gas will diffuse throughout the container than that it will become concentrated in one half. This was with just four molecules. If we use a more realistic number of molecules the chance of finding the uniform distribution is considerably greater than finding the molecules all in one half. The word considerable is not strong enough—the factor can be of the order of $10^{10^{10}}$. Diffusion is a one-way process, concentrated to spread out, because the chance of the reverse direction process occurring is considerably less than that of concentrated to spread out. Chance is the factor which decides which way an event will occur. A spread-out arrangement is more likely than a concentrated arrangement because there are more ways the spread-out arrangement can be realized.

What about events where temperature rises occur? Here instead of being concerned with the spreading out of atoms we are concerned with the spreading out of quanta. Quanta are packets of energy.

A bouncing ball comes to rest and the temperature of the floor (and the ball) rises. The potential energy of the ball has been converted into quanta which have been spread out among the atoms in the floor (and the ball). The reverse event is a drop in temperature of the floor and the ball springing up from the floor. Quanta have been taken from the atoms in the floor and converted to potential energy of the ball. Why is the event with the rise in temperature the event that normally happens?

Consider two quanta shared amongst two atoms (Fig. 17.14)—there are three possible arrangements. If we add another quantum, making three quanta among two atoms, we have four possible arrangements. The extra quantum has increased the number of possible arrangements from three to four. If instead of adding a quantum we took one away, making one quantum among two atoms, then the number of ways drops from three to two. An arrangement which can be realized in more ways is a more likely arrangement.

The bouncing ball coming to rest increases the temperature of the floor and thus is giving quanta

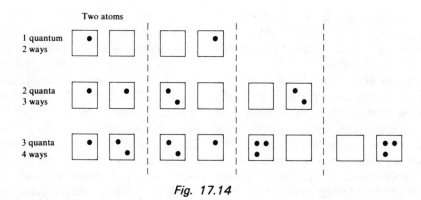

Fig. 17.14

to the floor. The ball springing up from the floor needs to derive its energy from the floor by the floor dropping in temperature; the ball thus needs to take quanta away from the floor. Giving quanta to the floor results in more possible arrangements than taking quanta from the floor and is thus the more likely event. The event that occurs most often is the one that occurs in most ways.

Second law of thermodynamics

A closed system will always end up in that condition which can be realized in the greatest number of ways.

n quanta among N atoms

The following is a brief mathematical interlude for those who feel they would like an algebraic equation for the number of ways n quanta can be spread among N atomic sites. We will assume that we cannot distinguish between individual quanta but only count the number occupying any one atomic site.

We have N atomic sites which we can write as

$$o \; o \; o \; o \; o \; o \; o \; o \; o \; o \; o \; o \ldots N$$

Each o represents a site. To spread among these sites we have n quanta, represented by x.

$$x \; x \; x \; x \; x \; x \; x \; x \; x \; x \ldots n$$

Each atom can have 0 or 1 or 2 or 3 or ... n quanta. Thus the first atom could have say 2

quanta, the second atom 1 quantum, the third atom 4 quanta, etc.

$$o \; x \; x \quad o \; x \quad o \; x \; x \; x \; x \quad o \; x \quad o \; x \; x \ldots$$

first   second   third   fourth
atom   atom   atom   atom

All together, when written in this way, there will be $N + n$ symbols, i.e., o or x, in this line. To find the number of ways n quanta can be arranged among N atoms we have to find the number of ways the symbols in this line can be arranged.

Consider an example, four atoms and two quanta. They can be arranged in the following ways.

$$o \; x \; x \; o \; o \; o$$
$$o \; o \; x \; x \; o \; o$$
$$o \; o \; o \; x \; x \; o$$
$$o \; o \; o \; o \; x \; x$$
$$o \; x \; o \; x \; o \; o$$
$$o \; x \; o \; o \; x \; o$$
$$o \; x \; o \; o \; o \; x$$
$$o \; o \; x \; o \; x \; o$$
$$o \; o \; x \; o \; o \; x$$
$$o \; o \; o \; x \; o \; x$$

In the first line we have the first site with two quanta and the second, third and fourth sites with zero quanta. In the last line the first two sites have zero quanta and the third and fourth sites have each one quantum. Figure 17.15, solid B, shows this written out as quanta in boxes. With our 4 atom sites and 2 quanta we have 6 symbols in the line. All but the first symbol can be rearranged to give different ways. The total number of ways of arranging the remaining 5 symbols is 5!, i.e., $5 \times 4 \times 3 \times 2 \times 1$. This is $(N - 1 + n)!$. But $5! = 120$ and we have only 10 ways. The error is due to our not being able to distinguish individual atoms or quanta—we do not know after reshuffling whether o is atom two or atom three, or x is quantum one or quantum two. We have thus overestimated by a factor $(N - 1)!$ for the atoms and $n!$ for the quanta. Thus the number of ways is given by

$$W = \frac{(N - 1 + n)!}{(N - 1)!n!}$$

Taking the four atoms sites and two quanta solid as an example, we have

$$W = \frac{(4 - 1 + 2)!}{(4 - 1)!2!} = \frac{5 \times 4 \times 3 \times 2 \times 1}{3 \times 2 \times 1 \times 2 \times 1} = 10$$

In this analysis we have assumed that we cannot distinguish between quanta.

Note: We have considered the distribution of quanta among atomic sites—really we should have considered quanta among localized and independent oscillators. In a solid each atom can have three modes of oscillation and thus N three-dimensional oscillators are equivalent to $3N$ one-dimensional oscillators. In our equation we are referring to the number of one-dimensional oscillators.

Temperature

When I put an object at, say, 10°C in thermal contact (i.e., thermal energy can pass between the objects) with another object at, say, 30°C then they will, if I wait long enough, come to the same temperature (some value between 10 and 30°C). We say that the two objects will reach thermal equilibrium. Two objects at, say 22°C will not of their own accord proceed to change their temperatures so that one ends up at 10°C and the other at 30°C. The event need not violate the conservation of energy principle. There is a one-way process towards thermal equilibrium.

Why should the process be one way? What do we mean by temperature? What is the difference between two objects at different temperatures? What is thermal equilibrium?

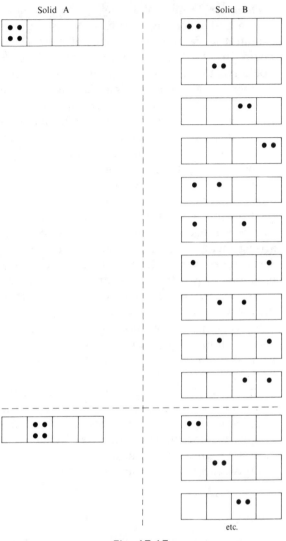

Fig. 17.15

Consider two very theoretical solids, solid A has four atoms and four quanta of energy and solid B has four atoms and two quanta. Which solid is at the higher temperature? If we put the two solids in thermal contact we would expect there to be a net flow of energy from the higher temperature solid to the lower temperature solid (we could define our terms high and low temperatures to mean this). Let us make an assumption: chance decides how the quanta move between the two solids.

385

MATTER

There are 35 ways of arranging the quanta in solid A and in solid B 10 ways. If A was to give a quantum to B then the number of ways for A would drop to 20 and the number of ways for B would rise to 20. How has this changed the total number of ways of arranging the quanta in the two solids? Initially the number of ways was 35 × 10 = 350, after the movement of one quantum from A to B the number of ways became 20 × 20 = 400. The total number of ways has increased.

You may rightly query why the numbers of ways for the quanta in A and B were multiplied together to give the total number of arrangements. Each arrangement of quanta in solid A (i.e., way) can be arranged in turn with every one of the arrangements of quanta in solid B (Fig. 17.15). Thus there are initially ten different combinations of B with each arrangement of A. As there are initially 35 possible ways for A then there will be 35 × 10 total arrangements.

What happens if we take a quantum from B and give it to A? The number of ways for A rises from 35 to 56. The number of ways for B drops from 10 to 4. The total number of ways changes from 350 to 56 × 4 = 224, a drop. Taking the quantum from A to B gave an increase in the number of ways and thus this would be the direction the event would tend to go. We conclude that A is at a higher temperature than B.

Consider another example:

Solid A   Solid C

4 quanta, 4 atoms   2 quanta, 2 atoms
35 ways   3 ways

Total of 35 × 3 = 105 ways

A gives a quantum to C

3 quanta, 4 atoms   3 quanta, 2 atoms
20 ways   4 ways

Total of 20 × 4 = 80 ways

This is a drop in the number of ways and thus is unlikely to occur.

C gives a quantum to A

5 quanta, 4 atoms   1 quantum, 2 atoms
56 ways   2 ways

Total of 112 ways

This is an increase in the number of ways from the initial state and is likely to occur. C is thus at a higher temperature than A.

A and C have the same average number of quanta per atom, i.e., one quantum per atom, but they are at different temperatures. When two objects are at different temperatures and in thermal contact energy flows between the two, giving one a net gain, until the two are at the same temperature. When two objects are at the same temperature energy can still pass between the two but neither object makes a net gain.

Solid A   Solid D

4 atoms, 4 quanta   7 atoms, 9 quanta
35 ways   5005 ways

Total of 35 × 5005 = 175 175 ways

A gives one quantum to D

4 atoms, 3 quanta   7 atoms, 10 quanta
20 ways   8008 ways

Total of 20 × 8008 = 160 160 ways

This is a drop in the number of ways and thus is unlikely to occur.

D gives one quantum to A

4 atoms, 5 quanta   7 atoms, 8 quanta
56 ways   3003 ways

Total of 56 × 3003 = 168 168 ways

This is a drop in the number of ways and thus is unlikely to occur. Both the movement of a quantum from A to D and from D to A give decreases in the number of ways. A and D are thus at the same temperature.

As this last example shows, temperature is not

on the microscopic scale the average number of quanta per atom. Two objects at the same temperature can have different numbers of quanta per atom.

How can we distinguish between objects at different temperatures? We can ascertain what happens when we supply energy, i.e., how W, the number of ways, changes.

Let us look at our first example again:

Solid A, higher temperature
4 atoms, 4 quanta
35 ways

Addition of one quantum gives 56 ways. This has increased the number of ways by a factor of 1.6, i.e., 56/35.

Solid B, lower temperature
   4 atoms, 2 quanta
   10 ways

Addition of one quantum gives 20 ways. This has increased the number of ways by a factor of 2.0, i.e., 20/10.

If A and B had been at the same temperature the effect of adding a quantum to each would be to change the number of ways by the same factor. You can check this with solids A and D which are at the same temperature. Addition of a quantum of energy seems to have a much greater effect on the factor by which the number of ways changes for the lower temperature solid than for the higher temperature solid.

Solid F
4 atoms, 6 quanta
84 ways

Addition of one quantum gives 120 ways. This has increased the number of ways by a factor of 1.4, i.e., 120/84. By putting F in thermal contact with, in turn, A and B and considering the combined numbers of ways we find that F is at a higher temperature than A or B.

Solid G
4 atoms, 8 quanta
165 ways

Addition of one quantum gives 220 ways. This has increased the number of ways by a factor 1.3, i.e., 220/165. By putting G in thermal contact with A, B, and F we find that G is at a higher temperature than A, B, or F.

Solid	Atoms	Quanta	Factor by which ways are changed when one quantum is given to the solid	
B	4	2	2.0	
A	4	4	1.6	increasing
F	4	6	1.4	temperature
G	4	8	1.3	↓

The larger the factor by which the number of ways change when one quantum is supplied the lower the temperature. We could use this factor to specify the temperature of a solid, without recourse to any temperature scale defined by reference to melting or boiling points of substances. Why not

factor by which ways are changed when one quantum is given to the solid $\left(\dfrac{W'}{W}\right) \propto \dfrac{1}{T}$

where T is the temperature? We could have said $1/T^2$ or $1/T^3$. The reciprocal has to be used if an increasing temperature is to mean a decreasing factor.

Is this a reasonable temperature scale? The lowest temperature we could envisage would be when our four-atom solid had no energy quanta. With no quanta there is just one way a solid can distribute its energy—all atoms with none. If we give this solid one quantum the number of ways rises from one to four. With one quantum and four atoms there are four ways—each atom in turn having the quantum. The factor W'/W is thus four for the lowest temperature. If we had a real solid with its very large number of atoms the number of ways would have risen from one to a number equal to the number of atoms, when one quantum was added. W'/W would thus be very large for a real solid. As each further quantum was added W'/W would become smaller until it reaches 1.0 for very large numbers of quanta.

For 4 atoms, 100 quanta	$W'/W = 1.03$
4 atoms, 1000 quanta	$W'/W = 1.003$

Suppose the constant of proportionality in the equation relating W'/W and T is one. Our lowest temperature, with a large number of atoms, becomes the reciprocal of a very large number. Our highest temperature becomes the reciprocal of 1.0, i.e., 1.0. The absolute temperature scale goes from zero to infinity. There is no reason why our new scale should do the same but it might be more convenient. We can make our high temperature value infinity by taking the logarithm of W'/W to be proportional to $1/T$. Without the logarithm the highest temperature becomes

$$T \propto \frac{1}{W'/W} \propto \frac{1}{1.0}$$

With the logarithm

$$\ln\left(\frac{W'}{W}\right) \propto \frac{1}{T}$$

$$T \propto \frac{1}{\ln(W'/W)} \propto \frac{1}{\ln(1.0)} \propto \frac{1}{0}$$

This would seem to be a scale similar to the absolute scale of temperature.

Using the logarithm also has other advantages. For one quantum added:

$$\ln\left(\frac{W'}{W}\right) = \ln 1.5$$

when we have four atoms and 5 quanta. Suppose we add two quanta to give 7 quanta, then:

$$\ln\left(\frac{W''}{W}\right) = \ln (1.5^2)$$

$$= \ln 1.5 + \ln 1.5 = 2 \ln 1.5$$

One quantum changes the number of ways from 56 to 84, a change by a factor of 84/56 or 1.5. Two quanta change the ways from 56 to 120, a change by a factor of 120/56 or 2.1. This is approximately 1.5×1.5. Three quanta extra change the factor by approximately $1.5 \times 1.5 \times 1.5$. Thus we have

$$\ln\left(\frac{W'''}{W}\right) = 3 \log 1.5$$

The logarithm of the factor is directly proportional to the number of quanta added, i.e., the total energy supplied to the solid.

$$\ln\left(\frac{W'''}{W}\right) = \ln W''' - \ln W = \Delta \ln W$$

The change in the logarithm of the number of ways is directly proportional to the thermal energy supplied (ΔQ)

$$\Delta \ln W \propto \Delta Q$$

Incorporating this with our temperature equation we can write

$$\Delta \ln W \propto \frac{\Delta Q}{T}$$

or by introducing a constant

$$k \, \Delta \ln W \propto \frac{\Delta Q}{T}$$

k is known as Boltzmann's constant. We choose the value of the constant to give our temperature scale, generally known as the Kelvin scale, the same size degrees as the absolute temperature scale. The value given is 1.38×10^{-23} J K^{-1}.

A consequence of defining temperature in this way is that T cannot have the value zero.

Third law of thermodynamics

The absolute zero of temperature can never be reached.

Entropy

A bouncing ball comes to rest—this is the natural direction for such an event. A ball suddenly springing up from the floor is unnatural. When an event proceeds in the 'natural' direction we say that the entropy is increasing. If the event is considered for the 'unnatural' direction the entropy decreases. At equilibrium any change results in a decrease in entropy. The term change in entropy ΔS is used to denote the quantity $k \, \Delta \ln W$ or $\Delta Q/T$. An increase in the number of ways of arranging energy means an increase in entropy.

Thermal energy ΔQ supplied to an object at temperature T produces a change (increase) in entropy for that object of $\Delta Q/T$. We could determine entropy changes by calculating the changes in the number of ways. A more practical method of determining the change is to measure $\Delta Q/T$.

A convention has been adopted that at absolute zero the entropy of a pure substance is zero. (This is another way of writing the Third Law.) By measuring all the $\Delta Q/T$ terms necessary to bring a substance up to a particular temperature we can give that substance an absolute entropy value at that temperature. For example, we would measure the energy ΔQ_1 needed to raise the temperature of the substance by, say, 2 K from an initial temperature of 0 K. The entropy change would be

$$\frac{\Delta Q_1}{1}$$

T is taken as the mean temperature, 1 K. The entropy change in going from 2 K to 4 K would be

$$\frac{\Delta Q_2}{3}$$

where ΔQ_2 is the energy used to raise the temperature from 2 to 4 K. By summing all these increments we arrive at the absolute entropy at some temperature T.

$$S = \frac{\Delta Q_1}{1} + \frac{\Delta Q_2}{3} + \frac{\Delta Q_3}{5} + \ldots + \frac{\Delta Q}{T}$$

Typical entropy values are:
1 mole of water, 1 atmosphere pressure, as liquid at 273 K

$$S = 63 \text{ J K}^{-1}$$

1 mole of water, 1 atmosphere pressure, as solid at 273 K

$$S = 41 \text{ J K}^{-1}$$

The difference between these two values is due to the latent heat needed to make the change from solid to liquid. If it were possible to have water in a vapour state at 273 K and 1 atmosphere pressure then its entropy would (by extrapola-

tion) be about 180 J K^{-1}. Liquid and solid water are in equilibrium at 273 K so the liquid should not change into the solid or the solid to liquid. The entropy of the liquid is, however, larger than that of the solid so apparently a change from solid to liquid will give an entropy increase and should be the natural direction of the event. We should not find solid water at 273 K because it has all turned into liquid. This is obviously wrong. The error we have made is not to take into account the energy which must be extracted from the surroundings in order to melt the solid water. The entropy of the surroundings must change, as well as the entropy change for the water. The energy needed to change 1 mole of water from solid to liquid is 5.94×10^3 J mol^{-1}. The entropy of the surroundings must therefore decrease by $5.94 \times 10^3/273$ or 22 J K^{-1}. This is in fact the difference between the entropy values for the solid and liquid water, $63 - 41 = 22$ J K^{-1}. Solid and liquid water are in equilibrium at 273 K because a change from solid to liquid or liquid to solid would not produce any increase in entropy. If we were to increase the temperature to 274 K then the entropy decrease for the surroundings becomes 21 J K^{-1} and there is an entropy increase when solid water changes to liquid water. The natural course of events is for solid water to change into liquid water at 274 K. If we were to decrease the temperature to below 273 K then the entropy decrease for the surroundings becomes more than the difference in entropy values between the solid and liquid.

To summarize: an event will occur if it results in an increase in entropy. Equilibrium exists when any change results in a decrease in entropy.

Engines

An engine converts fuel energy into mechanical energy. The fuel is used to increase the temperature of something, often steam, which is then used to turn perhaps a turbine and in the process becomes cool. The efficiency of even the most modern engines is only about 30 per cent—only 30 per cent of the energy available from the fuel appears as mechanical energy. The rest of the energy is given to the surroundings—perhaps via cooling towers or a river. Power stations have lots of energy to dispose of—lots of energy they 'waste'. Does this have to be so?

Suppose the fuel in a furnace supplies 100 MW to a boiler. If the efficiency is 30 per cent the mechanical energy produced by the steam from the boiler will be 30 MW. The rest of the energy, 70 MW, is dissipated to the surroundings by, say, a cooling tower.

The entropy changes during the above are:

$$\text{Entropy drop at the furnace} = \frac{100 \times 10^6}{T_H}$$

where T_H is the temperature of the furnace;

$$\text{Entropy gain by the surroundings} = \frac{70 \times 10^6}{T_C}$$

where T_C is the temperature of the surroundings. The net entropy change is

$$\frac{70 \times 10^6}{T_C} - \frac{100 \times 10^6}{T_H}$$

For entropy to increase we must have

$$\frac{70 \times 10^6}{T_C} > \frac{100 \times 10^6}{T_H}$$

$$\frac{T_H}{T_C} > \frac{100 \times 10^6}{70 \times 10^6}$$

If T_C = 300 K, then T_H must be greater than 430 K.

The higher the temperature of the steam entering the turbine the greater the possible efficiency. For 70 per cent efficiency T_H must be greater than 1000 K. The limitation on the efficiency of an engine is set by the requirement that entropy must increase.

In no event can we convert all our fuel energy into mechanical energy.

Further reading

J. F. Sandford (1962) *Heat Engines*, Heinemann Science Study Series, No. 22.

Specific heat capacities

We can use the arguments already presented to arrive at the way the temperature of a solid depends on the energy supplied.

$$W = \frac{(N + n - 1)!}{(N - 1)!n!}$$

W is the number of ways of arranging n quanta among N atoms.

When one quantum is added we have

$$W' = \frac{(N + n + - 1)!}{(N - 1)!(n + 1)!}$$

Hence

$$\frac{W'}{W} = \frac{(N + n)}{n + 1}$$

You can check this formula against the earlier results.

$$k \, \Delta \ln W = \frac{\Delta Q}{T}$$

Hence

$$k \ln\left(\frac{N + n}{n + 1}\right) = \frac{\varepsilon}{T}$$

where ε is the energy of one quantum. Thus

$$\frac{N + n}{n + 1} = e^{\varepsilon/kT}$$

Neglecting the 1 on the bottom line as being insignificant in comparison with n gives on rearranging:

$$n = \frac{N}{e^{\varepsilon/kT} - 1}$$

n is the total number of quanta given to the solid. Thus $n\varepsilon$ is the total amount of energy given to the solid.

$$n\varepsilon = \frac{N\varepsilon}{e^{\varepsilon/kT} - 1}$$

The number of atoms in the solid is $N/3$, because N is the number of independent oscillators and each atom can have three independent modes of oscillation. If we consider one mole of atoms and write L for Avogadro's number then

$$\text{Energy supplied to 1 mole} = \frac{3L\varepsilon}{e^{\varepsilon/kT} - 1}$$

As $\varepsilon = hf$, the equation becomes

$$\text{Energy supplied per mole} = \frac{3Lhf}{e^{hf/kT} - 1}$$

This equation tells us how the temperature of one mole of a crystalline solid depends on the energy supplied.

At high temperatures, i.e., when hf/kT is small

$$e^{hf/kT} \approx 1 + \frac{hf}{kT}$$

Thus energy supplied per mole =

$$\frac{3Lhf}{1 + (hf/kT) - 1}$$

$$= 3LkT$$

Hence the molar heat capacity (at constant volume)

$$C_V = \frac{\Delta(\text{energy})}{\Delta T} = 3Lk$$

As $Lk = R_0$, the gas constant, this can be written as

$$C_V = 3R_0$$

An alternative way of arriving at this equation is given earlier in this chapter. The other way does not, however, give the equation at temperatures other than high.

Energy distribution

n quanta among N atoms—how are the quanta arranged? At some instant how many atoms have 0 quanta, how many 1 quantum, how many 2 quanta, etc.? Suppose we put our quanta into our solid and let chance determine how many an atom will acquire. One way you can represent this is to make a board with six squares by six, i.e., a total of 36 squares, and having put the quanta in some way on the atoms (use counters), then use the chance throws of two dice to pick on a site from which to take a quantum and then use the two dice to determine which site to move the quantum to. Figure 17.16 shows a possible first move in such a game. After many moves the distribution becomes more or less static. Figure 17.17 shows the situation after 100 moves. The distribution begins to look as though it may be an

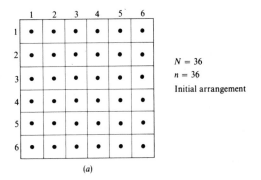

$N = 36$
$n = 36$
Initial arrangement

(a)

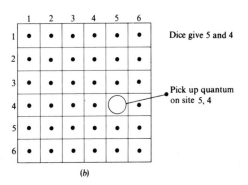

Dice give 5 and 4

Pick up quantum on site 5, 4

(b)

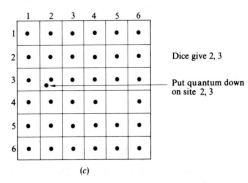

Dice give 2, 3

Put quantum down on site 2, 3

(c)

Fig. 17.16

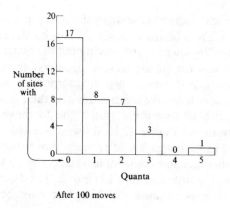

Fig. 17.17

exponential. Figure 17.18 shows the situation with 900 sites and 900 quanta after 10 000 moves; the distribution is quite a good exponential. There are twice as many sites with 0 quanta as with 1 quantum, twice as many sites with 1 quantum as with 2 quanta, twice as many with 2 quanta as with 3, etc. Figure 17.19 shows the result when 900 sites shared 300 quanta; there are now four times as many sites with 0 quanta as with 1 quantum, four times as many with 1 quantum as with 2 quanta, etc. With fewer quanta we have a steeper exponential; this is a lower temperature.

For $N = 100$, $n = 900$

$$\frac{\text{Number of sites with 0 quanta}}{\text{Number of sites with 1 quantum}} = 2$$

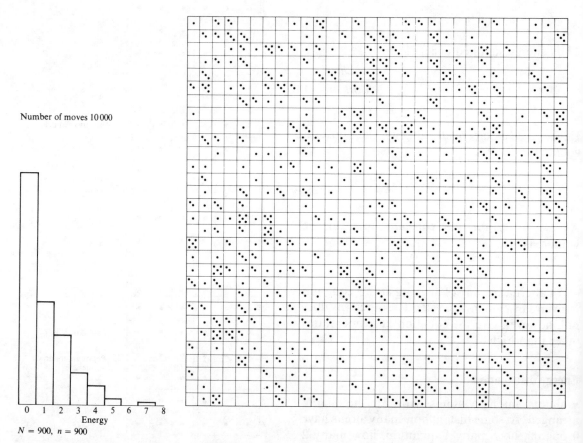

Fig. 17.18   N = 900, n = 900. (Nuffield Foundation Science Teaching Project (1972, Advanced Physics. Unit 9, Penguin)

But

$$\frac{W'}{W} = \frac{N + n}{n + 1} \approx 2$$

For $N = 900$, $n = 300$

$$\frac{\text{Number of sites with 0 quanta}}{\text{Number of sites with 1 quantum}} = 4$$

But

$$\frac{W'}{W} = \frac{N + n}{n + 1} \approx 4$$

It would seem that

$$\frac{\text{Number of sites with 0 quanta}}{\text{Number of sites with 1 quantum}} = \frac{W'}{W}$$

$$= e^{\varepsilon/kT}$$

Thus

$$\frac{\text{Number of sites with energy } n\varepsilon}{\text{Number of sites with energy}(n + 1)\varepsilon} = e^{-\varepsilon/kT}$$

ε is the energy of a quantum.

Note: In this chapter it has been assumed that the atoms can accept any number of equally sized quanta, i.e., they have equally spaced energy levels. The arguments can still be applied if this is not the case. See Appendix B of *Nuffield Advanced Physics*, Unit 9, Penguin, 1972.

Evaporation

In a liquid we can consider the number of molecules with an energy E greater than that of

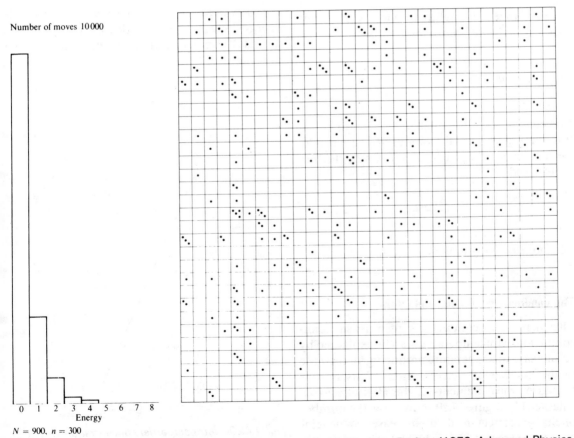

Number of moves 10 000

$N = 900$, $n = 300$

Fig. 17.19 N = 900, n = 300. (Nuffield Foundation Science Teaching Project (1972, Advanced Physics. Unit 9, Penguin)

another group of molecules to be

$$\frac{n_1}{n_2} = e^{-E/kT}$$

If n_1 is the number of molecules that escape as vapour and n_2 the number of liquid molecules, then E is of the order of the escape energy.

$$E = \frac{\Delta H_{\text{vap}}}{L}$$

where L is Avogadro's number. Thus

$$n_1 = n_2 e^{-\Delta H_{\text{vap}}/LkT}$$

But the pressure of the vapour will be proportional to the number of vapour molecules ($PV = \frac{1}{3}mnc^2$), thus

$$\text{vapour pressure } p \propto n_2 e^{-\Delta H_{\text{vap}}/LkT}$$

n_2 will change only slightly with temperature and thus a reasonable approximation is

$$p = A\, e^{-\Delta H_{\text{vap}}/LkT}$$

or as $Lk = R_0$

$$p = A\, e^{-\Delta H_{\text{vap}}/R_0 T}$$

This equation is a reasonable description of the graph in Fig. 16.32. If the vapour pressure results are replotted as $\ln p$ against $1/T$ a straight line is produced.

$$\ln p = -\frac{\Delta H_{\text{vap}}}{R_0 T} + \ln A$$

The slope of the graph is $\Delta H_{\text{vap}}/R_0 T$.

The conductivity of semiconductors

The increase in conductivity of intrinsic semiconductors with temperature can be explained by an increase in temperature producing an increase in the number of charge carriers. This is confirmed by measurements of the Hall effect (see Chapter 14). Figure 17.20 shows how the number of charge carriers in silicon increases as the temperature increases. This is typical of semiconductors. As the graph indicates the relationship

between the number density of charge carriers and temperature is of the form

$$\log n = -\frac{m}{T} + c$$

where m and c are constants. c is the value of $\log n$ when m/T is zero; we can simplify the equation by writing $\log n_0$ for c.

$$\log n = -\frac{m}{T} + \log n_0$$

or

$$\log\left(\frac{n}{n_0}\right) = -\frac{m}{T}$$

where m is the gradient of the graph. What physical quantity, or quantities, does m represent?

n/n_0 is the ratio of the number of atoms with energy greater than this release energy value to the total number of atoms in the same volume of solid.

$$\frac{n_2}{n_1} = e^{-E/kT}$$

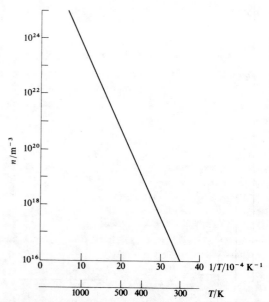

Fig. 17.20 Intrinsic carrier concentration for silicon. (After F. J. Morin and J. P. Maita. Phys. Rev., **94**, 1525, 1954)

where n_2/n_1 is the ratio of the number of particles in energy levels which differ by E. k is Boltzmann's constant. This is not quite the same as our ratio n/n_0 but if $n_0 > n$ it may be a reasonable approximation. Thus

$$\frac{n}{n_0} = e^{-E/kT}$$

or

$$\ln\left(\frac{n}{n_0}\right) = -\frac{E}{kT}$$

The gradient m becomes E/k, where E is the energy needed for an electron to escape from an atom, still, however, remaining within the solid.

The gradient of the graph for silicon, Fig. 17.20, is about

$$\frac{\ln 10^{24} - \ln 10^{17}}{20 \times 10^{-4}} \left(= \frac{E}{k}\right)$$

when the logarithm is used for the vertical axis. Taking k as 1.38×10^{-23} J K^{-1} gives E as 13.2×10^{-20} J or about 0.7 eV.

A way of representing these results is to use what is known as energy band pictures (see Chapter 11). There is an energy band in which electrons exist which have insufficient energy to take part in conduction and there is a band, called the conduction band, in which the 'free' electrons are located. The difference in energy between the top of the lower band and the bottom of the conduction band is the value of E. An energy gap exists between the two bands.

Thermal conduction, convection and radiation

Heat is the transfer of energy caused by a temperature difference. There are three basic mechanisms by which such a transfer can occur: conduction, convection and radiation. Thermal conduction and convection require a material through which the transmission can occur, radiation does not. Thermal conduction differs from convection in not involving mass movement of parts of the material, thus while conduction can take place in solids, liquids or gases, convection can only occur in liquids and gases.

Thermal conduction can take place in a number of ways. In a metal the energy transfer takes place through the conduction electrons (i.e., the free electrons) behaving rather like gas molecules in simple kinetic theory. If one end of a metal bar has its temperature increased, the electrons at that end have a higher mean kinetic energy than those at the colder end of the bar. By collisions between electrons this energy is gradually shared out and thus energy transferred down the bar from hot to the cold end.

Thermal conduction in liquids and non-metallic solids involves a different mechanism. The molecules vibrate about fixed positions which are relatively close together. This has the effect of coupling the vibrations, i.e., the vibration of one molecule affects the vibration of neighbouring molecules. Thus the energy transfer takes place as a transfer of vibrational energy from energetic to less energetic molecules until the vibrational energies become the same.

Thermal conduction in gases is the result of a transfer of energy by means of collisions between gas molecules.

Energy transfer by convection can occur as a result of a gas or liquid decreasing in density as a result of expansion when it becomes hot. The lower density gas or liquid then rises through the more dense, colder material. Thus the hot material physically moves. Convection can also occur as a result of the gas or liquid being moved by a pump or fan.

Energy transfer by radiation is a transfer of electromagnetic radiation between two bodies, there being a net flow in the direction from hot to cold body.

Thermal conductivity

Figure 17.21 shows how the temperature varies with distance along a solid bar when there is a temperature difference between its ends. The result depends on whether the bar is lagged so that the rate at which energy enters the hot end is the same as that leaving the cold end, with no energy being dissipated from the sides of the bar.

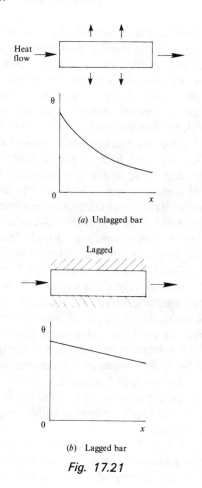

(a) Unlagged bar

Lagged

(b) Lagged bar

Fig. 17.21

In such a condition the temperature gradient along the bar is constant.

The rate at which energy is transferred through material, such as the bar in Fig. 17.21, can be investigated. Investigation is easiest with the lagged bar, one end perhaps being heated by an electrical heater wrapped round it and the other with water being passed through a pipe wrapped round it. Such a form of apparatus is called Searle's bar and is used when the material is a good conductor. The heat ΔQ passing through the bar in a time interval of Δt can be measured by either a measurement of the current and potential difference to the heater or the rise in temperature of the water being piped around the end of the bar, ΔQ = (mass flowing in time Δt) × c × (change in temperature). The temperature gradient along the bar can be measured by two

thermometers inserted in the bar a distance x apart. When steady-state conditions occur, i.e., the thermometer readings remain constant, then it is found that (Fig. 17.22):

$$\Delta Q \propto \Delta t$$

$$\Delta Q \propto \frac{\Delta \theta}{\Delta x}$$

$$\Delta Q \propto A$$

Also ΔQ depends on what material is used for the bar. These variables can be combined in the equation

$$\frac{\Delta Q}{\Delta t} = - \lambda A \frac{\Delta \theta}{\Delta x}$$

where λ is a constant for a particular material and is called the thermal conductivity. The reason for the minus sign is that the energy transfer is in the direction of decreasing θ, down the temperature gradient and not up it.

In the limiting case this equation becomes

$$\frac{dQ}{dt} = - \lambda A \frac{d\theta}{dx}$$

The unit of thermal conductivity is W m^{-1} K^{-1}. Copper, a good conductor, has a thermal conductivity of 3.9×10^2 W m^{-1} K^{-1}, air which is a bad conductor 2.4×10^{-2} W m^{-1} K^{-1}.

What is the energy transmitted through a brick wall of thickness 12 cm and area 6.0 m^2 in 1 hour if the temperature on one side is 0°C and on the other 20°C? The thermal conductivity of brick is 0.13 W m^{-1} K^{-1}.

If we assume that the energy per unit time

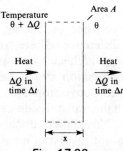

Fig. 17.22

entering one face is the same as that leaving the other face of the wall in the same time, then

$$\frac{\Delta Q}{3600} = 0.13 \times 6.0 \times \frac{(20 - 0)}{12 \times 10^{-2}}$$

$$\Delta Q = 4.7 \times 10^5 \text{ J}$$

Many situations involving thermal conduction concern the energy transfer occurring through more than one material. Thus in the case of the brick wall of a house we would normally have not just a single layer of brick but a cavity wall involving an air gap between two layers of brick. To illustrate how such 'compound' situations can be tackled, consider the two layer object described by Fig. 17.23. Assuming the energy entering the face of the first material is the same as that leaving it and entering the face of the second material and then leaving from the opposite face, then for the first layer of material:

$$\frac{\Delta Q}{\Delta t} = \lambda_1 A \frac{(\theta_1 - \theta_2)}{x_1}$$

For the second layer

$$\frac{\Delta Q}{\Delta t} = \lambda_2 A \frac{(\theta_2 - \theta_3)}{x_2}$$

We can determine $\Delta Q/\Delta t$ when we know θ_1 and θ_3, a common problem, by rearranging the equations and then adding them, i.e.

$$\theta_1 - \theta_2 = \frac{\Delta Q}{\Delta t} \frac{x_1}{A\lambda_1}$$

$$\theta_2 - \theta_3 = \frac{\Delta Q}{\Delta T} \frac{x_2}{A\lambda_2}$$

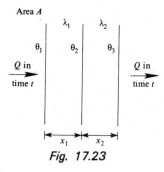

Area A

λ_1 λ_2

θ_1 θ_2 θ_3

Q in
time t

Q in
time t

x_1 x_2

Fig. 17.23

Hence

$$\theta_1 - \theta_3 = \frac{\Delta Q}{\Delta T} \times \frac{1}{A} \left(\frac{x_1}{\lambda_1} + \frac{x_2}{\lambda_2} \right)$$

$$\frac{\Delta Q}{\Delta t} = UA(\theta_1 - \theta_3)$$

$$U = \frac{1}{\left(\dfrac{x_1}{\lambda_1} + \dfrac{x_2}{\lambda_2} \right)}$$

where U is called the overall heat transfer coefficient or just referred to as the U-value. If there had been three layers of material rather than just the two in our example, the same basic equation would apply, the only difference being the inclusion of another x/λ term in the U-value.

Invariably in practice when involved with questions concerning, say, the transmission of heat through a glass window or a brick wall, the answer arrived at using just the thermal conductivity of the glass or wall material is not quite correct. This is because of what is termed 'air boundary layers'. There are layers of stagnant air close to all surfaces and since air has a low thermal conductivity they have a significant effect on calculations. An overall U-value can, however, be given for a structure which takes account of these layers.

Analogies between thermal and electrical conductivities

Both thermal conductivity and electrical conductivity can be considered as being concerned with flow, heat in one case and charge in the other. Heat flows between two points at a different temperature, charge flows (i.e., a current occurs) between two points at a different potential difference. The rate of flow of heat dQ/dt is comparable with the rate of flow of charge or current. Ohm's law $V = IR$ expresses the relationship between potential difference and current for electrical conduction; what is the equivalent of resistance for heat? We are thus enquiring about the relationship between $\Delta\theta$ and dQ/dt. But our thermal conductivity equation gives

$$\Delta\theta = \frac{L}{\lambda A} \frac{dQ}{dT}$$

where L is the length of conductor across which we have the temperature difference $\Delta\theta$. If we call $L/\lambda A$ the thermal resistance R and represent dQ/dt by ϕ, then

$$\Delta\theta = R\,\phi$$

The unit of thermal resistance is $K\ W^{-1}$.

We can compare thermal resistance $R = L/\lambda A$ with electrical resistance $R = L/\sigma A$ where σ is electrical conductivity.

If we consider our earlier equation for heat passing through two layers of material, then we can write it in the form

$$\Delta\theta = \phi\,\frac{1}{A}\left(\frac{x_1}{\lambda_1} + \frac{x_2}{\lambda_2}\right) = \phi(R_1 + R_2)$$

For heat flow in series through materials, our thermal resistances add up in the same way as electrical resistances.

$$\text{Total } R = R_1 + R_2$$

Convection

Convection which occurs as a result of a density change of a hot fluid is called natural convection, when it occurs as a result of a pump of fan forcing the fluid into motion it is called forced convection. For forced convection the rate of loss of heat per unit area by a hot object is proportional to the temperature difference between that object θ and its surroundings θ_s. This is known as Newton's law of cooling.

$$\frac{\Delta Q}{A\,\Delta t} \propto (\theta - \theta_s)$$

For natural convection the rate of loss of heat per unit area is found to be reasonably proportional to the temperature difference between the object and its surroundings raised to the power 5/4.

$$\frac{\Delta Q}{A\,\Delta t} \propto (\theta - \theta_s)^{5/4}$$

Thus if we have an object cooling in a draught in a room at a temperature of 20°C, the rate of cooling by convection when it is at a temperature of 60°C compared with its rate of cooling at 40°C is

$$\frac{\text{Rate at } 60°C}{\text{Rate at } 40°C} = \frac{(60-20)}{(40-20)} = 2.0$$

Radiation

Herschel, in 1800, moved thermometers along through the colours of the continuous spectrum produced by the sun's rays passing through a prism. The result was—a greater rise in temperature at the red end of the spectrum than at the violet end. Even stranger, when the thermometers were moved past the red end of the spectrum even larger temperature rises were found—the sun was emitting invisible rays. These rays we now call the infrared. Herschel found that the rays were capable of refraction and reflection.

Measurements of the energy at different wavelengths emitted by a hot solid show a maximum whose wavelength depends on the temperature of the hot body (Fig. 17.24). The wavelength of maximum energy is found to be inversely proportional to the absolute temperature.

$$\lambda_{max} \propto \frac{1}{T}$$

This is called Wien's law, first arrived at in 1894, and generally written as

$$\lambda_{max}T = \text{a constant}$$

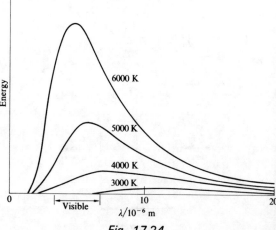

Fig. 17.24

The constant has the value 2.8978×10^{-2} m K, the wavelength being in metres and the temperature in kelvins.

Any hot body will emit energy, the lower the temperature of the body the longer the wavelength at which maximum emission occurs. All bodies, however, emit the very long wavelengths. Such wavelengths are not in the visible region of the spectrum but in the far infrared and radio regions.

The sun's surface temperature is about 6000 K and thus its maximum energy wavelength is about 4.8×10^{-7} m, almost the middle of the visible region. Since the peak of the radiation curve is fairly flat the sun appears yellowish. Other stars have their wavelength of maximum energy at different wavelengths. Stars cooler than the sun can appear red, stars hotter than the sun appear blue. Blue stars have their wavelength of maximum energy in the ultraviolet.

Name	Temperature, K	Colour
Alpha Crucis	23 000	bluish
Spica	20 400	bluish
Acherna	15 500	bluish
Rigel	12 300	bluish
Sirius	10 700	white
Altair	8530	white
Procyon	6800	straw
Sun	6000	yellow
Sigma Eridani A	5360	yellow
Epsilon Eridani	4910	orange
61 Cygni A	3900	orange
Lacaille 9352	3200	red

Adapted from G Gamow (1964) *A Star called the Sun*. Reprinted by permission of the Viking Press, Inc, New York, and Macmillan, London and Basingstoke.

The average temperature of the earth is about 281 K and thus its wavelength of maximum energy is about 1×10^{-5} m, deep in the infrared. The intensity of emission at all the wavelengths is not, however, expected to be the same as the curve given by a hot 'black body'. A 'black body' is defined as a body that absorbs all the radiation that falls on it, hence it appears black because no radiation is reflected, and it re-emits all the radiation. Most bodies are 'grey bodies' absorbing only a certain percentage of the radiation falling on them and hence emitting only that percentage of the radiation that would have been emitted by a 'black body'. The peak energy wavelength is not changed but the intensity at any wavelength is a certain fraction of the 'black body' intensity. This fraction is called the emissivity. The usefulness of the 'black body' energy distribution graphs is that the shape of the graphs are common to many substances; all that may have to be changed is the scale for the intensity (Fig. 17.25).

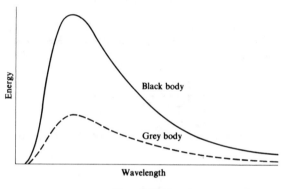

Fig. 17.25

In 1879 J. Stefan deduced (a fortuitous deduction, being essentially based on a few very poor results) from an examination of experimental evidence that the total energy radiated per unit surface area per second from a black body was proportional to the fourth power of the absolute temperature of the body.

$$E \propto T^4$$

or by introducing a constant, σ, called Stefan's constant,

$$E = \sigma T^4$$

σ has the value 5.67×10^{-8} J s^{-1} m^{-2} K^{-4}. A firm experimental foundation for this equation was provided in 1897 and a theoretical proof by Boltzmann in 1884.

We can use this equation to obtain estimates of the temperature of the sun. The only experimental information necessary is the amount of energy radiated per unit area per second from the sun. We can measure the amount of radiation reaching unit area of the earth per second. As some of the radiation would be absorbed in the earth's atmosphere we need either to estimate the amount not reaching the surface of the earth or make the measurements above the earth's atmosphere. Both types of measurement have been made and we can take the energy per second per square metre as being 1338 J s^{-1} m^2. This is known as the solar constant. The earth is 149 450 000 km from the sun, so the total radiation emitted by the sun will be

$$4\pi(1.495 \times 10^{11})^2 \times 1338$$

The sun has a radius of about 695 300 km so the energy emitted per unit area of the sun's surface per second is

$$\frac{4\pi(1.495 \times 11^{11})^2 \times 1338}{4\pi(6.953 \times 10^8)^2}$$

or 6.176×10^7 J s^{-1} m^{-2}. This gives a temperature of 5765 K.

Supplementary material

Sources of energy

Energy sources can be classified as renewable or non-renewable. Renewable sources include:

1. The direct use of solar energy
2 Water power
3. Wind power
4. Tidal energy
5. Geothermal energy
6. Biofuels

Non-renewable sources include:

1. Fossil fuels: coal, oil, natural gas
2. Fissionable isotopes
3. Fusion materials

The sun radiates energy, as a result of internal nuclear fusion processes, at the rate of about 4×10^{26} W. Virtually all this is radiated as frequencies in the ultraviolet–visible–infrared part of the electromagnetic spectrum. At the top of the earth's atmosphere this radiation amounts to about 1.35 kW per square metre averaged over the year. This is called the solar constant. Just under a half of this energy reaches the surface of the earth.

The above figure for the solar constant is an average over the year and over the entire surface of the earth. Thus at noon on a clear summer day in the south of England about 1 kW of solar radiation will fall on a 1 m^2 horizontal surface. In Scotland this would be about 0.8 kW. If it is cloudy it might drop to only about 0.2 kW. In winter all the figures are much lower, in the south of England about a tenth and in Scotland about a twentieth. In those parts of the world close to the equator the solar constant is much higher.

There are many forms of solar collectors. One version which is commonly used for domestic purposes consists of water, or some other fluid, circulating through tubes bonded to a blackened absorber plate (Fig. 17.26). Pumps are generally used to circulate the fluid, often being activated to pump fluid only when there is useful heat to be collected by a heat sensor. The warmed fluid is then, in an indirect system, passed through pipes immersed in a hot water tank from which water is drawn when required for the domestic heating or hot water system.

Water power can involve the water mills referred to in Chapter 4 or hydroelectricity. Both are essentially the result of solar energy causing water at low levels to evaporate and become

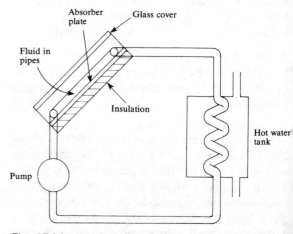

Fig. 17.26 *An example of a domestic solar collector system*

deposited at high levels. The water thus gains potential energy which it can then convert to kinetic energy in flowing as a river back down to the sea, so completing the cycle. A hydroelectric scheme might involve the damming of a river (Fig. 17.27) to create a reservoir from which the water can be constrained to fall through pipes and hit turbine blades, hence generating electricity. The loss in potential energy of the falling water is its gain in kinetic energy, thus if about 1×10^4 kg of water fall through 50 m and hit the turbine blades per second, the gain in kinetic energy per second is about $mgh = 1 \times 10^4 \times 9.8 \times 50$ or about 5×10^6 J. If the turbine converts 80 per cent of this to electricity then the power is 4 MW.

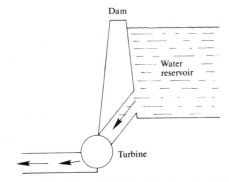

Fig. 17.27 The principle of hydroelectricity

Winds result from the non-uniform heating of the earth's surface by the sun producing convection currents in the atmosphere, affected by the rotation of the earth. Wind power can be produced when wind hits the blades of a turbine (i.e., a windmill in modern form). A moderate breeze has a wind speed of about 6 m s^{-1}, a gale about 18 m s^{-1} and a violent storm about 30 m s^{-1}. For air of density ρ and velocity v normal to the turbine blades, all the air within a distance vt will hit the blades in time t and so the mass of air hitting the blades in this time will be $vtA\rho$, where A is the area of the blades exposed to the wind. The kinetic energy of this air is $\frac{1}{2}(vtA\rho)v^2$ and thus the power is $\frac{1}{2}\rho Av^3$. Since the turbine will not be 100 per cent efficient in converting this power into electricity, then the output power will be some fraction of $\frac{1}{2}\rho Av^3$. Efficiencies of the order of 35 per cent are

usual. Thus if a 200 kW turbine output with 35 per cent efficiency is required with a wind velocity of 10 m s^{-1}, the area of the turbine blades must be, since $\rho = 1.2$ kg m^{-3}, given by

$$200 \times 10^3 = 0.35 \times \frac{1}{2} \times 1.2 \times A \times 10^3$$
$$A = 95 \text{ m}^2$$

Large area blades are thus indicated.

Tidal energy is based on the rise and fall of the tides, this being determined by gravitational forces between the moon, the sun, and the seas of the earth, and the earth's rotation. The tidal range, i.e., the difference between high and low tides, depends on geographical location. It is much affected by features such as the continental shelf and the funnelling effect of estuaries and bays. The tidal power station in the estuary of La Rance, France, is based on there being a difference in water level between water on either side of a dam placed across the estuary. Figure 17.28 illustrates the principle. When the water is rising and higher on the sea side of the dam than the land side, the turbines can operate; similarly when the water is higher on the land side than the sea side. The tidal range at La Rance averages about 8 m.

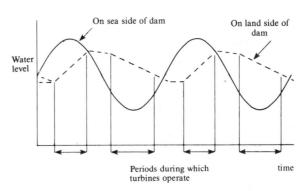

Fig. 17.28 Tide power

Geothermal energy is based on there being a heat flow at the earth's surface from the interior. In some parts of the earth the rate of flow can be quite high. Geothermal power stations consist essentially of a hole down into the ground and from which high velocity steam emerges, this then being used to rotate a turbine.

Biofuels involve the burning of wood, straw, municipal refuse, and other wastes to heat water and generate steam for driving turbines.

All the renewable energy sources are as the term implies renewable, unlike fossil fuels and nuclear reactor fuels. The world's stock of fossil fuels has been estimated as about:

Coal	2000×10^{20} J
Oil	120×10^{20} J
Natural gas	110×10^{20} J
Tar sand and shale oil	30×10^{20} J

This is a total stock of about 2260×10^{20} J. We are now using about 3×10^{20} J per year, but the demand is increasing at an alarming rate—it has been suggested that the demand may be about 7×10^{20} by the year 2000.

Uranium and thorium, naturally radioactive materials from which fissionable isotopes can be obtained, occurs in very small concentration in many parts of the world. However, the reserves which are likely to be economic to mine are of the order of 10^6 tonnes of uranium oxide. A typical burner reactor supplying 1000 MW of power will require initially 600 tonnes and then 150 tonnes per year of this oxide to supply its fuel. However, the reactor does produce plutonium which in turn can be used as a nuclear fissionable fuel. This production is enhanced in breeder reactors. Thorium is only recently becoming used as a source of fissionable isotopes, the world's economically extractable reserves having been estimated at about 10^7 tonnes.

Energy supply and demand in the UK

Energy is more than just a physicist's concept; it is a vital factor in a country's economy. Figure 17.29 summarizes the energy supply and demand picture for the UK in 1983. The UK is about 80 per cent energy self-sufficient, indeed it is a major exporter of oil with the level of exports almost as high as those of energy imports (the reason for imports is the requirement to get the right balance among the types of fuel). Of the order of 30 per cent of the energy supplied for use in the UK is lost in the conversion of the fuels to the energy supply form required by the consumer and their distribution. The main energy consumers are industry, domestic consumers and transport. We

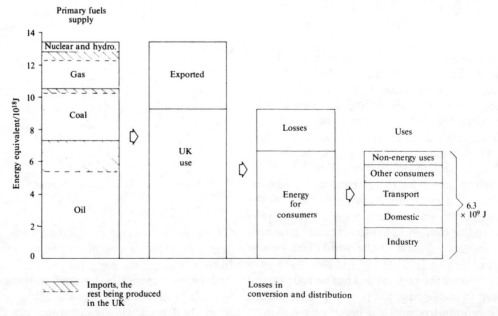

Fig. 17.29   Energy supply and demand for the UK in 1983 (based on Department of Energy information)

use almost as much energy in the home as industry uses.

The population of the UK is about 60 million and thus for the energy supplied for use in the UK of about 9×10^{18} J, each individual on average effectively 'consumes' about 1.5×10^{11} J per year. This is the equivalent of about 5 tonnes of coal or 3.5 tonnes of oil per year.

Problems

1. (a) What is meant by a thermometric property? What qualities make a particular property suitable for use in a practical thermometer?

A Celsius temperature scale may be defined in terms of a thermometric property X by the following equation:

$$\theta = \frac{X - X_0}{X_{100} - X_0} \times 100°C \qquad (1)$$

where X_0 is the value of the property at the ice point, X_{100} at the steam point, and X at some intermediate temperature. If X is plotted against θ a straight line always results no matter what thermometric property is chosen. Explain this.

(b) On the graph, Fig. 17.30, line A shows how X varies with θ (following equation (1) above), line B shows how a second thermometric property Q varies with θ, the temperature measured on the X scale.

(i) Describe, in principle, how you would conduct an experiment to obtain line B.

(ii) If $\theta = 40°C$ recorded by an X-scale thermometer, what temperature would be recorded by a Q-scale thermometer?

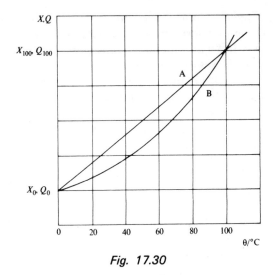

Fig. 17.30

(iii) At what two temperatures will the X and Q scales coincide?

(c) The ideal gas scale of temperature is one based on the properties of an ideal gas. What is the particular virtue of this scale? Describe very briefly how readings on such a scale can be obtained using a thermometer containing a real gas.

(University of London, Q9,
Paper 2, January 1984)

2. Explain what is meant by a scale of temperature, discussing how, in principle, a scale would be established.

The following table gives an example of a thermometer, the associated physical property and the measurement taken. Make a list giving the entries for the blank spaces (a)–(d) in the table.

Instrument	Physical property	Measurement taken
Constant volume gas thermometer	Pressure change of gas	Differences in manometer levels supported by the pressure of a fixed volume of nitrogen
Liquid-in-glass thermometer	(a)	(b)
Thermocouple	(c)	(d)

Why is it not convenient to use a constant volume gas thermometer in most practical situations? To what use is it actually put?

The masses of hydrogen and oxygen atoms are 1.66×10^{-27} kg and 2.66×10^{-26} kg respectively. What is the ratio of the 'average' speed of hydrogen and oxygen atoms at the same temperature? What is usually meant by the term 'average' speed in this case?

For the thermocouple give, with reasons, a situation for which it would be particularly suitable.

(University of London, Q9, Paper 2, June 1981)

3. (a) When bodies are in thermal equilibrium, their temperatures are the same. Explain in energy terms the conditions for two bodies to be in thermal equilibrium with one another.

(b) The temperature of a beaker of water is to be measured using a mercury-in-glass thermometer.

(i) Why is it necessary to wait before taking the reading?
(ii) Explain briefly how you might estimate the heat capacity (energy required per unit temperature rise) of a mercury-in-glass thermometer.
(iii) If the beaker contains 120 g of water at 60°C, what temperature would be recorded by the mercury-in-glass thermometer if it was initially at 18°C and had a heat capacity of 30 J K^{-1}? (Assume the specific heat capacity of water to be 4200 J kg^{-1} K^{-1} and ignore the heat losses to the beaker and surroundings while the temperature is being taken)
(iv) Why, if a more accurate value of the temperature were required in this case, might you use a thermocouple?
(v) Describe briefly how you would calibrate a thermocouple and use it to measure the temperature of the water. Show how you would calculate the temperature of the water from your readings.

(University of London, Q9, Paper 2, January 1985)

4. At a temperature of 100°C and a pressure of 1.01×10^5 Pa, 1.00 kg of steam occupies 1.67 m^3 but the same mass of water occupies only 1.04×10^{-3} m^3. The specific latent heat of vaporization of water at 100°C is 2.26×10^6 J kg^{-1}. For a system consisting of 1.00 kg of water changing to steam at 100°C and 1.01×10^5 Pa, find

(a) the heat supplied to the system,
(b) the work done by the system,
(c) the increase in internal energy of the system.

(University of Cambridge, Q10, Paper 1, June 1979)

5. (a) The specific heat capacities of air are 1040 J kg^{-1} K^{-1} measured at constant pressure and 740 J kg^{-1} K^{-1} measured at constant volume. Explain briefly why the values are different.

(b) A room of volume 180 m^3 contains air at a temperatue of 16°C having a density of 1.13 kg m^{-3}. During the course of the day the temperature rises to 21°C. Calculate an approximate value for the amount of energy transferred to the air during the day. Assume that air can escape from the room but no fresh air enters. Explain your reasoning.

(University of London, Q1, Paper 2, June 1984)

6. The cylinder in figure 17.31a holds a volume $V_1 = 1000$ cm^3 of air at an initial pressure $p_1 = 1.10 \times 10^5$ Pa and temperature $T_1 = 300$ K. Assume that air behaves like an ideal gas. Figure 17.31b shows a sequence of changes imposed on the air in the cylinder.

(a) AB—the air is heated to 375 K at constant pressure. Calculate the new volume, V_2.

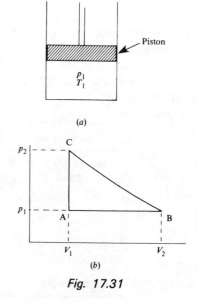

Fig. 17.31

(b) BC—the air is compressed isothermally to volume V_1. Calculate the new pressure, p_2.

(c) CA—the air cools at constant volume to pressure p_1. State how a value for the work done on the air during the full sequence of changes may be found from the graph in Fig. 17.31b.

(University of London, Q1,
Paper 2, June 1985)

7. (a) The first law of thermodynamics may be written $\Delta Q = \Delta U + \Delta W$. Explain the meaning of this equation as applied to the heating of a gas. Use the equation to justify the fact that the molar heat capacity of a gas at constant pressure is greater than the molar heat capacity at constant volume.

(b) Explain the meaning of the terms isothermal change and adiabatic change. What is meant by a reversible change?

A mass of gas is expanded isothermally and then compressed adiabatically to its original volume. What further operation must be performed on the gas to restore it to its original state? Sketch a labelled p–V graph to represent the series of operations. What quantity is represented by the area enclosed?

(c) An ideal gas at an initial temperature of 15°C and pressure of 1.10×10^5 Pa is compressed isothermally to one-quarter of its original volume. What will be its final pressure and temperature? What would have been the pressure and temperature if the compression had been adiabatic? (Ratio of the principal specific heat capacities of the gas = 1.40)

(AEB, QB12, Paper 3, November 1982)

8. What is meant by the specific latent heat of vaporization of a liquid? Explain how latent heat of vaporization can be regarded as molecular potential energy.

Calculate the potential energy per molecule released when 18 g of steam condenses to water at 100°C.

(Specific latent heat of vaporization of water = 2.26×10^6 J kg^{-1}. Mass of 1 mole of water = 18 g. Number of molecules in a mole of molecules = 6.02×10^{23})

(University of London, Q1,
Paper 2, January 1981)

9. List four factors that affect the rate at which the temperature of a beaker of hot water falls.

Explain why a beaker containing 0.5 litre of hot water cools faster than the same beaker containing 1.0 litre of water initially at the same temperature and cooling under identical conditions.

(University of London, Q1,
Paper 2, June 1981)

10. A double-glazed window consists of two panes of glass each 4 mm thick separated by a 10-mm layer of air. Assuming the thermal conductivity of glass to be 50 times greater than that of air calculate the ratios

(i) temperature gradient in the glass, to temperature gradient in the air gap,
(ii) temperature difference across one pane of glass to temperature difference across the air gap.

Sketch a graph showing how the temperature changes between the surface of the glass in the room and the surface of the glass outside, i.e., across the double-glazed window, if there is a large temperature difference between the room and the outside.

Explain why, in practice, the value of the ratio calculated in (i) is too high.

(University of London, Q1,
Paper 2, January 1984)

11. A copper hot water cylinder of length 1.0 m and radius 0.20 m is lagged by 2.0 cm of material of thermal conductivity 0.40 W m^{-1} K^{-1}. Estimate the temperature of the outer surface of the lagging, assuming heat loss is through the sides only, if heat has to be supplied at a rate of 0.25 kW to maintain the water at a steady temperature of 60°C.

Assume that the temperature of the inside surface of the lagging is 60°C.

(University of London, Q1,
Paper 2, January 1982)

12. (a) (i) Describe how you would determine the coefficient of thermal conductivity of copper. Your account should include details of how each measurement is taken.
(ii) State one way in which the behaviour of the apparatus used differs from that assumed in calculating the thermal conductivity. What is the cause of the difference and how does it affect the result?

(b) The cabin of a light aircraft can be regarded as an approximately rectangular box, sides 1.5 m by 1.5 m by 2 m. The windows are made of Perspex, 10 mm thick, and having a total area of 3 m^2; the remainder of the cabin wall is made of thin aluminium-alloy sheet lined with insulating material, 20 mm thick. The cabin heater is able to maintain a temperature of 20°C in the cabin when the outside temperature is $-10°C$.

Assuming that the temperature difference across the aluminium alloy may be neglected, calculate:

(i) the power of the heater;
(ii) the percentage of the total energy which is lost through the Perspex.

Explain why, in practice, the power of the heater needed would be much less than that calculated.
(Take the thermal conductivity of Perspex to be 0.2 W m^{-1} K^{-1} and that of the insulating material to be 3.5×10^{-2} W m^{-1} K^{-1})

(Oxford Local Examinations, Q4, Paper 1, June 1981)

13. (a) Discuss the analogy between the flow of heat under a temperature gradient and the electrical current under a potential gradient, and write down the corresponding expressions for the thermal conductivity and electrical conductivity.

In the case of a metal, why is thermal conductivity much the more difficult of the two to measure accurately?

(b) Describe how you would measure the thermal conductivity of copper. Mention the chief precautions which must be taken to obtain a reasonably accurate result.

(c) Figure 17.32 shows two cylindrical bars of aluminium and copper, each 0.3 m long, which have just been set up in good thermal contact with the flat surfaces of two large reservoirs maintained at 100°C and 0°C respectively. The diameter of the aluminium bar is 30 mm and that of the copper bar is 40 mm. Both bars are well lagged. The thermal conductivity, specific heat capacity, and density of each metal are:

	Aluminium	Copper
Thermal conductivity in W m^{-1} K^{-1}	235	380
Specific heat capacity in J kg^{-1} K^{-1}	840	360
Density in kg m^{-3}	2700	8800

(i) In the steady state, calculate the rate of flow of heat down each bar.
(ii) Assuming that both were initially at 15°C, estimate the energy that has been gained by each bar during the attainment of the steady state.
(iii) Which bar should reach the steady state first? Why?

(Oxford Local Examinations, Q6, Paper I, June 1978)

14. (a) At room temperature diamond is an extremely good conductor of heat, many times better than copper. Suggest a suitable way of measuring its thermal conductivity.

(b) The average rate of flow of heat per unit area from the interior of the Earth as measured at the surface is 3.8×10^{-3} W m^2. Taking the thermal conductivity of an average sample of the surface to be 6.0 W m^{-1} K^{-1}, estimate the temperature gradient at the surface. Suggest a suitable way of measuring the rate of flow of heat per unit area and the temperature gradient.

(c) The specific latent heat of fusion of ice at 0°C is 3.36×10^5 J kg^{-1}, its density is 910 kg m^{-3} and its thermal conductivity is 2.3 W m^{-1} K^{-1}. Find the rate at which the thickness of the ice on a pond is increasing when the water just below it is at 0°C, the air above it is at $-5°C$ and the ice is already 25 mm thick. How long will it take, under

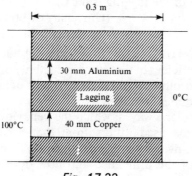

Fig. 17.32

these conditions for the thickness to increase to 50 mm?

(Oxford Local Examinations, Q5, Paper S, June 1979)

15. (a) Sketch graphs showing the distribution of the energy radiated by a black body with wavelength, for three temperatures. Label the axes of these graphs clearly. How is the total energy radiated by the body related to these graphs?

(b) A perfectly black sphere maintained at a temperature of 373 K in an enclosure at 0 K radiates heat at a rate of 200 W. At what rate will the black sphere radiate in the following cases?

(i) Its radius is doubled; other factors remain unchanged.

(ii) The temperature of the sphere is raised to 746 K; other factors remain unchanged.

(iii) The temperature of the enclosure is raised to 300 K; other factors remain unchanged.

What would be the net rate of heat loss of the original sphere if the enclosure were also at a temperature of 373 K?

(Explain your answers in each of the above.)

(c) If the Earth is assumed to be a perfectly black body radiating uniformly in all directions, a calculation of its equilibrium temperature gives a value of approximately 250 K. In fact the equilibrium temperature of the Earth's surface is considerably higher than this. Explain why this is so.

(University of London, Q9, Paper 2, January 1982)

16. Explain what is meant by black body radiation, and state Stefan's law.

The metal filament of an electrical lamp has a diameter of 0.2 mm. In normal operation, the current taken by the lamp is 5 A, and the resistance of the filament is 22 Ω m^{-1}. Estimate the temperature of the filament, stating the assumptions you make.

(The Stefan constant = 5.6×10^{-8} W m^{-2} K^{-4})

Draw sketch curves, on one set of axes, to show qualitatively how the energy radiated at different wavelengths varies with the wavelength for the two cases, when the lamp is operated with currents (a) 5 A, (b) 7 A.

(Southern Universities, Q5, Paper 2, June 1980)

17. Explain what is meant by thermal equilibrium. Describe the energy transfer mechanism by means of which thermal equilibrium will be attained in the case of

(a) a small 'hot' sphere inside a larger, hollow 'cold' sphere (from which all the air has been removed), and

(b) a vessel, the top half of which contains a 'hot' gas and the bottom half a 'cold' gas. (Assume that no energy is lost through the walls of the vessel.)

Explain why in case (a) energy transfer still takes place even when thermal equilibrium is established, and why in case (b) all the gas molecules will not have the same speeds when thermal equilibrium is established.

Sketch graphs showing the distribution of speeds among the molecules of case (b) for (i) the hot gas, (ii) the cold gas, and (iii) the mixture when thermal equilibrium is achieved.

The zeroth law of thermodynamics states that if a body A is in thermal equilibrium with a body B and body B is in thermal equilibrium with a body C then body A is in thermal equilibrium with body C. How may the temperature of a body be defined using this law? Explain how it relates to the interpretation of temperature provided by the simple kinetic theory of gases.

Explain how the absolute or ideal gas scale of temperature is defined and outline briefly how such a scale is realized in practice.

(University of London, Q3, Special paper, June 1980)

18. There are a number of physical processes which depend on the ratio of numbers of particles having energies differing by E being given, as least approximately, by the Boltmann factor $\exp(-E/kT)$.

(a) Give an example (other than that in (c) below) of such a process, explaining the significance of the factor $\exp(-E/kt)$ in that case, including the nature of the energy difference E.

(b) What is the connection between the Boltmann factor and the manner in which energy is shared among particles?

(c) Viscosity, that is the resistance to flow of a liquid, can be an example of such a process, if flow occurs by molecules needing extra energy E to push between their neighbours.

(i) If viscosity was thought to be inversely proportional to the number of molecules with the extra energy E needed to push between neighbours, what straight line graph derived from measurements of viscosity and temperature could you plot to test the theory?

(ii) Suppose the theory is correct for a given motor oil. If its viscosity falls by a factor e ($= 2.718$) when the temperature rises from 27°C to 77°C, what is the energy E? ($k = 1.4 \times 10^{-23}$ J K^{-1})

(Oxford and Cambridge, Nuffield special paper, Q4, June 1983)

19. R. Feynman in *The character of physical law* (BBC) states 'Temperature is like "ease of removing energy".'

(a) In what way is a solid at a higher temperature different from one at a lower temperature?

(b) If two solids are at the same temperature what have they in common?

(c) How valid do you think Feynman's definition of temperature is?

20. Hydrogen normally exists as H_2 molecules. But if 1 mole of H_2 changes to two moles of H atoms the entropy of the hydrogen increases from 130 to 230 J K^{-1}.

(a) Why does hydrogen remain as molecules if an entropy increase would result by it dissociating?

(b) At what temperature should hydrogen spontaneously dissociate?

Energy to break the H—H bond = 430 kJ mol^{-1}.

18 Atoms and quanta

Millikan's experiment

A characteristic of charge is that it comes in packets with the charge on any object always being an integral number of basic charges; we say that charge is quantized. The size of the basic charge is fixed, being the charge carried by the electron and the proton.

One of the pieces of evidence for this idea was the classic experiment by Millikan in 1911. He measured the charge on a large number of drops of oil and other liquids. It did not matter what liquid he used, or what size the drops were, the charge carried by a drop was always an integral multiple of the basic charge. For example, he found drops carrying charges of 6.397, 8.005, 9.662, 11.231, 12.814 × 10^{-19} C. These are all, within the limits of experimental error, multiples of the basic charge e of 1.602 × 10^{-19} C.

n	ne	Experimental value
4	6.408	6.397
5	8.010	8.005
6	9.612	9.662
7	11.214	11.231
8	12.816	12.814

The apparatus used by Millikan was essentially just two parallel, horizontal, metal plates (Fig. 18.1). Drops of oil were produced by means of an atomizer (essentially a scent spray) and some fell through a pinhole in the top plate into the space between the plates. They were viewed by a telescope, appearing as bright star-like objects against a dark background.

The velocity of a freely falling oil drop was determined from a measurement of the time taken for it to fall through a measured distance. The velocity was constant because it was the terminal velocity attained by an object falling in a viscous medium (see Chapter 16). A potential difference was then applied between the parallel plates. The resulting electric field caused the velocity of the oil drop to change, the new value being determined.

For the free fall, using Stokes' law

$$mg = 6\pi\eta r v_1 \qquad (1)$$

where m is the apparent mass of the drop (apparent because there is an upthrust on it due to the air of $V\sigma g$, where V is its volume and σ the air density). For fall if there is an opposing electric field the force acting on a drop carrying a charge q is Eq, where E is the field strength ($E = V/d$, with d being the plate separation and V the potential difference between them). Thus

$$mg - Eq = 6\pi\eta r v_2$$

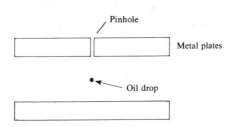

Fig. 18.1 The essential principle of Millikan's experiment

Hence

$$\frac{v_1}{v_2} = \frac{mg}{mg - Eq}$$

Thus if m is known the charge q can be determined. m can be determined using Eq. (1).

Taking account of the upthrust force, Eq. (1) can be written as

$$\frac{4}{3}\pi r^3(\rho - \sigma)g = 6\pi\eta r v_1$$

Hence r can be determined.

The specific charge of electrons

The term specific charge for a particle is used for its charge per unit mass. An early measurement of this quantity for electrons was by J. J. Thomson in 1897 and this, together with other experimental evidence, was to be the justification for the identification of the existence of electrons as discrete particles having a constant charge and mass.

In modern forms of this experiment, electrons are produced either directly from a heated filament or indirectly when a hot filament heats an electrode and causes it to emit electrons. The electrons are then accelerated by a potential difference V applied between the filament or electrode, called the cathode, and a perforated anode. If e is the charge on an electron and m its mass, it gains a kinetic energy of $\frac{1}{2}mv^2$ where

$$\frac{1}{2}mv^2 = eV \qquad (2)$$

The electron beam then passes through the anode into a region where there is a magnetic field B at right angles to the beam. This causes the beam to be acted on by a force, at right angles to both the beam and the magnetic field. The result is that the beam moves in a circular path of radius r, where

$$Force = Bev = \frac{mv^2}{r} \qquad (3)$$

Figure 18.2 shows one form of this apparatus, called a fine beam tube. The beam of electrons is made visible through collisions with hydrogen

Fig. 18.2 *Magnetic field everywhere at right angles to the electron beam*

gas which is in the tube under low pressure. The radius r can be measured. Since Eq. (3) gives

$$mv = Ber$$

We can eliminate r from this equation by using Eq. (2), where

$$v^2 = \frac{2eV}{m}$$

and so

$$\frac{e}{m} = \frac{2V}{B^2r^2}$$

Since V, B and r can be measured, a value for e/m can be obtained. The specific charge for an electron is 1.76×10^{11} C kg^{-1}.

The photoelectric effect

In 1887 Hertz, while doing experiments on electric waves, found that when ultraviolet light from a spark shone on his apparatus, two metal spheres with a high potential difference between them, sparks came more readily. In 1888

Hallwachs found that a negatively charged zinc plate lost its charge when illuminated with ultraviolet light; a positively charged zinc plate did not lose its charge. Later, in 1899, Lenard showed that the ultraviolet light was causing electrons to be emitted by metal plates. The sparks passed more readily between Hertz's metal spheres because ultraviolet light was causing the emission of electrons to occur from them. Hallwachs' zinc plate lost charge because it was emitting electrons under the action of the ultraviolet light. Only the negatively charged plate lost charge because it repelled the emitted electrons, the positively charged plate attracted the electrons back to its surface and none escaped. This emission of electrons due to the action of 'light' is known as photoelectricity.

Lenard in his experiments obtained some surprising results which could not be explained. When the metal is illuminated by monochromatic light the electrons are released with all energies up to a definite maximum value. The value of this maximum energy was found to be directly proportional to the frequency of the light used. Changing the intensity of the illumination at the metal surface had no effect on the value of the maximum energy, though more electrons were released. On the basis of the wave theory of light it would be expected that an increase in the intensity of illumination would produce an increase in the maximum energy of the electrons—for a wave an increase in intensity means an increase in energy. Why should the colour (frequency) of the light have anything to do with the energy of the emitted electrons—a change in frequency means on the wave theory a change of wavelength and not a change of energy. An explanation was given by Einstein in 1905.

'On a Heuristic Point of View about the Creation and Conversion of Light

... According to the assumption considered here, when a light ray starting from a point is propagated, the energy is not continuously distributed over an ever increasing volume, but it consists of a finite number of energy quanta, localized in space, which move without being divided and which can be absorbed or emitted as a whole....

The usual idea that the energy of light is continuously distributed over the space through which it travels meets with especially great difficulties when one tries to explain photoelectric phenomena, as was shown in the pioneering paper by Mr. Lenard.

According to the idea that the incident light consists of energy quanta with an energy (hf) ..., one can picture the production of ... [electrons] by light as follows. Energy quanta penetrate into a surface layer of the body, and their energy is at least partly transformed into electronic kinetic energy. The simplest picture is that a light quantum transfers all of its energy to a single electron; we shall assume that that happens. We must, however, not exclude the possibility that electrons only receive part of the energy from light quanta. An electron obtaining kinetic energy inside the body will have lost part of its kinetic energy when it has reached the surface. Moreover, we must assume that each electron on leaving the body must produce work W, which is characteristic for the body. Electrons which are excited at the surface and at right angles to it will leave the body with the greatest normal velocity. The kinetic energy of such electrons is

$$hf - W$$

If the body is charged to a positive potential V and surrounded by zero potential conductors, and if V is just able to prevent the loss of electricity by the body, we must have

$$Ve = hf - W$$

where e is the ... (charge) of the electron.... ... If the formula derived here is correct, V must be, if drawn in Cartesian coordinates as a function of the frequency of the incident light, a straight line, the slope of which is independent of the nature of the substance studied.

As far as I can see, our ideas are not in contradiction to the properties of the photoelectric action observed by Mr. Lenard. If every energy quantum of the incident light transfers its energy to electrons independently of all other quanta, the velocity distribution of the electrons ... will be independent of the intensity of the incident light; on the other hand ... the number of electrons leaving the body should be proportional to the intensity of the incident light. ...'

A. Einstein (1905) *Ann. Physik* **17**, 132. Translation in D. ter Haar (1967) *The Old Quantum Theory*, Pergamon.

According to Einstein light comes in packets, quanta. The energy carried by a quantum is directly proportional to the frequency of the light.

$$E = hf$$

where h is Planck's constant, 6.6×10^{-34} J s. The intensity of the light is proportional to the number of quanta reaching a surface in unit time. The term photons has been used to describe light quanta.

Figure 18.3 shows the type of experimental arrangement that might be used to investigate photoelectricity. The cathode of the photocell is coated with a material such as caesium. This is illuminated with light of just one frequency. The emitted electrons can be collected by an anode. If this anode is made sufficiently positive, all the electrons can be collected as fast as they are produced. The current then depends only on the intensity of illumination and, in a graph of current against potential difference across the photocell, corresponds to the horizontal part of the graph when the current becomes independent of the potential difference. We can, however, measure the maximum energy of the electrons by finding the potential difference necessary to stop the electrons reaching the anode. This means making the anode negative with respect to the cathode. The potential difference is adjusted until there is no current. This stopping potential is independent of the intensity of illumination, depending only on the frequency of the light used. A graph of this stopping potential plotted against frequency gives a straight line (Fig. 18.3c), which is described by the equation

$$Ve = hf - W$$

$$V = \left(\frac{h}{e}\right)f - \frac{W}{e}$$

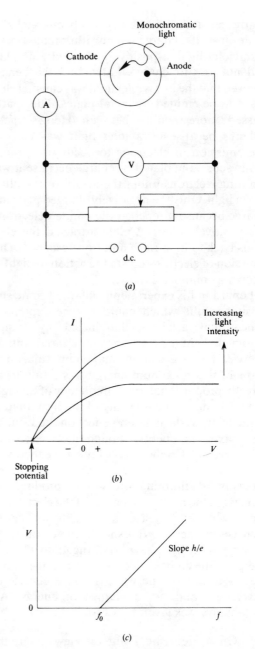

Fig. 18.3 The photoelectric experiment. (a) The apparatus. (b) and (c) The experimental results

The slope of the graph is (h/e) and hence h, Planck's constant, can be derived from its measurement. The slope is independent of the cathode material, this only determining the intercept on the graph axis. f_0 is the minimum frequency for which emission will occur, $f_0 = W/h$. For lower frequencies no emission of electrons occurs, regardless of the intensity of the illumination.

One of the consequences of Einstein's photoelectric equation is that as the energy is directly proportional to the frequency, high-frequency radiation can do things that low-frequency radiation cannot do. Ultraviolet light can kill bacteria—red light cannot; ultraviolet light has a higher frequency and hence higher energy per quantum than red light. Ultraviolet light has much more effect on a photographic emulsion than red light.

If the energy of a photon is less than W, the energy needed to get an electron out of a metal, then no electron emission can occur. With most metals red light can cause no electron emission, because the energy is less than W. However bright or intense the red light, no emission can occur if $W > hf$.

If the photoelectric effect is observed with very small metal particles, another piece of evidence in favour of light quanta emerges. Small metal pieces fall between two charged plates and light of the appropriate frequency is shone on them. When an electron is emitted from a piece of metal the balance of charge on the piece is disturbed, it becomes positively or more positively charged. The instant an electron is emitted the piece of metal will thus show a sudden change in its rate of fall between the charged plates. When the experiment is done it is found that on occasions emission of electrons starts to occur as soon as the light is switched on. The emission of electrons from the metal pieces is found to occur in a random manner with no apparent time lag being necessary before emission can take place. If light came in energy packets then this seems feasible—a piece of metal could take in enough energy for the ejection of an electron almost immediately the light was switched on, if it happened to pick up a quantum. If, however, we think of light as a wave motion we would expect that emission could not occur until a sufficient amount of wave energy had arrived at the metal piece—the wave energy is not localized but spread thinly over an entire wave front. Thus with waves we would expect a time lag which would be the same each time we did the experiment; there would appear to be no random element with waves.

Light, waves or particles?

We face a dilemma if we describe light as a wave motion—we cannot explain the photoelectric effect; we face an equal dilemma if we describe light as particulate—we cannot explain interference and diffraction. We seem to need both models if we are to describe the behaviour of light. As Sir William Bragg has said, in the early twenties, 'On Mondays, Wednesdays and Fridays light behaves like waves, on Tuesdays, Thursdays and Saturdays like particles, and like nothing at all on Sundays.'

Monochromatic light incident on two narrow slits placed close together gives an interference pattern (Young's experiment)—a series of fringes—a series of regions where light interferes to give constructive interference, a bright fringe, and where light interferes to give destructive interference, a dark fringe. We use the wave theory of light to calculate where the positions of the constructive and destructive interferences will be. Instead of looking at the interference fringes with the eye, we could use a photocell which we move across the interference pattern. What does the photocell detect?—photons. In the constructive interference fringes the photocell detects a large number of photons, in the destructive interference fringes only a few photons are detected. The photons seem to go to the regions forecast by our wave model. But what happens to a single photon moving up to the double slits? Which slit does it go through? Where does it go—to a constructive or destructive interference region? If it only goes through one slit surely it should be able to land anywhere—for interference we need light from two slits. G. I. Taylor, in 1909, took interference photographs with light so feeble that an exposure time of three months was necessary—the light was so feeble that the chance of there being more than one photon en route to the photographic plate at any instant was rather remote—he still obtained an interference pattern, even though only single photons were involved. Somehow a photon interferes with itself—it goes through both slits!

413

Critical potentials

When a table-tennis ball falls onto a smooth hard surface it bounces and kinetic energy is almost conserved. Collisions in which kinetic energy is conserved are called elastic collisions. When a piece of 'Plasticine' hits the surface rebounding does not occur—kinetic energy is not conserved. Such collisions are called inelastic collisions.

Is it to be expected that kinetic energy will be conserved when electrons hit atoms? If kinetic energy is conserved then the energy of an electron after a collision will be the value it had before the collision.

Franck and Hertz in 1914 carried out a series of experiments involving collisions between electrons and atoms, Fig. 18.4a showing the principles of their apparatus. Electrons were emitted from a hot filament, C. These were accelerated by a potential difference V_{GC} between a grid G and C. These electrons pass through the grid and into the space between G and a collecting electrode A. This electrode A is made negative with respect to the grid. However, since V_{GA} is less than V_{GC}, electrons passing through the grid should have sufficient energy to reach A. In the tube, however, was mercury vapour. The electrons would inevitably collide with mercury atoms in passing down the tube. However, provided the collisions were elastic they would not lose energy and so would still have enough energy to reach A. Inelastic collisions in which they lost energy would leave them with insufficient energy to overcome V_{GA} and reach A.

The results of such an experiment are shown in Fig. 18.4b. As V_{GC} is increased from zero, so the number of electrons able to reach A increases. This continues until V_{GC} is 4.9 V. Then there is a sudden drop in the current. Inelastic collisions occur when electrons have the energy acquired by acceleration through 4.9 V, we say they have an energy of 4.9 eV (electron-volts, where 1 eV = 1.6 × 10^{-10} J). As V_{GC} is further increased the current picks up again until at 2 × 4.9 V there is again a sudden drop in current. We can explain these changes by the electrons which had lost 4.9 eV energy being again accelerated. When, however, they had received another 4.9 eV energy they again lose their energy in inelastic collisions. This event keeps on being repeated every time V_{GC} is a multiple of 4.9 V. The value of 4.9 V is called a critical potential for mercury.

Later experiments showed that mercury has a number of excitation potentials: 4.9 V, 5.4 V, 6.8 V 7.7 V, 8.8 V, etc. When, however, the potential reaches 10.4 V the incident electrons have enough energy to knock electrons out of the mercury atoms. This is called ionization and the potential at which it occurs the ionization potential or energy.

The ionization energy varies from element to element. Figure 18.5 shows how it varies from element to element in the sequence given by the periodic table. The alkali elements, lithium Li

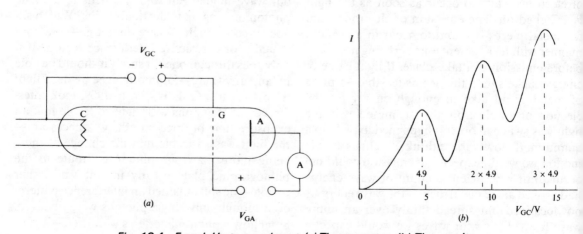

Fig. 18.4 Franck-Hertz experiment. (a) The apparatus. (b) The results

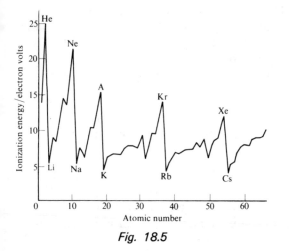

Fig. 18.5

sodium Na, potassium K, etc., have low ionization energies, i.e., it is easier to remove one electron from them than from other elements. Such elements are very reactive. The inert elements, helium He, neon Ne, argon A, etc., have high ionization energies and are very unreactive.

Energy levels

When an atom absorbs energy, perhaps as the result of an electron with the right energy hitting it, we consider that one of the atom's electrons has acquired the energy and become raised to a higher energy level. The atom is said to be excited. Since there are a number of critical potentials then an atom has a number of energy levels to which its electrons can be excited. We can think of the situation being rather like a ladder, with an atomic electron able to absorb energy only when it is sufficient for it to jump up to a rung at a higher level.

The unexcited atom is said to be in its ground state, we designate this level as $n = 1$ (n being what is called a quantum number). The rung above this ground state is designated as $n = 2$, the next rung $n = 3$, etc. Unlike a ladder, however, the rungs of this energy level pattern are not equally spaced.

The emission and absorption of radiation

When an atom makes a downward energy jump, from an energy level of more to an energy level of less energy, the energy released appears as a photon. Only a photon whose energy fits the jump between the levels can be emitted (Fig. 18.6a). The frequency of the photon is given by

$$E = hf$$

where E is surplus energy, equal to the difference in energy between the two energy levels, h is Planck's constant, and f the frequency of the photons.

In a similar way to emission, an atom can only absorb radiation (photons) whose energy fits one of the possible energy jumps between energy levels (Fig. 18.6b).

If we pass white light (i.e., a wide range of frequencies and hence photon energies) through a gas, absorption can only occur for those photons whose energy corresponds to the energy difference between two energy levels in the gas atoms. When white light is passed through sodium vapour the resulting spectrum shows all

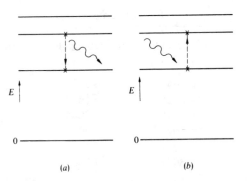

Fig. 18.6 (a) Emission of a photon, an atom drops down the energy level ladder. (b) Absorption of a photon, an atom climbs up the energy level ladder

frequencies with the exception of the yellow sodium lines (Fig. 18.7). The absorption spectrum of the sodium vapour is at the same frequencies as sodium vapour normally gives in an emission spectrum. The sodium vapour has in fact absorbed the photons with the energy corresponding to that which gives the yellow spectrum lines. The atoms which acquire this surplus energy later re-emit the energy, as the same frequency photons. The photons are, however, not necessarily emitted in the same direction as the incident photons. The result is that the white light has fewer yellow photons moving in the initial direction.

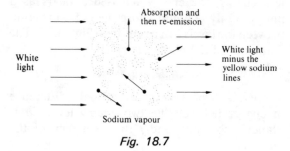

Fig. 18.7

The hydrogen spectrum

One of the important characteristics of the hydrogen atom is the spectrum lines produced by hydrogen. The spectrum lines occur in groups. Figure 18.8 shows one of the groups. The one shown is called the Balmer series, after J. J. Balmer who in 1885 found a rule for the frequencies of the lines in the series.

The Lyman series gives many more lines, up to a limit of frequency 32.881×10^{14} Hz, the Balmer series reaches a limit of 8.228×10^{14} Hz (wavelength 3.6456×10^{-7} m).

The relationship arrived at by Balmer can be expressed in the form

$$\text{Frequency of line } f = cR \left(\frac{1}{2^2} - \frac{1}{n^2} \right)$$

where c is the speed of light and R a constant, called the Rydberg constant and equal to 10 968 000 m^{-1}. n is an integer greater than 2.

For the Lyman series the formula becomes

$$f = cR \left(\frac{1}{1^2} - \frac{1}{n^2} \right)$$

n is an integer greater than 1.
For the Paschen series

$$f = cR \left(\frac{1}{3^2} - \frac{1}{n^2} \right)$$

n is an integer greater than 3.

The first two frequencies in the Lyman series are 24.659 and 29.226×10^{14} Hz. The difference between these two frequencies is 4.563×10^{14} Hz, but this is the first line in the Balmer series. The difference between the first and third line in the Lyman series is 6.165×10^{14} Hz—the second line in the Balmer series. The Balmer series has the frequencies of the differences between the first line in the Lyman series and each successive line.

Lyman series		Balmer series		Paschen series	
Wavelength /10^{-7} m	Frequency /10^{14} Hz	Wavelength /10^{-7} m	Frequency /10^{14} Hz	Wavelength /10^{-7} m	Frequency /10^{14} Hz
1.2157	24.659	6.5647	4.5665	18.756	1.5983
1.0257	29.226	4.8626	6.1649	12.822	2.3380
0.9725	30.824	4.3416	6.9044	10.941	2.7399
0.9497	31.564	4.1029	7.3064	10.052	2.9822
0.9378	31.966	3.9712	7.5487	9.5484	3.1395
0.9307	32.208	3.8901	7.7060	. . .	
0.9262	32.365	. . .			
. . .					

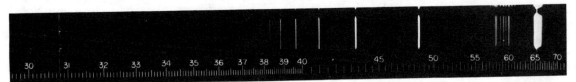

Fig. 18.8 The hydrogen spectrum. (Nuffield Foundation Science Teaching Project, Advanced Physics.
Unit 10, Penguin)

The Paschen series has the frequencies of the differences between the second line in the Lyman series and each successive line.

In terms of energy levels, the Lyman series of frequencies are produced by jumps from energy levels to the $n = 1$ level, the Balmer series are produced by jumps to the $n = 2$ level and the Paschen series by jumps to the $n = 3$ level. Thus rewriting the Lyman, Balmer, and Paschen equations we have

$$f = \frac{cR}{1^2} - \frac{cR}{n^2} \quad \text{Lyman series}$$

and as $E = hf$ we have

$$\text{Energy release} = \frac{hcR}{1^2} - \frac{hcR}{n^2}$$

For the Balmer series

$$\text{Energy release} = \frac{hcR}{2^2} - \frac{hcR}{n^2}$$

and for the Paschen series

$$\text{Energy release} = \frac{hcR}{3^2} - \frac{hcR}{n^2}$$

Thus the hydrogen atom has energy levels at energies of

$$-\frac{hcR}{1^2}, -\frac{hcR}{2^2}, -\frac{hcR}{3^2}, -\frac{hcR}{4^2}, -\frac{hcR}{5^2}, \text{etc.}$$

Figure 18.9 shows these energies on an energy level diagram. The energies are proportional to $1/n^2$ and given by $-21.8 \times 10^{-19}/n^2$ J. The minus sign appears because we take the view that the atom is an energy well, it needs 21.8×10^{-19} J to dig out the $n = 1$ electron and bring it to the surface where we take the energy to be zero. The more energy we supply to the atom the higher up the energy level ladder we can progress, i.e., the larger the value of n. Escape is when n is infinity.

Electrons, particles or waves?

Charge comes in packets. This is the evidence given by an experiment such as the Millikan

Fig. 18.9 Energy levels for hydrogen

experiment where the charge on oil drops was measured and found to be integral multiples of a basic charge. Assuming that the charges on the drops were produced by adding or removing electrons then this gave the charge on an electron. The charge-to-mass ratio for electrons can be measured. The results of such experiments give for the charge on the electron 1.6×10^{-19} C and for the mass 9.1×10^{-31} kg (at speeds not comparable with the speed of light). Electrons would certainly seem to be particles.

In 1925 Davisson, while doing experiments involving the scattering of electrons by a platinum target, had an accident—a liquid air bottle exploded when the target was at a high temperature. The experimental tube was broken and the platinum target became heavily oxidized by the in-rushing air. Davisson managed to rid the platinum target of the oxide by prolonged heating at high temperatures. When, however, he repeated his scattering experiment the results were completely different. The difference was found to be due to the target having previously been composed of small crystals but after the heating it was just a few large crystals. Why should the scattering from a polycrystalline target be different from that of just a few large crystals? Davisson's experiment with electron beams probing into platinum was to give information about the distribution of the atomic electrons in the platinum. Changing the crystalline structure of the platinum would not have been expected to change the distribution of atomic electrons.

A year earlier, 1924, de Broglie in his Ph.D. thesis had put forward a novel suggestion. In his own words:

'... I assumed that the existence of waves and particles, perceived by Einstein in 1905 in respect of light in his theory of light quanta, should be extended to all types of particle in the form of coexistence of a physical wave with a particle incorporated in it. ...'

L. de Broglie (1971) *Physics Bull.*, 149.

De Broglie was suggesting that not just light but all matter should have both a wave and a particle characteristic. Other than for light, there was no experimental evidence to justify this suggestion.

De Broglie's work was nothing more than speculation. He thesis was, however, to lead to a Nobel prize.

De Broglie suggested that the wavelength of all matter is given by

$$\lambda = \frac{h}{\text{momentum}}$$

This was essentially arrived at by equating $E = hf$ and $E = mc^2$.

Using de Broglie's equation for the wavelength of the electrons $\lambda = h/\text{momentum}$ (the momentum can be calculated from a measurement of the potential difference, V, through which the electrons had been accelerated: $\frac{1}{2} mv^2 = Ve$), Davisson found that the angles at which reflection of electron beams from crystals occurred fitted the idea of the crystal surface being a line grating, spacing d, and the electron a wave. The equation which fitted his results was the diffraction grating equation $n\lambda = d \sin \theta$. The experimental evidence was thus—electrons have wave properties.

Since Davisson's results there have been many more experiments with electrons which reveal the wave nature of electrons, the wavelength being that given by de Broglie's equation. Only a few months after Davisson (and Germer) published their first paper giving evidence of the wave nature of electrons, Thomson and Reid in England fired electrons at a thin sheet of celluloid and found that a photographic plate exposed to the transmitted electrons showed diffraction haloes (Fig. 18.10), a pattern that would be expected for waves diffracted by molecules of definite size orientated at random. Thomson used other materials in place of the celluloid. With aluminium and then gold films he found that the results were again rings: rings whose diameters agreed with what would be expected from waves, wavelength calculated from de Broglie's equation, being diffracted from an array of scattering centres of known spacing (measured by X-rays). Figure 18.11 shows the results for gold for electrons of two different energies.

The above evidence is overwhelming in favour of electrons showing a wave characteristic. The de Broglie equation was not, however, restricted to electrons but applies to all matter.

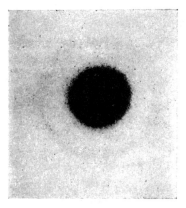

Fig. 18.10   Diffraction haloes for celluloid. (G. P. Thomson, Contemporary Physics, **9,** *8, Fig. 5, 1968)*

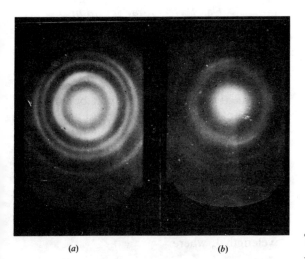

(a)   (b)

Fig. 18.11   Diffraction rings for gold. (a) Higher energy electrons than (b). (G. P. Thomson, Contemporary Physics, **9,** *9, Fig. 7, 1968)*

X-rays

1896 started with the main headlines and stories of the newspapers devoted to events in the Boer war.

'CRISIS IN THE TRANSVAL
DR. JAMESON CROSSES THE FRONTIER WITH 700 MEN'

The Times, 1 January 1896.

The papers were not, however, without the conventional news for that time of the year.

'THE LEAGUE MATCHES.—FIRST DIVISION

Many thousand people witnessed the defeat of Derby County by Bolton Wanderers yesterday at Bolton by two goals to one.

Everton won their match with Blackburn Rovers at Blackburn yesterday by three goals to two....'

The Times, 1 January 1896.

However, on the sixth of January a report hit the headlines of an event which was to have worldwide significance.

'The noise of the war's alarm should not distract attention from the marvellous triumph of science which is reported from Vienna. It is announced that Prof. Routgen [should be Röntgen] of the Wurzburg University has discovered a light which for the purpose of photography will penetrate wood, flesh, cloth, and most other organic substances. The professor has succeeded in photographing metal weights which were in a closed wooden case, also a man's hand which showed only the bones, the flesh being invisible.' [see Fig. 18.12]

Daily Chronicle, 6 January 1896.

The production of X-rays

In Röntgen's first apparatus the X-rays were produced by applying a high potential difference between two electrodes enclosed in a tube containing air under a low pressure. Stray ions and electrons were present in the tube (they would be produced by cosmic radiation and natural radioactivity) and these became accelerated by the potential difference. The X-rays were noticed as emanating at the anode and thus the source identified as being the 'collision' of electrons with a solid. Modern X-ray tubes produce the electrons by heating the cathode: thermionic emission (Fig. 18.13).

A ruled grating or a crystal can be used to determine how the intensity of the emitted rays varies with wavelength. Figure 18.14 shows a typical

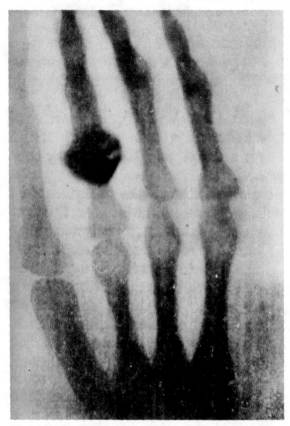

Fig. 18.12 Röntgen's original photograph. (Nature **53**, 274, 1896)

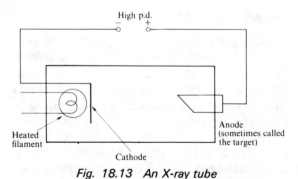

Fig. 18.13 An X-ray tube

result. Superimposed on a continuous background there are a number of sharp wavelength spikes. The continuous background is for the same accelerating p.d. the same for all elements, its shape depending only on the accelerating p.d.

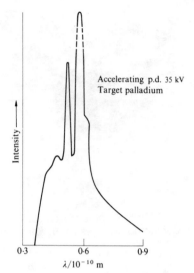

Fig. 18.14 X-ray spectrum

The interpretation placed on this is that the continuous X-rays are produced by the slowing down of the electrons in the target.

The maximum energy that can be converted into a photon is when the entire energy of an accelerated electron is transformed into a photon. Since the energy of such an electron is Ve, where V is the accelerating potential difference, then the maximum photon frequency f is given by

$$hf = Ve$$

The maximum frequency means a minimum wavelength λ, where

$$\lambda = \frac{c}{f} = \frac{hc}{Ve}$$

with c being the speed of electromagnetic waves. Thus for $V = 35$ kV we have

$$\lambda = \frac{6.6 \times 10^{-34} \times 3.0 \times 10^8}{35 \times 10^3 \times 1.6 \times 10^{-19}}$$

$$= 3.6 \times 10^{-11}$$

This is illustrated in Fig. 18.14.

In addition to the continuous spectrum produced by electrons slowing down there are sharp wavelength spikes or lines. These are characteristic of the target material and consist of groups of lines called the *K*, *L*, *M*, etc. groups (in order of increasing wavelength). These X-ray photon are produced as a result of the movements of the innermost electrons in atoms.

Interaction of X-rays with matter

X-rays which have been produced as a result of a high potential difference in the X-ray tube are called hard X-rays, those produced with a lower potential difference soft X-rays. These terms are used to describe what is called the quality of the X-rays, hard X-rays being able to pass through matter more readily than soft X-rays.

The intensity *I* of X-rays after having passed through a thickness *x* of matter is given by

$$I = I_0 e^{-\mu x}$$

where I_0 is the incident X-ray intensity and μ a constant called the absorption coefficient of the material.

The thickness $x_{1/2}$ required to reduce the intensity of X-rays by half is called the half thickness and is given by

$$I = \tfrac{1}{2} I_0 = I_0 e^{-\mu x}$$

Thus

$$x_{1/2} = \frac{\ln 2}{\lambda}$$

Water has an absorption coefficient for X-rays with a wavelength of about 1 nm of 0.15 cm^{-1}. Thus the thickness of water required to reduce the intensity of such X-rays by a half is ln 2/0.15 = 4.6 cm.

The thickness of water required to reduce the intensity to a quarter, i.e., half of a half, is two half-thicknesses, 9.2 cm. To reduce the intensity to an eighth, i.e., half of a half, of a half, is three half-thicknesses, 13.8 cm.

Bone has an absorption coefficient about 150 times greater than that of water. It is for this reason that X-rays can be taken of the human body, essentially just water and bone, and reveal the bone structure.

The discussion so far of absorption has assumed a fixed distance between the X-ray source and some detector, different absorbers being put between the two. We can, however, vary the

distance between the source and the detector. For distances *d* where we can effectively regard the X-ray source as being a point source the intensity follows an inverse square law, like any other electromagnetic radiation.

$$I \propto \frac{1}{d^2}$$

Thus if the distance is doubled the X-ray intensity is reduced to a quarter.

X-ray absorption spectrum

The X-ray absorption spectrum of a material can be examined by passing a beam of X-rays, having a continuous spectrum and so a wide range of wavelengths, through the material concerned. The resulting beam of X-rays can then be examined by a Bragg X-ray spectrometer (see Chapter 16). Figure 18.15 shows the type of absorption spectrum produced. At certain wavelengths there is an abrupt change in the absorption.

Below the wavelength λ_K the frequency of an X-ray photon is very high. It is high enough to eject electrons from any level within the atom. However, at the wavelength λ_K the energy just becomes insufficient to eject *K*-level electrons and so the absorption falls. At higher wavelengths similar discontinuities occur whenever the X-ray photon energy becomes just insufficient to eject electrons at particular energy levels.

Use can be made of this effect in producing filters which can preferentially absorb certain regions of X-ray wavelengths.

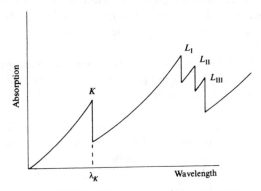

Fig. 18.15 X-ray absorption spectrum

Natural radioactivity

The discovery of radioactivity followed within a year of the discovery of X-rays by Röntgen. The X-rays had seemed to originate on the glass wall of Röntgen's X-ray tube where cathode rays hit and produced fluorescence. It thus seemed worth while considering other cases where fluorescence occurred to see if X-rays were also produced in those situations. H. Becquerel thus investigated a uranium salt which fluoresced, putting the uranium salt on top of a photographic plate which was wrapped in light-proof black paper. The photographic plate was affected, a radiation had penetrated the black paper. He then tried a variety of uranium compounds, some of which did not fluoresce, and found that all gave the same effect. The radiation was not linked with the fluorescence but emanated from the uranium.

What was this radiation? Experiments by Rutherford and others soon showed that the radiation from the uranium was made up of more than one component. One of the radiations was of very low penetrating power, being virtually stopped by a sheet of paper. This was called alpha radiation. A radiation of higher penetrating power was called beta radiation and a very penetrating component gamma radiation. The beta radiation requires several millimetres of aluminium to stop it while the gamma radiation can require considerably greater thicknesses. If an experiment is carried out in which for a fixed distance between a radioactive source and a detector different thicknesses of a material are interposed, then if the radiation is not homogeneous a graph of the logarithm of the detected intensity plotted against absorber thickness will show a result which is reasonably clearly the sum of two different straight line relationships (Fig. 18.16).

There were also other differences between the radiations. The alpha and beta radiations could be deflected by electric and magnetic fields, the directions of the deflections being such as to indicate that alpha radiation carried positive charges and beta radiation negative charges. Measurements of such deflections enabled the specific charge, i.e., charge to mass ratio, to be determined. The beta radiation gave results

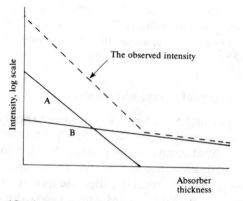

Fig. 18.16   The absorption curve when two different radiations are present

which were the same as those given by electrons; the alpha radiation, however, gave results which could be explained if the radiation was composed of helium atoms that had lost two electrons.

Conclusive evidence in favour of this was obtained by Rutherford and Royds in 1909. Figure 18.17 shows the apparatus they used. A radioactive, alpha-emitting gas was enclosed in the very thin walled glass tube A. The glass was thin enough for alpha radiation to pass through it into an outer tube which had been evacuated and in which it became trapped. When, after two days, the mercury level was raised in the outer tube to compress the gas into V, where it could be examined by means of a spectroscope, the helium spectrum was found.

Gamma radiation was not deflected by magnetic or electric fields. In all its properties it was similar to X-rays. Final confirmation was the use of crystals as diffraction gratings in a measurement of the wavelength. Gamma radiation is an electromagnetic wave of very short wavelength.

Ionizing radiations

Alpha, beta, and gamma radiations ionize air, the alpha radiation producing considerably more ions than the beta and the beta more than the gamma. Becquerel was able to use a charged electroscope to determine the presence of the radiation: the radiation caused the electroscope

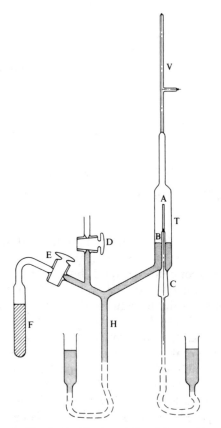

Fig. 18.17   Rutherford and Royds' experiment

alpha particle's range than near the beginning because it is moving more slowly and spends more time in those regions. Figure 18.18 shows the ionization curve.

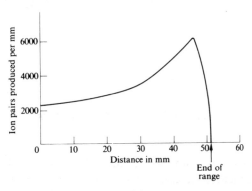

Fig. 18.18

Alpha particles are massive by comparison with electrons and thus little energy is lost by an alpha particle in collisions with electrons. This is, however, not the case with beta particles—they lose a lot of their energy by collisions with electrons, and are more easily deflected from their path.

Alpha and beta particles lose their energy in a number of collisions. Gamma radiation, being composed of photons, generally loses all its energy at a single encounter. Gamma radiation is extremely penetrating only because encounters between photons and atoms are not too frequent.

Radiation detectors

A charged gold-leaf electroscope discharges when ions produced inside the electroscope chamber neutralize the charge on the deflected gold leaf. The rate at which the leaf's deflection changes is a measure of the number of ions produced in the chamber. A more convenient way of detecting this is to produce the ions between a pair of electrodes. If the electrodes have a potential difference applied between them they will have become charged; they are a capacitor. If the charges on the two electrodes are partially neutralized by the ions produced in the chamber a current will flow in the electrode circuit as the p.d.

to discharge. The rate of discharge of the electroscope was taken as a measure of the intensity of the radiation.

An alpha particle of energy 5 MeV has a range in air of about 6.5 cm. Along its track it will ionize the air (see cloud chamber photographs in Chapter 4). To ionize oxygen or nitrogen takes about 30 eV. As in a distance of 6.5 cm an alpha particle loses 5 MeV it must, if we assume it only loses energy by ionization and not just by transfer to molecules, produce

$$\frac{5 \times 10^6}{30} \text{ ion pairs}$$

This is 1.7×10^5 ion pairs. This is an average of 2600 ion pairs per millimetre of path.

In fact the number of ion pairs produced per millimetre of path is greater near the end of the

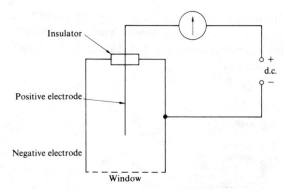

Fig. 18.19   Ionization chambers

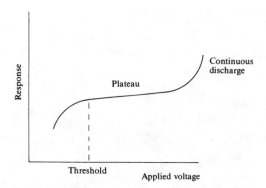

Fig. 18.20   Geiger–Müller tube characteristic

again charges up the electrodes (Fig. 18.19). This arrangement is called an ionization chamber.

If the air pressure inside the ionization chamber is reduced below atmospheric pressure the ions are able to reach high velocities, and hence high kinetic energies, in their passage to the electrodes. They are being produced in the electric field given by the p.d. applied between the two electrodes. Reducing the pressure increases the mean free path of the ions. If the ions have high enough kinetic energy they can produce further ions when they collide with gas atoms in the chamber. With a suitable combination of low pressure and high voltage the ion current may be multiplied by many thousands by these further ionizations. With a high enough voltage an avalanche of ions is produced as each ion produces more ions which in turn produce more ions which in turn . . . and so on. Each primary ion may give rise to 10^9 further ion pairs before reaching an electrode. A chamber operating under these conditions is called a Geiger–Müller tube (first produced in 1928). This is a simplified account.

Figure 18.20 shows how the response of a Geiger–Müller tube depends on the applied voltage, the graph being called the characteristic. When the voltage reaches the threshold value the response becomes almost independent of the voltage over the region referred to as the plateau. At higher voltages the tube goes into continuous discharge and is thereby damaged. The tube is thus operated at about the mid point of the plateau.

Cloud and bubble chambers can be used to show the tracks of ionizing radiations. If the ions occur in a region in which there is vapour just about to condense or liquid about to boil, then the trail of ions left in the wake of the radiation encourages the formation of vapour droplets or bubbles. These then can be seen and thus so can the track, the 'density' of the track being a measure of the number of ionizing events occurring. Alpha radiation thus gives heavy, dense tracks while beta gives more sparse tracks. Gamma radiation gives a number of short, curly tracks, these resulting from the paths of electrons knocked out of atoms by the radiation. The Wilson cloud chamber produces the right vapour conditions by a sudden adiabatic expansion of the vapour in the chamber, the expansion cooling the vapour to give supersaturated conditions. The diffusion cloud chamber produces the cooling of a vapour by direct cooling.

Scintillation methods were widely used by Rutherford and his coworkers. The impact of radiation on some materials causes the emission of light. While Rutherford painstakingly sat in the dark watching for the flashes of light when radiation hit a zinc sulphide screen, modern methods use crystals of suitable materials and observe and count the flashes of light by means of photomultiplier tubes.

The nuclear atom

Suppose there was a small metal object located somewhere in a haystack. One way of locating the object and estimating its size would be to fire bullets at the haystack. Those bullets that did not encounter the object would pass straight through the stack and would not be significantly deviated from their straight line paths. Those bullets that did encounter the object would be deviated from their straight line paths. By raining bullets on the haystack information about the object inside the haystack can be obtained. This is essentially the technique used by Geiger and Marsden when they discovered the existence of nuclei within atoms. The projectiles were alpha particles emitted at high speed from a radioactive source, the target was a thin gold foil.

'Now I myself was very interested in the next stage, ... and I would like to use this example to show how you often stumble upon facts by accident. In the early days I had observed the scattering of alpha particles, and Dr. Geiger in my laboratory had examined it in detail. He found, in thin pieces of heavy metal, that the scattering was usually small, of the order of one degree. One day Geiger came to me and said, "Don't you think young Marsden, whom I am training in radioactive methods, ought to begin a small research?" Now I had thought that too, so I said, "Why not let him see if any alpha particles can be scattered through a large angle?" I may tell you in confidence that I did not believe that they would be, since we knew that the alpha particle was a very fast massive particle, with a great deal of energy, and you could show that if the scattering was due to the accumulated effect of a number of small scatterings the chance of alpha particles being scattered backwards was very small. Then I remember two or three days later Geiger coming to me in great excitement and saying, "We have been able to get some of the alpha particles coming backwards ... " It was the most incredible event that has happened to me in my life. It was almost as incredible as if you fired a 15-inch shell at a piece of tissue paper and it came back and hit you. On consideration I realized that the scattering backwards must be the result of a single collision, and when I made calculations I saw that it was impossible to get anything of that order of magnitude unless you took a system in which

the greater part of the mass of the atom was concentrated in a minute nucleus. It was then that I had the idea of an atom with a minute massive centre carrying a charge.'

E. Rutherford (1937) 'The development of the theory of atomic structure', *Background of Modern Science* (1938), ed. J. Needham, page 1, CUP.

The calculations Rutherford made were based on the use of the conservation of momentum, the conservation of energy, the inverse square law force between electric charges, and geometry. The experimental results agreed with the idea of a nuclear atom.

'It is well known that α and β particles suffer deflections from their rectilinear paths by encounters with atoms of matter. This scattering is far more marked for the β than for the α particle on account of the much smaller momentum and energy of the former particle. There seems to be no doubt that such swiftly moving particles pass through the atoms in their path, and that the deflections observed are due to the strong electric field traversed within the atomic system. It has generally been supposed that the scattering of a pencil of α or β rays in passing through a thin plate of matter is the result of a multitude of small scatterings by the atoms of matter traversed. The observations, however, of Geiger and Marsden on the scattering of α rays indicate that some of the α particles must suffer a deflection of more than a right angle at a single encounter. They found, for example, that a small fraction of the incident α particles, about 1 in 20 000, were turned through an average angle of 90° in passing through a layer of gold foil about 0.000 04 cm thick, which was equivalent in stopping power of the α particle to 1.6 mm of air. Geiger showed later that the most probable angle of deflection for a pencil of α particles traversing a gold foil of this thickness was about 0.87°. A simple calculation based on the theory of probability shows that the chance of an α particle being deflected through 90° is vanishingly small. In addition, it will be seen later that the distribution of the α particles for various angles of large deflection does not follow the probability law to be expected if such large deflections are made up of a large number of small deviations. It seems reasonable to suppose that the deflection through a large angle is due to a single atomic encounter, for the chance of a second encounter of a kind to produce a large deflection must in most cases be exceedingly small. A simple calculation shows that the atom must be a seat of an intense electric field in order to produce such a large deflection at a single encounter.'

E. Rutherford (1911) *Phil. Mag.*, **21**, 699.

This was the introduction by Rutherford of the idea of atoms having a central minute nucleus surrounded by a diffuse region containing the electrons.

How big is a nucleus? Geiger and Marsden found that for a metal foil, 4×10^{-7} m thick, 1 in 20 000 particles were turned back through 90° or more. If we take the atoms in the foil as being about 2.5×10^{-10} m apart then there will be

$$\frac{4 \times 10^{-7}}{2.5 \times 10^{-10}} = 1.6 \times 10^3$$

layers of atoms. One layer could therefore be expected to turn back about

$$\frac{1}{20\,000 \times 1.6 \times 10^3} = \frac{1}{32 \times 10^6}$$

particles. Thus in the first layer the actual area which turns back alpha particles is

$$\frac{1}{32 \times 10^6}$$

of the surface area of the foil. If each atom occupies an area of about $(2.5 \times 10^{-10})^2$ m² and each nucleus an area of d^2

$$\frac{d^2}{(2.5 \times 10^{-10})^2} = \frac{1}{32 \times 10^6}$$

$$\approx 5 \times 10^{-14}$$

The radius of the nucleus is about one-ten-thousandth of the radius of the atom.

What is the charge on the nucleus? We could ask, the same question, what is the number of electrons in an atom? As an atom is neutral there must be equal amounts of negative and positive charge. The deflection of alpha particles by the nuclei of atoms in a foil depends on both the charge carried by the alpha particles and the charge carried by the nuclei of the foil atoms. At a particular angle the number of particles deflected is in fact proportional to the square of the number of charges carried by the nucleus.

Geiger and Marsden in the work which led to the concept of the nucleus deduced that the charge on the nucleus of an atom was roughly ½Ae, where A is the atomic mass and e the charge on the electron. Later (1913) van den Broek suggested that the nuclear charge might be proportional to the atomic number of the element. The atomic number was the number of the element when all the elements were placed in order of increasing atomic mass. J. Chadwick in 1920 repeated the alpha scattering experiment with the intent of finding the charge on the atomic nucleus. The following are his results, taken from *Phil. Mag.*, 6th Ser., **40**, 742, 1920.

	Nuclear charge	Atomic mass	Atomic number
Platinum	77.4e	195	78
Silver	46.3e	108	47
Copper	29.3e	63.5	29

The results clearly show that the charge on the nucleus is equal to the atomic number times the charge on the electron. The nuclear charge is carried by particles called protons. Hence the number of protons in the nucleus equals the atomic number, being the same as the number of electrons in an unionized atom.

The hydrogen atom, being the simplest, has an atomic number of 1 and hence just one proton in the nucleus. The atomic mass of an element such as copper in the above table was, however, greater than the mass of just the protons and so there had to be some other particle in the nucleus.

The discovery of the neutron

'It has been shown by Bothe and others that beryllium when bombarded by α particles of polonium emits a radiation of great penetrating power.... Recently Mme Curie-Joliot and M. Joliot found, when measuring the ionization produced by this beryllium radiation in a vessel with a thin window, that the ionization increased when matter containing hydrogen was placed in front of the window. The effect appeared to be due to the ejection of protons with velocities up to a maximum of nearly 3×10^9 cm per sec.... These results, and others I have obtained in the course of the work, are very difficult to explain on the assumption that the radiation from beryllium is a quantum radiation, if energy and momentum are to be conserved in the collisions. The difficulties disappear, however, if it be assumed that the radiation consists of particles of mass 1 and charge 0, or neutrons. The capture of the α particle by the Be 9 nucleus may be supposed to result in the formation of a C 12 nucleus and the emission of the neutron....'

J. Chadwick (1932) *Nature*, No. 3252, **1291**, 312.

The nuclear reaction for the neutron production obtained by Chadwick was

$$^9_4\text{Be} + {}^4_2\text{He} \rightarrow {}^{12}_6\text{C} + {}^1_0\text{n}$$

When matter containing hydrogen was placed in the path of the neutrons, protons were ejected. Figure 18.21 illustrates this.

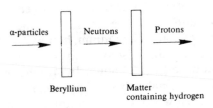

| Beryllium | Matter containing hydrogen |

Fig. 18.21 Chadwick's experiment

Atomic and mass numbers

Nuclear particles are called nucleons and consist of just neutrons and protons. The atomic number Z of an element is the number of protons in the nucleus. Atoms with the same atomic number belong to the same chemical element. The mass number A of an atom is the number of nucleons in the nucleus, i.e., the sum of the number of protons and neutrons. The term nuclide is used for a particular species of atom, one whose nuclei all contain the same number of protons and the same numbers of neutrons—they all have the same atomic number and mass number. Those which have the same atomic number but different mass numbers are called isotopes.

A given nuclide can be represented by the symbol ^A_ZX, where X is the chemical symbol for the element. Thus $^{12}_6\text{C}$ is carbon with all its atoms having atomic number of 6 and mass number 12, i.e., the nuclei contain 6 protons and $(12 - 6) = 6$ neutrons. $^{14}_6\text{C}$ is an isotope of carbon, all its atoms containing 6 protons and $(14 - 6) = 8$ neutrons.

Radioactive decay

Figure 18.22 shows how the current in an ionization chamber varied with time when a radioactive gas was present, the graph being taken from a paper written by Rutherford in 1900. Rutherford observed that the current, which is directly proportional to the activity of the radioactive gas, diminishes exponentially with time.

This means that, in the case of the radioactive gas used by Rutherford, in one minute the activity

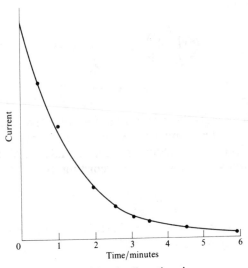

Fig. 18.22 Radioactive decay

decreases by a factor of two. In the next minute it decreases by a factor of two from what it was at the beginning of that minute. This means that if the activity initially was 32 units, then after one minute the activity would be 16 units, after the second minute it would be 8 units, after the third minute 4 units. The term 'half-life' is used to describe the time taken for the activity to decrease by a factor of two. In this case the half-life is 1 minute.

For such a type of change (see Chapter 0) the rate at which the activity changes is proportional to the amount of active material present, i.e.

$$\frac{dN}{dt} = -\lambda N \qquad (4)$$

where dN/dt is the rate at which nuclei are decaying and emitting radiation, N is the number of active nuclei present and λ is a constant with a unit of s^{-1} called the decay constant. The negative sign is because N is decreasing with time.

The rate of decay is called the activity A, where

$$A = \frac{dN}{dt}$$

The unit of activity is the Becquerel, with 1 Bq being 1 disintegration per second.

If we solve the differential equation (4) we have

$$\int_{N_0}^{N} \frac{dN}{dt} = -\lambda \int_{0}^{t} dt$$

$$N = N_0 e^{-\lambda t}$$

where N_0 is the original number of active nuclei and N the number remaining after a time t.

Since $A = dN/dt$ and this equals $-\lambda N$, the activity varies with time according to

$$A = -\lambda N_0 e^{-\lambda t}$$

But at $t = 0$, then $A = -\lambda N$. Hence if we called this activity A_0 we have

$$A = A_0 e^{-\lambda t}$$

The half-life is the time taken for the activity to be reduced from A_0 to $\frac{1}{2}A_0$ or, in other words, the time taken for the number of active nuclei to be reduced from N_0 to $\frac{1}{2}N_0$. Thus

$$\frac{1}{2}A_0 = A_0 e^{-\lambda t} \quad \text{and} \quad e^{-\lambda t} = \frac{1}{2}$$

where t is the half-life. If we denote this by $t_{\frac{1}{2}}$ then

$$t_{\frac{1}{2}} = \frac{\ln 2}{\lambda} = \frac{0.693}{\lambda}$$

Consider a radioactive isotope of strontium which has a half-life of 28 years. If initially 14 years ago there had been 6.0 µg of it then there would now be

$$\lambda = \frac{\ln 2}{28} \quad \text{and so } \lambda t = \frac{\ln 2}{28} \times 14 = 0.35$$

Thus as $N = N_0 e^{-\lambda t}$ we have

$$\text{Mass now} = 6.0 \, e^{-0.35}$$

$$= 4.2 \, \text{µg}$$

Growth and decay

Many radioactive isotopes do not decay into a stable isotope but into another radioactive isotope which itself decays. There may be many radioactive isotopes in the sequence before a stable isotope is reached. For example, the thorium isotope (mass 232) decays by alpha emission to give a radium isotope (mass 228), the half-life being 1.90 years. The radium, however, decays to give an actinium isotope (mass 228) by beta emission, half-life 6.1 hours. In turn the actinium decays. The final stable end product is an isotope of lead. How does the amount of radium, or actinium, present vary with time?

Consider isotope A decaying into isotope B which in turn decays into isotope C. The amount of B being produced per unit time is equal to the rate at which B is produced by the decay of A minus the rate at which B decays into C. The rate at which A decays into B is given by

$$\frac{\Delta A}{\Delta t} = -k_A A$$

Thus the rate at which B is produced from A is given by

$$\frac{\Delta B'}{\Delta t} = k_A A$$

k_A is the rate constant for the decay of A into B. The rate at which B decays into C is given by

$$\frac{\Delta B''}{\Delta t} = -k_B B$$

Thus the rate at which the amount of B present increases with time is given by

$$\frac{\Delta B}{\Delta t} = k_A A - k_B B$$

Consider the decay of parent A to daughter B to be similar to that of the thorium decay to radium, i.e., one with a long half-life (very small value of k), and the decay of B to C to be similar to that of radium to actinium, i.e., a short half-life (large value of k). If we consider time intervals of an hour then over a period of, say, ten hours there will have been very little change in the amount of A (ΔA will be very small because of the smallness of k). The result of this will be that the production of B from the decay of A will be virtually constant over the period we are considering. Let us suppose that this is constant at 10 000 atoms of B being produced per hour.

At $t = 0$, $B = 0$.

We start with only thorium present.

At $t = 1$ hour, 10 000 atoms of B have been produced. If $k_B = 1/10$ per hour, then about 1000 of these atoms will decay. The total of B atoms after 1 hour is thus 9000.

At $t = 2$ hours, a further 10 000 atoms of B will have been produced. During this second hour 1/10 of the 19 000 B atoms will decay. The total after 2 hours is thus 17 100.

At $t = 3$ hours, a further 10 000 atoms of B will have been produced. Of the 27 100 atoms 2710 will decay leaving 24 390.

At $t = 4$ hours, a further 10 000 atoms of B will have been produced. Of the 34 390 atoms 3439 will decay to leave 30 951.

Figure 18.23 shows the resulting graph. The number of atoms of B rises until the rate of production of B is equal to the rate at which it decays. That happens when $k_B B = 10\,000$. When this happens the amount of B present will remain constant.

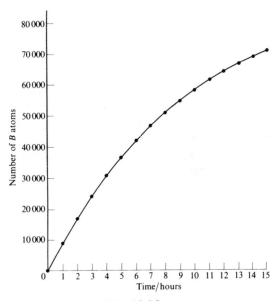

Fig. 18.23

In our example we considered the parent A to decay at a steady rate—not changing the number of disintegrations per hour during the period considered. This results in a graph, Fig. 18.24, where the number of B atoms rises to a maximum and remains at that maximum. This is only theoretically possible—the parent A will decay with time. The result of taking this into account is

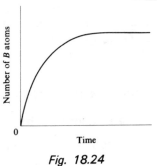

Fig. 18.24

429

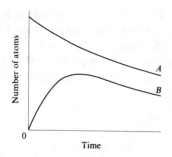

Fig. 18.25 Long life parent (A) with shorter life daughter (B).

to give a graph similar to that in Fig. 18.25. Here the parent A decays slowly with time and the daughter B rises to a maximum and then decays at the same rate as the parent. If the parent has a shorter life than the daughter a graph like Fig. 18.26 occurs. Here the daughter B rises to a maximum and then decays in the same manner as it would do in the absence of A.

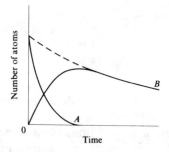

Fig. 18.26 Short lived parent (A) with longer life daughter (B).

Nuclear changes in decay

When a nuclide decays by alpha emission the mass number decreases by 4 and the atomic number by 2. Thus, for example, radium-223 which decays by alpha emission gives radon, where

$$^{223}_{88}\text{Ra} \rightarrow \ ^{219}_{86}\text{Rn} + \ ^{4}_{2}\text{He}$$

(radium) (radon) (alpha)

When a nuclide decays by beta emission the mass number does not change and the atomic number increases by 1. Thus, for example, thorium-231 decays by beta emission to proto-actinium, where

$$^{231}_{90}\text{Th} \rightarrow \ ^{231}_{91}\text{Pa} + \ ^{0}_{-1}\text{e}$$

(beta)

When a nuclide decays by gamma emission there is no change in either the mass number or the atomic number.

We can explain the above 'rules' by considering what happens to the protons and neutrons in the nuclei. Alpha emission involves the removal from a nucleus of two protons and two neutrons, a mass number loss of 4, and since the atomic number is the number of protons this must decrease by 2. With beta emission, since there are no electrons in the nucleus the electron must be the result of a neutron changing to a proton. This will give no change in the mass number and an increase in the atomic number by 1. Gamma emission represents the emission of energy from an excited nucleus returning to its ground state. In the same way we considered the emission of radiation from excited atoms in terms of atomic energy levels, we can think of the emission of gamma radiation from excited nuclei in terms of nuclear energy levels.

Important points to remember are that, in any radioactive decay, electric charge is always conserved and mass number is also conserved. This means that when we write down the equation for the decay, as for example that for ^{231}Th, the charge numbers must be the same on both sides of the equation. The charge number is the atomic number. This means we must write -1 for an electron. Also since mass number is conserved, the mass numbers must be the same on both sides of the equation.

In some nuclear reactions positrons are emitted, these have the same mass as the electron and the same size charge, but are positive. They are thus represented as $^{0}_{+1}\text{e}$.

Radioactive decay series

Uranium-235 decays by alpha emission to thorium-231, which in turn decays by beta emission to protoactinium-231, which, in turn decays by alpha emission to actinium-227, which in turn decays.... and so on down a long series of radioactive decays until we end up with lead-207 which is not radioactive. This is a total mass number change of $(235 - 207) = 28$. Since there is only a change in mass number when alpha emission occurs this means there is $28/4 = 7$ alpha-emitting decays in the series. The atomic number changes from uranium at 92 to lead at 82, a change of 10. Each alpha-emitting decay decreases the atomic number by 2 while each beta decay increases it by 1. Since we know there are 7 alpha-emitting decays the number of beta decays must be $(7 \times 2) - 10 = 4$.

Another decay series begins with uranium-238 and ends up after eight alpha and six beta decays at lead-206.

Bombarding nuclei

The first artificial transmutation was produced by Rutherford in 1919. He bombarded nitrogen atoms with alpha particles and found that a long-range radiation was produced which he identified as protons. Nitrogen had been changed into oxygen.

$$^{14}_{7}\text{N} + ^{4}_{2}\text{He} \rightarrow ^{17}_{8}\text{O} + ^{1}_{1}\text{H}$$

Rutherford and Chadwick later showed that many other light elements could be similarly transmuted. In all cases the bombardment was provided by the alpha particles.

It was the results of bombarding beryllium by alpha particles which led to the discovery of the neutron.

It was in the years round 1930 that the first accelerators were being built. These were for the production of high-speed particles with which to bombard matter, and find more transmutations. In 1932 Cockcroft and Walton bombarded lithium with protons, of energy about 250 keV. The lithium nucleus broke up to give two helium particles.

$$^{7}_{3}\text{Li} + ^{1}_{1}\text{H} \rightarrow ^{4}_{2}\text{He} + ^{4}_{2}\text{He}$$

The high-velocity protons were produced by accelerating them through a large potential difference, this being produced by an arrangement of rectifiers and capacitors.

Other means of accelerating charged particles were soon developed. In 1931 Van de Graaff invented the electrostatic generator now known by his name.

'The principle of the generator can be described by making reference to the diagram shown in figure [18.27]. The generator consists of a well-rounded high-voltage terminal supported from ground on an insulating column, and of a charge-conveying system consisting of one or more belts of an insulating material running between this terminal and ground. Electric charge of one polarity is sprayed by corona on the belt at its grounded end and is transported by the belt into the hollow terminal, where it is removed. Within the terminal, charge of the opposite polarity may be deposited on the belt and transferred to the ground. At any instant the terminal potential is $V = Q/C$, where Q is the stored charge and C the capacitance of the terminal to ground. The terminal potential rises initially at the rate $dV/dt = I/C$, where I is the net charging current to the terminal. This rate is commonly of the order of one million volts per second....'

R. J. Van de Graaf, J. G. Trump and W. W. Buechner (1948) *Reports on Progress in Physics*, **11**, 1.

Ions can be accelerated to high velocities by accelerating them through a large potential difference. There are, however, difficulties with this method: difficulties of insulation, discharges, the production of the high voltage. In the cyclotron the ions are accelerated in a number of small spurts and only relatively low potential differences are used. The following extract is taken from the paper by Lawrence and Livingston in which they describe the first cyclotron.

'Two electrodes A, B in the form of semi-circular hollow plates are mounted in a vacuum tube in coplanar fashion with their diametral edges adjacent [Fig. 18.28]. By placing the system between the poles of a magnet, a magnetic field is introduced that is normal to the plane of the plates. High frequency electric oscillations are applied to the plates so that there results an oscillating

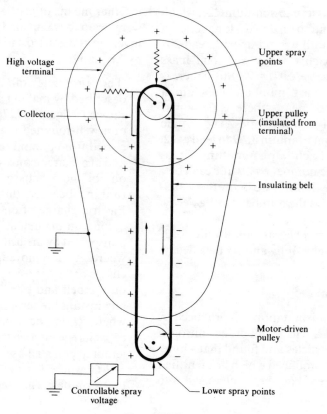

High voltage terminal

Upper spray points

Collector

Upper pulley (insulated from terminal)

Insulating belt

Motor-driven pulley

Controllable spray voltage

Lower spray points

Fig. 18.27

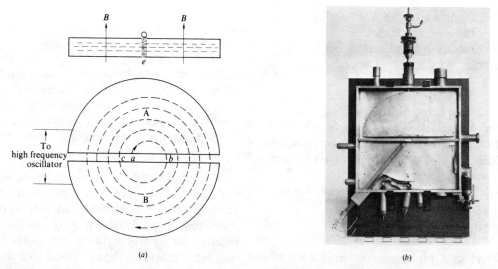

(a)

(b)

Fig. 18.28   (a) Diagram of experimental method for multiple acceleration of ions. (b) Tube for the multiple acceleration of light ions—with cover removed. (Lent to Science Museum, London by Professor E. O. Lawrence, Radiation Laboratory, University of California. Photo: Science Museum, London)

electric field in the diametral region between them.

With this arrangement it is evident that, if at one moment there is an ion in the region between the electrodes, and electrode A is negative with respect to electrode B, then the ion will be accelerated to the interior of the former. Within the electrode the ion traverses a circular path because of the magnetic field, and ultimately emerges again between the electrodes; this is indicated in the diagram by the arc $a . . b$. If the time consumed by the ion in making the semi-circular path is equal to the half period of the electric oscillations, the electric field will have reversed and the ion will receive a second acceleration, passing into the interior of electrode B with a higher velocity. Again it travels on a semi-circular path ($b . . c$), but this time the radius of curvature is greater because of the greater velocity. For all velocities (neglecting variation of mass with velocity) the radius of the path is proportional to the velocity, so that the time required for traversal of a semi-circular path is independent of the ion's velocity. Therefore, if the ion travels its first half circle in a half cycle of the oscillations, it will do likewise on all succeeding paths. Hence it will circulate around on ever widening semi-circles from the interior of one electrode to the interior of the other, gaining an increment of energy on each crossing of the diametral region that corresponds to the momentary potential difference between the electrodes. Thus, if, as was done in the present experiments, high frequency oscillations having peak values of 4,000 volts are applied to the electrodes, and protons are caused to spiral around in this way 150 times, they will receive 300 increments of energy, acquiring thereby a speed corresponding to 1,200,000 volts.

It is well to recapitulate these remarks in quantitative fashion. Along the circular paths within the electrodes . . .

$$\left[\frac{mv^2}{r} = Bev \right] \tag{1}$$

It follows that the time for traversal of a semi-

circular path is

$$t = \frac{\pi r}{v} = \ldots = \left[\frac{\pi m}{Be} \right] \tag{2}$$

which is independent of the radius r of the path and the velocity v of the ion. The particle of mass m and charge e thus may be caused to travel in phase with the oscillating electric field by suitable adjustment of the magnetic field.'
    E. O. Lawrence and M. S. Livingston (1932)
        Phys. Rev., **40**, 23.

Cyclotrons can accelerate particles up to energies of about 20 MeV. This limit is set by the velocity of the ions becoming appreciable when compared with the speed of light and so m changes. A changing value of m in the above equations means that ions will not arrive at the gap between the electrodes at the right time to be accelerated. This has been overcome by either varying the magnetic field or the frequency of the electric field during the acceleration of the ions. Such a modified cyclotron is known as a synchrocyclotron. Such instruments were first produced in about 1946.

Further reading

R. R. Wilson and P. Littauer (1960) *Accelerators*, Heinemann Science Study Series, No. 15.

Radiocarbon dating

The earth's atmosphere is bombarded by cosmic rays. These produce neutrons which on hitting nitrogen-14 atoms produce carbon-14.

$$^{14}_{7}\text{N} + ^{1}_{0}\text{n} \rightarrow ^{14}_{6}\text{C} + ^{1}_{1}\text{H}$$

Carbon-14 has a half-life of 5568 years. This radioactive carbon produced in the upper atmosphere combines with oxygen to give radioactive carbon dioxide. The radioactive carbon dioxide forms only a very small percentage of the atmospheric carbon dioxide. As plants live off carbon dioxide this means that all plants will show some radioactivity due to carbon-14. During

433

the lifetime of the plant it will take in carbon dioxide and the percentage of its carbon which is radioactive will remain constant, the same as that of the atmosphere. When, however, the plant dies it ceases to take in further supplies of carbon and the percentage of radioactive carbon within the plant decreases as the carbon-14 decays. Figure 18.29 shows how the number of disintegrations per minute per gramme of carbon changes with time. The results are taken from materials whose date could be established by other means. Thus by measuring the activity of the carbon-14 in a specimen it becomes possible to establish its age.

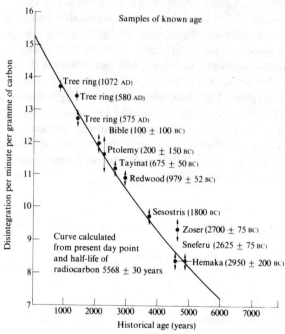

Fig. 18.29 Radiocarbon Dating, *2nd edn, Libby, University of Chicago Press, 1955*

Radioactive istopes

Bombardment of nuclei by high-energy particles can lead to the production of radioactive isotopes. Thus sodium, for example, which occurs naturally only as sodium-23, can be produced artificially as sodium isotopes of mass 20, 21, 22, 24, and 25. These isotopes are all radioactive. Sodium-24 can

be produced by bombarding sodium-23 with neutrons from a reactor.

$$\ce{^{23}_{11}Na + ^{1}_{0}n -> ^{24}_{11}Na + ^{0}_{0}\gamma}$$

Radioactive isotopes have numerous uses and the following list can only give a rough indication of these uses.

(a) Isotopes as labels.
(i) The investigation of the wear of a bearing. The bearing is made radioactive and thus the movement of the radioactive particles of bearing which wear off the bearing can be traced.
(ii) Fluid level gauge. A float has a radioactive source attached to it. The movement of the fluid surface can be followed by a Geiger counter following the movements of the float. This has application where the fluid is contained in a non-transparent container.
(iii) The movement of a particular element in a chemical reaction can be followed by making some of the atoms of that element radioactive.
(b) Absorption of radiation.
(i) Thickness gauges. The thickness of a sample can be determined by determining the amount of radiation absorbed by the sample. A radioactive source on one side of the sample and a Geiger tube on the other is an arrangement in which the output from the Geiger tube is a measure of the thickness of the sample passing between them.
(ii) A similar arrangement to the thickness gauge can be used to indicate whether a container is completely full.
(iii) Radiography. The presence of cracks or flaws in a sample can be shown by the difference in absorption of the radiation passing through such parts when compared with the radiation passing through the rest of the sample.

Mass spectroscopy

A mass spectroscope consists of three essential parts:

1. An ion source where ionized atoms or molecules of the substance being examined are produced as a result of bombardment by electrons from a heated filament.
2. An analyser which separates the ions into a

mass spectrum. This is a magnetic field which is at right angles to the path of the ion beam. Since $Bqv = mv^2/r$, if the ions have the same velocity then the radius of their path r in the magnetic field will be directly proportional to the mass of the ions.

3. A means of detecting the ions. This could be a photographic plate or some form of ionization chamber.

Because the ions produced in the source will not all have the same velocity, a velocity selector is sometimes interposed between the source and the analyser. Such a selector consists of an electric field and a magnetic field at right angles to each other and to the ion beam. The force on an ion due to the electric field E is thus Eq, while the force due to the magnetic field B is Bqv. If these forces are in opposite directions, only for ions with the velocity v for which the forces cancel, i.e. $Eq = Bqv$ and so $v = E/B$, will the ion beam be able to pass through into the analyser.

Figure 18.30 shows the principles of the Bainbridge mass spectroscope.

Nuclear binding energy

The mass of a neutral atom is slightly less than the sum of the masses of the individual constituent particles. The mass of the constituent particles of the deuterium atom differs by 2.96×10^{-30} kg from that of the neutral atom. In terms of atomic mass units (1 u = 1.66×10^{-27} kg)

Rest mass of one proton	1.007 276 u
Rest mass of one neutron	1.008 665 u
Rest mass of one electron	0.000 549 u
Total	2.016 490 u

The rest mass of the neutral deuterium atom is 2.001 410 2 u, an amount 0.002 388 u less than that of the total of the constituents' masses. This is referred to as the mass defect.

If we use Einstein's equation relating energy and mass

$$E = mc^2$$

then the above mass difference corresponds to an energy change of 3.55×10^{-13} J or 2.22 MeV. Combining the particles to form deuterium means that this energy must be released.

When hydrogen is bombarded with neutrons, deuterium can be produced. In the process gamma rays are produced; they have energy 2.22 MeV. This is how the surplus energy is carried off in this case.

If we want to break a deuterium atom down into hydrogen we have to bombard the hydrogen

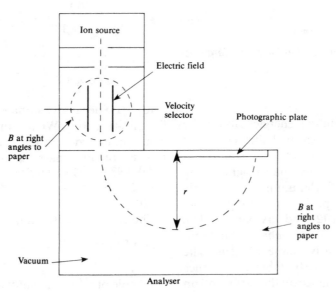

Fig. 18.30 The principles of the Bainbridge mass spectroscope

MATTER

with gamma rays of energy at least 2.22 MeV before the change can occur. 2.22 MeV can be considered as the binding energy of the deuterium nucleus.

Binding energy is the energy equivalence of the difference in mass between the unbound and the bound systems. For every 1 u difference in mass there is 931 MeV energy.

The binding energy increases as the number of particles in the nucleus increases. A convenient way of looking at binding energies is to consider the value of the average binding energy per nucleon. Figure 18.31 shows how this binding energy per nucleon varies with the atomic mass.

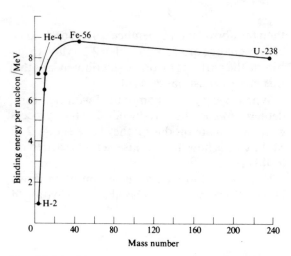

Fig. 18.31 *The general trend in binding energy per nucleon*

Some nuclei have binding energies above the graph curve which passes through the majority of points. Helium, mass 4, is one such example. It has a higher binding energy than neighbouring atoms with mass 3 or 5. Helium is a particularly stable nucleus. Other particularly stable nuclei are those of carbon-12 and oxygen-16. The binding energy per nucleon reaches a maximum at iron-56, a particularly stable nucleus. The elements that are particularly stable are the ones found in greatest abundance on the earth, and on the sun.

Energy release

The following are some calculations to indicate the order of magnitude of the energy released during radioactive decay.

(a) Radium-226 decays by alpha emission to radon-222. What is the energy of the alpha particle if the nuclide masses are $^{226}_{88}$Ra 226.025 406 u, $^{222}_{86}$Rn 222.017 574, $^{4}_{2}$He 4.002 603 u?

The energy released must be

$$226.025\ 406 - 222.017\ 574 - 4.002\ 603\ \text{u}$$

which, since 931.5 MeV is equivalent to 1 u, is 4.871 MeV. If we assume that all this energy is given to the alpha particle then this would be the alpha particle energy. It is in fact an overestimate since the radon nucleus recoils (to conserve linear momentum) when the alpha particle is emitted and so takes some of the energy. The actual alpha particle energy is 4.785 MeV and thus the recoiling nucleus has an energy of 0.086 MeV.

(b) The energy release from one gramme of radium raises the temperature of the radium to about 1.5 K above the surroundings. This is an energy release of 420 J per hour or 0.12 J per second. Since 1 g of radium emits about 3.7×10^{10} alpha particles per second this means an energy release per alpha particle of about

$$\frac{0.12}{3.7 \times 10^{10}} = 3.2 \times 10^{-13}\ \text{J}$$

$$= \frac{3.2 \times 10^{-13}}{1.6 \times 10^{-19}} = 2.0\ \text{MeV}$$

(c) ^{239}Pu decays by alpha emission with a half-life of 2.41×10^4 y. What is the power output that can be obtained from 1.00 g of this isotope? $^{239}_{94}$Pu has a nuclide mass of 239.052 158 u, $^{235}_{92}$U 235.043 925 u, $^{4}_{2}$He 4.002 603 u. Avogadro's number is 6.02×10^{23}. Number of seconds in a year $= 3.16 \times 10^7$.

The energy released must be

$$(239.052\ 158 - 235.043\ 925 - 4.002\ 603) \times 9315$$
$$= 5.24\ \text{MeV}$$

One mole of ^{239}Pu will contain 239 g. Thus 1.00 g is 1/239th of a mole. Since 1 mole will contain

6.02×10^{23} atoms, then there was $6.02 \times 10^{23}/239 = 2.52 \times 10^{21}$ atoms. Thus, since $dN/dt = -\lambda N = -(\ln 2/t_{\frac{1}{2}})N$, then

number of disintegrations per s =

$$\frac{2.52 \times 10^{21} \times \ln 2}{2.41 \times 10^4 \times 3.16 \times 10^7}$$

$$= 2.29 \times 10^9$$

Each disintegration liberates 5.24 MeV, thus the energy liberated per second, i.e., power, is

$$2.29 \times 10^9 \times 5.24 = 1.20 \times 10^{10} \text{ MeV per second}$$

$$= 1.20 \times 10^{10} \times 10^6 \times 1.6 \times 10^{-19}$$
$$= 1.92 \times 10^{-3} \text{ W}$$

Nuclear fission

Neutrons were discovered by Chadwick in 1932 and they were soon used as projectiles to bombard nuclei. In 1934 E. Fermi bombarded uranium with slow neutrons (about the speed of molecules in a room-temperature gas) hoping that the addition of the neutron to the uranium nucleus would give a new element, atomic number 93. His results were, however, puzzling. Fermi failed to identify the elements produced.

Early in January 1939 a clue emerged as to the nature of the elements produced by the bombardment of uranium with slow neutrons. O. Hahn and F. Strassmann, in Germany, found that one of the products of the bombardment was barium. Barium has an atomic number of 56, nowhere near that of uranium at 92. An explanation for this strange result was soon forthcoming, from L. Meitner and O. R. Frisch—the uranium nucleus had been split; nuclear fission was occurring.

'It seems . . . possible that the uranium nucleus has only small stability of form and may, after neutron capture, divide itself into two nuclei of roughly equal size (the precise ratio of sizes depending on finer structural features and perhaps partly on chance). These two nuclei will repel each other and should gain a total kinetic energy of c. 200 MeV. . . .'
L. Meitner and O. R. Frisch (1939) *Nature*, **143**, 239.

200 MeV is a lot of energy per atom. The implications of this large energy release were considerable.

Lise Meitner had been working under Hahn in Germany until 1938 when she fled from Nazi Germany. Hahn advised her of his discovery of barium in a letter which she received just before Christmas, 1938. Her nephew Otto Frisch was on holiday with her in Sweden and in discussing the implications of Hahn's letter they arrived at the idea of fission. On returning from holiday to Copenhagen Frisch mentioned the matter to Bohr who was just departing for a conference in the USA. Bohr acclaimed the idea and advised speedy publication. The news of fission set the conference alight and scientists rushed off to their laboratories to repeat the experiments. Within days of the announcement nuclear fission had been realized at many USA laboratories.

Uranium has three naturally occurring isotopes; about 0.006 per cent U-234, about 0.7 per cent U-235, and the remainder as U-238. Do all three undergo fission by neutrons? A mass spectrometer arrangement was used to separate the three isotopes and the minute samples so prepared were bombarded by neutrons. Only U-235 showed fission. U-238 captured neutrons which hit it while moving fast but failed to fission. U-235 was found to capture slow neutrons more easily than fast ones. When fission occurred the U-235 nucleus split to liberate more neutrons—fast neutrons. A chain reaction was possible if the neutrons emerging from the fissioned U-235 could be slowed down and hit other U-235 nuclei; they must not, however, hit U-238 nuclei and be absorbed. Because the greater bulk of natural uranium was U-238 a chain reaction in natural uranium was not possible.

A typical fission reaction with ^{235}U is

$$^{235}_{92}\text{U} + ^{1}_{0}\text{n} \rightarrow ^{93}_{37}\text{Rb} + ^{141}_{55}\text{Cs} + 2^{1}_{0}\text{n}$$
$$\text{(neutron)} \qquad\qquad\qquad \text{(2 neutrons)}$$

What happens to the U-238 when it absorbs fast neutrons? It changes via U-239 to a new element, neptunium (Np).

$$^{238}_{92}\text{U} + ^{1}_{0}\text{n} \rightarrow ^{239}_{93}\text{Np} + ^{0}_{-1}\text{e}$$

Neptunium is radioactive and decays to give another new element, plutonium (Pu).

$$^{239}_{93}Np \rightarrow ^{239}_{94}Pu + ^{0}_{-1}e$$

The half-life of neptunium-239 is 2.34 days, the half-life of plutonium-239 is 2.44×10^4 years. Plutonium is, however, fissionable by slow neutrons.

Because plutonium can be produced from the main bulk of natural uranium it provided a more readily available source of fissionable material than U-235. A chain reaction in plutonium seemed feasible.

For a chain reaction to be sustained the neutrons produced by fission must be slowed down and sufficient of them must find other fissionable nuclei. The neutrons must not be wasted by being absorbed or leaving the block of material. The neutrons can be slowed down by using carbon, the chance of the neutrons finding other fissionable nuclei can be increased if the size of the piece of fissionable material is increased. For a spherical piece of material the volume and hence the number of accessible fissionable nuclei goes up as the radius cubed, the number of neutrons lost, i.e., the surface area, only increases as the square of the radius. Hence the idea of a 'critical' size.

In 1942 Fermi produced the first 'divergent chain reaction'. The vital factor in a chain reaction is what is called the reproduction factor—the number of neutrons produced in the 'second generation' of fissions by a single neutron producing the 'first generation' fission. If the reproduction factor is less than 1 the reaction obtained is not self-sustaining. Fermi in the first chain reaction obtained a reproduction factor of 1.0006. Cadmium strips were used to control the reaction—cadmium absorbs neutrons and when inserted in the uranium pile rapidly reduces the reproduction factor. The pile consisted of lumps of uranium metal and uranium oxide embedded in graphite. About 6000 kg of uranium metal was used and the pile was near spherical with an effective radius of 3.55 m. The power produced was about 200 watts.

Nuclear reactors

In a nuclear reactor a controlled chain reaction is produced. The reactor consists of the fissionable material, perhaps uranium-235, surrounded by a moderator. The function of the moderator is to slow down the neutrons since for fission slow neutrons are required. Heavy water, i.e., water in which the ordinary hydrogen isotope has been replaced by deuterium, or carbon is used. The fission reaction is controlled by controlling the number of neutrons that are available to initiate fission. This is done by control rods, perhaps boron steel, which can be inserted in varying numbers and to varying extents in the reactor. Such material absorbs neutrons.

A number of methods have been used to extract the energy of the fission from the reactor. Boiling water reactors use water which circulates through pipes in the reactor. The water turns to steam and is then directly used to rotate a turbine and hence generate electricity. Pressurized water reactors involve water circulating under high pressure through pipes in the reactor. This water does not turn to steam, because of the high pressure involved, and is then used in turn to heat a second water system which then delivers steam to the turbine (as in Fig. 18.32). Liquid-metal reactors use liquid sodium in place of the water in the pressurized water reactor system. The advantage of sodium is that it has a higher specific heat capacity than water and so is better at transferring heat.

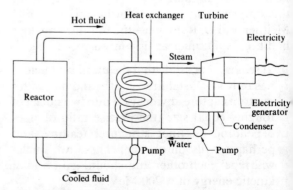

Fig. 18.32 *Simple diagram of a power-producing nuclear reactor*

Nuclear fusion

Fusion reactions are those in which the resulting nuclei have higher masses than those of initial particles. For example, when two protons combine to produce deuterium.

$$_1^1H + _1^1H \rightarrow _1^2H + _1^0e + \nu + 1.44 \text{ MeV}$$
positron   neutrino

This reaction between the two protons can only occur when the kinetic energies of the two are high enough for them to come close enough to react. The high kinetic energies can be produced by raising hydrogen to very high temperatures, millions of degrees. This reaction is thought to occur in the sun and be partially responsible for the energy released by the sun. The reaction forms part of a sequence of reactions involving hydrogen, deuterium, and tritium—the end product being helium and a considerable release of energy.

$$4\,_1^1H \rightarrow _2^4He + 2_1^0e + 26 \text{ MeV}$$

Four protons are effectively fused to produce helium.

Models of atoms

How are the electrons arranged in the Rutherford atom? Rutherford's atom with its minute nucleus was barely two years old when N. Bohr, a pupil of Rutherford, wrote a paper in which he put forward what was a revolutionary theory of the atom. The idea was that the atomic electrons orbited the nucleus in certain stable orbits or states. When they were in the orbits no emission of radiation occurred. This was only emitted when the electrons jumped between orbits.

On purely ordinary mechanics an electron moving in a circular parth was accelerating, towards the centre, and accelerating electrons radiate electromagnetic waves. Thus the electron is continually losing energy. If it loses energy, at the expense of its potential energy, it must spiral into the nucleus. Bohr 'solved' this problem by just stating that electrons in stable orbits did not radiate and that they only radiated when jumping from one orbit to another.

Only certain orbits were permitted and thus since an electron in such an orbit would have a specific kinetic energy and potential energy there was therefore specific values of energy associated with orbits, hence energy levels. When an electron moved from a higher-energy E_2 orbit to a lower-energy E_1 orbit, radiation of frequency f would be emitted where $E_2 - E_1 = hf$.

Bohr's atom gave an explanation of the spectrum lines of hydrogen. The cost of the explanation had been a number of arbitrary rules. The justification for these rules was that they gave an explanation of the hydrogen spectrum.

Quantum mechanics

In 1925 Heisenberg published a paper 'The interpretation of kinematic and mechanical relationships according to the quantum theory'. This was the beginning of quantum mechanics.

Heisenberg had discerned a basic limitation which exists on our experimental capabilities. Certain quantities are unobservable—not measurable. It is not that we might in the future be able to devise experimental techniques which will let us observe these quantities—they are just unobservable. In the case of a photon or electron passing through a single slit: if the slit is about one wavelength wide then the uncertainty about the position is λ—we know within a wavelength λ where the photon or electron goes; the momentum is $mv = h/\lambda$ and thus the uncertainty about the momentum is h/(uncertainty about position). A single slit of this width gives complete diffraction through 180°—the photon or electron beam spreads out into all directions on emerging from the slit, the sideways momentum the particle obtained at the slit is very indefinite when the particle could go anywhere on passing through the slit. If we make the slit wider we produce more uncertainty about position and less about momentum—the diffraction pattern is much narrower. We have:

(Uncertainty about position) ×
(Uncertainty about momentum) $\geqslant h$

A similar relationship exists for energy of a particle and spread of time over which the energy is determined. For a photon, the momentum is mc

439

and as $E = mc^2$ we have the uncertainty in momentum equal to (uncertainty about energy)/c. The photon travels with a speed c so that position is ct, and so the uncertainty in position means an uncertainty in time. Hence

(Uncertainty about energy) ×
(Uncertainty about time) $\geqslant h$

Suppose we think of an atom as being like a box with an electron bouncing backwards and forwards between an opposite pair of walls. If the walls are a distance L apart, then the uncertainty in position of the electron is L and hence the uncertainty in momentum is h/L. Thus we might suggest that the momentum be + or $-h/2L$. Between the walls the electron we will say has only kinetic energy. Thus the energy of the electron in the atom corresponding to this momentum will be

$$\text{energy} = \tfrac{1}{2}mv^2 = \frac{(mv)^2}{2m} = \frac{h^2}{8mL^2}$$

How big is the 'atom box'? We know that about 22×10^{-19} J is needed for an electron to escape from a hydrogen atom. This is the potential energy at a distance of about 1×10^{-10} m from a nucleus having a charge of 1.6×10^{-19} C.

$$\text{potential energy} = Ve = \frac{e^2}{4\pi\varepsilon_0 r}$$

where r is the radius of the atom. Thus we can think of walls being at this distance. For an electron to escape from the atom it would need to have 22×10^{-19} J to just reach the top of the wall. Taking L as 2×10^{-10} m, m as 9×10^{-31} kg and h as 6.6×10^{-34} J s gives the energy of the electron as about 14×10^{-19} J. We can have an electron in this size box.

If our atom had been the size of the nucleus, the uncertainty in momentum would be much higher because of the reduction in the uncertainty of the position. The nucleus is about 10 000 times smaller than the atom, and so the kinetic energy would be about $10\,000 \times 10\,000$ times larger, of the order of 10^{-11} J or about 100 MeV. This is an immense energy and indicates why electrons are

not thought to exist inside nuclei. The above argument thus gives some reason for atoms being the size they are. If they were smaller, the electron would have too high an energy to exist in the atom. The atom is about the smallest size box in which we can contain the electron.

Wave mechanics

In 1926 Schrödinger postulated that there was no need to invent rules about only certain orbits being possible in order to arrive at energy levels, they would occur naturally if we considered the conditions for standing electron waves in atoms, like standing waves on a string (Fig. 7.18b).

What would the wavelength of an electron have to be if it is to fit like a string inside an atom-sized box? The size of an atom is about 2×10^{-10} m, thus the wavelength of the fundamental oscillation will be about 4×10^{-10} m ($2L$).

As

$$\lambda = \frac{h}{mv}$$

the momentum of the electron giving this wavelength will be

$$mv = \frac{6.6 \times 10^{-36}}{4 \times 10^{-10}}$$

$$= 1.6 \times 10^{-24} \text{ kg m s}^{-1}$$

The kinetic energy of such an electron will be

$$\text{Kinetic energy} = \tfrac{1}{2}mv^2$$

and if $m = 9.1 \times 10^{-31}$ m s $^{-1}$

$$\text{Kinetic energy} = \frac{(1.6 \times 10^{-24})^2}{2 \times 9.1 \times 10^{-31}}$$

$$= 14 \times 10^{-19} \text{ J}$$

Could an electron with this energy be contained within the atom? Within the box the electron is only considered to have kinetic energy. The energy needed to remove an electron from the hydrogen atom is about 22×10^{-19} J. This is greater than the kinetic energy we calculated for the electron wave and thus the electron can have this energy and remain within the atom.

If the atom were half the size the kinetic energy is increased by a factor of four, to 56×10^{-19} J, and the energy the electron needs to escape is increased by a factor of two, to 44×10^{-19} J; the potential energy of the 'wall' is proportional to $1/r$. The electron could not be contained within an atom of this size. The electron could certainly not be contained within the nucleus—its kinetic energy would be much too large, about 14×10^{-13} J for a nucleus 2×10^{-10} m in size. The wavelength of a proton can fit within the nucleus, its wavelength being smaller because of its larger mass.

What about the other forms of oscillation of a string—can electron waves have these forms? The fundamental wave has just one loop, the next wave has two loops, the next three loops, and so on. The wavelength is $2L/n$, where n is the number of loops.

$$\text{Kinetic energy} = \frac{(mv)^2}{2m} = \frac{h^2}{2m\lambda^2}$$

$$= \frac{h^2 n^2}{8mL^2}$$

We imagine the electron shuttling back and forth in the box with this constant kinetic energy between walls. If within the box the potential energy is zero, the expression gives us the total energy possible for the electron. Unlike the Bohr atom where the integers had to be specifically introduced by assumption, they here spring naturally out of wave ideas.

We can apply this simple idea to the case of a dye molecule where electrons are able to move along the length of a chain of carbon atoms between walls of CH_3 molecules, these being the ends of the carbon chain. A particular dye has a carbon chain length of 8.4×10^{-10} m, thus the energy levels are 8.48×10^{-20} J, 33.92×10^{-20} J, 76.32×10^{-20} J, 135.68×10^{-20} J, 212.00×10^{-20} J, etc (Fig. 18.33). The colour of the dye is given by the transition from level 4 to level 3, an energy change of 59.36×10^{-20} J. This corresponds to a frequency

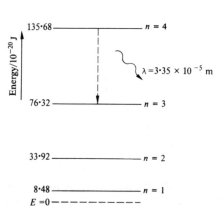

Fig. 18.33 Energy levels for a particle in a box. E $\propto n^2$

(E/h) of 8.94×10^{14} Hz, a wavelength of 3.35×10^{-5} m, and a resulting purple colour.

Our wave model is a crude model, a wave in a rectangular box. We can imagine it as a standing water wave produced between straight barriers. The kinetic energy of the electron is, however, dependent on how far away from the nucleus we consider it to be, the momentum thus depends on the distance and hence the wavelength is not constant over the entire atom. Our box containing the standing wave is not rectangular but is much more complex. A rectangular box is a rectangular potential well, the electron moving unimpeded between the walls and being unable to surmount them because its kinetic energy is not as large as the potential energy at the walls (Fig. 18.34a). Our box should have a $1/r$ shape, the electron having both kinetic and potential energy within the box.

$$V = -\frac{Q}{4\pi \varepsilon_0 r}$$

This is consistent with an inverse square law force. Thus, for a constant total energy, the kinetic energy will decrease as the potential energy increases. This occurs as r becomes larger.

441

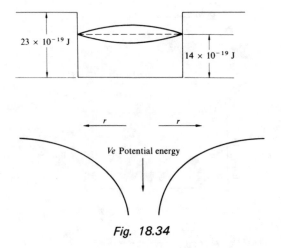

23×10^{-19} J

14×10^{-19} J

Ve Potential energy

Fig. 18.34

Then as $d \cos \theta$ is the projection of the length in the x direction we must have $n\lambda = 2d \cos \theta$. For the same wave projected onto the y-axis we have $m\lambda = 2d \sin \theta$. Hence, since $\sin^2\theta + \cos^2\theta = 1$ we have

$$\left(\frac{m\lambda}{2d}\right)^2 + \left(\frac{n\lambda}{2d}\right)^2 = 1$$

$$\left(\frac{m}{2d}\right)^2 + \left(\frac{n}{2d}\right)^2 = \frac{1}{\lambda^2}$$

In a similar way we can derive the three-dimensional case of

$$\left(\frac{l}{2d}\right)^2 + \left(\frac{m}{2d}\right)^2 + \left(\frac{n}{2d}\right)^2 = \frac{1}{\lambda^2}$$

where l, m and n are quantum numbers which can have the values 1, 2, 3, etc.

What do the electron waves represent? Schrödinger considered that the electron was smeared out over its wave pattern. Born later developed the interpretation that the wave was a phantom wave which guided the electron to regions of high and low probability. A large amplitude region on a standing wave indicates a region of high probability of finding an electron there. In an interference experiment with light incident on two slits we use the idea of light as a wave to find the regions where the interference fringes will be a maximum—the wave tells us where the greatest chance is of a photon being found. Thus in our atomic model, the greatest chance of finding an electron is where the amplitude of our standing wave is a maximum. The chance is proportional to the square of the amplitude (as the amplitude could be negative this means we do not have 'negative' chances.)

Figure 18.34b shows a $1/r$ potential well. What would the fundamental standing wave in such a well look like? Near the centre the kinetic energy would be high, where the potential energy is small, and thus the wavelength small; near the edge of the atom the kinetic energy would be smaller, the potential energy is higher, and thus the wavelength longer.

$$\text{Kinetic energy} \propto v^2 \propto \frac{1}{\lambda^2}$$

Figure 18.35 shows the type of fundamental wave pattern we might expect for our hypothetical string.

So far we have been considering waves confined to one dimension. For the wave in the box we thus had $n\lambda = 2L$. But atoms are three-dimensional, we need an equation which will give the one-dimensional result whichever axis we choose. Consider a two-dimensional situation where the standing wave is at some angle θ to the x direction.

Our hypothetical string in Fig. 18.35 has a maximum amplitude at the centre. The chance of finding an electron at a point would seem to be highest at the centre. Because atoms are three-dimensional it is generally more convenient to give the chance of finding the electron at a given distance from the centre, say at radius r. This radial charge density is $4\pi r^2 \Delta r$ times the chance of finding an electron at a point distance r from

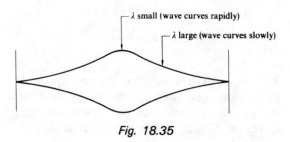

λ small (wave curves rapidly)

λ large (wave curves slowly)

Fig. 18.35

the centre. This is the chance of finding the electron in a shell of thickness Δr and radius r. At the centre r is zero and thus the radial charge density is zero. Figure 18.36 shows the result of expressing Fig. 18.35 as a radial distribution. Figure 18.37 shows another way of representing the radial distribution—the blackness of the shading in any region indicates the chance of finding the electron there. Our result looks like a fuzzy Bohr orbit.

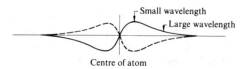

Fig. 18.36   n = 1 radial distribution

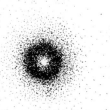

Fig. 18.37   n = 1 radial distribution

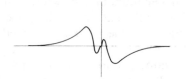

Fig. 18.38   n = 2 radial distribution

Fig. 18.39   n = 3 radial distribution

What would the other modes of oscillation look like? The next mode would have to fit the idea of the wavelength being smaller near the centre than farther out and have an extra maximum (Fig. 18.38). The next mode would have yet one more extra maximum (Fig. 18.39).

Supplementary material

Optoelectronics

A photoconductive cell, such as one made from the semiconductor compound cadmium sulphide, has the property that its resistance depends on the intensity of light falling on it. The resistance is high when the intensity is low and low when the intensity is high. When photons impinge on the semiconductor the energy given to electrons is sufficient to raise them into the conduction band. This increase in the number of charge carriers means a drop in resistance. Cadmium sulphide cells are made to have a spectral response similar to that of the eye. A problem with such cells, however, is that they respond fairly slowly to light changes, time lags of the order of 0.1 s occurring.

Photovoltaic cells involve the generation of a voltage when photons are absorbed by the cell material. Such cells are either a junction between a metal and a semiconductor, e.g., a gold-coated surface and selenium, or a p–n junction. When photons with sufficient energy impinge on the junction electron–hole pairs are created which can move across the junction, and hence give rise to a current through a load connected across the cell. Such cells are used for satellite solar cell panels.

Photodiodes and phototransistors depend on the same effect. If a reverse bias is set up across a p–n junction there is just a small leakage current. However, if photons of sufficient energy impinge on the junction, electron-hole pairs are created. On the n-side of the junction the extra electrons produced are fairly insignificant in terms of the number of conduction electrons; however, the holes produced give quite a large fractional increase in the hole population and so in the minority charge carriers. Similarly, on the p-side of the junction the fractional increase in the number of holes is quite small but there is quite a significant increase in the number of electrons, the minority charge carriers. The net result is that for the reverse biased p–n junction there is an increase in the leakage current when the junction is illuminated. This current passing through an external load resistance is proportional to the intensity of the light.

p–i–n photodiodes have an intrinsic layer of semiconductor material sandwiched between the p-type and n-type materials (hence the i for intrinsic in the name of the diode). When a fairly high reverse bias is applied across the diode an approximately uniform electric field is set up across the intrinsic layer of material. The result is that there is effectively a much wider depletion layer than normally occurs with a p–n junction, hence there is a greater volume within which photons can be absorbed and give rise to electron–hole pairs. Such photodiodes can respond very quickly to light changes (in about 1 ns).

Photoemissive cells are based on the photoelectric effect. Photons with sufficient energy impinging on a surface are able to cause electrons to be emitted. A vacuum photoemissive cell consists of a light-sensitive cathode and an anode sealed in an evacuated glass envelope. When the anode is positive with respect to the cathode a current flows which is proportional to the light intensity. Gas-filled photoemissive cells have a gas at a low pressure inside the envelope. The electrons produced by the impact of photons on the cathode can, when the potential difference between the cathode and anode is high enough, ionize gas molecules in the passage from cathode to anode. The result is a much larger current. The current is, however, not proportional to the light intensity.

Light-emitting diodes (LED) are junction diodes, made from the semiconducting compounds of gallium arsenide or gallium phosphide, which emit light when forward-biased. The effect of the forward-biasing is to move electrons from the conduction band of the n-type material to the p-side of the junction. Within the p-material these electrons may combine with holes in the valency band. In doing this they lose energy, an amount equal to the fall from the bottom of the conduction band to the top of the valency band. Gallium phosphide has an energy gap between its conduction and valency bands of 2.25 eV. Thus since $hf = 2.25 \times 1.6 \times 10^{-19}$ J, then the wavelength emitted is $c/f = 5.5 \times 10^{-7}$ m (a yellow colour). Gallium arsenide has an energy gap of 1.41 eV and so emits infrared radiation. By combining these two compounds in varying amounts to give gallium arsenide phosphide (the term used is a solid solution of one in the other) the energy gap can be fixed at any value between 1.41 eV and 2.25 eV and thus light emitted at any wavelength between 550 nm and 725 nm. Such photodiodes are used as indicator lamps and in arrays for displays of numbers on cash registers, clocks, etc. An important use is with optical fibres. They are cheap but, however, do have the limitation of only low intensity emission. Where higher intensities are required a laser would be used. They are, like the laser, monochromatic. However, no light source is completely monochromatic and the spread of the wavelength is greater with an LED than with a laser.

Lasers

The absorption and re-emission process can be summarized as—a photon of the right energy hits the atom, the atom becomes excited and moves to a higher energy level, at some time later the atom drops back down the energy level ladder and re-emits the photon. Re-emission can take place in a number of steps as the atom drops back down the steps of the energy ladder. This re-emmission occurs some time later than the absorption, after a time interval which is random. This form of emission is known as spontaneous emission.

The absorption and emission process we have just considered assumed that the atom being hit by the photon was able to absorb the photon's energy, i.e., the energy of the photon was just the right value to raise the atom from the energy level it was in to a higher energy level. If, however, the atom was already at this higher level then there is a chance that a process known as stimulated emission can occur. When this occurs the incident photon triggers the emission of an identical photon from the atom, the atom dropping to a lower energy level. Thus the incident photon results in two identical photons moving away from the atom. In this case there is no time lag between the two emerging photons and they both move off in the same direction. There is an increase in the intensity of the light (a factor of two as the number of photons has been doubled). The two photons are said to be coherent.

If the conditions are right for stimulated emissions, i.e., a large number of atoms already excited to the correct energy level, then a large build-up of intensity occurs. The light is monochromatic, i.e., one frequency, because it is produced by jumps between just one pair of energy levels. A device in which such intense beams of monochromatic radiation is produced is, in the case of visible light, known as a laser (light amplification by stimulated emission of radiation) and in the case of microwaves as a maser (microwave amplification by stimulated emission of radiation). The first such device was produced in 1954 and produced waves of wavelength 0.0125 m. Ammonia molecules were used as the photon target atoms. 1960 saw the first solid-state laser, a ruby giving a wavelength of 0.694×10^{-6} m (a bright red colour). 1961 saw the first gas laser, using a mixture of helium and neon.

All masers and lasers are amplifiers for just one narrow frequency band; a few photons, of the right energy, cause an avalanche of stimulated photons.

The basic requirement for a laser or maser is that there must be a large number of atoms or molecules in the correct excited state for stimulated emission to exceed spontaneous emission. This means that we must have more atoms at the higher energy level than the lower energy level. This is known as population inversion. Under normal conditions more atoms will be at a lower energy level than at a higher one; the population of atoms at a higher level is lower than the population at a lower level. Population inversion can be produced in a number of ways. In the ruby laser bright light from a xenon flashtube is focused on the ruby. The flashlamp only operates for a few microseconds and in that short time interval excites a considerable number of atoms. Because, in this case, the spontaneous decay of the atoms from this excited state takes quite a long time a population inversion is produced—the flash lamp is exciting atoms faster than they can decay. In the helium–neon laser the production of population inversion is achieved in two stages. A high voltage, of the order of 1 kV, is applied across the tube which contains about 85 per cent helium and 15 per cent neon at a combined pressure of about 1 mm of mercury. The high voltage accelerates ions in the tube and so excites the helium atoms to their lowest energy level of 19.8 eV above the ground state. The helium atoms collide with the neon atoms and because neon has an energy level at 19.8 eV energy can be transferred from the excited helium atoms to the neon atoms (Fig. 18.40). This 19.8 eV level is not the lowest level for neon. This results in the neon

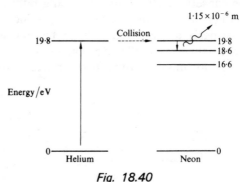

Fig. 18.40

having more atoms at the 19.8 eV level than its lower levels—a population inversion has been produced. When the neon atoms drop down to the next lower level, at 18.6 eV, photons of wavelength 1.15×10^{-6} m are produced. Photons of wavelength 0.633×10^{-6} m (a red colour) can also be produced because the helium energy level at 20.0 eV is the same as a neon level at 20.0 eV (Fig. 18.41).

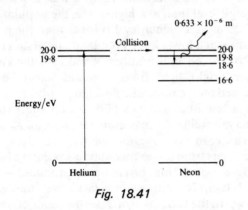

Fig. 18.41

When population inversion has been produced then stimulated emission can occur. To produce a large build-up in intensity the photons produced by stimulated emission must produce yet more photons so that a chain reaction can occur. This build-up can be in a controlled direction if the action takes place in a cavity formed between two reflectors. The photons which move along the axis between the mirrors (Fig. 18.42) are reflected back along the same line and so produce more stimulated emission. The stimulated photons move along the same direction as the photons hitting the atom—this must occur for momentum to be conserved. The result of placing reflectors on either side of the cavity is to produce an intense beam along the axis. Since the reflectors are not 100 per cent reflective, some photons are lost by transmission through the mirrors. In a

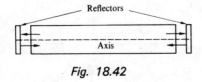

Fig. 18.42

typical gas laser, one mirror may be 99.9 per cent reflective and the other 99 per cent reflective. The lower reflectance of one mirror is to enable a beam of radiation to emerge from the laser.

Lasers produce highly monochromatic radiation. A high percentage of the input energy emerges at just one wavelength, unlike any other lamp where the energy is spread over a range of wavelengths. Also the light from a laser is coherent. When laser light is focused to a fine point by a lens we have large amounts of energy directed towards that point. The result can be the burning of holes through steel plate, the welding of a detached retina back into place in the human eye, or indeed any application where highly localized energy is required.

Age of the earth

How old is the earth? Ten million years? A hundred million years? A thousand million years? Five thousand million years? Figures like these were the subject of great controversy in the latter half of the nineteenth century. In 1858 Darwin published his book *The Origin of Species.*

‘ . . . if the variations useful to any organic being ever do occur, assuredly individuals thus characterized will have the best chance of being preserved for the struggle for life; and from the strong principle of inheritance, these will tend to produce offspring similarly characterized. This principle of preservation, or the survival of the fittest, I have called Natural Selection. . . . ’

C. Darwin (1858) *The Origin of Species.*

A vital point in this theory was the length of time the earth had supported life in order to allow for natural selection to evolve the various species. This required more time than if species had been separately created. The time necessary for man to evolve via apes would be much greater than the time in which man was somehow directly created as man.

W. Thomson (later Lord Kelvin) opposed Darwin's views because he considered that the earth was not old enough for evolution by natural selection to have occurred. His argument was based on a calculation of the rate at which the earth was cooling. Kelvin measured the temperature gradient of the earth's crust near the surface and the thermal conductivity of the surface material.

The rate of flow of heat from a cooling object, dQ/dt, is related to the temperature gradient, $d\theta/dx$, by

$$\frac{dQ}{dt} = \lambda A \frac{d\theta}{dx}$$

where λ is called the thermal conductivity, and A is the surface area of the object.

$\lambda = 3$ J m^{-1} K^{-1} s^{-1}
$d\theta/dx = 17 \times 10^{-3}$ K m^{-1} (Kelvin used 1/2776)
$A = 4\pi r^2 = 4\pi (6.4 \times 10^6)^2 = 5.2 \times 10^{14}$ m^2

$$\text{Thus } \frac{dQ}{dt} = 2.7 \times 10^{12} \text{ J s}^{-1}$$

Kelvin assumed that the beginning of time for the earth could be taken as the time when the earth was just solidifying. He took the temperature of solidification as 3900°C. The heat flow from a body cooling from 3900°C to about 0°C (assumed to be the average temperature of the earth) is

Q = mass × specific heat capacity × 3900
 = $6 \times 10^{24} \times 800 \times 3900$
 = 1.9×10^{31} J

If dQ/dt remained constant then it would need about 7×10^{18} s or about 10^{11} years. The rate of flow of heat at 3900°C might, however, be expected to be greater than that at 0°C; this would mean fewer years would be necessary. Kelvin suggested that the value would be about 10^8 years (a hundred million years).

'The limitation of geological periods imposed by physical science cannot, of course, disprove the hypothesis of transmutation of species; but it does seem sufficient to disprove the doctrine that transmutation has taken place through 'descent with modification by natural selection'.'

Kelvin (1894) *Popular Lectures and Addresses*, London, page 89.
L. Eiseley (1959) (*Darwin's Century*, Gollancz, page 240)

It was not many years before the error of Kelvin's calculation emerged—Kelvin had assumed that the earth was cooling without itself containing any source of energy which could replenish in any way the energy lost. A source was discovered—radioactivity. The energy released by 1 g of uranium is about 10^{-6} J s^{-1}. If we assume that uranium occurs throughout the earth's volume in the same proportions as the surface rocks, the total amount of uranium in the earth will be of the order of 10^{19} kg and the total energy released about 10^{13} J s^{-1}. This is about the same as the rate at which the earth is losing energy.

Our estimates are very rough; we have neglected the thorium in the earth and probably overestimated the uranium content (it is doubtful that there is the same proportion in the earth's interior as in the crust). The result is, however, sufficient to indicate that the age of the earth as estimated by Kelvin is probably a considerable underestimate.

Estimates of the ages of rocks can be made from measurements of their helium content. Radioactive materials, which decay by alpha emission, produce helium. If this is trapped in the rocks we can from a measurement of the amount of helium estimate the number of alpha particles produced over the lifetime of the rock. The mineral thorianite from Ceylon was found to contain 68 per cent of thorium and 11 per cent of uranium and yielded 8.9 cm^3 of helium gas (at 273 K and 76 cm pressure) per gramme of mineral. Knowing the rates at which uranium and thorium produce alpha particles, and hence helium, the age of the mineral can be estimated. The thorianite has been aged at 270 million years.

Uranium and thorium decay to give lead; uranium–238 decays to give lead–206, thorium–232 decays to give lead–208. Thus lead in uranium or thorium-bearing rocks would be expected to have a higher concentration of these particular lead isotopes than common lead. Measurement, using a mass spectroscope, of the relative amounts of these isotopes enables the rock to be aged. (See Mass spectroscopy, earlier in this chapter.)

Naturally occurring potassium contains a radioactive isotope, potassium-40. On decay this gives argon-40. The amount of argon in potassium-bearing minerals can therefore be used to age those minerals. Rubidium-87 occurs naturally in rocks and decays to give strontium-87. Measurements of the strontium-to-rubidium ratio can thus yield an estimate of the age of the rocks.

The oldest rocks on earth appear to have an age of about 4.7×10^9 years, meteorites an age of about 4.5×10^9 years, soil from the moon about 4.7×10^9 years. All the indications are that the earth, and the moon, solidified about 4.7×10^9 years ago.

Further reading

P. M. Hurley (1959) *How Old is the Earth?* Heinemann, Science Study Series No. 5.

Radiological protection

When nuclear and electromagnetic radiations pass through living tissue it can alter or damage the structure of molecules and so lead to the malfunctioning or death of cells. While some cells can recover others cannot, and the effects on tissues are cumulative. Chromosomes are particularly sensitive to ionizing radiations at the moment of cell division and the gene arrangement in the chromosomes can be seriously modified and so produces changes affecting future generations. Although genetic mutations have been responsible for the evolution of human beings to their present state, most mutations are probably harmful.

Medical research on the effects of radiation on humans has led to statements of the maximum permissible radiation levels for safety, these levels being almost constantly reviewed and modified as research continues. Dosage is measured in grays (Gy) where 1 Gy is an absorbed energy of 1 J per kilogram. The unit which this replaced was called the rad, 1 rad = 1 mGy. The biological effects of some radiations are more pronounced than others and so the dose may be stated in units of rem, with the dose in rem being the product of the dose in rad and a factor called the relative biological effectiveness (RBE) for the radiation concerned. Beta radiation has RBE as 1, while alpha radiation can have a value of 10 because of its greater ionization effect.

The maximum permissible levels for occupational exposure over the whole body, for workers over the age of 18, is 5 rem per year. For non-radiation workers the maximum permissible level is 170 mrem per year (1/30th that of the occupational exposure). It should, however, be borne in mind that the natural radiation and radioactivity background to which we are all subject does give everybody a dose of about 100 mrem per year.

For radiation workers there is thus a need to monitor the dose they receive and also to take precautions to ensure that they do not receive large doses. Film badges or pocket dosimeters (small ionization chambers) are worn and Geiger counter equipment modified to give direct readings of dose rate used for monitoring. Radioactive isotopes have to be stored in well-shielded and labelled rooms. Laboratories have to be capable of thorough and effective cleaning so that no traces of radioactive materials can accumulate in cracks on benches or corners. Special clothing may have to be worn so that the ordinary outdoor clothing of the worker does not become contaminated. During experiments, suitable shielding will be used as well as precautions taken to ensure that radioactive material does not come into contact with the skin. The above, in very simplistic terms, can only serve just to indicate some of the more basic points of radiological protection.

Medical uses of radioisotopes as tracers

Many medical diagnostic studies using radioisotopes involve a radioactively labelled compound being administered to the patient and which is then absorbed in the organ of concern. A detector outside the body is then used to monitor the radioactivity in that organ over a period of time. Two radioactive isotopes that are widely used are $^{99}_{43}Tc$ (technetium) which in the state it is used (called a metastable state) is a gamma emitter (energy 0.096 MeV) with a half-life of 6 h, and $^{131}_{53}I$ which decays by beta and gamma emissions with a half-life of 8.06 days.

A note of explanation is needed regarding the term metastable state. With natural radioactivity, gamma radiation is emitted by nuclei which have just formed as a result of alpha or beta decay;

these decay at the same rate as the decay of the alpha and beta activity. However, artificially produced activity sometimes exhibits gamma activity which is not closely identified with alpha or beta activity and thus has a half-life not related to alpha or beta activity The energy level in the nuclei from which such gamma radiation is emitted when it falls to a lower level is called a metastable level.

The choice of radioisotope depends on the organ being studied, the approach depending on the biochemistry of the body and the resulting selective localization of specific isotopes in certain organs. $^{131}_{53}I$, for example, tends to become localized in the thyroid, $^{49}_{19}K$ in muscle.

One way of monitoring the way in which the amount of radioisotope varies with time in a particular organ would be to put a counter against that part of the body close to the organ and monitor the count rate. This, however, only gives the activity over a small region of the body and does not enable movements of the radioactive isotope to be monitored from one organ to another or within an organ. For this purpose, imaging devices have to be used. These are based on the use of a crystal and a photomultiplier. The crystal emits flashes of light when struck by particles or photons. The photons emitted by the crystal then enter the photomultiplier tube (Fig. 18.43) and there strike a light-sensitive cathode.

Electrons are emitted and then accelerated by a potential difference to strike another electrode. Electrons are knocked out of this electrode by the impact, typically four electrons for every one electron hitting it. The resulting electrons are then accelerated by a further potential difference to another electrode, when each electron causes further emission of electrons. The result after, say, ten such collisions with electrodes is, for every electron emitted at the cathode, an amplification by 4^{10} or about a million.

In carrying out a scan the scintillation head, behind a collimator which only permits radiation from a small area to enter the crystal, is moved across the region of interest (Fig. 18.44). The pulses emerging from the photomultiplier tube can then be recorded in some way, perhaps on paper or photographic film. Another version of this arrangement which permits simultaneous observation of a large area employs a large scintillating crystal backed by an array of photomultipliers, each photomultiplier detecting the flashes of light in just a small area of the crystal (Fig. 18.45). A computer can then be used to convert the outputs from each area of the crystal into a picture which can be displayed on a cathode ray oscilloscope screen.

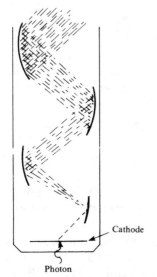

Fig. 18.43 A photomultiplier tube

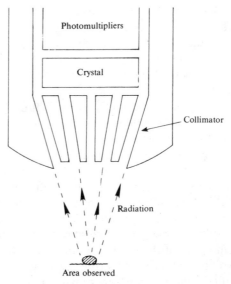

Fig. 18.44 A scintillation counter scan

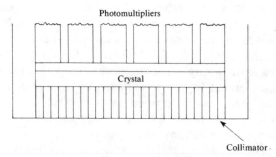

Fig. 18.45 A gamma camera

Problems

1. An electron beam passes between two parallel plates which are separated by 2.0 cm and across which there is a potential difference of 300 V. The deflection of this beam is just cancelled by a magnetic field of flux density 6.0×10^{-4} T applied in a direction normal to the electric field. Calculate the speed of the electrons. If the radius of curvature of the path of the electrons due to the magnetic field alone is 25 cm what is the value of the specific electronic charge, e/m?

(AEB, Q8, Paper 3, November 1981)

2. (a) A charged oil drop falls at constant speed in the Millikan oil drop experiment when there is no p.d. between the plates. Explain this.

(b) Such an oil drop, of mass 4.0×10^{-15} kg, is held stationary when an electric field is applied between the two horizontal plates. If the drop carries 6 electric charges each of value 1.6×10^{-19} C, calculate the value of the electric field strength.

(University of London, Q7, Paper 2, June 1985)

3. (a) Draw a labelled diagram to show how an electron, of mass m, carrying a charge e, travelling at a constant speed, is deflected on entering a uniform magnetic field of magnetic flux density B, at right angles to the direction of the field. Write down an expression for the force acting on the electron while it is in the field and then explain, using your knowledge of mechanics, why the path of the electron is the shape it is.

Explain carefully how the path would be modified if the electron were slowing down whilst in the magnetic field.

(b) Observations on single electrons are not possible. The path of a beam of electrons fired from an electron gun inside a spherical glass enclosure can be made visible by introducing into the enclosure a tiny amount of gas, e.g., argon. The path appears as a faint coloured glow through the gas. Explain this.

In such a tube, of dimensions shown in Fig. 18.46, electrons are ejected in the direction of the arrow from a gun, G, at a speed of 1.0×10^7 m s^{-1}. There is a uniform magnetic field at right angles to the plane of the diagram. Calculate the value of the magnetic flux density that would just confine the path of the beam to the tube without it hitting the walls.

(Specific charge of electron, $e/m = 1.76 \times 10^{11}$ C kg^{-1})

(University of London, Q15, Paper 2, June 1979)

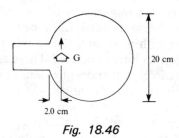

Fig. 18.46

4. The cut-off voltage (the reverse voltage that will just prevent any electron flow) for a photo-electric cell is measured for light of two frequencies. The following results are obtained:

Cutt-off voltage/V	0.93	1.41
Frequency/10^{14} Hz	6.10	7.30

Use this data to determine a value for the Planck constant.

(The electronic charge, $e = -1.6 \times 10^{-19}$ C)

(University of London, Q8, Paper 2, January 1982)

5. When light of frequency 5.4×10^{14} Hz is shone onto a metal surface the maximum energy of the electrons emitted is 1.2×10^{-19} J. If the same surface is illuminated with light of frequency

6.6×10^{14} Hz the maximum energy of the electrons emitted is 2.0×10^{-19} J. Use this data to calculate a value for the Planck constant.

(University of London, Q8, Paper 2, January 1981)

6. (a) Explain what is meant by the work function of a metal ϕ.

(b) Draw a diagram of the electric circuit you would use to find the 'stopping potential' of photoelectrons emitted from a metal surface in vacuum. Describe how you would determine the value of ϕ and of h/e, where h is the Planck constant and e the electronic charge.

(c) The work function of caesium is 1.90 electron volts, equal to 3.04×10^{-19} J. Calculate:

(i) the longest wavelength of light that can cause the emission of photoelectrons from a caesium surface;

(ii) the greatest speed with which electrons are emitted for incident light of wavelength 550 nm.

It has been suggested that photocells of some kind might eventually be developed as batteries to make use of solar energy. Supposing that the Sun's radiation is all of a single wavelength 550 nm:

(iii) estimate the e.m.f. of a caesium cell in sunlight.

With the same oversimplification, the power per unit area received at this wavelength from the Sun can be taken to be about 250 W m^{-2}.

(iv) Estimate the current per unit area from the caesium surface.

(v) State two difficulties in the way of constructing a practical source of electrical power from such cells.

(Take the value of the Planck constant h to be 6.63×10^{-34} J s, that of the electronic charge e to be 1.60×10^{-19} C, that of the electronic mass m_e to be 9.11×10^{-31} kg, and that of the speed of light c to be 3.00×10^8 m s^{-1})

(Oxford Local Examinations, Q13, Paper I, Summer 1979)

7. The accelerating voltage across an X-ray tube is 33.0 kV. Explain why the frequency of the X-radiation cannot exceed a certain value and calculate this maximum frequency. (The Planck constant $= 6.6 \times 10^{-34}$ J s; the charge on an electron $= 1.6 \times 10^{-19}$ C)

(AEB, Q8, Paper 3, June 1981)

8. Draw a diagram, and explain the action, of an X-ray tube.

Explain the presence in X-ray spectra of

(a) characteristic wavelengths,
(b) a continuous background.

The structure of a particular solid in which the spacing of the atomic planes is 0.30 nm is investigated by X-rays. First-order diffraction is observed from these planes at a Bragg angle of 30°. Calculate the X-ray wavelength and find the minimum potential difference across the X-ray tube needed to excite this wavelength. Explain your calculations clearly.

(The Planck constant, $h = 6.6 \times 10^{-34}$ J s. The charge on the electron, $e = -1.6 \times 10^{-19}$ C. The speed of light, $c = 3.0 \times 10^8$ m s^{-1})

(University of Cambridge, Q6, Paper 3, June 1980)

9. Explain the concept of energy levels of electrons in an atom. How does this concept enable the frequencies of spectral lines to be predicted? Explain the terms excitation potential and ionization potential.

(AEB, QA9, Paper 3, June 1982)

10. Figure 18.47 represents the scheme of the apparatus used by Franck and Hertz to investigate the collisions between electrons and mercury atoms. The tube contains mercury vapour, and electrons emitted from the hot cathode C are accelerated towards the openwork anode A, at a positive potential V_A which can be varied from

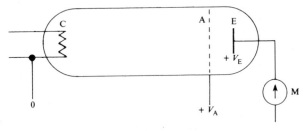

Fig. 18.47

zero up to about 20 V. The collecting electrode E is maintained at a positive potential V_E which is less than V_A by about 0.5 V, and M is a meter which reads the current flowing from E to earth.

(a) As V_A is increased from zero up to 4.9 V, the meter reading increases steadily. Why is this?

(b) At V_A = 4.9 V, there is a drop in the meter reading. How is this explained?

(c) Show on a sketch graph the way in which the meter reading varies with V_A as this potential is increased steadily up to about +20 V, and explain the form of this graph.

(d) The tube is observed to emit ultraviolet radiation of wavelength 253.7 nm at stage (b) and onward. How does this radiation originate?

(e) Why is this experiment said to give evidence for the existence of energy levels within the atom? Mention one other piece of evidence in support of this concept.

(Oxford Local Examinations, Q14, Paper 0, Summer 1981)

11. (a) Explain briefly what is meant by an emission spectrum. Describe a suitable source for use in observing the emission spectrum of hydrogen.

(b) Figure 18.48, which is to scale, shows some of the possible energy levels of the hydrogen atom.

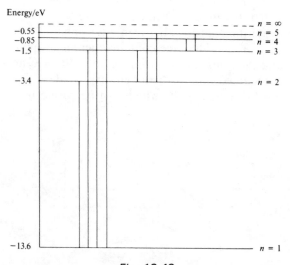

Energy/eV

Fig. 18.48

(i) Explain briefly how such a diagram can be used to account for the emission spectrum hydrogen.

(ii) When the hydrogen atom is in its ground state, 13.6 eV of energy are needed to ionise it. Calculate the highest possible frequency in the line spectrum of hydrogen. In what region of the electromagnetic spectrum does it lie?

(The frequency range of the visible spectrum is from 4×10^{14} Hz to 7.5×10^{14} Hz)

(iii) A number of transitions are marked on the energy level diagram. Identify which of these transitions corresponds to the lowest frequency that would be visible.

(c) The wavelengths of the lines in the emission spectrum of hydrogen can be measured using a spectrometer and a diffraction grating. If the grating has 5000 lines per cm, through what angle would light of frequency 4.6×10^{14} Hz be diffracted in the first-order spectrum?

($1\,\text{eV} = 1.60 \times 10^{-19}$ J. The Planck constant = 6.6×10^{-34} J s. Speed of light = 3.00×10^8 m s^{-1})

(University of London, Q10, Paper 2, January 1985)

12. Give an account of the evidence for the existence of energy levels within atoms that is afforded by (a) visible line spectra (such as the Balmer series of atomic hydrogen), (b) X-ray line spectra and absorption edges and (c) the results of electron bombardment of atoms, as in the experiment of Franck and Hertz.

The wavelength λ of the line emitted by the transition of the electron in the hydrogen atom from its $(n + 1)$th to its nth level is given by the formula

$$\frac{1}{\lambda} = R\left(\frac{1}{n^2} - \frac{1}{(n+1)^2}\right)$$

Where R is the Rydberg constant. Show that, when n is very large λ is given approximately by λ = $n^3/2R$.

Taking the value of R to be 1.097×10^7 m^{-1}, estimate the value of n concerned with the emission of the line for which λ = 0.21 m.

(Oxford Local Examinations, Q15, Paper II, Summer 1977)

13. Describe the principle of the experiment which established the nuclear model of the atom, explaining how the deduction is made from the observations.

The emission spectrum of the hydrogen atom consists of a series of lines. Explain why this suggests the existence of definite energy levels for the electron in the atom.

By considering the intervals between the energy levels explain the spacing of the lines in the visible hydrogen spectrum.

The ionisation potential of the hydrogen atom is 13.6 eV. Use the data below to calculate

(a) the speed of an electron which could just ionise the hydrogen atom;
(b) the minimum wavelength which the hydrogen atom can emit.

(Charge on the electron = -1.60×10^{-19} C, mass of an electron = 9.11×10^{-31} kg, the Planck constant = 6.63×10^{-34} J s, speed of light = 3.00×10^8 m s^{-1})

(University of London, Q15, Paper 2, January 1978)

14. Figure 18.49 shows a gold foil mounted across the path of a narrow, parallel beam of alpha particles. The fraction of incident particles reflected back through more than 90° is very small. How does this result lead to the idea that an atom has a nucleus

(a) whose diameter is small compared with the atomic diameter, and
(b) which contains most of the atom's mass.

(University of London, Q8, Paper 2, January 1985)

15. What are β and γ rays? Describe the structure and explain the action of a Geiger-Müller tube.

A source emitting both β and γ radiation was placed a fixed distance in front of a Geiger counter. Absorbers of various thicknesses x were placed between the source and the counter and the following readings of counts per second R were obtained:

R/s^{-1}	500	170	125	100	82	70	60
x/mm	0.1	0.3	0.4	0.5	0.6	0.7	0.8
R/s^{-1}	56	53	50	47	45	40	
x/mm	0.9	1.0	1.2	1.4	1.6	2.0	

Plot a graph of $\lg(R/\text{s}^{-1})$ against x/mm and discuss its shape.

Deduce how many β's were counted each second when the absorber was 0.5 mm thick. Show clearly how your result is obtained from your graph.

(University of Cambridge, Q6, Paper 3, November 1979)

16. (a) List, for α, β and γ radiation
(i) the mass, in terms of the electron mass, m_0, associated with each radiation,
(ii) the charge, in terms of the electronic charge, e, associated with each radiation,
(iii) their respective penetration of matter.

What effect, if any, does the emission of each of these radiations have on the nucleon number, A, and the proton number, Z, of the emitting nucleus?

(b) The energy of α-particles emitted by ^{210}Po is 3.9 MeV and their range in air at standard atmospheric pressure is approximately 30 mm. Each ionisation produced by α-particles colliding

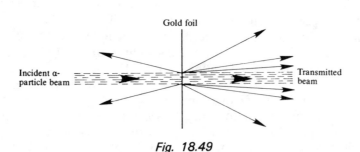

Fig. 18.49

with air molecules requires about 30 eV of energy. Estimate the average number of ionisations produced per mm of path. The number of ionisations per mm increases towards the end. Suggest a reason for this. If the pressure were reduced by a factor of 1/100, what would be the effect on the average number of ionisations produced per mm? Explain your answer.

(c) Describe in principle, an experiment whereby the range of α-particles in air may be found. You may assume you have a suitable source, and that any necessary circuitry for your detector is available and need not be described in detail. Discuss any limitation on the nature of the detector and explain the interpretation of the observations made.

(University of London, Q15, Paper 2, January 1982)

17. Figure 18.50 illustrates the principle of an experiment performed inside a cloud chamber to study the collision between an alpha particle and a proton. Alpha particles of energy 5.0 MeV were obtained from a radioactive source, and protons were 'knocked-on' from a thin sheet of polythene by the alpha particles. The diagram shows the result of a head-on collision between an alpha particle and a proton.

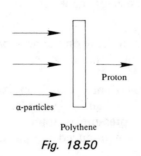

Fig. 18.50

(a)(i) Show that the speed of an incoming alpha particle of energy 5.0 MeV is approximately 1.5×10^7 m s^{-1}.

(ii) Calculate the momentum of the alpha particle.

(b) It can be shown that the change in momentum of a 5.0 MeV alpha particle colliding head-on with a proton is 4.6×10^{-20} kg m s^{-1}.

(i) What does this indicate about the direction of the motion of the alpha particle after the collision? Justify your answer.

(ii) By how much does the momentum of the proton change?

(iii) Calculate the speed of the knocked-on proton, stating any assumption made.

(c) The proton track in the cloud chamber is less dense (i.e., fainter) than the alpha particle tracks. Suggest a reason why this might be expected. Justify your answer.

(Mass of alpha particle 6.8×10^{-27} kg, mass of proton 1.7×10^{-27} kg)

(Oxford and Cambridge, Nuffield, Q2, Paper 2, June 1985)

18. (a) Radium has an isotope $^{226}_{88}$Ra of half-life approximately 1600 years. What is meant by the terms isotope and half-life?

(b) A sample of $^{226}_{88}$Ra emits both α-particles and γ-rays. State, and account for, any change in

(i) nucleon number, A,

(ii) proton number, Z,

which may occur as a result of the emission of these radiations.

(c) A mass defect of 8.8×10^{-30} kg occurs in the decay of a $^{226}_{88}$Ra nucleus. Calculate the energy released.

In a given sample it is found that most of the radium nuclei decay with the emission of an α-particle of energy 4.60 MeV and a γ-ray photon. What is the frequency of the γ-ray photon emitted? (Ignore the recoil energy of the decayed nucleus.)

(d) Outline briefly how you could show experimentally that both α-particles and γ-rays are present in emission from $^{226}_{88}$Ra.

How is it possible that, with a half-life of 1600 years, $^{226}_{88}$Ra occurs in measurable quantities in minerals 10^9 years old?

(Speed of light = 3.0×10^8 m s^{-1}. The Planck constant = 6.6×10^{-34} J s. Electronic charge = -1.6×10^{-19} C.)

(University of London, Q15, Paper 2, June 1983)

19. (a) Z protons and N neutrons are combined to form a nucleus $^{Z+N}_{Z}$X. Describe the energy changes which occur as the $(Z + N)$ free particles

are combined. Explain the concept of binding energy per nucleon which arises in this description.

Sketch a graph of binding energy per nucleon against nucleon number and use this graph to explain how the processes of nuclear fission and nuclear fusion are possible, indicating the values of nucleon number at which they may occur.

(b) A typical fission reaction is

$$^{235}_{92}U + ^1_0n \longrightarrow ^{148}_{57}La + ^{85}_{35}Br + \text{neutrons}$$

How many neutrons are released in this reaction? What is the importance of these neutrons in a nuclear reactor?

Why are the product isotopes of lanthanum (La) and bromine (Br) likely to be radioactive and what type of radioactivity are they likely to exhibit?

(University of London, Q15, Paper 2, January 1980)

20. Explain briefly how electrical energy is derived from the heat produced in a nuclear reactor.

In an nuclear reactor the process of nuclear fission is involved. Explain

(i) how useful energy is released in this process,
(ii) why fission generally only occurs for heavy nuclei,
(iii) why the release of several neutrons in each reaction is of fundamental importance,
(iv) why a nuclear reactor has to be heavily shielded.

A nuclear reactor produces 550 MW of electrical power. Waste heat is carried away by seawater supplied at the rate of $2.7 \times 10^4 \text{ kg s}^{-1}$. If the temperature rise of the seawater is 10.3 K, calculate the mass of nuclear fuel converted into energy in one year.
(1 year $\equiv 3.2 \times 10^7$ s; speed of light $= 3.0 \times 10^8$ m s^{-1}; specific heat capacity of seawater $= 4.0$ kJ kg^{-1} K^{-1})

(University of London, Q15, Paper 2, June 1981)

21. (a) Explain what is meant by the binding energy of an atomic nucleus.

(b) The uranium-238 isotope is an α-emitter,

and an atom (at rest) decays by the reaction

$$^{238}_{92}U \longrightarrow ^{234}_{90}Th + ^4_2He$$

Calculate, using the data given:

(i) the energy in MeV released in the reaction;
(ii) the recoil speed of the resulting thorium nucleus (assuming α-radiation only is emitted). (Mass of $^{238}_{92}U = 238.05081$ u; mass of $^{234}_{90}Th = 234.04363$ u; the atomic mass unit u $= 1.66 \times 10^{-27}$ kg $\equiv 930$ MeV; the electronic charge $e = 1.6 \times 10^{-19}$ C.

(c) The isotope of carbon ^{14}C, which has a half-life of 5600 years, is produced continuously in the upper atmosphere and is incorporated in living material. Measurements on newly formed natural carbon show that about 1 in 10^{12} of the atoms are of this isotope.

A 2 g sample of carbon from an archaeological specimen is found to have an activity of 5 disintegrations per minute.

(i) Estimate the age of the archaeological specimen.
(ii) Discuss the assumptions inherent in this method of archaeological dating.

(Take the Avogadro constant N_A to be 6×10^{23} mol^{-1})

(Oxford Local Examinations, Q15, Paper 0, Summer 1982)

22. (a) For a beam of singly-charged positive ions, show how:

(i) a uniform electric field acts as an energy selector;
(ii) a uniform magnetic field acts as a momentum selector.

In each case, draw diagrams to illustrate the path followed by the ions and the field direction.

(b) A combination of uniform electric field E and uniform magnetic field B, at right angles to each other and a beam of singly-charged positive ions, acts as a velocity selector. Ions of a particular velocity v are not deviated.

(i) Explain this and derive an expression for v.
(ii) Show clearly on a diagram what happens to ions of velocities $v_1 (> v)$ and $v_2 (< v)$.
(c) A beam of singly-charged neon ions ($^{20}_{10}Ne^+$

455

and $^{22}_{10}\mathrm{Ne}^+$) which have been accelerated through a p.d. of 2 kV enter a uniform magnetic field of flux density 0.25 T at right angles to the direction of the beam. Find the radial separation of the two neon isotopes.

(Take the specific charge on a proton to be 0.96×10^8 C kg^{-1})

(Oxford Local Examinations, Q14, Paper 0, Summer 1982)

23. (a) One of the basic tenets of quantum theory is the dual nature of matter, i.e. electromagnetic radiation possesses certain particle-like properties whereas particles such as electrons possess certain wave-like properties. The duality is expressed by the relationship $p = h/\lambda$, where p is momentum, λ is wavelength and h is the Planck constant, 6.6×10^{-34} J s.

(i) Discuss the experimental evidence which shows that electromagnetic radiation is quantized.

(ii) A beam of electrons has a speed equal to 5×10^6 m s^{-1}. Utilize the above relationship to suggest a possible way in which the wave properties of the electrons could be demonstrated.

(The mass of an electron may be taken as 9.0×10^{-31} kg)

(b) 'The existence of quantum numbers is a direct result of the existence of specified conditions at the boundaries of a system containing waves.' Illustrate this statement by discussing the waves in a string fixed at both ends.

What is the likely relationship between the number of dimensions of the system and the number of quantum numbers, each of which may have a range of values?

If an electron around a nucleus possesses wave properties, suggest, by analogy with the above, how quantization of electron energies is likely.

(University of London, Q8, Special paper, June 1980)

24. This question is about clarifying the idea of wave–particle duality.

Physicists claim both that things commonly regarded as particles can behave like waves and that things commonly regarded as waves can behave like particles.

(a) Outline experimental evidence which supports the claim that particles can behave like waves.

(b) Outline experimental evidence which supports the claim that waves can behave like particles.

(c) Explain why wave properties of particles may be important for electrons but not for tennis balls, and why particle properties of waves may be important for light waves but not for radio waves.

(d) Answer a critic who objects that these ideas are absurd because something cannot be both a wave and a particle at the same time.

(Oxford and Cambridge, Nuffield, Q2, Paper 3, June 1984)

25. (a) Each of the diagrams [Fig. 18.51] is said to represent an electron in a box. Explain why a diagram of potential energy against distance like this can be said to represent a box. Also explain how the curved lines in each box can be said to represent the electrons.

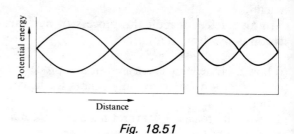

Fig. 18.51

(b) 'With a single particle in a box, the smaller the box the faster the particle will rattle around.' Use the diagrams above, and the relationship $p = h/\lambda$, to explain this statement.

(c) The electron in a hydrogen atom cannot be represented by diagrams like these. Draw a rough diagram that better represents an electron in a hydrogen atom 'box' with the electron in the lowest energy level. How and why does your diagram differ from those given above?

(Oxford and Cambridge Schools' Examination Board, Nuffield Advanced Physics, Physics I, Options paper, 1970)

Suggested answers to problems

Chapter 0

1. High latent heats occur for high melting points. You might have expected this if you thought of the latent heat and the melting point as both being a measure of the size of the inter-atomic forces. See Chapter 16 for a more detailed discussion.

Magnesium has a latent heat of 8.95 kJ mol^{-1} and vanadium 17.57 kJ mol^{-1}, not quite fitting the pattern.

2. Lead should be 2024 K. It seems reasonable to expect melting points, molar latent heat capacities, and boiling points to follow similar patterns.

3. The following are my suggestions, you may disagree.

(1) Makes an hypothesis.
(2) A deduction from earlier statements.
(3) An experimental fact.
(4) A deduction.

4. (a) N s^2 m^{-1}, (b) N s^2 m^{-4}, (c) N s.

5. (a) $[ML^{-3}]$, (b) $[MLT^{-1}]$, (c) $[MLT^{-1}]$.

6. $[MLT^{-2}] = [L^2][ML^{-3}][LT^{-1}]^x$, hence $x = 2$. $A = 4\pi r^2$, hence if upthrust is neglected $F = mg = 1.0 \times 9.8 = k \times 4\pi(50 \times 10^{-3})^2 \times 1.2 \times 11.0^2$ and $k = 2.1$.

7. Using dimensions, $v^2 = kas$.

8. $s = kt$, $[LT^{-1}]$.

9. Gradient $= A = 15$ cm^2 g^{-1} s^{-2}. Intercept $= -B = -15$ and so $B = 15$ cm^{-1} s^{-1}. $a = 0.2$ cm.

10. (a) p against h, gradient $= \rho g$ and intercept $= p_0$.
(b) v against $\sqrt{(1/R)}$, gradient $= \sqrt{(2gM)}$ and intercept $= 0$.
(c) F against $1/r^2$, gradient $= q_1 q_2/4\pi\varepsilon_0$ and intercept $= 0$.
(d) v^2 against s, gradient $= 2a$ and intercept $= v_0^2$.

11. (a) See text.
(b) (i) l, 2.5 per cent; D, 1.7 per cent; d, 2.0 per cent. (ii) 1.38×10^3 mm^3. (iii) 9.9 per cent. (iv) Measurement of the volume of water displaced when tube immersed, perhaps 1 or 2 per cent.

12. $T = 2.0 \pm 0.1$ s, hence $g = 9.8 \pm 1.0$ m s^{-2}.

13. (b) 2.82×10^{-2} N m^{-1}. (c) 3.45×10^{-2} N m^{-1}, -4.9×10^{-4} N m^{-1} per %.

14. (a) (i) 3600 μA V^{-1}. (ii) 11 per cent. (b) 6.3×10^{-4} μA, 25 V^{-1}. (c) 0.36 μA.

15. (a) and (b) are exponential decays, (e) and (f) are exponential growths. Curves (c) and (d) are $(4 - e^{-kt})$.

16. Phrases such as 'constant ratio changes, i.e., ...' and 'rate of change proportional to the amount present' might be useful in such an explanation.

17. (a) ln y against x. (b) ln y against $1/x$.

18. This is the motion of a particle described by the equation: Acceleration $= -g \sin \theta = -4.9$ m s^{-2}, or rate of change of distance–time graph $= -4.9$ m s^{-2}.

19. (a) The amplitudes of successive oscillations are in a constant ratio.

(b) The rate of change of amplitude with time would be doubled and thus the motion would die away more rapidly.

(c) An exponential decrease should be drawn.

Chapter 1

1. $2T \sin 10° = 5.0 \times 9.8$, hence $T = 141$ N.

2. Take moments about lower fixture point, hence $(500/\tan 40°)N = 10.0 \times 9.8 \times 500$ and so $N = 82$ N.

3. Take moments about A, hence $T \times 1.5 \cos \theta = 800 \times (2.0 - 0.01) + 1000 \times (2.5 - 0.01)$ and since $1.5/4.0 = \tan \theta$, then $T = 2.91$ kN. Horizontal force components: $T \cos \theta = N$ and so $N = 2.72$ kN. It has been assumed that all 'reaction' forces are normal ones.

4. Normal forces occur at the wheels. Hence taking moments about the pivot above the rear wheels gives $1.2L = 5000 \times 1.5 - 2.5N$. Equating all vertical forces gives $2N = 5000 + L$. Hence $L = 510$ N.

5. Taking moments about step base gives $160 \times 1.2 \times (0.3/2.0) + 50 \times (2.0 + 1.0)(0.3/2.0) = N_1 \times 0.6$, hence $N_1 = 8.5$ N. Since $N_1 + N_2 = 160 + 50$, then $N_2 = 124.5$ N.

6. $2T \sin 40° = 4.0 \times 9.8$ and hence $T = 61$ N.

7. $85g\bar{x} = 70g \times 1.1 + 15g \times 1.4$, hence $\bar{x} = 1.15$ m.

8. $21g\bar{x} = 15g \times 0.7 + 4 \times 1.5g \times \frac{1}{2} \times 0.7$ and so $\bar{x} = 0.6$ m above the floor and central since symmetrical. $\tan \theta = 0.5/0.6$ and hence $\theta = 40°$.

9. The centre of gravity has to be pushed 30 mm and so top has to be pushed $(260/120) \times 30 = 65$ mm.

Chapter 2

1. (a) See Fig. A.1.

(b) See Fig. A.2.

(c) Up to about 20 m s^{-1} there is an increase in acceleration with increasing velocity, above that the acceleration decreases.

2. $s = v_0t + \frac{1}{2}at^2 = 0 + \frac{1}{2} \times 1.5 \times 6.0^2 = 27$ m. $v = v_0 + at = 0 + 1.5 \times 60 = 9.0$ m s^{-1}.

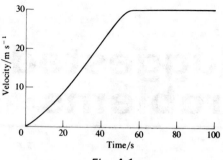

Fig. A.1

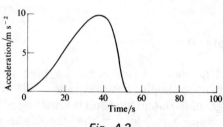

Fig. A.2

3. (a) $v = v_0 + at = 16 = 12 + 1.2t$, hence $t = 3.3$ s.

(b) $v^2 = v_0^2 + 2as = 16^2 = 12^2 + 2 \times 1.2s$, hence $s = 47$ m.

4. $v^2 = v_0^2 + 2as = 20^2 = 35^2 + 2 \times 500a$, hence a, $= -0.83$ m s^{-2}. $v = v_0 + at = 0 = 20 - 0.83t$, hence $t = 24$ s.

5. $s = v_0t + \frac{1}{2}at^2 = 2.0 = 0 + \frac{1}{2} \times 9.8t^2$, hence $t = 0.64$ s.

6. (a) $v^2 = v_0^2 + 2as = 0 = 12^2 - 2 \times 9.8s$, hence $s = 7.3$ m.

(b) $v = v_0 + at = 0 = 12 - 9.8t =$ time to greatest height $= 1.2$ s. Total time $= 2.4$ s.

7. Time = time of free fall with initial vertical velocity of zero. $s = \frac{1}{2}at^2 = 50 = \frac{1}{2} \times 9.8t^2$, hence $t = 10.2$ s. Horizontal motion is constant velocity motion of 2.0 m s^{-1}, hence $s = v_0t = 20$ m.

8. See text for derivation. (a) Deceleration to greatest height at B, then fall to C before rebounding back upwards again.

(b) Acceleration = gradient of graph. A, 17.5 m s^{-2} downwards; B, 10 m s^{-2} downwards; C, 3.3 m s^{-2} downwards. Air resistance, though the value of A greater than g is not easy to explain.

(c) Area under graph between A and B, about 5.6 m.

9. (a) $v^2 = 2as$, hence $v = 6.3$ m s^{-1}. (b) $v^2 = v_0^2 + 2as = 0 = v_0^2 - 2 \times 9.8 \times 1.6$, hence $v_0 = 5.6$ m s^{-1}. (c) $s = \frac{1}{2}at^2$, hence $t = 0.64$ s for fall. For rise, $v = v_0 + at = 0 = 5.6 - 9.8t$, hence $t = 0.57$ s. Time = 1.2 s.

10. For free fall $s = \frac{1}{2}at^2 = 0.70 = \frac{1}{2} \times 9.8t^2$ and so $t = 0.38$ s. Horizontal motion is constant velocity, $s = v_0 t = 0.15 = 0.38 \, v_0$ and so $v_0 = 0.39$ m s^{-1}.

11. You might guess that a bullet has a velocity of a few thousand metres per second. Thus in travelling 100 m it will be in the air, and falling, for about 0.05 s. In this time it falls a vertical distance of about 0.012 m, that is 12 mm. We have assumed that the bullet does not slow down over 100 m.

12. (a) You should find that R^3 is proportional to T^2.

(b) Bode's law works very well. Mercury has $n = -\infty$, Venus $n = 0$, Earth $n = 1$, Mars $n = 2$, the asteroids $n = 3$, Jupiter $n = 4$, and so on.

(c) 3.86 to 5.20 years.

13. Speed is a rate of covering distance and is not dependent on the total distance covered.

Chapter 3

1. (a) 392 N. (b) 424 N. (c) 392 N.
2. 510 N.

3. For the 3.0 kg mass, $3.0g - T = 3.0a$. For the 2.0 kg mass, $T = 2.0a$. Hence $a = 5.9$ m s^{-2}.

4. Momentum, $[MLT^{-1}]$; acceleration, $[LT^{-2}]$; force, $[MLT^{-2}]$. Possibly an experiment involving trolleys and ticker tape, or gliders on an air track with electrical timing. Conservation of charge and of energy. For derivation see text. See Fig. A.3.

5. $50 \times 4 = 250v$, hence $v = 0.8$ m s^{-1}.
6. $1400 \times 60 - 4200 \times 40 = 5600v$, hence $v = -15$ km h^{-1}.
7. $10 \times 300 = 510v$, hence $v = 5.9$ m s^{-1}.
8. $18 \times 1000 = 12 \times 1600 + 6v$, hence $v = -200$ m s^{-1}.
9. Force = rate of change of momentum = $4.0 \times 10^{-3} \times 400 = 1.6$ N.
10. $F - mg = ma$, hence $F = 1.95 \times 10^5$ N = rate of change of momentum = $2000 \, m$, hence $m = 97.5$ kg s^{-1}.

11. (a) Boat acquires an opposite momentum to that of the person so that the centre of mass remains in the same place. (b) Boat acquires an opposite momentum and so moves away from bank.

12. $F = \mu N = 0.50 \times 30 \times 9.8 = 147$ N. (a) No movement. (b) A small acceleration due to a resultant force of 3 N. (c) An acceleration due to a resultant force of 53 N.

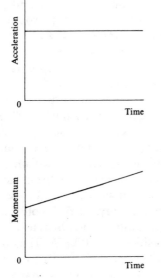

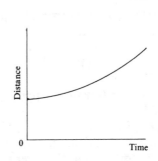

Fig. A.3

13. $\mu = \tan \theta = 0.58$.

14. (i) $1.6 \times 9.8 \sin 30° = 7.84$ N parallel to plane. At right angles $1.6 \times 9.8 \cos 30° = 13.6$ N. Limiting frictional force has not been reached and so since block is at rest frictional force is 7.84 N.

(ii) Impulse = change in momentum = $1.6 \times 0.3 = 0.48$ N s. Since $7.84 - F = ma$, then $F = 7.52$ N.

15. Resultant force on down cabin = $(2 \times 10^4 + 1.5 \times 10^4 + 4 \times 10^3) g \sin \theta - T = (2 \times 10^4 + 1.5 \times 10^4 + 4 \times 10^3) a$; resultant force on up cabin = $T - (2 \times 10^4 + 750) g \sin \theta = (2 \times 10^4 + 750) a$, where T is the tension in the cable and a the initial acceleration. Hence $a = 0.68$ m s^{-2}. This occurred for a time $t = v/a = 5/0.68 = 7.4$ s. The deceleration to stop occupied a time $t = v/a = 5/0.5 = 10.0$ s. The distance covered during the initial acceleration was $v^2/2a = 5^2/(2 \times 0.68) = 18.4$ m. The distance covered during deceleration = $v^2/2a = 5^2/(2 \times 0.5) = 25$ m. Hence distance at constant velocity = 196.6 m and hence time for this = $s/v = 196.6/5 = 39.3$ s. Hence total journey time = 56.7 s. Number of journeys per hour = $3600/(56.7 + 120) = 20.4$. The maximum number of people in one journey = $1.5 \times 10^4/750 = 20$ and hence number of passengers = 19. Thus maximum number of passengers per hour = $20 \times 19 = 380$. For up journey the initial acceleration is reduced and so time of journey increased. Hence fewer passengers per hour. Safety precautions—automatic brake in case of cable break.

Chapter 4

1. See Fig. A.4.

2. (a) $h = \frac{1}{2}gt^2 = 29.4$ m. (b) $Fs = \frac{1}{2}mv^2 = mgh$ and so $F = 256$ N.

3. $mv = (M + m)V$; $\frac{1}{2}(M + m)V^2 = Fs$; $F = \mu N = \mu(M + m)g$, hence $s = 0.042$ m.

4. $\frac{1}{2}mv^2 = Fs$, hence $F = 2.1 \times 10^4$ N.

5. $mv = (M + m)V$ and $\frac{1}{2}(M + m)V^2 = (M + m)gh$, hence $v = 173$ m s^{-1}.

6. Power = $Fs/t = Fv = (mg \sin \theta + \mu mg \cos \theta)$, hence $v = 33$ m s^{-1}.

7. Power = $Fs/t = Fv = mgv \sin \theta = 96$ W.

8. Gain in momentum for coal per second = 120×2 kg m s^{-1}, i.e., force of 240 N. Power = $Fs/t = Fv = 240 \times 2.0 = 480$ W.

9. (a) See previous chapter. (b) Momentum conserved in all cases, kinetic energy only in first. During fall, gain in downward momentum of ball equals gain in upward momentum of earth, momentum being conserved. At point of impact of the ball and earth, the rate of change of momentum of the ball is opposite and equal in size to the rate of change of momentum of the earth. The upward momentum gained by the ball equals the downward momentum gained by the earth. At all times momentum is conserved and has a net zero value. During the fall the ball gains kinetic energy. On impact with the earth this is transformed into strain energy, the ball and earth becoming slightly deformed. This energy then is partly transferred to the ball as kinetic energy, the remainder showing as a rise in temperature of ball and earth. See Fig. A.5 (page 462).

10. (a) See previous chapter. (b) (i) Momentum of dart = momentum of dart plus board. (ii) Momentum of ball before collision = momentum of ball after collision plus momentum of table, i.e., momentum of table $MV = 2mv$. (iii) Horizontal component of ball's momentum before equals horizontal component of ball's momentum after collision plus horizontal component of earth's momentum; vertical component of ball's momentum before collision equals vertical component of ball's momentum after collision plus vertical component of earth's momentum. (c) See text and previous question. Because kinetic energy would not be conserved. (d) $mv = (M + m)V$ and $\frac{1}{2}(M + m)V^2 = (M + m)gh$, hence $v = 43$ m s^{-1}.

11. See previous chapter. (a) Kinetic energy of system constant and equal to initial kinetic energy of incident particle. The angle between the subsequent tracks must be 90°. See the discussion on cloud chamber tracks in this chapter. (b) Since $mv_0 = (2m)v$ then kinetic energy changes from $\frac{1}{2}mv_0^2$ to $\frac{1}{2}(2m)v^2 = \frac{1}{2} \times \frac{1}{2}mv^2$. There is a loss of kinetic energy from the system of half of the initial kinetic energy. For the neutrons, if E is initial energy, after 1 collision energy is $(1 - 0.14)E$, after two collisions $(1 - 0.14)^2E$, after n collisions $(1 - 0.14)^nE$. Thus $6.0 \times 10^{-21} = (1 - 0.14)^n \times 6.0 \times 10^{-13}$ and so $n = 122$.

12. See the previous chapter. $\frac{1}{2}m_P v_P^2 + \frac{1}{2}m_Q v_Q^2 = 24$, also $m_P v_P + m_Q v_Q = 0$ and so $v_P = 2$ m s^{-1} and

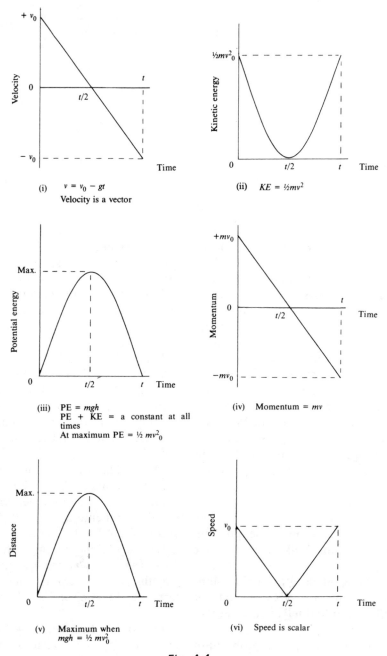

(i) $v = v_0 - gt$
Velocity is a vector

(ii) $KE = \frac{1}{2}mv^2$

(iii) $PE = mgh$
$PE + KE = $ a constant at all times
At maximum $PE = \frac{1}{2} mv_0^2$

(iv) Momentum $= mv$

(v) Maximum when $mgh = \frac{1}{2} mv_0^2$

(vi) Speed is scalar

Fig. A.4

$v_Q = -6$ m s^{-1}. For the helicopter, mass of air moved in time t is ρAvt and so momentum given to air is ρAv^2t. Hence force $= \rho Av^2$ and $v = 14.8$ m s^{-1}. Power $= Fs/t = Fv = \rho Av^3 = 117$ kW.

13. (a) Change in momentum of n balls is $n(2mv) = 3600$ kg m s^{-1}. Force on balls $=$ rate of change of momentum $= 3600/12 = 300$ N. The force on wall is therefore 300 N (Newton's third law). The graph will show a number of 'blips', each corresponding to one collision. The average

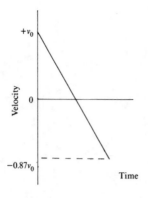

Fig. A.5

force can be obtained by drawing a line parallel to the time axis such that the area under the line equals the area above the line under the force-time blips. This is the basis of simple kinetic theory, see later chapter. (b) $\frac{1}{2}mv^2 = 5000$ J, $mv = 10\,000$ kg m s^{-1}. Car kinetic energy to strain energy when car is deformed to perhaps kinetic energy of some pieces and a rise in internal energy. Force = rate of change of momentum = $10\,000/0.2 = 50\,000$ N. Average because some parts stopped before others. Doubling the impact time, for instance, halves the force. The lower the force the less the effect on the passenger. This assumes the passenger is brought to rest in the same time as the car. A safety belt can increase this time. A front of car that crumples can increase the time.

14. (a) Whenever a quantity is counted it gives the same number. This is only one possible answer, you can no doubt think of many other forms.

(b) Prohibition: keep off the grass. Permission: keep left. A law of permission tells you what you can do, a law of prohibition tells you what you cannot do.

(c) The laws can be read in both prohibition and permission forms. A force enables you to have an acceleration: no acceleration is permitted without a force.

Chapter 5

1. 8.0 N m.
2. $I = \frac{1}{2}(\rho \times \pi r^2 t)r^2 = 0.013$ kg m^2.

3. 2.0 kg m^2.
4. $I = 300 \times 0.50^2$ kg m^2 and $\alpha = 2\pi f/t = 2\pi \times 3.0/50$ rad s^{-2}, hence $T = I\alpha = 28.3$ N m.
5. The hollow sphere must have more mass at about the radial distance than the solid cylinder, hence it has the greater moment of inertia.
6. 1.88 kJ.
7. $T = P/\omega = 3.2$ N m.
8. $P = T\omega = 7.54 \times 10^6$ W.
9. (a) $\frac{1}{2}I\omega^2 = 1000$ J. (b) In the absence of friction no power would be needed to keep it rotating with a constant angular velocity, thus 50 W is used to make up frictional losses. $T = P/\omega = 0.50$ N m.
10. Angular momentum is conserved, hence $I_0\omega_0 = I_1\omega_1$ and so $I_1/I_0 = 2/6$.
11. Initial angular momentum = $2\pi \times 33I$, new angular momentum = $2\pi \times 30(I + 0.020 \times 0.150^2)$ and so $I = 4.5 \times 10^{-3}$ kg m^2.
12. Angular momentum of running children = $I\omega = (mr^2) \times (v/r) = 60 \times 1.6 \times 2.5$ kg m^2 s^{-1}. Angular momentum is conserved and so for turntable $I\omega = 60 \times 1.6 \times 2.5$ and $\omega = 1.3$ rad s^{-1}.
13. (a) $L = I\omega$, where $\omega = 2\pi/T$ with $T = 24$ h. Hence $L = 5.8 \times 10^{33}$ kg m^2 s^{-1}. (b) KE = $\frac{1}{2}I\omega^2 = 2.1 \times 10^{29}$ J. Decreases both. For angular momentum to be conserved the moon must be affected.
14. PE to translational kinetic energy of mass and rotational kinetic energy of flywheel. $mgh = \frac{1}{2}mv^2 + \frac{1}{2}I\omega^2$, hence $\omega = 15.4$ rad s^{-1}.
15. (a) See text. (b) (i) $\frac{1}{2}I(2\pi f)^2 = 2.0 \times 10^7$ J. (ii) Time between stations = $d/(36 \times 10^3/3600) = d/10$ s,

hence $P = 20 \times 10^3 = 2.0 \times 10^7/(d/10)$ and so $d = 10^4$ m.

16. (a) See text. $[LT^{-2}] = [LT^{-1}]^2[L]^{-1}$. (b) (i) Continues with constant velocity. (ii) See Chapter 3 for discussion of weightlessness. Everything in satellite has same acceleration. (c) $\tan \theta = v^2/rg$ and hence $\theta = 79°$. The angle to horizontal $= 11°$.

Chapter 6

1. See Fig. A.6.

2. a is the amplitude. See Fig. A.7. Maximum kinetic energy $= \frac{1}{2}m\omega^2a^2 = 0.20$ J.

3. Still T, since the restoring force depends on the force constant of the spring and not the acceleration due to gravity.

4. (a) At maximum displacement. (b) At the equilibrium position or zero displacement. (c) At maximum displacement. (d) At the equilibrium position or zero displacement. (e) At maximum displacement.

5. (a) Restoring force is proportional to the displacement and always directed towards the

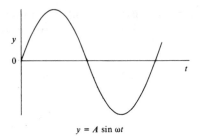

$y = A \sin \omega t$

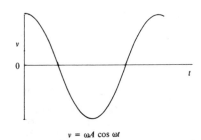

$v = \omega A \cos \omega t$

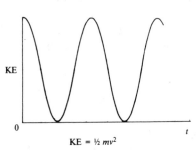

$KE = \frac{1}{2} mv^2$

Fig. A.7

zero displacement position, hence acceleration $a \propto -x$.

(b) This equation has been derived from $T = 2\pi\sqrt{(m/k)}$ by substituting for m/k using $F = mg = kx_0$. A mass of 200 g means a force of about 2.0 N and hence $x_0 = 70$ mm. Thus $T = 0.53$ s and so $f = 1/T = 1.9$ Hz.

(c) PE $= \frac{1}{2}m\omega^2A^2 = \frac{1}{2}kA^2 = \frac{1}{2}mgx_0 = 0.069$ J.

6. When one column depressed by distance x the other rises by x. Thus excess pressure $= 2x\rho g$ and hence restoring force $= -2x\rho gA$. Acceleration $a = F/m = -2x\rho gA/LA\rho = -(2g/L)x$. The motion is simple harmonic since $a \propto -x$, hence $T = 2\pi\sqrt{(L/2g)}$.

7. (a) See text and Fig. A.7. (b) At equilibrium $F = kx_0$ and so $k = 0.2g/0.16$ N. Hence restoring force $= kx = (0.2g/0.16)0.08 = 0.98$ N. $T = 2\pi\sqrt{(m/k)} = 0.80$ s. KE $= \frac{1}{2}m\omega^2A^2 = 0.039$ J.

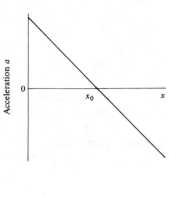

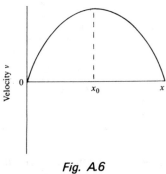

Fig. A.6

8. The motion is not simple harmonic motion because the restoring force is not proportional to the displacement.

Force causing the spring extension =

$$k\left(\frac{L}{\cos\theta} - L\right)$$

The restoring force is $F\sin\theta$ =

$$k\left(\frac{L}{\cos\theta} - L\right)\sin\theta.$$

9. When the trolley is displaced to one side by a distance x the extension of one spring is increased to $X + x$ and the extension of the other spring decreased to $X - x$. The resultant force on the trolley is thus $k(X + x) - k(X - x)$ or $2kx$. The restoring force is thus proportional to the displacement and the motion is simple harmonic.

$$f = \frac{1}{2\pi}\sqrt{\left(\frac{2k}{\text{mass}}\right)}$$

10. Assume Hooke's law applies. $F = mg = kx$ and so $T = 2\pi\sqrt{(m/k)} = 2\pi\sqrt{(x/g)}$ and $f = 1/T = 10$ Hz. See the text on resonance. Change in k or damping.

11. The natural frequency is proportional to $\sqrt{k}$, hence changing the springs will change the natural frequency of the oscillations produced by the sudden deflection of the springs produced by the bump.

12. See text. At top of the motion. Maximum amplitude occurs when $a = -g = -\omega^2 x$ and so maximum amplitude is 0.062 m.

13. (a) New period $= \sqrt{2} \times 0.5$ s.

(b) Similar to Fig. 6.16. Resonance occurs at 2 Hz.

(c) Every 2 s the forcing and natural oscillations will be in step and a large amplitude oscillation will be produced. Half way between these maximum oscillations the forced and natural oscillations will be out of step and minimum amplitude will occur. The amplitude of the oscillations will fluctuate with a period of 2 s. This phenomena is called beats. The beat frequency is equal to the difference between the natural and forcing frequencies, 0.5 Hz.

(d) The damping will change and the maximum amplitudes reached will be larger than those in (c). Otherwise the motion will be the same.

(e) When the frequency of the forcing vibration produced by the road is the same as the natural vibration frequency of the car springs, resonance will occur. The more comfortable car has a natural frequency far removed from the forcing frequencies that may arise. When a car goes round a sharp corner the springs are given a sudden deflection, oscillations will occur unless the motion is heavily damped.

Chapter 7

1. See text.

2. See Fig. 7.2.

3. See text.

4. See Fig. 7.18b. $f = c/2L, f = c/L$.

5. (a) See text. (b) See Fig. A.8. A hollow box has a wire attached to one end of its upper surface and passing over a pulley at the other end to a hanger on which masses can be placed. The length of the wire in which standing waves is set up is determined by the position of two bridges. The wire is plucked at the middle and, for a constant tension, the length adjusted until the sound of the vibrating wire has the same frequency as that of a tuning fork. Different forks can be used and different lengths obtained. The frequency is proportional to $1/L$ for a given wire and constant tension. The experiment can then be repeated with a constant length but the tension varied for different tuning forks. The frequency is

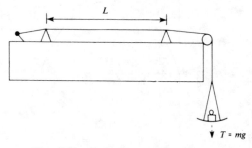

Fig. A.8 A sonometer experiment

proportional to the square root of the tension. (c) $\lambda = 20/100 = 0.20$ m. Hence the points are $\frac{1}{4}\lambda$ apart, i.e. $\frac{1}{4} \times 2\pi = \frac{1}{2}\pi$ rad phase difference.

6. See the text for differences. See Fig. A.9. The frequency applied to the rubber cord is varied and the standing wave patterns obtained at different frequencies. See Fig. A.10, $\frac{3}{4}\pi$ corresponds to $3/8\lambda$, the minimum path difference. For the first mode $\lambda = L$, the length of string. For next mode $3\lambda = L$, hence the frequency is $100 \times 3 = 300$ Hz.

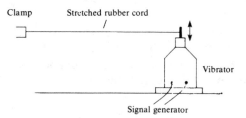

Fig. A.9 Melde's experiment

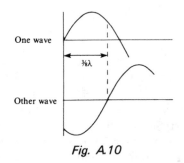

Fig. A.10

7. See the text.

8. (a) (i) $2A$, (ii) $2\pi/\omega$, (iii) $c = \lambda\omega/2\pi = \omega/k$. (b) This is essentially the Doppler effect with a moving observer and fixed source (see the next chapter). For the stationary boat there would be f waves in 1 s, f being the frequency of the water waves. Because the boat is moving in the same direction as the waves, then because in 1 s the boat moves a distance v the number of waves f_0 would be $f - v/\lambda = f - vf/c$. Hence period $= 1/f_0 = 1/f(1 - v/c) = 2\pi/(\omega - kv)$.

Chapter 8

1. Nearest is $340 \times 2 \times 10^{-3} = 0.68$ m, furthest is $340 \times 7 \times 10^{-2} = 23.8$ m.

2. $v = \sqrt{(E/\rho)} = 5.1 \times 10^3$ m s^{-1}.

3. $v = x\sqrt{(k/m)}$—see text, with $m = 63.6 \times 10^{-3}/6.0 \times 10^{23}$ kg. Hence $k = 24$ N m^{-1}.

4. $E = k/x$ and $v = \sqrt{E/\rho} = \sqrt{(k/\rho x)}$. Hence $k = 32$ N m^{-1}.

5. (a) When an object is set into oscillation by some external, periodic, driving force. (b) The vibration with which an object would freely oscillate in the absence of any externally imposed vibration. (c) When large-amplitude oscillations build up as a result of the external, periodic, driving force having a frequency equal to the free vibration frequency. See Fig. 6.15—the driver pendulum supplies a periodic, driving force to the other pendulum. This other pendulum has a free vibration frequency and when the two frequencies are the same, i.e., resonance, large-amplitude oscillations are produced.

See the text on standing waves in tubes and for the factors affecting the speed of sound.

6. See text. (a) The bench is caused to vibrate and because a greater area is involved in the movement the sound is louder. (b) Standing waves in the tube. Other examples of standing waves could be vibrating strings (as in previous chapter) or water waves being incident on a plane reflector and superposition of the incident and reflected waves occurring. See the resonance tube experiment for the wavelength measurement and the text for the factors affecting the speed and hence the wavelength.

7. $0.30 + \delta = \frac{1}{4}\lambda$ and $0.96 + \delta = \frac{3}{4}\lambda$, hence $\lambda = 1.32$ m and $v = f\lambda = 330$ m s^{-1}. $\delta = 0.03$ m.

8. (a) See text. (b) See previous chapter. (c) See Fig. 8.9. $L = \frac{1}{4}\lambda, \frac{3}{4}\lambda, \frac{5}{4}\lambda, \frac{7}{4}\lambda$, etc. Hence the next member is 0.34 m. $v/\lambda = f$, hence 137.5 Hz, 412.5 Hz, 687.5 Hz, 970.6 Hz.

9. (a) (i) See text. (ii) Characteristic gas constant $R = R_0/M_r$, where R_0 is the universal gas constant. Hence $v = \sqrt{(\gamma R_0 T/M_r)}$ and so $v \propto \sqrt{(\gamma/M_r)}$. (iii) On a foggy day there is more water vapour in the air and this affects both the values of γ and M_r, decreasing γ slightly and M_r by a greater amount. The net effect is an increase in v. (iv) See Fig. 8.4a for the night and Fig. 8.4b for the day. (b) $L = \frac{3}{2}\lambda$ and hence $\lambda = 1.2$ m. For air $f = v/\lambda = 283$ Hz. $v = \sqrt{(\gamma R_0 T/M_r)}$ and so $\sqrt{(RT)} = 340\sqrt{(28.8/1.41)}$. Hence for helium $v = 340\sqrt{(1.67 \times 28.8/1.41 \times 4)}$

and so $f = 827$ Hz.

10. (a) $f_0 = f_s(1 + v_0/c) = 1059$ Hz. (b) $f_0 = f_s(1 - v_0/c) = 941$ Hz.

11. (a) 1200 Hz. (b) $f_0 = cf_s/(c - v_s) = 1338$ Hz.

12. When source is a distance x nearer to the surface, the image moves a distance x, hence the distance between source and image is reduced by $2x$. Hence the velocity of the image is twice that of the surface. For the image $f_0 = cf_s/(c - v_s)$. But $f_s - f_0 = 15$, hence $f_s - cf_s/(c - v_s) = v_s f_s/(c - v_s) = 15$ and $v_s = 5.2$ m s^{-1}. Hence speed of surface = 2.6 m s^{-1}.

Chapter 9

1. $d = \lambda D/x = 7.3 \times 10^{-4}$ m.

2. Central white fringe with coloured edges, see text.

3. (a) λ decreases so x decreases. (b) x is doubled. (c) Only a single slit diffraction pattern is observed. (d) d decreased so x increases.

4. They are not coherent, see text, and even if they were the separation would be too great for observable fringes.

5. See text.

6. See text.

7. Because a phase change of $\frac{1}{2}\lambda$ occurs at one reflection. Lifting the lens increases the film thickness at all points and extra fringes appear. The centre will change from dark to light to dark, and so on, as the distance is gradually increased.

8. See text.

9. (a) See text. (b) See Fig. 9.1, with D about 1 m, d about 0.5 mm. Instead of the screen a vernier microscope would be used for the x measurement. It would also be used to measure d, a rule being suitable for D. The light passing through the slits has to diffract otherwise no superposition would occur. (i) See Fig. 9.9. The fringes produced by the grating will be sharper. (ii) The fringes produced by the grating will be much further apart. With red light, i.e., longer wavelength, the fringes are further apart.

10. (a) (b) (c) See text. (d) $2d \sin \theta = 2\lambda_r = 3\lambda_v$. This is valid since λ_r is about 6×10^{-7} m and λ_v about 4×10^{-7} m.

11. The white area is due to the maxima for both yellow and blue coinciding. $600 \times 10^{-9} m = 450 \times 10^{-9} (m + 1)$, hence $m = 3$ and so $\theta = m\lambda/2s = 1.5 \times 10^{-4}$ rad.

12. (a) See text, dispersion occurring because the angle at which reinforcement occurs depends on the wavelength, other than for $m = 0$.

(b) In water the wavelength is less than in air and thus the angle of the diffracted beam changes. (i) $d \sin \theta = m\lambda$, hence $\lambda_a = 6.25 \times 10^{-7}$ m. (ii) $n = \lambda_a/\lambda_w$, hence $\lambda_w = 4.70 \times 10^{-7}$ m. (iii) 22.1°. (iv) 48.8°.

13. (a) See text. (b) The telescope and collimator are set at 90°. The grating is then rotated until the reflected image of the slit appears on the cross-wires. The light is then at 45° to the grating and a further 45° rotation brings the light to normal incidence. (c) $2d \sin \frac{1}{2}(\beta - \alpha) = 2\lambda$, hence $d = 8.332 \times 10^{-7}$ m. Line 1 – 486 nm, line 2 – 608 nm, line 3 – 656 nm. Hydrogen and carbon dioxide. For hydrogen, $3 \times 410 < 2 \times 656$.

14. (a) (b) See text. (c) (i) Dark lines are where destructive interference occurs for a particular wavelength. For transmitted light no phase change occurs and so $2nt = (p + \frac{1}{2})\lambda$. (ii) $558(p + \frac{1}{2}) = 499(p + 1\frac{1}{2}) = 452(p + 2\frac{1}{2})$, thus $p = 8$. For $p = 7$ and 6, $\lambda = 632$ nm and 730 nm.

15. (a) (i) See text. (ii) There can be a constant phase difference between radio transmitters, but not between two lamps. (iii) See Fig. 9.6. (b) See the answer to question 13(b). (c) (i) See Fig. 9.14b. (ii) $2d \sin \theta = m\lambda$, hence $d = 8.4 \times 10^{-5}$ m.

16. A parallel-sided thin film is produced and interference occurs when the waves reflected from the upper surface superpose with those reflected from the lower surface. Different colours are produced because the path difference depends on the angle at which the film is viewed. As the oil spreads out the thickness decreases and so the colours at any particular position change. When the thickness is small only one or two colours may reinforce along a particular viewing direction in which others cancel. This gives a more brilliant colour than when many values of wavelength give reinforcement at greater thicknesses.

Oil film thickness = $0.20/1.0 \times 10^4 = 2.0 \times 10^{-5}$ cm. Because the film appears black there must be destructive interference. $2nt + \frac{1}{2}\lambda = (m + \frac{1}{2})\lambda$, hence if $m = 1$, then $n = 1.4$. This is a more reasonable value for n than would be given with higher m orders.

Could be (i) Young's double slit experiment, (ii) two different, but close, frequencies supplied to a loudspeaker, (iii) a standing wave on a string or perhaps a sound wave in a resonance tube.

17. (a) Intensity varies as $1/(SA)^2$, i.e., an inverse square law. At $SA = 3d$, one-ninth. Rotation shows the wave is plane polarized. (b) Standing waves. $6 \times \frac{1}{2}\lambda = 8.7$ and so $\lambda = 2.9$ cm. $f = c\lambda = 1.0 \times 10^{10}$ Hz. (c) Of one frequency, one colour. Maxima every $1\frac{1}{2}$ cm with alternate maxima double intensity.

18. See the text on Young's double slit experiment. The third slit is to isolate just a narrow segment of the source so that both the double slits receive essentially the same coherent light. Superposition is occurring between waves from the source S and its image in the reflector. The pattern is thus essentially half of that given by the double slit type of experiment. The bigger the wavelength the further apart the maxima, hence for the movement D the wavelength has been increased, the frequency decreased.

Image is 160 km above S, hence receiver 200 km from image. Path difference $= 200 - 120 = 80$ km. Ignoring any possible phase changes, $80 \times 10^3/200 = m$ and $80 \times 10^3/180 = m + p$. Hence number of maxima $p = 44$.

19. (a) See text. Radio waves transmitted from an aerial source are plane polarized. Light from a source, ordinary light, is generally not polarized. Ordinary light contains electric field vectors in all possible directions, plane polarized light contains only one.

(b) See Fig. 9.20. It can be shown by passing the light through a sheet of 'Polaroid', at one particular angle of the 'Polaroid', that no light will be transmitted. Sunglasses can be made of polarizing materials to reduce the glare of light polarized by reflection from shiny surfaces such as the sea. (c) See the text.

20. (a) They are in phase. (b) A maximum. The path difference is a whole number of wavelengths. (c) More than.

21. (a) The electric vector is vertical, the magnetic vector horizontal. (b) The pulse would have the vectors appropriate to $\frac{1}{3}\lambda$ further on. (c) (i) Along the direction of the electric vector. (ii) With its plane in the plane of the electric vectors. (iii) At right angles to the plane of the electric vectors and $\lambda/4$ behind the aerial. There is a phase change of $\lambda/2$ at the reflector. (d) The electric vector is only in one plane. Rotation of the receiving aerial can be used to determine whether the wave is plane polarized.

Chapter 10

1. When $\sin i$ is greater than n_1/n_2 and light moves from medium 2 towards the 2–1 interface.

2. Plot $\sin i_1$ against $\sin i_2$, the slope being n.

3. $1/f = 1/u + 1/v$, hence for $u = 1.00$ m, $v = 136$ mm. From 136 mm to 120 mm.

4. As far as the converging lens is concerned the object is still 40 cm from it when the diverging lens is present, hence the image distance for the diverging lens is -20 cm and so as $1/f = -1/20 + 1/30$ then $f = -60$ cm.

5. The telescope is not in normal adjustment (see Fig. A.11). For the eyepiece $1/2.0 = 1/24 + 1/u$ and so $u = 2.18$ cm. $I_2/I_1 = v/u = 24/2.18$ and as I_2

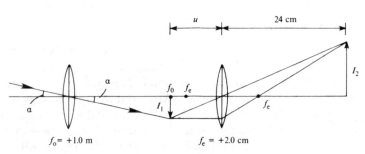

$f_o = +1.0$ m $f_e = +2.0$ cm

Fig. A.11

= 10 cm then I_1 = 0.91 cm. Angle subtended α = I_2/f_0 = 9.1 × 10^{-3} rad.

6. The telescope is in normal adjustment since separation of lenses = $f_0 + f_e$. Since $1/f_e = 1/v + 1/u$, where $u = f_0 + f_e$, then v = 0.0204 m. The advantage is that the maximum amount of light enters the eye.

7. (a) See Fig. A.12. (b) See text. (i) Because the light path is reversible the two values of i_1 for a particular deviation represent the incident and emergent angles. Thus at D = 39° we have i_i = 39° and 60.5°, hence A = 60.5°. (ii) At D_{min}, i_i = 49° and D = 37.2°. Thus i_2 = 48.7°, effectively the same as i_1 bearing in mind the limited accuracy with which the graph can be read. At all other incident angles D is greater. For D = 42°, i_1 = 33° or 68°. The light path is reversible. For maximum deviation the light must either enter face PQ at grazing incidence or leave PR at grazing incidence. Thus $D = (i_i + 90°) − 60.5° = 58°$ and so i_1 = 28.50. (c) They produce dispersion; also not all angles of deviation are possible. Also see Fig. 10.12.

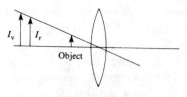

Fig. A.13

light is changed by $(5.6/16)^2 = 1/2^3$ and hence speed becomes 1/15 s. An increase in the depth of field which is effectively in focus.

9. See text and Fig. 10.29. See 'Resolving power' in previous chapter. The diameter of the lens or the wavelength used could be changed.

10. (a) See text and Fig. 10.29. (b) See 'Resolving power' in previous chapter. (iii) Roughly doubles the minimum angle at which resolution can occur. (c) 2 × 60/2 = 60.

11. (a) See text. (b) For image at infinity α = h/d and β = h/f, hence $M = d/f$. See text for $M = (1 + d/f)$. (c) This is not normal adjustment. For eyepiece $1/50 = 1/u − 1/250$, hence u = 42 mm. For objective $1/20 = 1/u + 1/(220 − 42)$, hence u = 23 mm. α = $h_1/(220 − 42)$ and β = $h_1/42$, where h_1 is height of intermediate image (see Fig. A.14). Hence $M = (220 − 42)/42 = 4.2$. (d) Fill out the rays in Fig. A.14.

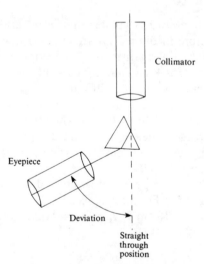

Fig. A.12

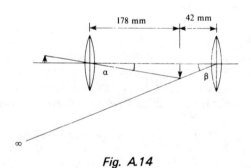

Fig. A.14

8. (a) (b) See text. (c) This is because the lens enables the object to be brought to a nearer position to the eye than the least distance of distinct vision. All the images subtend the same angle at the eye and so an image free of chromatic aberration is seen (Fig. A.13). (d) The amount of

12. (a) See Fig. A.15. The rays are at right angles to the wavefronts. (b) See Fig. A.16. AE and CB are parallel, therefore angle EAB = angle ABC. But triangle ABC is isosceles, hence angle ABC = angle BAC = r. Hence angle EAC = $2r = i$. Thus for small angles $n = i/r = 2$. See Fig. A.17. By considering the angles, AB must be a line cutting two parallel lines. (c) See text.

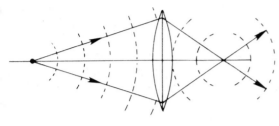

Fig. A.15

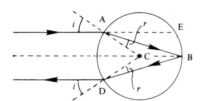

Fig. A.16

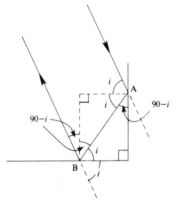

Fig. A.17

Chapter 11

1. (a) See text. (b) $I = P/V = 625 \times 10^{-3}/2.5 = 0.25$ A. $2E = V + 2rI$ and so $r = 1.0$ Ω. Energy dissipated in each cell $= I^2r = 0.0625$ W.

2. $50 \times 10^{-3} = 4.0 \times 10^{-3}(1 + 25/R_s)$, hence $R_s = 2.2$ Ω.

3. p.d. across instrument with shunt $= 40 \times 10 \times 10^{-3} = 0.40$ V. Without shunt $1.0 = 10 \times 10^{-3}(40 + R_m)$, hence $R_m = 60$ Ω. Hence with shunt $I = 1.0$ A and so p.d. across $R_m = 60$ V and hence a full-scale deflection is produced with 60.40 V.

4. $1.50 = 15 \times 10^{-3}(1 + 5/R_s)$, hence $R_s = 0.051$

Ω. $R_\theta = R_0(1 + \alpha\theta) = 0.056$ Ω. Hence $I = 15 \times 10^{-3}(1 + 5/0.056) = 1.35$ A.

5. To make the resistance as low as possible increase area and decrease thickness. The higher the voltage the greater the current, and hence the easier it is to measure.

6. (a) See text. (b) (1) Resistance is inversely proportional to current, hence ratio lamp to wire is about $0.75/0.40 = 0.19$. (2) $0.03/0.25 = 0.12$. The resistance of the lamp increases as the current increases, that of the wire being independent of current. The resistance increases because the temperature of the filament is increasing. (c) Slope of graph gives the resistance, for wire about 16 Ω. Hence ρ is about 1.3×10^{-6} Ω m. Ratio is thus about $1.3 \times 10^{-6}/1.8 \times 10^{-8} = 72$. Power dissipated $= I^2R$, hence the larger the resistance the more power is dissipated. The resistance per unit length of fire element is much greater than the resistance per unit length of connecting cable.

7. (a) See text. (b) You could use the metre bridge version of a Wheatstone bridge, with a coil of fine copper wire. (c) At $1750°C$ $R = V^2/P = 4.0$ Ω. Since $R_{1750} = R_0(1 + 1750\alpha)$ and $R_{20} = R_0(1 + 20\alpha)$ then $R_{20} = 0.389$ Ω. (d) For the lamps in parallel the p.d. across each is the same and thus the current at a particular p.d. is the sum of the currents for the two lamps.

8. (a) (i) (ii) See text. (iii) (a) No, B same potential as C since no current through Y, (b) No, B same potential as A, (c) No, A and B same potential, (d) Possible, (e) No, A and C same potential, (f) Possible.

(b) (iv) From Fig. 11.26, (f) would have no current through Y and hence B and C would be same potential, therefore it must be (d). (v) From Fig. 11.25 current through X = current through Y, hence $X/Y = 0.33/0.66$ and $Y = 0.5X$. p.d. between A and C = p.d. across 15 Ω so combined resistance is 15 Ω. Thus $1/15 = 1/Z + 1/(X + Y) = 1/Z + 1/1.5Y$. From Fig. 11.26 current through Z = current through Y, hence $Z/Y = 0.42/0.28 = 1.5$. Thus $1/15 = 1/1.5Y + 1/1.5Y$ and $Y = 20$ Ω. Hence $X = 10$ Ω and $Z = 30$ Ω.

9. (a) (i) R_3 and R_4. (ii) R_1 to vary p.d. across wire, R_2 to vary sensitivity of galvanometer, R_5 to vary current through R_3 and R_4 and hence potential differences being measured. (iii) The potentiometer should be changed from connections E

469

and F to G. (iv) One of the cells was connected the reverse way round to that indicated in figure. The p.d. between E and F was greater than that between B and D. (v) Not necessary since the resistances are being compared. (b) The upper half of figure with E positive and F negative. Figure A.18 circuit between E and F.

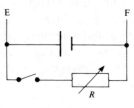

Fig. A.18

Balance lengths L are recorded for different values of R, including $R =$ infinity when the switch is open. The result is a measure of the potential difference between the terminals of the cell when different currents are taken from it. This p.d. is $(\varepsilon - Ir)$. Thus $(\varepsilon - Ir)/\varepsilon = L/L_0$, where L_0 is the balance length with the switch open. But $\varepsilon = I/(R + r)$, hence $R/(R + r) = L/L_0$, or $1/L = (r/L_0)(1/R) + 1/L_0$. A graph of $1/L$ against $1/R$ gives a straight line with a slope of (r/L_0).

10. (a) See text. Potential difference—pressure difference across tap, charge—volume or mass of water, current—rate of flow of water, resistance—the restriction offered by the pipe through which the water flows. Semiconductors, electrolytes, diodes, gases, see Fig. 11.1. (b) With circuit 1, the ammeter is measuring the sum of the currents through both the resistor and the voltmeter. With circuit 2, the voltmeter is measuring the p.d. across both the ammeter and resistor, A Wheatstone bridge or potentiometer could be used. (c) Current through ABC = $6/(6 + 12)$ A and so p.d. between A and B = $6 \times 6/(6 + 12) = 2$ V. Current through ADC = $6/(12 + 6)$ A and so p.d. between A and D = $12 \times 6/(12 + 6) = 4$ V. Hence the p.d. btween B and D must be $4 - 2 = 2$ V. If the 12 Ω is replaced by R, then p.d. between A and D = $R \times 6/(R + 6)$. This must equal the p.d. between A and B of 2 V, hence $R = 3\ \Omega$. To make the 12 Ω into 3 Ω, a 4 Ω resistor needs to be put in parallel with it.

11. (a) See text. (b) See text. (i) increases, (ii) no change, (iii) movement of donor electrons into conduction band, (iv) donor atoms fully ionized, decrease in drift velocity, (v) movement of electrons from valency to conduction bands. (c) (vi) $m = zIt = 7.9 \times 10^{-4}$ kg. (vii) $7.9 \times 10^{-4} \times 600/12 \times 10^{-3} = 39.5$ cm^3. (viii) $Av = 39.5$, hence $v = 0.40$ cm s^{-1}.

12. (a) (b) (i) (ii) See text. (iii) $\rho = 2m/ne^2\tau = 7.12 \times 10^{-8}\ \Omega$ m. (iv) Increase in vibration of ions results in bigger scattering centres and so shorter time between collisions.

Chapter 12

1. $g = GM/R^2$, hence $g_s/g_e = R^2/(3R/2)^2$ and so $g_s = 4.4$ N kg^{-1}. Hence $F = mg_s = 880$ N.

2. $mg = mv^2/R$, $= gR$ and $v = 7852$ m s^{-1}. $T = 2\pi R/v = 5249$ s.

3. (a) See text. (b) $T = 2\pi r/v$, but $mv^2/r = GMm/r^2$, hence $T^2 = 4\pi^2 R^3/GM$.

4. $g_e = GM/R^2, g_p = GM/(R - \Delta R)^2$, hence $\Delta g = GM[1/(R - \Delta R)^2 - 1/R^2] \approx 2GM\Delta R/R^2 = 0.0643$ m s^{-2}. At the poles an object has no rotation about the earth's axis, at the equator it has and so there is a centripetal acceleration at the equator.

5. (a) See text. (b) (i) $(150 \times 10^9)^3/1^2 \approx (778 \times 10^9)^3/11.8^3$. (ii) $mv^2/R = GMm/R^2$ and since $v = 2\pi R/T$, then $M = 4\pi^2 R^3/(GT)^2 = 2.01 \times 10^{30}$ kg.

6. (a) See text. (b) Potential $V = -GM/R$, hence PE $= Vm = -GMm/(r + h)$. But $g_0 = GM/r$, hence PE $= -mrg_0/(r + h)$. KE $= \frac{1}{2}mv^2$. But $mv^2/(r + h) = GMm/(r + h)^2 = mrg_0/(r + h)^2$, and so KE $= \frac{1}{2}mrg_0/(r + h)$. Total energy $=$ PE $+$ KE $= -\frac{1}{2}mrg_0/(r + h)$. Change in energy $= -\frac{1}{2}mrg_0 [1/(r + 300 \times 10^3) - 1/(r + 299 \times 10^3)] = -65$ J. $Fs = 65$, hence $F = 0.065$ N.

7. See text, $g = dV/dR$. See previous question, change in energy $= 1.1 \times 10^3$ J. At the altitude the speed is adjusted to give the right v value. If the procedure fails the satellite will move to a different orbit.

8. See text. $mg = GMm/r^2$, hence $gr^2 =$ constant. $GM_e/x^2 = GM_m/(D - x)^2$ and $GM_e = g_e r_e^2$, also $GM_m = g_m r_m^2$. Hence $x = 395\,000$ km. See Fig. A.19. (b) See Fig. A.19, a potential hill has to be climbed.

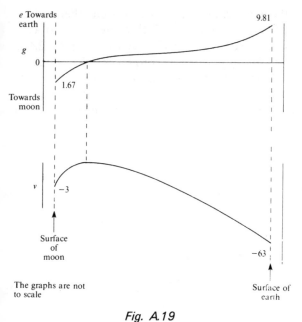

The graphs are not to scale

Fig. A.19

9. (a) See text. (b) $mv^2/R^2 = GMm/R^2$, also $v = 2\pi R/T$ and $M = \frac{4}{3}\pi r^3\rho$. Hence $R^3 = Gr^3\rho T^2/3\pi$ and $R = 2.03 \times 10^7$ m. (c) $\omega = v/r$ and so $m\omega^2 R = GMm/R^2$ and $\omega^2 \propto 1/R^3$. Thus $\omega_1/\omega_2 = 19.9$.

10. (a) See text. (b) (i) $g = GM/r^2$. (ii) $T^2 = 4\pi^2(r + h)^3/GM$. (iv) $v^2 = 2GM/r$. (c) (i) $M = \frac{4}{3}\pi r^3\rho$ and so $\rho = 2.55 \times 10^{17}$ kg m^{-3}. (ii) $g = GM/r^2 = 1.34 \times 10^{12}$ N kg^{-1}. (iii) $F = Ah\rho g$, thus $3.6 \times 10^6 = F/A = h\rho g$ and $h = 9.95 \times 10^{-10}$ m. (iv) The atoms are brought so close together that all electrons and protons are expelled and the star consists entirely of just neutrons.

Chapter 13

1. Because at all other positions there would be a resultant force from the summation of the forces due to the two charges. Beyond Q_2 towards B, since force $\propto 1/d^2$. E is zero at point and this does not depend on charge at point.

2. $1/r^2$. See Fig. 13.9 and text.

3. Summing E due to each charge gives 5.7×10^7 V m^{-1}.

4. $V = -q/4\pi\varepsilon_0 R$ and $E = q/4\pi\varepsilon_0 R^2$. Hence $E = -V/R$ and $V = 1.8 \times 10^5$ V.

5. (a) 1.0×10^{-7} C. (b) 1000 V. (c) Initially $\frac{1}{2}CV^2 = 2.0 \times 10^{-5}$ J, finally 5.0×10^{-5} J. Work done $= 3.0 \times 10^{-5}$ J.

6. Stick foil to glass and with foil sides facing separate by some thin, small pieces of insulator. Separation a minimum, area facing a maximum. If $d = 0.2$ mm, $C = \varepsilon_0 A/d = 4.5 \times 10^{-8}$ F. By a factor of 4. See text.

7. (a) The earthed plate is at zero potential and so bringing it close means that the potential on the plate must decrease to maintain the same potential gradient and hence the same electric field ($E = \sigma/\varepsilon_0$). Separating the plates decreases C and for constant Q increases energy stored ($\frac{1}{2}Q^2/C$). Work is done by an external agent in pulling the plates apart. (b) See text. (c) (i) $\frac{1}{2}CV^2$, 2.0×10^{-2} J, 4.0×10^{-2} J. (ii) It really is zero, since there are equal amounts of positive and negative charge, but probably what is expected is 8.0×10^{-4} C. (iii) 6.0 µF. (iv) 1.3×10^2 V. (v) 5.1×10^{-2} J. Because of heat produced by current when capacitors were connected together.

8. (a) (i) See text. (ii) See text, energy = $\frac{1}{2}QV$, but V = e.m.f. = energy/Q and so energy = VQ from source. (b) (i) A_1 and A_2 show same direction current, decreasing from 1.2 mA to zero. V in same time decreases from 24 V to zero. (ii) $A_1 = A_2 = 0$, $V = 0$. (iii) $A_1 = A_2 = 1.2$ mA in opposite direction decreasing to zero, V in same time decreases from 24 V to zero. $\frac{1}{2}CV^2 = 0.63$ J. $I = -(V_m/R)e^{-t/RC} = -0.76$ mA. Hence $P = I^2R = 0.012$ W.

9. (a) (b) See text. (iii) Net charge on B is zero but electric force causes charge to redistribute so that unlike charge is on side of B nearest A and like charge on opposite side. (iv) B is left with just opposite charge to that on A, thus force increases. (c) (i) $Q = CV = 4\pi\varepsilon_0 rV = 1.7 \times 10^{-6}$ C. (ii) $\frac{1}{2}QV = 0.21$ J. (iii) $E = Q/4\pi\varepsilon_0 r^2 = 4.3 \times 10^6$ V m^{-1}. Breakdown of the air.

10. (a) See text for measurement of C for a parallel plate capacitor. With material between plates and A and d measured, the relative permittivity can be determined if ε_0 is assumed. (b) $I = 35 \times 10^{-6} = 6.0/R$ and so $R = 1.71 \times 10^5$ Ω. Q = area under graph $= 3.3 \times 10^{-3}$ C. (i) $\frac{1}{2}QV = 9.9 \times 10^{-3}$ J. (ii) 5.5×10^{-4} F.

11. (a) (i) The capacitance would decrease. (ii) The p.d. would decrease. (b) The p.d. would rise to

471

the original value. (c) To obtain as large a capacitance as possible. (d) 0.01 s. (e) (i) The p.d. would drop. (ii) The p.d. would remain constant. (f) (i) The 50 Hz signal is moving the diaphragm inwards and outwards in a time comparable with that of the time constant. The 10 000 Hz signal gives times which are much smaller than the time constant. (ii) The time constant must be made bigger, perhaps by increasing the resistance in the circuit.

Chapter 14

1. $F = \mu_0 I_1 I_2 L/2\pi r$, hence $F/L = 3.0 \times 10^{-6}$ N m^{-1}.

2. See Fig. 14.10. (a) The force variation would be always attractive but fluctuating from zero to a maximum. (b) The force variation would be always repulsive but fluctuating from zero to a maximum.

3. See the text on the Hall effect.

4. Approaching and just entering, increasing e.m.f. Entering, e.m.f. drops to zero when in coil. On emerging, e.m.f. increases in opposite direction and then decreases as magnet moves away from coil.

5. See text on self-inductance.

6. Eddy currents, see homopolar generator.

7. (a) $F = ILB \sin \theta$, see text. (b) See text on damping of galvanometer.

8. See text. $\varepsilon - L\,dI/dt = IR$, hence $L = 4.0 \times 10^{-3}$ H.

9. See text. $V = BI/(nhq)$, hence $n = 2.14 \times 10^{22}$ m^{-3}. The sign of the majority charge carrier.

10. (a) (i) See Fig. 14.5. (ii) $3.0 \times 10^{-9}\theta = 4.2 \times 10^{-9}$, hence $\theta = 1.4$ rad. (iii) $\theta = 1.4 \times (2/100)$ rad and thus arc $= r\theta = 0.20$ mm. (iv) 50 µA, no effect. (b) (i) A shunt 0.10 Ω. (ii) With a half-wave or full-wave rectifier circuit (see Chapter 15). For half a cycle average $= (1/\pi)\int_0^\pi I \sin \theta \, d\theta = I_m/(\pi/2)$. This is the meter current for full-wave rectification; for half-wave it is half this.

11. (a) See text, Wb m^{-2} = V s m^{-2} = kg s^{-2} A^{-1}. (b) (i) $B = \mu_0 NI/L = 0.031$ T. (ii) $\phi = BA = 3.7 \times 10^{-5}$ Wb. (iii) $\varepsilon = \pi r^2 fB = AfB = 1.1$ mV. A potentiometer with a resistor in series with the potentiometer wire.

12. (a) Flux—number of lines of force passing through an area; flux density—number of lines per unit area. (b) (i) Within the solenoid away from the ends. (ii) $I = BL/\mu_0 N$. (iii) $\phi = BA = 2.42 \times 10^{-6}$ Wb. (c) (i) The a.c. produces a changing flux. (ii) Length of trace $= 2\varepsilon_m$. (iii) B varies from $+1.51$ mT to -1.51 mT in 10 s, hence flux change per turn of 8-turn coil in 10 s $= 3.88 \times 10^{-5}$ Wb. Thus $\varepsilon = -N\,d\phi/dt = -3.88$ mV. See Fig. A.20.

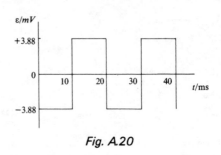

Fig. A.20

13. (a) Double h. (b) No change. (c) Some reduction in h. (d) Doubles the frequency of the probe coil output and doubles h.

Chapter 15

1. $V = \sqrt{(V_R^2 + V_L^2)}$, hence since $V_R = P/I = 110$ V then $V_L = 213$ V. $V_L = IX_L = I \times 2\pi fL$, hence $L = 0.34$ H.

2. R and C in series. At low frequency Z is predominantly X_C, at high frequencies R. Thus $R = V/I = 32/2.0 \times 10^{-3} = 16$ kΩ.

3. Test 1: $Z = 10/42 \times 10^{-3} = \sqrt{(R^2 + (2\pi 50L)^2)}$. Test 2: $Z = 20/62 \times 10^{-3} = \sqrt{(R^2 + (2\pi 100L)^2)}$. Hence $R = 202$ Ω and $L = 0.40$ H.

4. (a) $I = 1000/200 = 5.0$ A, hence $R = (250 - 200)/5.0 = 25$ Ω. (b) $Z = 250/5 = \sqrt{(R^2 + X_L^2)}$. Since $R = (200/5) + 5$, and $X_L = 2\pi fL$, $L = 0.069$ H. Less power dissipated in 5 Ω than 25 Ω.

5. Resonance. $Z = R = V/I = 10$, hence resistance of inductor $= 8.0$ Ω. $f = 1/2\pi\sqrt{LC} = 50$ Hz.

6. (a), (b), (c) See text. (d) $I = 120/50 = 2.4$ A, hence $Z = 180/2.4 = 75$ Ω. $Z = \sqrt{(R^2 + X_L^2)}$, hence since $X_L = 2\pi fL$, $R = 41$ Ω.

7. (a) See text. (b) (i) Zero. (ii) Virtually zero since X_L is very high. (iii) Resonance, $f = 1/2\pi\sqrt{LC} = 356$ Hz. (iv) $I = V/R = 0.10$ A. (v) $V_R =$

10 V, $V_L = V_C = IX_C = IX_L = 22$ V. They are not in phase.

8. (a) $X_L = 2\pi fL = 2830\ \Omega$. (b) 2830 Ω. (c) $X_C = 1/2\pi fC$, hence $C = 9.37 \times 10^{-8}$ F. (d) $I = V/R = 1.25$ A. See Fig. 15.9. $V_{PN} = \sqrt{(V_R^2 + V_L^2)} = \sqrt{(250^2 + (IX_L)^2)} = 3546$ V. Tan $\phi = X_L/R$, hence $\phi = 86°$. Increases the current and sharpness of resonance. Increases I by a factor of 10, V_L by a factor of 10, V_R unchanged. Hence new $V_{PN} = 35\,376$ V, an increase of 897 per cent.

9. See text.

10. (a) See Chapter 11. (b) See this chapter. (c) (i) Source, (ii) C. Maximum source p.d. = 12 × $\sqrt{2}$ = 17 V. The capacitor will be charged to 17 V. With S open and a.c. also in reverse bias, maximum p.d. = 2 × 17 = 34 V.

11. (a) (b) (c) See Chapter 11. (c) See this chapter.

12. (a) See text. (b) (i) Simple potential divider circuit. (ii) −4 V to +0.5 V, +1 V to +6 V. (iii) See Fig. A.21. (iv) +0.5 V to +1.0 V. A bias of 0.75 V.

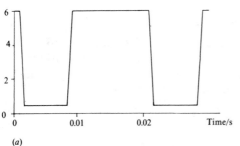

(a)

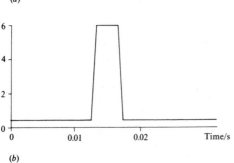

(b)

Fig. A.21

13. (a) No, it just selects a frequency. (b) Amplifier. (c) Change C or L. (d) Speaker. (e) No, the 10^3 Hz is the modulation signal.

14. (a) See Fig. 15.42. (b) See Fig. 15.43. (c) Either calibrate time base with a known frequency or use Lissajous figures for a comparison with a known frequency. (d) 30°, see Fig. 15.44.

Chapter 16

1. See text.

2. $2d \sin \theta = 1\lambda$, hence $d = 2.7 \times 10^{-10}$ m.

3. (a) See text. (b) $2d \sin \theta = 1\lambda$, hence $d = 2.3 \times 10^{-10}$ m.

4. A is shorter than B. Force against strain. Slope = EA.

5. (a) $EA(\Delta L/L) =$ a constant, hence ratio = 1.50. (b) 6.00 mm, 4.00 mm, since sum of extensions = 0.0100 m. (c) Force = $EA(\Delta L/L) = 780$ N.

6. (a) $F = EA(\Delta L/L)$, so $F_A/F_B = 8$. (b) $8F_Bx = F_B(D − x)$, hence $x = D/9$.

7. (a) (i) $E = (F/A)/(\Delta L/L) = 2.0 \times 10^{11}$ Pa. (ii) A pair of steel wires suspended from a rigid beam with the difference in length being measured when one is loaded. The control wire allows for temperature variations. A vernier arrangement will be needed for the measurement. (b) (i) Applies to other diameter and length copper wires. (ii) See Fig. 16.14. (iii) $F =$ stress $\times A = 50$ N. Work done per unit volume = area under graph, hence work = $2 \times 10^7 \times 2.0 \times 0.25 \times 10^{-6} = 10$ J. (c) (i) See Fig. A.22. (ii) It would get warm. Area marked in figure.

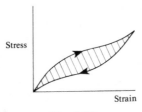

Fig. A.22

8. (a) (b) See previous answer (a) (ii). (c) Repulsion as interatomic separation decreases, attraction when increases. (d) ½stress × strain = 5.8×10^4 J m^{-3}.

9. (a) See answer 7(a) (ii). (b) 0 to 1.5 mm. $E = (F/A)/(\Delta L/L) = 1.7 \times 10^{11}$ Pa. (c) Area about 0.34 J. (d) See text, energy dissipated.

10. (a) (ii). (b) Small-amplitude oscillations where restoring force is reasonably proportional to displacement.

11. It would spread since γ is reduced.

12. (a) $\text{Pa} \times \text{m} = \text{N m}^{-2} \times \text{m} = \text{N m}^{-1}$. $\text{J m}^{-2} = \text{N m} \times \text{m}^{-2} = \text{N m}^{-1}$. (b) See text. (c) $2\gamma A = 4.5 \times 10^{-4}$ J (two surfaces). If all PE converted to KE, $\frac{1}{2}mv^2 = 2\gamma A$ and $v = 17.3$ m s^{-1}.

13. (a) See text. (b) AB $\sin \theta \times \rho g = 2\gamma/r$, hence $\gamma = 7.2 \times 10^{-2}$ N m^{-1}. Reflection and position of image.

14. $\frac{4}{3}\pi r^3 g(\rho - \sigma) = 0.057v$, hence $v = 0.12$ m s^{-1}. (a) Zero rising to a constant value. (b) Initially g and then decreasing to zero.

15. See text.

16. (a) (i) $p/\rho = 1.5 \times 10^5/1.75$, hence $c = 507$ m s^{-1}. (ii) Higher, since higher p/ρ value and so higher c. (iii) Ideal gas. (iv) Density $\propto 1/V$, hence a Boyle's law apparatus. (b) (i) Increase the most probable speed and the spread of molecular speeds. (ii) About 450 m s^{-1}. About $0.8c$.

17. (a) (b) See text. (c) $(A/V) > (A/V + B)$. Intermolecular attractive forces.

18. (i), (ii), (iii) See text. $p = \frac{1}{3}(2 \times 10^{-3}/6.0 \times 10^{23})5.3 \times 10^{15} \times (2.1 \times 10^3)^2 = 2.6 \times 10^{-5}$ Pa.

19. $9.5pV = 19 \times 278R$ and $10pV = 300mR$, hence $\Delta m = 19 - m = 0.33$ kg.

20. Air pressure $= 100 - 20 = 80$ kPa. New air pressure $= 150 - 20 = 130$ kPa. $80 \times 120 = 130V$, hence $V = 74$ cm^3.

21. $11.3A(1.01 \times 10^5 - 1 \times 10^3)/283 = LA(1.01 \times 10^5 - 3 \times 10^3)/298$, hence $L = 12.1$ cm.

22. See text.

23. (a) No attractive forces. (b) See text. Nitrogen is at all times a gas, butane is initially liquid and the SVP remains constant.

24. (a) (b) See text. (c) $k = 25$ nN/50 pm $= 500$ N m^{-1}. (d) See Chapter 6. $f = (1/2\pi)\sqrt{(k/m)} = 8.6 \times 10^{13}$ Hz.

25. (a) (i) Equilibrium 3.00×10^{-10} m, maximum 3.33×10^{-10} m. (ii) Estimating area, subtracting above axis area from below, gives about 1.2×10^{-21} J. (iii) Minimum value is at equilibrium separation 3.00×10^{-10} m. Hence PE from area estimate is about 1.3×10^{-21} J. (b) (i) (ii) See text. (iii) Greater than maximum attractive force so attractive force decreasing. (c) Slope F/r at 3.00×10^{-10} m. 83 N m^{-1}. 2.8×10^{11} Pa.

Chapter 17

1. (a) See text. (b) (i) A and B perhaps in a heated water bath with the temperature varying slowly with time so that A and B are in thermal equilibrium when the two are measured. (ii) About 25°C, since Q is about 15 per cent of $(Q_{100} - Q_0)$. (iii) 0°C and 100°C. (c) Independent of gas. See text.

2. See text. $\frac{1}{2}m_1c_1^2 = \frac{1}{2}m_2c_2^2$, hence $c_1/c_2 = 4.00$. Thermocouple—temperature at a point on a surface or a rapidly changing temperature.

3. (a) Net transfer of energy between the two is zero. (b) (i) Time for thermometer to reach thermal equilibrium. (ii) Measure with another thermometer the change in temperature when the thermometer is put into a liquid. (iii) $120 \times 10^{-3} \times 4200 \times (60 - \theta) = 30(\theta - 18)$, hence $\theta = 57.6$C. (iv) Small heat capacity. (v) See answer **1**.

4. (a) 2.26×10^6 J. (b) $p(V_2 - V_1) = 1.69 \times 10^5$ J. (c) 1.99×10^6 J.

5. (a) See text. (b) $180 \times 1.13 \times 1040 \times 5 = 1.06 \times 10^6$ J.

6. (a) $V/T =$ constant, hence $V_2 = 1250$ cm^3. (b) $pV =$ constant, hence $p_2 = 1.38 \times 10^5$ Pa. (c) Area ABC.

7. (a) (b) See text. Figure A.23. Cooling at constant volume. Work done. (c) $pV =$ constant, hence $p = 4.40 \times 10^5$ Pa, $\theta = 15$°C. $pV^\gamma =$ constant, hence $p = 7.66 \times 10^5$ Pa. $pV/T =$ constant, hence $T = 505$ K, $\theta = 232$°C.

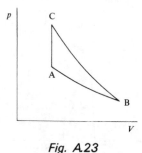

Fig. A.23

8. See text. $18 \times 10^{-3} \times 2.26 \times 10^6/6.02 \times 10^{23} = 6.76 \times 10^{-20}$ J.

9. Surface area, mass air flow, temperature of water and surroundings. Smaller mass and surface area. See Newton's law of cooling.

10. (i) $\lambda_a/\lambda_g = 1/50$. (ii) $x_g\lambda_a/x_a\lambda_g = 8.0 \times 10^{-3}$. Dirt and a stagnant layer of air against glass gives a low thermal conductivity layer.

11. $0.25 \times 10^3 = 2\pi \times 0.20 \times 1 \times 0.40 (60 - \theta)/2 \times 10^{-2}$, hence $\theta = 50.1°C$.

12. (a) Searle's bar, see text. Assumes perfect lagging. Higher temperature gradient occurs and so underestimate of λ. (b) (i) For Perspex $Q/t = 3 \times 0.2 \times 30/10 \times 10^{-3} = 1800$ W. For walls $Q/t = 3.5 \times 10^{-2} \times 30/20 \times 13.5 \times 10^{-3} = 709$ W. Total power $= 2.5$ kW. (ii) $(1800/2500) \times 100$ per cent $= 72$ per cent. Heat generated by passengers.

13. (a) See text. Difficulty in confining flow to just along the length of the sample. (b) Searle's bar, see text. (c) (i) Aluminium: $Q/t = 235 \times \frac{1}{4}\pi \times 0.030^2 \times 100/0.3 = 55.4$ W. Copper: $Q/t = 380 \times \frac{1}{4}\pi \times 0.040^2 \times 100/0.3 = 159.2$ W. (ii) Mean temperature 50°C, hence aluminium $mc\Delta\theta = 1.68 \times 10^4$ J, copper 4.18×10^4 J. (iii) Copper, since energy/flow rate is bigger.

14. (a) Could be a Searle's bar type of arrangement with very accurate measurement of the temperature gradient using possibly a thermocouple. (b) $d\theta/dt = (dQ/A\, dt)/(1/\lambda) = 6.3 \times 10^{-2}$ K m^{-1}. Possibly put an object in 'series' with the earth and measure the heat flow through that, e.g., stand a copper block on the surface, insulate its sides, and measure the heat flow using perhaps the method used with Searle's bar. The temperature could be measured with possibly thermocouples or resistance thermometers. (c) $dQ/dt = \lambda A\theta/x$. But $dQ = (L\rho A)dx$ and so $dx/dt = \lambda\theta/L\rho x = 1.50 \times 10^{-6}$ m s^{-1}. Since $x/dx = (\lambda\theta/L\rho)dt$, if we integrate this between $x = 25$ mm to 50 mm we obtain 2.49×10^4 s.

15. (a) Figure 17.24. Area under graph. (b) (i) 4×200 W since area $\propto r^2$. (ii) $2^4 \times 200$ W, since proportional to T^4. (iii) Net radiation $= 116$W since we now have $\sigma(T^4 - T_s^4)$. When $T_s = 0$, net rate $= 0$.
(c) Radioactivity in the earth produces heat.

16. See text. $I^2R = 5^2 \times 22L = A\sigma T^4$, hence $T = 2000$ K. Assume a black body and all the energy radiated, none conducted through filament supports. As Fig. 17.24 with the area under the 7 A graph $7^2/5^2$ the area under the 5 A graph. Also the maximum energy occurs at a shorter wavelength for the 7 A graph.

17. See text. (a) Radiation. (b) Molecular movement and collisions (not convection but conduction since direction downwards). Radiation occurs at all temperatures, being proportional to T^4. Only same average energy, but distribution of speeds. See Fig. 16.30. At equilibrium, intermediate temperature and distribution. See text.

18. (a) See text. (b) Ratio number of sites with energy $(n + 1)E$ to number with nE.(c) (i) $\eta \propto e^{E/kT}$, hence $\ln \eta$ against $1/T$. (ii) $\ln(\eta_1/\eta_2) = E/kT_1 - E/kT_2$. Hence $E = 2.9 \times 10^{-20}$ J.

19. (a) The higher the temperature the smaller the factor by which the number of ways is changed when a quantum is added.
(b) The number of ways is changed by the same factor when a quantum is given each. Taking a quantum from one solid to the other does not increase the combined number of ways.
(c) Ease of removing or ease of adding; temperature is a measure of the effect on the number of ways of adding or removing quanta—the higher the temperature the less fractional effect. We are only allowed to take or give energy quanta to a solid if the total number of ways increases.

20. (a) The dissociation results in an increase of 100 J K^{-1} in the entropy of the hydrogen. Breaking the hydrogen molecule apart requires energy—which has to come from the surroundings. The temperature of the surroundings must therefore drop. At 300 K the entropy decrease resulting from this temperature drop will be $430 \times 10^3/300 = 1400$ J K^{-1}. The net entropy change by the dissociation would be -1300 J K^{-1}, an entropy decrease. For this reason dissociation at 300 K is unlikely.
(b) About 4300 K.

Chapter 18

1. $Bev = Ee$, hence $v = 2.5 \times 10^7$ m s^{-1}.
2. (a) Terminal velocity due to viscosity of air.
(b) $E = F/q = mg/6e = 4.1 \times 10^4$ V m^{-1}.
3. (a) Circular, $F = mv^2/r = Bev$. r would increase. (b) Excitation of argon atoms by colliding electrons. $B = mv/er = 6.3 \times 10^{-3}$ T.

4. $hf_1 = V_1 e + \phi$, also $hf_2 = V_2 e + \phi$, and so $h(f_1 - f_2) = (V_1 - V_2)e$ and $h = 6.4 \times 10^{-34}$ J s.

5. $hf_1 = E_1 + \phi$, also $hf_2 = E_2 + \phi$, and so $h(f_2 - f_1) = E_2 - E_1$ and $h = 6.7 \times 10^{-34}$ J s.

6. (a) (b) See text. (c) (i) $hf = hc/\lambda = \phi$, hence $\lambda = 6.51 \times 10^{-7}$ m. (ii) $\frac{1}{2}mv^2 = hc/\lambda - \phi$, hence $v = 3.51 \times 10^5$ m s^{-1}. (iii) $Ve = \frac{1}{2}mv^2 = 0.35$ V. (iv) Number of photons per s per m^2 = $250/hf$. If each ejects an electron, charge moved per s per m^2 = $(250/hf)e = 111$ A m^{-2}. (v) Photocell has a high internal resistance, sunlight not always at 250 W m^{-2}.

7. See text. $Ve = hf$, hence $f = 8.0 \times 10^{18}$ Hz.

8. See text. $2d \sin \theta = 1\lambda$, hence $\lambda = 0.30$ nm. $Ve = hf = hc/\lambda$, hence $V = 4.1$ kV.

9. See text.

10. See text.

11. (a) See text. (b) (i) See text. (ii) $f = E/h = 3.3 \times 10^{15}$ Hz, ultraviolet. (iii) $n = 4$ to 3. (c) $(1/N) \sin \theta = 1/\lambda = c/f$, hence $\theta = 19°$.

12. See text. $[(n + 1)^2 - n^2]/n^2(n + 1)^2 = (2n + 1)/n^2(n + 1)^2$ or approximately $2/n^3$, hence $\lambda = n^3/2R$. Hence $n = 166$.

13. See text. (a) $\frac{1}{2}mv^2 = 13.6 \times 1.6 \times 10^{-19}$, hence $v = 2.2 \times 10^6$ m s^{-1}. (b) $hc/\lambda = 13.6 \times 1.6 \times 10^{-19}$, hence $\lambda = 9.1 \times 10^{-8}$ m.

14. See text.

15. See text. $\lg R = 2.00$ of which 1.77 is due to gamma. Hence for beta $R = 41$ s^{-1}.

16. (a) See text. (b) Number per mm = $3.9 \times 10^6/(30 \times 30) = 4.3 \times 10^3$. It goes slower near end of path and so chance of ionizing an atom increases since it is there longer. Reducing pressure by 1/100 reduces number of molecules by 1/100. Hence chance of alpha particle causing ionization reduced by 1/100. So number of ionization events per mm reduced by 1/100. (c) Ionization chamber. Alpha particles must be able to get into detector since they are absorbed by very thin layers of matter.

17. (a) (i) $\frac{1}{2}mv^2 = 5.0 \times 10^6 \times 1.6 \times 10^{-19}$, hence $v = 1.5 \times 10^7$ m s^{-1}. (ii) $mv = 1.02 \times 10^{-19}$ kg m s^{-1}. (b) (i) Little change. (ii) 4.6×10^{-20} kg m s^{-1}. (iii) 2.7×10^7 m s^{-1}, in same direction as incident particle. (c) Only half the charge and one-quarter mass.

18. (a) See text. (b) For γ no change. α: $A = 222$, $Z = 86$. (c) $8.8 \times 10^{-30} \times (3.0 \times 10^8)^2 = 7.92 \times$ 10^{-13} J. $hf = 7.92 \times 10^{-13} - (4.60 \times 10^6 \times 1.6 \times 10^{-19})$, hence $f = 8.5 \times 10^{19}$ Hz. (d) Absorption experiment. It is part of a decay series (from $^{232}_{90}$Th).

19. (a) See text. (b) $235 + 1 = 148 + 85 - x$, hence number of neutrons $x = 3$. Chain reaction. Both have a considerable excess of neutrons over protons and thus they are likely to be beta active.

20. (i) (iii) See text. (ii) The addition of a neutron to heavy nuclei causes them to become unstable. According to the liquid drop model the nuclear drop is set into oscillation and in an elongated shape is liable to break into two drops. This is because the large nuclear size means that the nuclear forces are fairly weak for surface nucleons compared with the electrostatic forces of repulsion between the protons. (iv) The fission products are unstable and decay, emitting radiations. Total energy released per second = $2.7 \times 10^4 \times 4.0 \times 10^3 \times 10.3 + 550 \times 10^6 = 1.7 \times 10^9$ J. Hence per year $1.7 \times 10^9 \times 3.2 \times 10^7 = 5.4 \times 10^{16}$ J. Hence $m = E/c^2 = 0.60$ kg.

21. (a) See text. (b) (i) $(238.050\,81 - 234.043\,63 - 4.002\,60)930 = 4.26$ MeV. (ii) Conservation of momentum: $234v_T = 4v_H$; conservation of kinetic energy: $(\frac{1}{2} \times 234v_T^2 + \frac{1}{2} \times 4v_H^2) \times 1.66 \times 10^{-27} = 4.26 \times 10^6 \times 1.6 \times 10^{-19}$. Hence $v_T = 1.7 \times 10^5$ m s^{-1}. (c) (i) Number of active atoms N_0 in 2 g = $6 \times 10^{23} \times 2/(12 \times 10^{12}) = 1 \times 10^{11}$. $dN/dt = 5/60 = -\lambda N = -\lambda N_0 e^{-\lambda t}$. Since $\lambda = (\ln 2)/5600$ then $t = 1.52 \times 10^{10}$ y.

22. (a) (b) See text. (c) $eV = \frac{1}{2}mv^2$ and $Bev = mv^2/r$, hence $r = (2mV/B^2 e)^{1/2}$. For $^{20}_{10}$Ne the mass to charge ratio is $20m/10e = (20/10)/0.96 \times 10^8$ C kg^{-1}. For $^{22}_{10}$Ne the ratio is $(22/10)/0.96 \times 10^8$ C kg^{-1}. Radial separation = 1.78 mm.

23. (a) (i) Photoelectricity. (ii) $\lambda = h/mv = 1.5 \times 10^{-10}$ m, comparable with lattice spacing in a crystal, hence electron diffraction by a crystal. (b) See text. Each dimension a quantum number.

24. (a) Electron diffraction. (b) Photoelectricity. (c) Wavelength of electrons comparable with 'apertures' and 'obstacles' they encounter. For tennis balls, the wavelength is considerably smaller. For light waves, momentum comparable with that of 'objects' encountered, e.g., electrons, while for radio waves the momentum is much too small. (d) We only use the macroscopic properties of waves and particles as models for microscopic behaviour. The models are not the real thing.

25. (a) An abrupt change in potential energy signifies a force which suddenly acts on a particle—like when an object meets a wall. The amplitude represents the chance of finding an electron at the point concerned. (b) $\lambda = L$, hence decreasing L increases p. (c) See text.

Index